STATISTICS
IN PSYCHOLOGY
AND EDUCATION

◇◇

"If we take in our hand any volume . . . let us ask, *Does it contain any abstract reasoning concerning quantity or number? No. Does it contain any experimental reasoning concerning matter of fact and existence? No.* Commit it then to the flames: for it can contain nothing but sophistry and illusion!"

HUME, DAVID, *An Enquiry concerning Human Understanding* (1777).

STATISTICS

IN PSYCHOLOGY AND EDUCATION

HENRY E. GARRETT, Ph.D.

PROFESSOR EMERITUS OF PSYCHOLOGY
COLUMBIA UNIVERSITY

WITH AN INTRODUCTION BY
R. S. WOODWORTH

PROFESSOR EMERITUS OF PSYCHOLOGY
COLUMBIA UNIVERSITY

SIXTH EDITION

DAVID McKAY COMPANY, INC.

NEW YORK

GARRETT

STATISTICS IN PSYCHOLOGY AND EDUCATION

SIXTH EDITION

LIBRARY OF CONGRESS CATALOG CARD NUMBER 66-18866

Printed in the United States of America

INTRODUCTION

BY R. S. WOODWORTH

MODERN PROBLEMS and needs are forcing statistical methods and statistical ideas more and more to the fore. There are so many things we wish to know which cannot be discovered by a single observation, or by a single measurement. We wish to envisage the behavior of a man who, like all men, is rather a variable quantity, and must be observed repeatedly and not once for all. We wish to study the social group, composed of individuals differing from one another. We should like to be able to compare one group with another, one race with another, as well as one individual with another individual, or the individual with the norm for his age, race or class. We wish to trace the curve which pictures the growth of a child, or of a population. We wish to disentangle the interwoven factors of heredity and environment which influence the development of the individual, and to measure the similarly interwoven effects of laws, social customs and economic conditions upon public health, safety and welfare generally. Even if our statistical appetite is far from keen, we all of us should like to know enough to understand, or to withstand, the statistics that are constantly being thrown at us in print or conversation—much of it pretty bad statistics. The only cure for bad statistics is apparently more and better statistics. All in all, it certainly appears that the rudiments of sound statistical sense are coming to be an essential of a liberal education.

Now there are different orders of statisticians. There is, first in order, the mathematician who invents the method for performing a certain type of statistical job. His interest, as a mathematician, is not in the educational, social or psychological problems just alluded to, but in the problem of devising instruments for handling such matters. He is the tool-maker of the statistical industry, and one good tool-maker can supply many skilled workers. The latter are quite another order of statisticians. Supply them with the mathematician's formulas, map out the procedure for them to follow, provide working charts, tables and calculating machines, and they will compute from your data the necessary averages, probable errors and correlation coefficients. Their interest, as computers, lies in the quick and accurate handling of the tools of the trade. But there is a statistician of yet another order, in between the other two. His primary interest is psychological, perhaps, or it may be educational. It is he who has selected the scientific or practical problem, who has organized his attack upon the problem in such fashion that the data obtained can be handled in some sound statistical way. He selects the statistical tools to be employed, and, when the computers have done their work, he scrutinizes the results for their bearing upon the scientific or practical problem with which he started. Such an one, in short, must have a discriminating knowledge of the kit of tools which the mathematician has handed him, as well as some skill in their actual use.

The reader of the present book will quickly discern that it is intended primarily for statisticians of the last-mentioned type. It lays out before him the tools of the trade; it explains very fully and carefully the manner of handling each tool; it affords practice in the use of each. While it has little to say of the tool-maker's art, it takes great pains to make clear the use and limitations of each tool. As anyone can readily see who has tried to teach statistics to the class of students who most need to know the subject, this book is the product of a genuine teacher's experience, and is exceptionally well adapted to the student's use. To an unusual degree, it succeeds in meeting the student upon his own ground.

PREFACE

TO THE SIXTH EDITION

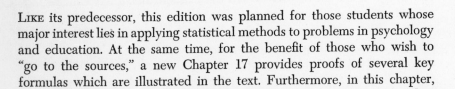

LIKE its predecessor, this edition was planned for those students whose major interest lies in applying statistical methods to problems in psychology and education. At the same time, for the benefit of those who wish to "go to the sources," a new Chapter 17 provides proofs of several key formulas which are illustrated in the text. Furthermore, in this chapter, several techniques have been outlined which may be almost essential in specific problems, but are not sufficiently general for inclusion in the main body of the book.

Revisions often have a way of growing quantitatively rather than qualitatively. For this reason, among others, only a few changes have been made in the text itself, and little new material has been added, as the book already covers more topics than can easily be taught in one semester. Analysis of variance is treated briefly, and the value of this attack upon certain problems is indicated. But highly specialized techniques such as factor analysis have not been included, as these do not properly belong in a first course in statistics.

In a short course, the first five chapters plus linear correlation are probably all that can be covered. In a longer course, topics from Parts II and III dealing with mental tests and with individual and group differences may be added.

Suggestions and criticisms offered by those who have used the book over the years have always been appreciated and often incorporated in the text.

HENRY E. GARRETT

May, 1966

CONTENTS

◇◇ ᠘◇᠘◇᠘◇

PART I

DESCRIPTIVE
STATISTICS

CHAPTER 1

THE FREQUENCY
DISTRIBUTION

◇◇

I. MEASURES IN GENERAL

1. Ways of measuring

Measurement may be of several kinds and may be taken to various degrees of precision. When people or objects have been ranked or arranged in an *ordinal* series with respect to some trait or attribute, we have perhaps the simplest sort of measurement. School children may be put in 1,2,3 order for height, marks on an examination, or regularity of school attendance; salesmen for experience or sales volume over the year; advertisements for amount of color used, or for cost, or sales appeal. Rank order gives us serial position in the group, but it does not provide an exact measurement. We cannot add or subtract ranks as we do inches or pounds, as a person's rank is always relative to the ranks of other members of his group and is never absolute, i.e., in terms of some known unit.

Measurement of individual performance by means of tests is usually expressed as a *score*. Scores may be in terms of time taken to complete a task or amount done in a given time; less often scores are expressed in terms of difficulty of the task or excellence of result. Mental test scores vary with performance, and changes in score parallel closely changes in performance.

Many mental tests are not scaled in equal units. When scores are expressed in equal units they constitute an *interval scale*. Standard psychological tests are usually interval scales, as they have equal units or equal steps; but they do not possess a true zero. Scaled test scores may be added or subtracted just as we add or subtract inches. But we cannot say that a score of 40 is twice as good as a score of 20, as neither is taken from a zero of just no ability.

1

When measures are expressed in equal units, and are also taken from a true zero, they constitute *ratio scales*. Examples are the "c.g.s." scales (centimeters, grams, seconds) found in the physical sciences. Measures from c.g.s. scales may be added and subtracted, and a "score" of 20 inches is twice a "score" of 10 inches. Ratio scales are rarely encountered in the behavioral sciences. The measurements of certain sensory functions such as pitch and loudness, to be sure, may be expressed in ratio scales. But in the measurement of mental and social variables and traits we must generally be content with interval scales.

2. Continuous and discrete series

In measuring mental and physical traits, most of the variables * with which we deal fall into *continuous* series. A continuous series is one which is capable of any degree of subdivision, though in practice divisions smaller than some convenient unit are rarely met. I.Q.'s, for example, are usually thought of as increasing by increments of *one* unit along an ability continuum which runs from idiot to genius. But with more refined methods of measurement it is conceivable that we might get I.Q.'s of 100.8 or even 100.83. Physical measures as well as mental test scores fall into continuous series: within the given range any "score," integral or fractional, may exist and have meaning. Gaps in a truly continuous series can be attributed to failure to get enough data,† or to crudity of the measuring instrument, or to some other factor of the same sort, rather than to the lack of measures within the gaps.

Series which exhibit real gaps are called *discrete*. A salary scale in a department store, for example, may run from $50 per week to $60 per week in units of $1: no one receives, let us say, $57.53 per week. Again, the average family in a certain community may be reported to consist of 2.57 children, though there is obviously a real gap between two children and three children. Fortunately, most of the variables dealt with in psychology and education are continuous or may profitably be treated as continuous. Hence, we shall be concerned in later chapters primarily with methods for handling continuous data.

In the following sections we shall define more precisely what is meant by a score, and shall show how scores may be classified into what is called a *frequency distribution*.

* Variables are attributes or qualities which exhibit differences in magnitude, and which vary along some dimension.

† Data are figures, ratings, check lists and other information collected in experiments, surveys and descriptive studies.

3. The meaning of test scores in a continuous series

Scores or other numbers in continuous series are to be thought of as *distances* along a continuum, rather than as discrete points. An inch is the linear magnitude between two divisions on a foot rule; and, in like manner, a score in a mental test is a unit distance between two limits. A score of 150 upon an intelligence examination, for example, represents the interval 149.5 up to 150.5. The exact midpoint of this score interval is 150 as shown below.

Score 150

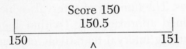

Other scores may be interpreted in the same way. A score of 12, for instance, includes all values from 11.5 to 12.5, i.e., any value from a point .5 unit *below* 12 to a point .5 unit *above* 12. This means that 11.7, 12.0 and 12.4 would all be scored 12. The usual mathematical meaning of a score is an interval which extends along some dimension from .5 unit below to .5 unit above the face value of the score.

There is another and somewhat different meaning which a test score may have. According to this second view, a score of 150 means that an individual has done *at least* 150 items correctly, but not 151. Hence, a score of 150 represents any value *between* 150 and 151. Any fractional value greater than 150, but less than 151, e.g., 150.3 or 150.8, since it falls within the interval 150–151, is scored simply as 150. The middle of the score is 150.5 (see below).

```
                    Score 150
                 |     150.5      |
               150        ^       151
```

Both of these ways of defining a score are valid and useful. Which to use will depend upon the way in which the test is scored and on the meaning of the units of measurement employed. If each of ten boys is recorded as having a height of 64 inches this will ordinarily mean that these heights fall between 63.5 and 64.5 inches (middle value 64 in.), and not between 64 and 65 inches (middle value 64.5 in.). On the other hand, the ages of twenty-five children, all recorded as being 9 years old, will most probably lie between 9 and 10 years; will be greater than 9 and less than 10 years (middle value 9.5). But "9 years old" must be taken in many studies to mean 8.5 up to 9.5 years with a middle value of 9 years. The point to remember is that results obtained from treating scores under our second definition will always be .5 unit higher than results obtained when scores are taken under the first or mathematical definition. The student will often have to decide, sometimes arbitrarily, what meaning a score should have. In general, it is safer to take the mathematical meaning of a score unless it is clearly indicated otherwise. This is the method followed throughout this book. Scores of 62 and 231, for example, will mean 61.5–62.5 and 230.5–231.5 and not 62 up to 63 and 231 up to 232.

II. DRAWING UP A FREQUENCY DISTRIBUTION

I. Tabulating measures or scores

Data collected from tests and experiments may have little meaning to the investigator until they have been arranged or classified in some systematic way. The first task, therefore, is to organize our material and this leads naturally to a grouping of the scores under subheads or into classes. Rules for classifying scores into what is called a frequency distribution may be laid down as follows:

(1) Determine the *range* or the gap between the highest and the lowest scores. The highest score in Table 1 (1) is 197 and the lowest is 142, so that the range is 55 (i.e., 197–142). The 50 scores in Table I represent the test performance of 50 college students upon a modified form of the Army Alpha intelligence examination.

(2) Settle upon the number and size of the groupings to be used in making a classification. Commonly used grouping intervals are 3, 5, 10 units in length, as these are somewhat easier to work with in later calculations. A good rule is to select by trial a grouping unit which will yield from 5 to 15 categories. The number of intervals which a given range will yield can be determined approximately (within 1 interval) by dividing the range by the grouping interval tentatively chosen. In Table 1, for instance, 55, the range, divided by 5 (the interval tentatively chosen) gives 11, which is 1 less than the actual number of intervals shown in Table 1 (2), namely, 12. An interval of 3 units will yield 19 classes; an interval of 10, 6 classes. An interval of 3 would spread the data out too much, thus losing the benefit of grouping; whereas an interval of 10 would crowd the scores into too coarse categories. Accordingly, an interval of 5 was chosen as best suited to the data of Table 1.

(3) Tally the scores in their proper intervals as shown in Table 1 (2). In the first column of the table the class intervals have been listed serially from the smallest scores at the bottom of the column to the largest scores at the top. Each class interval covers 5 scores. The first interval "140 up to 145" begins with score 140 and ends with 144, thus including the

TABLE I The tabulation of Army Alpha scores made by 50 college students

1. The original scores ungrouped

185	166	176	145	166	191	177	164	171	174
147	178	176	#142	170	158	171	167	180	178
173	148	168	187	181	172	165	169	173	184
175	156	158	187	156	172	162	193	173	183
* 197	181	151	161	153	172	162	179	188	179

* Highest score   # Lowest score

2. The same 50 scores grouped into a frequency distribution

(1) Class Intervals	(2) Tallies	(3) f (frequency)
195 up to 200	/	1
190 " " 195	//	2
185 " " 190	////	4
180 " " 185	/////	5
175 " " 180	///// ///	8
170 " " 175	///// /////	10
165 " " 170	///// /	6
160 " " 165	////	4
155 " " 160	////	4
150 " " 155	//	2
145 " " 150	///	3
140 " " 145	/	1
		$N = 50$

5 scores 140, 141, 142, 143 and 144. The second interval "145 up to 150" begins with 145 and ends with 149, that is, at score 150. The topmost interval "195 up to 200" begins with score 195 and ends at score 200, thus including 195, 196, 197, 198 and 199. In column (2), marked "Tallies," the separate scores have been listed opposite their proper intervals. The first score of 185 is represented by a tally placed opposite interval "185 up to 190"; the second score of 147 by a tally placed opposite interval "145 up to 150"; and the third score, 173, by a tally placed opposite "170 up to 175." The remaining scores have been tabulated in the same way. When all 50 have been listed, the total number of tallies on each class interval (i.e., the frequency) is written in column (3) headed f (frequency). The sum of the f column is called N. When the total frequency within each class interval has been tabulated opposite the proper

interval, as shown in column (3), our 50 Alpha scores are arranged in a frequency distribution.

The student will note that the beginning score of the first interval in the distribution (140 up to 145) has been set at 140 although the lowest score in the series is 142. When the interval selected for tabulation is 5 units it facilitates tabulation as well as computations which come later if the score limits of the first interval, and, accordingly, of each successive interval, are multiples of 5. A class interval "142 up to 147" is just as good theoretically as a class interval "140 up to 145"; but the second is easier to handle from the standpoint of the arithmetic involved.

2. Methods of describing the limits of the class intervals in a frequency distribution

Table 2 illustrates three ways of expressing the limits of the class intervals in a frequency distribution. In (A), the interval "140 up to 145" means, as we have already seen, that all scores from 140 up to but not including 145 fall within this grouping. The intervals in (B) cover the same distances as in (A), but the upper and lower limits of each interval are defined more exactly. We have seen (p. 3) that a score of 140 in a

TABLE 2 Methods of grouping scores into a frequency distribution

(Data from Table 1, 50 Army Alpha scores)

(A)			(B)			(C)		
Class Intervals	Mid-point	f	Class Intervals	Mid-point	f	Class Intervals	Mid-point	f
195–200	197	1	194.5–199.5	197	1	195–199	197	1
190–195	192	2	189.5–194.5	192	2	190–194	192	2
185–190	187	4	184.5–189.5	187	4	185–189	187	4
180–185	182	5	179.5–184.5	182	5	180–184	182	5
175–180	177	8	174.5–179.5	177	8	175–179	177	8
170–175	172	10	169.5–174.5	172	10	170–174	172	10
165–170	167	6	164.5–169.5	167	6	165–169	167	6
160–165	162	4	159.5–164.5	162	4	160–164	162	4
155–160	157	4	154.5–159.5	157	4	155–159	157	4
150–155	152	2	149.5–154.5	152	2	150–154	152	2
145–150	147	3	144.5–149.5	147	3	145–149	147	3
140–145	142	1	139.5–144.5	142	1	140–144	142	1
	$N = 50$			$N = 50$			$N = 50$	

continuous series ordinarily means the interval 139.5 up to 140.5; and that a score of 144 means 143.5 up to 144.5. Accordingly, to express precisely the fact that an interval *begins* with 140 and *ends* with 144, we may write 139.5 (the beginning of score 140) as the lower limit, and 144.5 (end of score 144 or beginning of score 145) as the upper limit of this step. The class intervals in (C) express the same facts more clearly than in (A) and less exactly than in (B). Thus, "140–144" means that this interval begins *with* score 140 and ends *with* score 144; but the precise limits of the interval are not given. The diagram below will show how (A), (B), and (C) are three ways of expressing identically the same facts:

Class Interval
140 up to 145
139.5–144.5
140–144

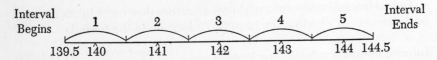

Interval Begins   1   2   3   4   5   Interval Ends

139.5 140   141   142   143   144 144.5

For the rapid tabulation of scores within their proper intervals, method (C) is to be preferred to (B) or (A). In (A) it is fairly easy, even when one is on guard, to let a score of 160, say, slip into the interval "155 up to 160," owing simply to the presence of 160 at the upper limit of the interval. Method (B) is clumsy and time consuming because of the need for writing .5 at the beginning and end of every interval. Method (C), while easiest for tabulation, offers the difficulty that in later calculations one must constantly remember that the *expressed* class limits are not the *actual* class limits: that interval "140–144" begins at 139.5 (not 140) and ends at 144.5 (not 144). If this is clearly understood, method (C) is as accurate as (B) or (A). It will be generally used throughout this book.

3. The midpoint of an interval in a frequency distribution

The scores grouped within a given interval in a frequency distribution are considered to be spread evenly over the entire interval. This assumption is made whether the interval is 3, 5, or 10 units. If we wish to represent *all* of the scores within a given interval by some single value, the midpoint of the interval is the logical choice. For example, in the interval 175–179 [Table 2, method (C)] all 8 scores upon this interval are represented by the single value 177, the midpoint of the interval.* Why 177 is the midpoint of this interval is shown graphically below:

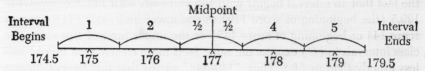

A simple rule for finding the midpoint of an interval is

$$\text{Midpoint} = \text{lower limit of interval} + \frac{(\text{upper limit} - \text{lower limit})}{2}.$$

In our illustration,

$$174.5 + \frac{(179.5 - 174.5)}{2} = 177.$$

Since the interval is 5 units, it follows that the midpoint must be 2.5 units from the *lower limit* of the class, i.e., $174.5 + 2.5$; or 2.5 units from the *upper limit* of the class, i.e., $179.5 - 2.5$.

To find interval midpoints, when *scores* rather than *exact* limits are used in the frequency distribution, i.e., (C), substitute in the formula

$$\text{Interval midpoint} = \text{beginning interval score} + \frac{(\text{upper score} - \text{lower score})}{2}$$

In the example above,

$$\text{Midpoint} = 175 + \frac{(179 - 175)}{2} \text{ or } 177.$$

The assumption that the midpoint is the most representative value within an interval holds best when the number of scores in the distribution is large, and when the intervals are not too broad. But even when neither of these conditions fully obtains, the midpoint assumption is not greatly in error and is the best that we can make. In the long run, about as many scores will fall above as below the various midpoint values; and lack of balance in one interval will usually be offset by the opposite condition in another interval.

III. THE GRAPHIC REPRESENTATION OF THE FREQUENCY DISTRIBUTION

Aid in analyzing numerical data may often be obtained from a graphic or pictorial treatment of the frequency distribution. The advertiser has long used graphic methods because these devices catch the eye and hold the attention when the most careful array of statistical evidence fails to

* The same value (namely, 177) is, of course, the midpoint of the interval when methods (A) and (B) are used.

attract notice. For this and other reasons the research worker also utilizes the attention-getting power of visual presentation; and, at the same time, seeks to translate numerical facts—often abstract and difficult of interpretation—into more concrete and understandable form.

Four methods of representing a frequency distribution graphically are in general use. These methods yield the *frequency polygon*, the *histogram*, the *cumulative frequency graph*, and the *cumulative percentage curve* or *ogive*. The first two graphic devices will be treated in the following sections; the second two in Chapter 4.

1. Graphic representation of data; General principles

Before considering methods of constructing a frequency polygon or histogram, we shall review briefly the simple algebraic principles which apply to all graphic representation of data. Graphing or plotting is done with reference to two lines or *coördinate axes*, the one the vertical or *Y* axis, the other the horizontal or *X* axis. These basic lines are perpendicular to each other, the point where they intersect being called *O*, or the *origin*. Figure 1 represents a system of coördinate axes.

The origin is the zero point or point of reference for both axes. Distances measured along the *X* axis to the *right* of *O* are called positive,

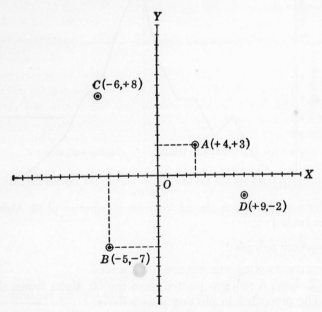

FIG. 1 A system of coördinate axes

distances measured along the X axis to the *left* of O negative. In the same way, distances measured on the Y axis *above* O are positive; distances *below* O negative. By their intersection at O, the X and Y axes form four divisions or quadrants. In the upper right division or first quadrant (see Fig. 1), both x and y measures are positive $(+ +)$. In the upper left division or second quadrant, x is minus and y plus $(- +)$. In the lower left or third quadrant, both x and y are negative $(- -)$; while in the lower right or fourth quadrant, x is plus and y minus $(+ -)$.

To locate or plot a point "A" whose coördinates are $x = 4$, and $y = 3$, we go out from O four units on the X axis, and up from the origin three units on the Y axis. Where the perpendiculars to these points intersect, we locate the point "A" (see Fig. 1). The point "B," whose coördinates are $x = -5$, and $y = -7$, is plotted in the third quadrant by going left from O along the X axis five units, and then down seven units, as shown in the figure. In like manner, any points "C" and "D" whose x and y values are known can be located with reference to OY and OX, the coördinate axes. The distance of a point from O on the X axis is commonly called the *abscissa*; and the distance of the point from O on the Y axis the *ordinate*. The abscissa of point "D" is $+9$, and the ordinate, -2.

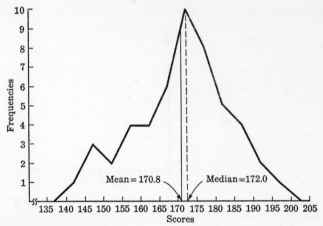

FIG. 2 Frequency polygon plotted from the distribution of 50 Alpha scores in Table I

2. The frequency polygon *

(1) CONSTRUCTION OF THE FREQUENCY POLYGON

Figure 2 shows a polygon plotted from the 50 Alpha scores shown in Table 1. The procedure in plotting is as follows:

* Polygon means "many-angled figure."

(a) *Labeling the points on the base line.* There are several ways of labeling the intervals along the base line or X axis of the frequency polygon. Exact score limits are sometimes used (for illustration, see Fig. 2) but marking off score limits of the successive intervals is easier and for most purposes just as accurate. The distribution in Table 1 begins at 140 and ends with score 200. Two additional points, one just below 140 (at 135) and one just above 200 (at 205), have been added for reasons which will appear later. The break in the X axis (∫∫) indicates that the vertical axis has been moved in for convenience.

(b) *Plotting midpoints.* Frequencies on each interval are plotted above the midpoints of the intervals on the X *axis.* There is 1 score on the first interval, 140 to 145. To represent this frequency, go out to 142, midpoint of the interval, and put a dot a distance of 1 unit up on the Y axis above this midpoint. The frequency on the next interval (145 to 150) is 3, so that the second point must be plotted above 147 and 3 units up on the Y axis. The 2 frequencies on interval 150 to 155, the 4 frequencies on 155 to 160, etc., are represented in each instance by a dot the specified distance up on Y and midway between the lower and upper limits of the interval upon which it falls.

(c) *Drawing in the frequency polygon.* When all of the points have been located in the diagram, they are joined by a series of short lines to form the frequency polygon shown in Figure 2. In order to complete the figure (i.e., bring it down to the base line), one additional interval (135 to 140) at the low end and one additional interval at the high end (200 to 205) of the distribution are included on the X scale. The frequency on each of these intervals is, of course, zero; hence, by adding them to the scale we begin the polygon one-half interval *below* the first, and end it one-half interval *above* the last, interval on the X axis.

(d) *Dimensions of the frequency polygon.* In order to give symmetry and balance to the polygon, care must be exercised in the selection of unit distances to represent the intervals on the X axis and the frequencies on the Y axis. A too-long X unit tends to stretch out the polygon, while a too short X unit crowds the separate points. On the other hand, a too-long Y unit exaggerates the changes from interval to interval, and a too-short Y unit makes the polygon too flat. A good general rule is to select X and Y units which will make the *height* of the figure approximately 75% of its *width.* The ratio of height to width may vary from 60–80% and the figure still have good proportions; but it can rarely go below 50% and leave the figure well balanced. The frequency polygon in Figure 2 illustrates the "75% rule." There are thirteen class intervals laid off on the X axis—twelve full intervals plus one-half interval at the beginning and at the end of the range. Hence, our polygon should be 75% of thirteen, or about ten X axis units high. These 10 units (each equal to *one* interval) are laid off on the Y axis. To determine how many scores (f's) should be assigned to *each unit* on the Y axis, we divide 10, the largest f, by 10, the number of intervals laid off on Y. The result (i.e., 1) makes each Y unit exactly equal to one f or one score, as shown in Figure 2.

The polygon in Figure 5 is another illustration of how X and Y units must be selected so as to preserve balance in the figure. The polygon represents the distribution of 200 scores on a cancellation test shown in Table 3. Exact interval limits have been laid off along the base line or

TABLE 3 Scores achieved by 200 adults on a cancellation test

Class interval = 4		
Class Intervals (Scores)	Midpoints (X)	f
135.5–139.5	137.5	3
131.5–135.5	133.5	5
127.5–131.5	129.5	16
123.5–127.5	125.5	23
119.5–123.5	121.5	52
115.5–119.5	117.5	49
111.5–115.5	113.5	27
107.5–111.5	109.5	18
103.5–107.5	105.5	7
	N =	200

X axis. In all, there are 10 intervals—9 full intervals plus one-half of an interval at the beginning and one-half of an interval at the end of the range. Since 75% of 10 is 7.5, the height of our figure could be either 7 or 8 X axis units. To determine the "best" value for each Y unit, we divide 52, the greatest frequency (on 119.5–123.5), by 7, getting 7⅜; and then by 8, getting 6½. Using whole numbers for convenience, evidently we may lay off on the Y axis 7 units, each representing 8 scores; or 8 units each representing 7 scores. The first combination was chosen because a unit of 8 f's is somewhat easier to handle than one of 7. A slightly longer Y unit representing 10 f's would perhaps have been still more convenient.

(e) *Area of the polygon.* The total frequency (N) of a distribution is represented by the *area* of its polygon; that is, the area bounded by the frequency surface and the X axis. That part of the area lying above any given interval, however, cannot be taken as proportional to the number of cases within the interval, owing to irregularities in the frequency surface. To show the positions of the mean and the median on the graph, we have located these points on the X axis as shown in Figures 2 and 4. Perpendiculars erected at these points on the base line show the approximate frequency of scores at the mean and the median.

Steps to be followed in constructing a frequency polygon may be summarized as follows:

(1) Draw two straight lines perpendicular to each other, the vertical line near the left side of the paper, the horizontal line near the bottom. Label the vertical line (the Y axis) OY, and the horizontal line (the X axis) OX. Put the O where the two lines intersect. This point is the *origin*.

(2) Lay off the score intervals of the frequency distribution at regular distances along the X axis. Begin with the interval *next below* the lowest in the distribution, and end with the interval *next above* the highest in the distribution. Label the successive X distances with the score interval limits. Select an X unit which will allow all of the intervals to be represented easily on the graph paper.

(3) Mark off on the Y axis successive units to represent the scores (the frequencies) on the different intervals. Choose a Y scale which will make the largest *frequency* (the height) of the polygon approximately 75% of the width of the figure.

(4) At the midpoint of each interval on the X axis go up in the Y direction a distance equal to the number of scores on the interval. Place points at these locations.

(5) Join the points plotted in (4) with straight lines to give the frequency surface.

(2) SMOOTHING THE FREQUENCY POLYGON

Because the sample is small ($N = 50$) and the frequency distribution somewhat irregular, the polygon in Figure 2 tends to be jagged in outline. To iron out chance irregularities, and also get a better notion of how the figure might look if the data were more numerous, the frequency polygon may be "smoothed" as shown in Figure 3. In smoothing, a series of "moving" or "running" averages are taken from which new or adjusted frequencies are determined. The method is illustrated in Figure 3. To find an adjusted or "smoothed" f, we add the f on the given interval and the f's on the *two* adjacent intervals (the interval just below and the interval just above) and divide the sum by 3. For example, the smoothed f for interval 175–179 is $\frac{5+8+10}{3}$ or 7.67; for interval 155–159 it is $\frac{4+4+2}{3}$ or 3.33. The smoothed f's for the other intervals may be found in the table

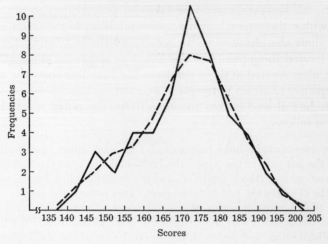

FIG. 3 Original and smoothed frequency polygons. The original and smoothed f's are given on page 14.

below (see also Fig. 3). To find the smoothed f's for the two intervals at the extremes of the distribution, namely, 140–144 and 195–199, a slightly different procedure is necessary. First, we add 0, the f on the step interval *below* or *above*, to the f on the given interval and to the f on the adjacent interval, and divide by 3. The smoothed f for 140–144 is $\dfrac{0+1+3}{3}$

(Data from Table 1)

Scores	f	Smoothed f
200–204	0	.33
195–199	1	1.00
190–194	2	2.33
185–189	4	3.67
180–184	5	5.67
175–179	8	7.67
170–174	10	8.00
165–169	6	6.67
160–164	4	4.67
155–159	4	3.33
150–154	2	3.00
145–149	3	2.00
140–144	1	1.33
135–139	0	.33
	50	50.00

or 1.33; and the smoothed f for 195–199 is $\dfrac{2+1+0}{3}$ or 1.00. The smoothed f for the intervals 135–139 and 200–204, for which the f in the original distribution is 0, is in each case $\dfrac{1+0+0}{3}$ or .33. Note that if we omit these last two intervals the N for the smoothed distribution will be less than 50, as the smoothed distribution has f's outside the range of the original distribution.

If the already smoothed f's in Figure 3 are subjected to a second smoothing, the outline of the frequency surface will become more nearly a continuous flowing curve. It is doubtful, however, whether so much adjustment of the original f's is often warranted. When an investigator presents only the smoothed frequency polygon and does not give his original data, it is impossible for a reader to tell with what he started. Moreover, smoothing gives a picture of what an investigator *might* have gotten (not what he did get) if his data had been more numerous, or less subject to error than they were. If N is large, smoothing may not greatly change the shape of a graph, and hence is often unnecessary. The frequency polygon in Figure 5, for example, which represents the distribution of 200 cancellation test scores, is quite regular without any adjustment of the ordinate (i.e., the Y) values. Probably the best course for the beginner to follow is to smooth data as little as possible. When smoothing seems to be indicated in order better to bring out the facts, one should be careful always to present original data along with "adjusted" results.

3. The histogram or column diagram

A second way of representing a frequency distribution graphically is by means of a histogram or column diagram. This type of graph is illustrated in Figure 4 for the same distribution of 50 Alpha scores depicted by the frequency polygon in Figure 2. The two figures are constructed in much the same way with this important difference. In the frequency polygon, all of the scores within a given interval are represented by the midpoint of that interval, whereas in a histogram the scores are assumed to be spread uniformly over the entire interval. Within each interval of a histogram the frequency is shown by a rectangle, the base of which is the length of the interval, and the height of which is the number of scores within the interval. In Figure 4 the base line is labeled with the score intervals rather than with the exact limits. Thus, the first interval in the histogram actually begins at 139.5, the exact lower limit of the interval, and ends at 144.5, the exact upper limit of the interval. The one score on

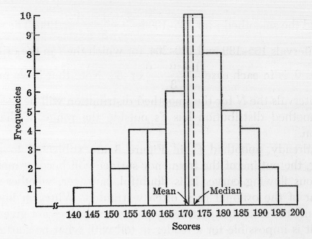

FIG. 4 Histogram of the 50 Alpha scores given in Table I

interval 140–145 is represented by a rectangle the base of which is the length of the interval and the height of which is one unit up on the Y axis. The 3 scores on the next interval are represented by a rectangle one interval long and 3 Y units high. The heights of the other rectangles vary with the f's on the intervals, the bases all being one interval in length. When the same number of scores is found on two or more adjacent intervals, as in the intervals 155 to 160 and 160 to 165, the rectangles are the same height. The highest rectangle, of course, is on interval 170 to 175 which has 10, the largest f, as its height. In selecting scales for the X axis and the Y axis, the same considerations as to height and width of figure outlined on page 11 for the frequency polygon should be observed.

While each interval in a histogram is represented by a separate rectangle, it is not necessary to project the sides of the rectangles down to the base line as is done in Figure 4. The rise and fall of the boundary line shows the increase or decrease in the number of scores from interval to interval and is usually the important fact to be brought out (see Fig. 5). As in a frequency polygon, the total frequency (N) is represented by the area of the histogram. In contrast to the frequency polygon, however, the area of each rectangle in a histogram is directly proportional to the number of measures within the interval. For this reason, the histogram presents an accurate picture of the relative proportions of the total frequency from interval to interval.

In order to provide a more detailed comparison of the two types of frequency graph, the distribution in Table 3 is plotted upon the same coördinate axes in Figure 5 as a frequency polygon and as a histogram. The increased number of cases and the more symmetrical arrangement of scores in the distribution make these figures more regular in appearance than those in Figures 2 and 4.

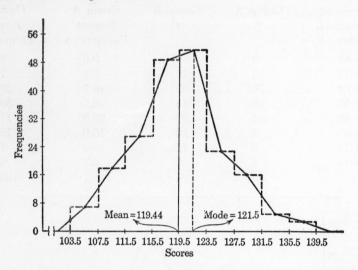

FIG. 5 Frequency polygon and histogram of 200 cancellation scores shown in Table 3

4. Plotting two frequency distributions on the same axes, when samples differ in size

Table 4 gives the distributions of scores on an achievement examination made by two groups, A and B, which differ considerably in size. Group A has 60 cases, Group B, 160 cases. If the two distributions in Table 4 are plotted as polygons or as histograms on the same coördinate axes, the fact that the f's of Group B are so much larger than those of Group A makes it hard to compare directly the range and quality of achievement in the two groups. A useful device in cases where the N's differ in size is to express both distributions in percentage frequencies as shown in Table 4. Both N's are now 100, and the f's are comparable from interval to interval. For example, we know at once that 26.7% of Group A and 30% of Group B made scores of 50 through 59, and that 5% of the A's and 7.5% of the B's scored from 70 to 79. Frequency polygons representing the two distributions, in which percentage frequencies instead of original f's have been plotted on the same axes, are shown in Figure 6. These polygons provide an immediate comparison of the rela-

TABLE 4

(1)	(2)	(3)	(4)	(5)
Achievement Examination Scores	Group A f	Group B f	Group A Percent Frequencies	Group B Percent Frequencies
80–89	0	9	0.0	5.6
70–79	3	12	5.0	7.5
60–69	10	32	16.7	20.0
50–59	16	48	26.7	30.0
40–49	12	27	20.0	17.0
30–39	9	20	15.0	12.5
20–29	6	12	10.0	7.5
10–19	4	0	6.7	0.0
	60	160	100.1	100.1

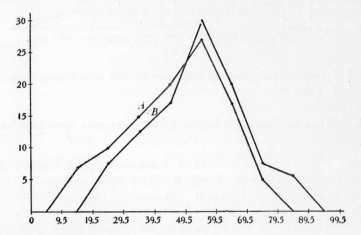

FIG. 6 Frequency polygons of the two distributions in Table 4. Scores are laid off on the X axis, percentage frequencies on the Y axis.

tive achievement of our two groups not given by polygons plotted from original frequencies.

Percentage frequencies are readily found by dividing each f by N and multiplying by 100. Thus $3/60 \times 100 = 5.0$. A simple method of finding percentage frequencies when a calculating machine is available is to divide 100 by N and, putting this figure in the machine, to multiply each f in turn by it.

For example: 1.667 (i.e., 100/60) $\times 3 = 5.0$; $1.667 \times 10 = 16.7$, etc.; .625 (i.e., 100/160) $\times 9 = 5.6$; $.625 \times 12 = 7.5$, etc. What percentage frequencies do, in effect, is to scale each distribution down to the same total N of 100, thus permitting a comparison of f's for each interval.

5. When to use the frequency polygon and when to use the histogram

The question of when to use the frequency polygon and when to use the histogram cannot be answered by citing a general rule which will cover all cases. The frequency polygon is less precise than the histogram in that it does not represent accurately, i.e., in terms of area, the frequency upon each interval. In comparing two or more graphs plotted on the same axes, however, the frequency polygon is likely to be more useful, as the vertical and horizontal lines in the histograms will often coincide.

Both the frequency polygon and the histogram tell the same story and both enable us to show in graphic form how the scores in the group are distributed—whether they are piled up at the low (or high) end of the scale or are evenly and regularly distributed over the scale. If the test is too easy, scores accumulate at the high end of the scale, whereas if the test is too hard, scores will crowd the low end of the scale. When the test is well suited to the abilities of the group, scores will be distributed symmetrically around the mean, a few individuals scoring quite high, a few quite low and the majority falling somewhere near the middle of the scale. When this happens the frequency polygon approximates to the ideal or normal frequency curve described in Chapter 5.

IV. STANDARDS OF ACCURACY IN COMPUTATION *

"How many places" to carry numerical results is a question which arises persistently in statistical computation. Sometimes a student, by discarding decimals, throws away legitimate data. More often, however, he tends to retain too many decimals, a practice which may give a false appearance of great precision not always justified by the original material.

In this section are given some of the generally accepted principles which apply to statistical calculation. Observance of these rules will lead to greater uniformity in calculation. They should be followed carefully in solving the problems given in this book.

* This section should be reviewed frequently, and referred to in solving the problems given in succeeding chapters.

1. Rounded numbers

In calculation, numbers are usually "rounded" off to the standard of accuracy demanded by the problem. If we round off 8.6354 to two decimals it becomes 8.64; to one decimal, 8.6; to the nearest integer, 9. Measures of central tendency and variability, coefficients of correlation, and other indices are rarely reported to more than two decimal places. A mean of 52.6872, for example, is usually reported as 52.69; a standard deviation of 12.3841 as 12.38; and a coefficient of correlation of .6350 as .63, etc. It is very doubtful whether much of the work in mental measurement warrants accuracy beyond the second decimal. Convenient rules for rounding numbers to two decimals are as follows: When the third decimal is less than 5 drop it; when greater than 5, increase the preceding figure by 1; when exactly 5, compute the fourth decimal and correct back to the second place; when exactly 5 followed by zeros, drop it and make no correction.

2. Significant figures

The measurement 64.3 inches is assumed to be correct to the nearest tenth of an inch, its true value lying somewhere between 64.25 and 64.35 inches. Two places to the left of the decimal point and one to the right are fixed, and hence 64.3 is said to contain *three* significant figures. The numbers 643 and .643 also contain three significant figures each.

In the number .003046 there are *four* significant figures, 3, 0, 4 and 6, the first two zeros serving merely to locate the decimal point. When used to locate a decimal point only, a zero is not considered to be a significant figure; .004, for example, has only *one* significant figure, the two zeros simply fixing the position of 4, the significant digit. The following illustrations should make clear the matter of significant figures:

136 has *three* significant figures.

136,000 has *three* significant figures also. The true value of this number lies between 136,500 and 135,500. Only the first three digits are definitely fixed, the zeros serving simply to locate the decimal point or fix the size of the number.

1360. has *four* significant figures; the decimal indicates that the zero in the fourth place is known—and hence significant.

.136 has *three* significant figures.

.1360 has *four* significant figures; the zero fixes the fourth place.

.00136 has *three* significant figures; the first two zeros merely locate the decimal point.

2.00136 has *six* significant figures; the integer, 2, makes the two zeros to the right of the decimal point significant.

3. Exact and approximate numbers

It is necessary in calculation to make a distinction between *exact* and *approximate* numbers. An exact number is one which is found by counting: 10 children, 150 test scores, 20 desks are examples. Approximate numbers result from the measurement of variable quantities. Test scores and other measures, for example, are approximate since they are represented by intervals and not exact points on some scale. Thus a score of 61 may be any value from 60.5 up to 61.5 and a measured height of 47.5 inches may be any value from 47.45 up to 47.55 inches (see p. 3). Calculations with exact numbers may, in general, be carried to as many decimals as we please, since we may assume as many significant figures as we wish. For example, 110 test scores, which means that exactly 110 subjects were tested, could be written $N = 110.000$ . . . i.e., to n significant figures. Calculations based upon approximate numbers depend upon, and are limited by, the number of significant figures in the numbers which enter into the calculations. This will be made clearer in the following rules.

4. Rules for computation

(1) ACCURACY OF A PRODUCT

(*a*) The number of significant figures in the product of two or more approximate numbers will equal the number of significant figures in that one of the numbers which contains the smaller (or smallest) number of significant figures. To illustrate:

125.5 × 7.0 = 880, not 878.5, because 7.0, the less accurate of the two numbers, contains only two significant figures. The number 125.5 contains four significant figures.

125.5 × 7.000 = 878.5. Both numbers now contain four significant figures; hence their product also contains four significant figures.

(*b*) When multiplying an exact number by an approximate number, the number of significant figures in the product is determined by the number of significant figures in the approximate number. To illustrate:

If each of 12 children (12 is an exact number) has an M.A. of 8 years (8 is an approximate number) the product 12 × 8 must be written either as 90 or 100, since the approximate number has only *one* significant digit. If, however, each M.A. of 8 years can be written as 8.0, the product 12 × 8.0 can be written as 96, since 8.0 contains *two* significant digits.

(2) ACCURACY OF A QUOTIENT

(a) When dividing one approximate number by another approximate number, the significant figures in the quotient will equal the significant figures in that one of the two numbers (dividend or divisor) which is less accurate, i.e., which has the smaller number of significant digits. Illustrations:

$\dfrac{9.27}{41}$ should be written .23, not .22609, since 41 (the less accurate number) contains only two significant figures.

$\dfrac{16}{4724}$ should be written .0034, not .0033869, since 16 (the less accurate number) has two significant figures.

(b) In dividing an approximate number by an exact number, the number of significant figures in the quotient will equal the number of significant figures in the approximate number. Illustrations:

$\dfrac{9.27}{41}$ should be written .226, since 9.27, the approximate number, has three significant figures. The number 41 is an exact number.

$\dfrac{8541}{50}$ should be written 170.8, not 170.82, since 8541, the approximate number, contains only four significant figures.

(c) In dealing with exact numbers, quotients may be written to as many decimals as one wishes.

(3) ACCURACY OF A ROOT OR POWER

(a) The square root of an approximate number may legitimately contain as many significant figures as there are in the number itself. However, the number of figures retained in the root is usually less than the number of significant figures in the number. For example, $\sqrt{159.5600}$ will more often be written 12.63 than 12.63171, although the original number, 159.5600 contains seven significant figures.

(b) The square, or higher power, of an approximate number contains as many significant figures as there are in the original number (and no more). For example, $(.034)^2 = .0012$ (two significant figures) and not .001156 (four significant figures).

(c) Roots and powers of exact numbers may be taken to as many decimal places as one wishes.

(4) ACCURACY OF A SUM OR DIFFERENCE

The number of decimal places to be retained in a sum or difference should be no greater than the *number of decimals* in the least accurate of the numbers added or subtracted. Illustrations:

$362.2 + 18.225 + 5.3062 = 385.7$ not 385.7312, since the least accurate number (362.2) contains only one decimal

$362.2 - 18.245 = 344.0$, not 343.955, since the less accurate number (362.2) contains only one decimal.

PROBLEMS

1. Indicate which of the following variables fall into continuous and which into discrete series: (a) time; (b) salaries in a large business firm; (c) sizes of elementary school classes; (d) age; (e) census data; (f) distance traveled by car; (g) football scores; (h) weight; (i) numbers of pages in 100 books; (j) mental ages.

2. Write the exact upper and lower limits of the following scores in accordance with the two definitions of a score in continuous series, given on pages 3 and 4:

| 62 | 175 | 1 |
| 8 | 312 | 87 |

3. Suppose that sets of scores have the ranges given below. Indicate how large an interval, and how many intervals, you would suggest for use in drawing up a frequency distribution of each set.

Range	Size of Interval	Number of Intervals
16 to 87		
0 to 46		
110 to 212		
63 to 151		
4 to 12		

4. In each of the following write (a) the exact lower and upper limits of the class intervals (following the first definition of a score, given on p. 3), and (b) the midpoint of each interval.

| 45–47 | 162.5–167.5 | 63–67 | 0–9 |
| 1–4 | 80 up to 90 | 16–17 | 25–28 |

5. (a) Tabulate the following twenty-five scores into two frequency distributions, using (1) an interval of three, and (2) an interval of 5 units. Let the first interval begin with score 60.

72	75	77	67	72
81	78	65	86	73
67	82	76	76	70
83	71	63	72	72
61	67	84	69	64

(b) Tabulate the following 100 scores into three frequency distributions, using intervals of 3, 5 and 10 units. Let the first interval begin with 45.

63	78	76	58	95
78	86	80	96	94
46	78	92	86	88
82	101	102	70	50
74	65	73	72	91
103	90	87	74	83
78	75	70	84	98
86	73	85	99	93
103	90	79	81	83
87	86	93	89	76
73	86	82	71	94
95	84	90	73	75
82	86	83	63	56
89	76	81	105	73
73	75	85	74	95
92	83	72	98	110
85	103	81	78	98
80	86	96	78	71
81	84	81	83	92
90	85	85	96	72

6. The following lists represent the final grades made by two sections of the same course in general psychology.

(a) Tabulate the grades into frequency distributions using an interval of 5. Begin with 45 in Section I and 50 in Section II.

(b) Represent these frequency distributions as frequency polygons on the same axes.

Section I ($N = 64$)								Section II ($N = 46$)				
70	71	67	90	51	70	90		84	73	78	58	84
67	79	81	81	58	76	72		80	74	86	52	74
51	76	76	90	71	72	62		90	87	92	78	62
89	90	76	71	88	66	81		82	76	85	85	90
91	71	65	63	65	76			84	79	54	94	81
79	80	71	76	54	80			70	97	65	66	77
72	63	87	91	90	45			89	69	56	57	
69	66	80	79	71	75			77	78	71	63	
58	50	47	67	67	52			62	95	65	71	
64	88	54	70	80	92			79	85	70	71	

7. (a) Plot frequency polygons for the two distributions of 25 scores found in 5(a), using intervals of 3 and of 5 score units. Smooth the second dis-

tribution (see p. 13) and plot the smoothed f's and the original scores on the same axes.

(b) Plot a frequency polygon of the 100 scores in 5(b) using an interval of 10 score units. Superimpose a histogram upon the frequency polygon, using the same axes.

8. Reduce the distributions A and B below to percentage frequencies and plot them as frequency polygons on the same axes. Is your understanding of the achievement of these groups advanced by this treatment of the data?

Scores	Group A	Group B
52–55	1	8
48–51	0	5
44–47	5	12
40–43	10	58
36–39	20	40
32–35	12	22
28–31	8	10
24–27	2	15
20–23	3	5
16–19	4	0
	65	175

9. (a) Round off the following numbers to two decimals:

3.5872   74.168   126.83500
46.9223   25.193   81.72558

(b) How many significant figures in each of the following:

.00046   91.00   1.03
46.02   18.365   15.0048

(c) Write the answers to the following:

$127.4 \times .0036 =$ (both numbers approximate)
$200.0 \div 5.63 =$ "   "   "
$62 \times .053 =$ (first number exact, second approximate)
$364.2 + 61.596 =$
$364.2 - 61.596 =$
$\sqrt{47.86} =$
$(18.6)^2 =$

ANSWERS

2. 61.5 to 62.5 and 62.0 to 63.0; 174.5 to 175.5 and 175.0 to 176.0; 7.5 to 8.5 and 8.0 to 9.0; 311.5 to 312.5 and 312.0 to 313.0; .5 to 1.5 and 1.0 to 2.0
86.5 to 87.5 and 87.0 to 88.0

3.

Size of Interval	No. of Intervals
5	15
4 or 5	12 or 10
10	11
10	9
1	9

4.

	Midpoint
44.5 to 47.5	46.0
.5 to 4.5	2.5
162.5 to 167.5	165.0
79.5 to 89.5	84.5
62.5 to 67.5	65.0
15.5 to 17.5	16.5
−.5 to 9.5	4.5
24.5 to 28.5	26.5

9. (a)

3.59	74.17	126.83
46.92	25.19	81.73

(b)

2	4	3
4	5	6

(c)

.46
35.5
3.3
425.8
302.6
6.918 or 6.92
346

CHAPTER 2

MEASURES OF CENTRAL TENDENCY

◇◇

When scores or other measures have been tabulated into a frequency distribution, as shown in Chapter 1, usually the next task is to calculate a measure of *central tendency*, or central position. The value of a measure of central tendency is twofold. First, it is an "average" which represents *all* of the scores made by the group, and as such gives a concise description of the performance of the group as a whole; and second, it enables us to compare two or more groups in terms of typical performance. There are three "averages" or measures of central tendency in common use, (1) the *arithmetic mean,* (2) the *median,* and (3) the *mode.* The "average" is the popular term for the arithmetic mean. In statistical work, however, "average" is the general term for any measure of central tendency.

I. CALCULATION OF MEASURES OF CENTRAL TENDENCY

I. The arithmetic mean (M)

(1) CALCULATION OF THE MEAN WHEN DATA ARE UNGROUPED

The arithmetic mean or more simply the mean is the sum of the separate scores or measures divided by their number. If a man earns $3.00, $4.00, $3.50, $5.00 and $4.50 on five successive days his mean daily wage ($4.00) is obtained by dividing the sum of his daily earnings by the number of days he has worked. The formula for the mean (M) of a series of ungrouped measures is

$$M = \frac{\Sigma X}{N} \qquad (1)$$

(arithmetic mean calculated from ungrouped data)

27

in which N is the number of measures in the series, X stands for a score or other measure, and the symbol Σ means "sum of," here sum of separate measures.

(2) CALCULATION OF THE MEAN FROM DATA GROUPED INTO A FREQUENCY DISTRIBUTION

When measures have been grouped into a frequency distribution, the mean is calculated by a slightly different method from that given above. The two illustrations in Table 5 will make the difference clear. The first example shows the calculation of the mean of the 50 Alpha scores tabulated into a frequency distribution in Table 1. First, the fX column is found by multiplying the midpoint (here X) of each interval by the number of scores (f) on it; the mean (170.80) is then simply the sum of

TABLE 5   The calculation of the mean, median, and crude mode from data grouped into a frequency distribution

1. Data from Table 1, 50 Army Alpha scores
Class interval = 5

Class Intervals Scores	Midpoint X	f		fX
195–199	197	1		197
190–194	192	2		384
185–189	187	4		748
180–184	182	5 ↓		910
175–179	177	8	20	1416
170–174	172	10		1720
165–169	167	6	20	1002
160–164	162	4 ↑		648
155–159	157	4		628
150–154	152	2		304
145–149	147	3		441
140–144	142	1		142
		$N = 50$		8540
		$N/2 = 25$		

(1) Mean $= \dfrac{\Sigma fX}{N} = \dfrac{8540}{50} = 170.80$

(2) Median $= 169.5 + \dfrac{5}{10} \times 5 = 172.00$

(3) Crude Mode falls on class interval 170–174 or at 172.00

TABLE 5—(Continued)

2. Scores made by 200 adults upon a cancellation test
Class interval = 4

Class Intervals Scores	Midpoint X	f		fX
135.5–139.5	137.5	3		412.5
131.5–135.5	133.5	5		667.5
127.5–131.5	129.5	16	↓	2072.0
123.5–127.5	125.5	23		2886.5
119.5–123.5	121.5	52	99	6318.0
115.5–119.5	117.5	49		5757.5
111.5–115.5	113.5	27	52	3064.5
107.5–111.5	109.5	18	↑	1971.0
103.5–107.5	105.5	7		738.5
		$N = 200$		23888.0
		$N/2 = 100$		

(1) Mean $= \dfrac{\Sigma fX}{N} = \dfrac{23{,}888.0}{200} = 119.44$

(2) Median $= 115.5 + \dfrac{48}{49} \times 4 = 119.42$

(3) Crude Mode falls on class interval 119.5 to 123.5 or at 121.50

the fX (namely, 8540) divided by N (50). Scores grouped into intervals lose their identity and must be represented by the midpoint of that particular interval on which they fall. Hence, we multiply the midpoint of each interval by the frequency upon that interval; add the fX and divide by N to obtain the mean. The formula is

$$M = \frac{\Sigma fX}{N} \qquad (2)$$

*(arithmetic mean calculated from scores grouped into
a frequency distribution)*

in which fX is the sum of the midpoints weighted by their frequencies.

The second example in Table 5 is another illustration of the calculation of the mean from grouped data. This frequency distribution represents 200 scores made by a group of adults on a cancellation test. Scores have been classified into 9 intervals; and since the intervals are 4 units in length, the midpoints are found by adding one-half of 4 to the exact lower limit of each. For example, in the first interval, $103.5 + 2.0 = 105.5$.

The fX column totals 23,888.0; and N is 200. Hence, applying formula (2), the mean is found to be 119.44 (to two decimals).

(3) THE MEAN FROM COMBINED SAMPLES OR GROUPS

Suppose that on a certain test the mean for a group of 10 children is 62, and that on the same test the mean for a group of 40 children is 66. Then the mean of the two groups combined is $\dfrac{62 \times 10 + 66 \times 40}{50}$ or 65.2. The formula for the weighted mean of n groups is

$$M_{comb} = \frac{N_1 M_1 + N_2 M_2 + \ldots\ldots\ldots + N_n M_n}{N_1 + N_2 + \ldots\ldots + N_n} \tag{3}$$

(*weighted arithmetical mean obtained from combining*
n groups)

When only two groups are combined, the weighted mean formula becomes

$$M_{comb} = \frac{N_1 M_1 + N_2 M_2}{N_1 + N_2}$$

2. The median (Mdn) *

(1) CALCULATION OF THE MEDIAN WHEN DATA ARE UNGROUPED

When ungrouped scores or other measures are arranged in order of size, the median is the *midpoint* in the series. Two situations arise in the computation of the median from ungrouped data: (*a*) when N is *odd*, and (*b*) when N is *even*. To consider, first, the case where N is odd, suppose we have the following integral "mental ages": 7, 10, 8, 12, 9, 11, 7, calculated from seven performance tests. If we arrange these seven scores in order of size

$$7 \quad 7 \quad 8 \quad (9) \quad 10 \quad 11 \quad 12$$

the median is 9.0 since 9.0 is the midpoint of that score which lies midway in the series. Calculation is as follows: There are three scores above, and three below 9, and since a score of 9 covers the interval 8.5 to 9.5, its midpoint is 9.0. This is the median.

Now if we drop the first score of 7 our series contains six scores

$$7 \quad 8 \quad 9 \quad \overset{9.5}{\uparrow} \quad 10 \quad 11 \quad 12$$

and the median is 9.5. Counting three scores in from the beginning of the series, we *complete* score 9 (which is 8.5 to 9.5) to reach 9.5, the *upper* limit of score 9. In like manner, counting three scores in from the end

* The median is also designated *Md.*

of the series, we move *through* score 10 (10.5 to 9.5) reaching 9.5, the *lower* limit of score 10.

A formula for finding the median of a series of ungrouped scores is

$$Median = the \frac{(N+1)}{2} th \text{ measure in order of size} \qquad (4)$$

(*median from ungrouped data*)

In our first illustration above, the median is on the $\frac{(7+1)}{2}$ or 4th score counting in from either end of the series, that is, 9.0 (midpoint 8.5 to 9.5). In our second illustration, the median is on the $\frac{(6+1)}{2}$ or 3.5tb score in order of size, that is, 9.5 (upper limit of score 9, or lower limit of score 10).

(2) CALCULATION OF THE MEDIAN WHEN DATA ARE GROUPED INTO A FREQUENCY DISTRIBUTION

When scores in a continuous series are grouped into a frequency distribution, the median by definition is the 50% *point* in the distribution. To locate the median, therefore, we take 50% (i.e., $N/2$) of our scores, and count into the distribution until the 50% point is reached. The method is illustrated in the two examples in Table 5. Since there are 50 scores in the first distribution, $N/2 = 25$, and the median is that point in our distribution of Alpha scores which has 25 scores on each side of it. Beginning at the small-score end of the distribution, and adding up the the scores in order, we find that intervals 140–144 to 165–169, inclusive, contain just 20 fs—five scores short of the 25 necessary to locate the median. The next interval, 170–174, contains 10 scores assumed to be spread evenly over the interval (p. 29). In order to get the five extra scores needed to make exactly 25, we take $5/10 \times 5$ (the length of the interval) and add this increment (2.5) to 169,5, the beginning of the interval 170–174. This puts the *Mdn* at 169.5 + 2.5 or at 172.0. The student should note carefully that the median like the mean is a *point* and not a *score*.

A second illustration of the calculation of the median from a frequency distribution is given in Table 5 (2). There are 200 scores in this distribution; hence, $N/2 = 100$, and the median must lie at a point 100 scores distant from either end of the distribution. If we begin at the small-score end of the distribution (103.5–107.5) and add the scores in order, 52 scores take us *through* the interval 111.5–115.5. The 49 scores on the next interval (115.5–119.5) plus the 52 already counted off total 101—*one* score too many to give us 100, the point at which the median falls. To get the 48 scores needed to make *exactly* 100 we must take $48/49 \times 4$ (the length of the interval) and add this amount (3.92) to 115.5, the beginning of interval 115.5–119.5. This procedure takes us exactly 100 scores into the distribution, and locates the median at 119.42.

A formula for calculating the *Mdn* when the data have been classified into a frequency distribution is

$$Mdn = l + \left(\frac{\frac{N}{2} - F}{f_m}\right) i \qquad (5)$$

(*median computed from data grouped into a frequency distribution*)

where

l = exact lower limit of the class interval upon which the median lies

$\dfrac{N}{2}$ = one-half the total number of scores

F = sum of the scores on all intervals *below* l

f_m = frequency (number of scores) *within* the interval upon which the median falls

i = length of class interval

To illustrate the use of formula (5), consider the first example in Table 5. Here $l = 169.5$, $N/2 = 25$, $F = 20$, $f_m = 10$, and $i = 5$. Hence, the median falls at $169.5 + \dfrac{(25 - 20)}{10} \times 5$ or at 172.0. In the second example, $l = 115.5$, $N/2 = 100$, $F = 52$, $f_m = 49$, and $i = 4$. The median is $115.5 + \dfrac{(100 - 52)}{49} \times 4$ or 119.42.

The steps involved in computing the *Mdn* from data tabulated into a frequency distribution may be summarized as follows:

(1) Find $N/2$, that is, one-half of the cases in the distribution.
(2) Begin at the small-score end of the distribution and count off the scores in order up to the exact lower limit (l) of the interval which contains the median. The sum of these scores is F.
(3) Compute the number of scores necessary to fill out $N/2$, i.e., compute $N/2 - F$. Divide this quantity by the frequency (f_m) on the interval which contains the median; and multiply the result by the size of the class-interval (i).
(4) Add the amount obtained by the calculations in (3) to the exact lower limit (l) of the interval which contains the *Mdn*. This procedure will give the median of the distribution.

The median may also be computed by counting off one-half of the scores from the top down in a frequency distribution; but counting up from the low score end is usually more convenient. If we count down from the top of the distribution, the quantity found in step (3) must be subtracted from the exact upper limit of the interval upon which the median falls.

To illustrate with the data of Table 5 (1), counting down in the f column, 20 scores *complete* interval 175–179, and we reach 174.5, the exact upper limit of the interval 170–174. Five scores of the 10 on this interval are needed to make 25 ($N/2$). Hence we have $174.5 - \frac{5}{10} \times 5 =$ 172.0, which checks our first calculation of the median. In Table 5 (2), the median found by counting down is $119.5 - \frac{1}{49} \times 4$ or 119.42.

(3) CALCULATION OF THE Mdn WHEN (a) THE FREQUENCY DISTRIBUTION CONTAINS GAPS; AND WHEN (b) THE FIRST OR LAST INTERVAL HAS INDETERMINATE LIMITS

(a) Difficulty arises when it becomes necessary to calculate the median from a distribution in which there are gaps or zero frequency upon one or more intervals. The method to be followed in such cases is shown in Table 6. Since $N = 10$, and $N/2 = 5$, we count *up* the frequency column

TABLE 6 Computation of the median when there are gaps in the distribution

Class Intervals Scores	f	
20–21	2	
18–19	1	
16–17	0	
14–15	0	
12–13	2	10–13
10–11	0	
8–9	0	6–9
6–7	2	
4–5	1	
2–3	1	
0–1	1	
	$N = 10$	
	$N/2 = 5$	

$$Mdn = 9.5 + \frac{0}{2} \times 2 = 9.5$$

5 scores through 6–7. Ordinarily, this would put the median at 7.5, the exact lower limit of interval 8–9. If we check this median, however, by counting *down* the frequency column five scores, the median falls at 11.5, the lower limit of 12–13. Obviously, the discrepancy between these two values of the median is due to the two intervals 8–9 and 10–11 (each of which has zero frequency) which lie between 6–7 and 12–13. In order to have the median come out at the same point, whether computed from the top or the bottom of the frequency distribution, the procedure usually followed in cases like this to have interval 6–7 *include* 8–9, thus becoming 6–9; and to have interval 12–13 *include* 10–11, becoming 10–13. Lengthening these intervals from two to four units eliminates the zero frequency on the adjacent intervals by spreading the numerical frequency over them. If now we count off five scores, going *up* the frequency column through 6–9, the median falls at 9.5, the upper limit of this interval. Also, counting *down* the frequency column five scores, we arrive at a median value of 9.5, the *upper* limit of 6–9, *or* the *lower* limit of 10–13. Computation from the two ends of the series now gives consistent results—the median is 9.5 in both instances.

Table 6 represents an extreme case of a distribution with gaps. When N is small (as here) and gaps are numerous, it is always wise to get further data before computing a median. The procedure suggested for dealing with gaps in a distribution is not to be taken as a substitute for good data in the first instance.

(*b*) When scores scatter widely, the last interval in a frequency distribution may be designated as "80 and above" or simply as 80+. This means that all scores at or above 80 are thrown into this interval, the upper limit of which is indeterminate. The same lumping together of scores may occur at the beginning of the distribution, when the first interval, for example, may be designated "20 and below" or 20–; or a number of scores may be put into an interval marked D.N.C. (did not complete). The lower limit of the beginning interval is now indeterminate. In incomplete distributions like these, the median is readily computed since each score is simply counted as one frequency whether accurately classified or not. But it is impossible to calculate the mean exactly when the midpoint of one or more intervals is unknown. The mean depends upon the absolute size of the scores (or their midpoints) and is directly affected by indeterminate interval limits.

3. The mode

In a simple ungrouped series of measures the "crude" or "empirical" mode is that single measure or score which occurs most frequently. For example, in the series 10, 11, 11, 12, 12, 13, 13, 13, 14, 14, the most often recurring measure, namely, 13, is the crude or empirical mode. When data are grouped into a frequency distribution, the crude mode is usually taken to be the midpoint of that interval which contains the largest frequency. In example 1, Table 5, the interval 170–174 contains the largest frequency and hence 172.0, its midpoint, is the crude mode. In example 2, Table 5, the largest frequency falls on 119.5–123.5 and the crude mode is at 121.5, the midpoint.

When calculating the mode from a frequency distribution, we distinguish between the "true" mode and the crude mode. The true mode is the point (or "peak") of greatest concentration in the distribution; that is, the point at which more measures fall than at any other point. When the scale is divided into finely graduated units, when the frequency polygon has been smoothed, and when N is large, the crude mode closely approaches the true mode. Ordinarily, however, the crude mode is only approximately equal to the true mode. A formula for approximating the true mode, when the frequency distribution is symmetrical, or at least not badly skewed (p. 99) is

$$Mode = 3\ Mdn - 2\ Mean \qquad (6)$$

(*approximation to the true mode calculated from a frequency distribution*)

If we apply this formula to the data in Table 5, the mode is 174.40 for the first distribution, and 119.38 for the second. The first mode is somewhat larger and the second slightly smaller than the crude modes obtained from the same distributions.

The crude mode is an unstable measure of central tendency. But this instability is not so serious a drawback as it might seem. A crude mode is usually employed as a simple, inspectional "average," to indicate in a rough way the center of concentration in the distribution. For this purpose it need not be calculated as exactly as the median or mean.

II. CALCULATION OF THE MEAN BY THE "ASSUMED MEAN" OR SHORT METHOD

In Table 5 the mean was calculated by multiplying the midpoint (X) of each interval by the frequency (number of scores) on the interval, summing these values (the fX column) and dividing by N, the number of scores. This straightforward method (called the Long Method) gives accurate results but often requires the handling of large numbers and entails tedious calculation. Because of this, the "Assumed Mean" method, or simply the Short Method, has been devised for computing the mean. The Short Method does not apply to the calculation of the median or the mode. These measures are always found by the methods previously described.

The most important fact to remember in calculating the mean by the Short Method is that we "guess" or "assume" a mean at the outset, and later apply a correction to this assumed value (AM) in order to obtain the actual mean (M) (see Table 7). There is no set rule for assuming a

TABLE 7   The calculation of the mean by the short method

(Data from Table 1, 50 Army Alpha scores)

(1) Class Intervals Scores	(2) Midpoint X	(3) f	(4) x'	(5) fx'
195–199	197	1	5	5
190–194	192	2	4	8
185–189	187	4	3	12
180–184	182	5	2	10
175–179	177	8	1	8
170–174	172	10	0	+43
165–169	167	6	−1	−6
160–164	162	4	−2	−8
155–159	157	4	−3	−12
150–154	152	2	−4	−8
145–149	147	3	−5	−15
140–144	142	1	−6	−6
		$N = 50$		−55

$$AM = 172.00$$
$$ci = -1.20$$
$$M = 170.80$$

$$c = -\frac{12}{50} = -.240$$
$$i = 5$$
$$ci = -.240 \times 5 = -1.20$$

mean.* The best plan is to take the midpoint of an interval somewhere near the *center* of the distribution; and if possible the midpoint of that interval which contains the largest frequency. In Table 7, the largest f is on interval 170–174, which also happens to be almost in the center of the distribution. Hence the AM is taken at 172.0, the middle of this interval. The question of the AM settled, we determine the correction which must be applied to the AM in order to get M. Steps are as follows:

* The method outlined here gives consistent results no matter where the mean is tentatively placed or assumed.

(1) First, we fill in the x' column,* column (4). Here are entered the deviations of the midpoints of the different steps measured from the AM in *units of class interval.* Thus 177, the midpoint of 175–179, deviates from 172, the AM, by *one* interval; and a "1" is placed in the x' column opposite 177. In like manner, 182 deviates *two* intervals from 172; and a "2" goes in the x' column opposite 182. Reading on up the x' column from 172, we find the succeeding entries to be 3, 4 and 5. The last entry, 5, is the interval deviation of 197 from 172; the actual score deviation, of course, is 25.

Returning to 172, we find that the x' of this midpoint measured from the AM (from itself) is zero; hence a zero is placed in the x' column opposite 170–174. Below 172, all of the x' entries are negative, since all of the midpoints are less than 172, the AM. So the x' of 167 from 172 is -1 interval; and the x' of 162 from 172 is -2 intervals. The other x's are -3, -4, -5, and -6 intervals.

(2) The x' column completed, we compute the fx' column, column (5). The fx' entries are found in exactly the same way as are the fX in Table 5. Each x' in column (4) is multiplied or "weighted" by the appropriate f in column (3). Note again that in the Short Method we multiply each x' by its deviation from the AM in *units of class interval,* instead of by its actual deviation from the mean of the distribution. For this reason, the computation of the fx' column is much more simple than is the calculation of the fX column by the method given on page 000. All fx' on intervals *above* (greater than) the AM are *positive;* and all fx' on intervals *below* (smaller than) the AM are *negative,* since the signs of the fx' depend upon the signs of the x'.

(3) From the fx' column the correction is obtained as follows: The sum of the positive values in the fx' column is 43; and the sum of the negative values in the fx' column is -55. There are, therefore, 12 more *minus* fx' values than *plus* (the algebraic *sum* is -12); and -12 divided by 50 (N) gives $-.240$ which is the correction (c) in *units of class interval.* If we multiply c $(-.240)$ by i, the length of the interval (here 5), the result is ci (-1.20) the score correction, or the correction in *score units.* When -1.20 is added to 172.00, the AM, the result is the actual mean, 170.80.

The process of calculating the mean by the Short Method may be summarized as follows:

(1) Tabulate the scores or measures into a frequency distribution.
(2) "Assume" a mean as near the center of the distribution as possible, and preferably on the interval containing the largest frequency.
(3) Find the deviation of the midpoint of each class interval from the AM in units of interval.

* x' is regularly used to denote the deviation of a score X from the assumed mean (AM); x is the deviation of a score X from the actual mean (M) of the distribution.

(4) Multiply or weight each deviation (x') by its appropriate f—the f opposite it.

(5) Find the algebraic sum of the plus and minus fx' and divide this sum by N, the number of cases. This gives c, the correction in units of class interval.

(6) Multiply c by the interval length (i) to get ci, the score correction.

(7) Add ci algebraically to the AM to get the actual mean. Sometimes ci will be positive and sometimes negative, depending upon where the mean has been assumed. The method works equally well in either case.

III. WHEN TO USE THE VARIOUS MEASURES OF CENTRAL TENDENCY

The student of statistical method is often puzzled to know what measure of central tendency is most appropriate for a given problem. The M is generally preferred to other averages as it is rigidly defined mathematically $(\Sigma X/N)$ and is based upon all of the measures. But there are instances where the Mdn or the mode is the better statistic. While there is no substitute for experience, certain general rules may be set down as follows:

1. Use the mean

(1) When the scores are distributed symmetrically around a central point, i.e., when the distribution is not badly skewed (p. 99). The M is the center of gravity in the distribution, and each score contributes to its determination.

(2) When the measure of central tendency having the greatest stability is wanted (p. 185). Why the M is more stable than either the Mdn or the mode will appear later in Chapter 8.

(3) When other statistics (e.g., SD, coefficient of correlation) are to be computed later. Many statistics are based upon the mean.

2. Use the median

(1) When the exact midpoint of the distribution is wanted—the 50% point.

(2) When there are extreme scores which would markedly affect the mean. Extreme scores do not disturb the median. For example, in the series 4, 5, 6, 7and 8, both mean and median are 6. But if 8 is replaced by 50, the other scores remaining the same, the median is still 6 but the mean is 14.4.

(3) When it is desired that certain scores should influence the central tendency, but all that is known about them is that they are above or below the median (p. 33).

3. Use the mode

(1) When a quick and approximate measure of central tendency is all that is wanted.

(2) When the measure of central tendency should be the most typical value. When we describe the style of dress or shoes worn by the "average woman," for instance, the modal or most popular fashion is usually meant. In like manner, in speaking of the average wage in a certain industry, we often mean the modal wage under specified conditions.

PROBLEMS

1. Calculate the mean, median, and mode for the following frequency distributions. Use the Short Method in computing the mean.

(1)

Scores	f	x
70–71	2	
68–69	2	
66–67	3	
64–65	4	
62–63	6	
60–61	7	
58–59	5	
56–57	4	
54–55	2	
52–53	3	
50–51	1	
	N = 39	

$m = 60.76$
$Mdn. 60.79$
$\sigma - 4.99$

$Q = 3.37$

(2)

Scores	f
90–94	2
85–89	2
80–84	4
75–79	8
70–74	6
65–69	11
60–64	9
55–59	7
50–54	5
45–49	0
40–44	2
	N = 56

$m = 67.36$
$s = 66.77$
$\sigma = 11.83$
34
14
$Q = 8.12$
14

(3)

Scores	f
120–122	2
117–119	2
114–116	2
111–113	4
108–110	5
105–107	9
102–104	6
99–101	3
96–98	4
93–95	2
90–92	1
	N = 40

(4)

Scores	f
100–109	5
90–99	9
80–89	14
70–79	19
60–69	21
50–59	30
40–49	25
30–39	15
20–29	10
10–19	8
0–9	6
	N = 162

34

115

(5) Scores	f		(6) Scores	f
120–139	50		15	1
100–119	150		14	2
80–99	500		13	3
60–79	250		12	6
40–59	50		11	12
	$N = 1000$		10	15
			9	22
			8	31
			7	18
			6	6
			5	2
			4	2
				$N = 120$

2. Compute the mean and the median for each of the two distributions in problem 5(a), page 23, tabulated in 3- and 5-unit intervals. Compare the two means and the two medians, and explain any discrepancy found. (Let the first interval in the first distribution be 61–63; the first interval in the second distribution, 60–64.)

3. (a) The same test is given to the three sections of Grade VI. Results are: Section I, $M = 24$, $N = 32$; Section II, $M = 31$, $N = 54$; Section III, $M = 35$, $N = 16$. What is the general mean for the grade?
   (b) The mean score on AGCT in Camp A is 102, $N = 1500$; and in Camp B 106, $N = 450$. What is the mean for Camps A and B combined?

4. (a) Compute the median of the following 16 scores by the method of page 33.

Scores	f
20–21	2
18–19	2
16–17	4
14–15	0
12–13	4
10–11	0
8–9	4
	$N = 16$

   (b) In a group of 50 children, the 8 children who took longer than 5 minutes to complete a performance test were marked D.N.C. (did not complete). In computing a measure of central tendency for this distribution of scores, what measure would you use, and why?
   (c) Find the medians of the following arrays of ungrouped scores by formula (4) page 31:

(1) 21, 24, 27, 29, 29, 30, 32, 33, 35, 38, 42, 45.
(2) 54, 59, 64, 67, 70, 72, 73, 75, 78, 83, 90.
(3) 7, 8, 9, 9, 10, 11.

5. The time by your watch is 10:31 o'clock. In checking with two friends, you find that their watches give the time as 10:25 and 10:34. Assuming that the three watches are equally good timepieces, what do you think is probably the "correct time"?

6. What is meant popularly by the "law of averages"?

7. (a) When one uses the term "in the mode" does he have reference to the mode of a distribution?
   (b) What is approximately the modal time for each of the following meals: breakfast, lunch, dinner. Explain your answers.
   (c) Why is the median usually the best measure of the typical contribution in a church collection?

8. Suppose that the mean weekly pay of 5 brothers (after deductions) is $60 and the median is $50.
   (a) How much money do the brothers take home?
   (b) If John, the best paid brother, gets a pay raise of $10 per week, what is the new mean? The new median?

ANSWERS

1. (1) Mean = 60.76   Median = 60.79   Mode = 60.85
   (2) Mean = 67.36   Median = 66.77   Mode = 65.59

   (3) Mean = 106.00   Median = 105.83   Mode = 105.49
   (4) Mean = 55.43   Median = 55.17   Mode = 54.65

   (5) Mean = 87.5   Median = 87.5   Mode = 87.5
   (6) Mean = 8.85   Median = 8.55   Mode = 7.95

2. Class interval = 3   Mean = 72.92   Median = 71.75
   Class interval = 5   Mean = 73.00   Median = 72.71

3. (a) 29.43   (b) 103 (to the nearest whole number)

4. (a) Median = 14.5
   (c) (1) Median = 31.0
       (2) Median = 72.0
       (3) Median = 9.0

5. Mean is 10:30.

8. (a) $300
   (b) $62 $50

CHAPTER 3

MEASURES OF VARIABILITY

◇◇

In Chapter 2 the calculation of three measures of central tendency—measures typical or representative of a set of scores as a whole—was outlined. Ordinarily, the next step is to find some measure of the *variability* of our scores, i.e., of the "scatter" or "spread" of the separate scores around their central tendency. It will be the task of this chapter to show how indices of variability may be computed.

The usefulness of a statistic which provides a measure of variability can be seen from a simple example. Suppose a test of arithmetic reasoning has been administered to a group of 50 boys and to a group of 50 girls. The mean scores are, boys, 34.6, and girls, 34.5. So far as the means go there is no difference in the performance of the two groups. But suppose the boys' scores are found to range from 15 to 51 and the girls' scores from 19 to 45. This difference in range shows that in a general sense the boys "cover more territory," are more *variable,* than the girls; and this greater variability may be of more interest than the lack of a difference in the means. If a group is *homogeneous,* that is, made up of individuals of nearly the same ability, most of its scores will fall around the same point on the scale, the range will be relatively short and the variability small. But if the group contains individuals of widely differing capacities, scores will be strung out from high to low, the range will be relatively wide and the variability large.

This situation is represented graphically in Figure 7, which shows two frequency distributions of the same area (N) and same mean (50) but of very different variability. Group A ranges from 20 to 80, and Group B from 40 to 60. Group A is three times as variable as Group B—spreads over three times the distance on the scale of scores—though both distributions have the same central tendency.

Four measures have been devised to indicate the variability or dispersion within a set of measures. These are (1) the *range,* (2) the *quartile*

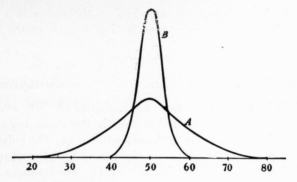

FIG. 7 Two distributions of the same area (N) and mean (50) but of very different variability

deviation or *Q*, (3) the *average deviation* or *AD*, and (4) the *standard deviation* or *SD*.

I. CALCULATION OF MEASURES OF VARIABILITY

I. The range

We have already had occasion to use the range in Table 1. It may be defined again simply as that interval between the highest and the lowest scores. In Figure 7 the range of the boys' scores was 51–15 or 36 and the range of the girls' scores 45–19 or 26. The range is the most general measure of spread or scatter, and is computed when we wish to make a rough comparison of two or more groups for variability. The range takes account of the extremes of the series of scores only, and is unreliable when *N* is small or when there are large gaps (i.e., zero *f*'s) in the frequency distribution. Suppose that the highest score in a distribution is 120 and there is a gap of 20 points before we reach 100, the score next below. If the lowest score is 60, the single high score of 120 increases the range from 40 (100–60) to 60 (120–60).

2. The quartile deviation or Q

The *quartile deviation* or *Q* is one-half the scale distance between the 75th and 25th percentiles in a frequency distribution. The 25th percentile or Q_1 is the *first quartile* on the score scale, the point below which lie 25% of the scores. The 75th percentile or Q_3 is the *third quartile* on the score scale—the point below which lie 75% of the scores. When we have these two points the quartile deviation or Q is found from the formula

$$Q = \frac{Q_3 - Q_1}{2} \tag{7}$$

(quartile deviation or Q calculated from a frequency distribution)

To find Q, it is clear that we must first compute the 75th and 25th percentiles. These statistics are found in exactly the same way as was the median, which is, of course, the 50th percentile or Q_2. The only difference is that 1/4 of N is counted off from the low end of the distribution to find Q_1 and that $3/4 N$ is counted off to find Q_3. The formulas are

$$Q_1 = l + i \frac{(N/4 - cum\ f_l)}{f_q} \tag{8}$$

and

$$Q_3 = l + i \frac{(3N/4 - cum\ f_l)}{f_q} \tag{9}$$

(quartiles Q₁ and Q₃ computed from a frequency distribution)

where

   $l =$ the exact lower limit of the interval in which the quartile falls
   $i =$ the length of the interval
$cum\ f_l =$ cumulative f up to the interval which contains the quartile
   $f_q =$ the f on the interval containing the quartile

Table 8 shows the computations needed to get Q in the distribution of 50 Alpha scores shown in Table 1. First, to find Q_1 we count off 1/4 of N or 12.5 from the low-score end of the distribution. When the scores are added in order, the first 4 intervals (140–144 through 155–159) contain 10 scores and take us up to 159.5. Q_1 must fall on the next interval (160–164) which contains 4 scores. From Table 8 we have that

   $l = 159.5$, exact lower limit of the interval on which Q_1 falls
$1/4\ N = 12.5$
$cum\ f_l = 10$, cumulated scores up to the interval containing Q_1
   $f_q = 4$, the f on the interval on which Q_1 falls
   $i = 5$, the length of the interval

Substituting in formula (8), we have that

$$Q_1 = 159.5 + \frac{5(12.5 - 10)}{4}$$

$$= 162.62$$

To find Q_3, we count off $3/4\ N$ from the low-score end of the distribution. From Table 8 it is clear that $3/4\ N$ is 37.5; and that the f's on intervals 140–144 through 170–174, inclusive, total 30. Q_3 must fall on the next interval (175–179) which contains 8 scores. Substituting the necessary data from Table 8 we have that

$l = 174.5$, exact lower limit of interval which contains Q_3
$3/4\,N = 37.5$
$cum\ f_l = 30$, sum of scores up to interval which contains Q_3
$f_q = 8$, f on the interval containing Q_3
$i = 5$

and from formula (9)

$$Q_3 = 174.5 + \frac{5(37.5 - 30)}{8}$$
$$= 179.19$$

Finally, substituting in formula (7) we have that

$$Q = \frac{179.19 - 162.62}{2}$$
$$= 8.28$$

TABLE 8   The calculation of the Q, AD and SD from data grouped into a frequency distribution

$M = 170.80$

1. Data from Table 1, p. 5, 50 Army Alpha scores

(1) Intervals (Scores)	(2) Midpoint X	(3) f		(4) x	(5) fx	(6) fx²
195–199	197	1		26.20	26.20	686.44
190–194	192	2		21.20	42.40	898.88
185–189	187	4		16.20	64.80	1049.76
180–184	182	5		11.20	56.00	627.20
175–179	177	8		6.20	49.60	307.52
170–174	172	10	30	1.20	12.00	14.40
165–169	167	6		−3.80	−22.80	86.64
160–164	162	4		−8.80	−35.20	309.76
155–159	157	4	10	−13.80	−55.20	761.76
150–154	152	2		−18.80	−37.60	706.88
145–149	147	3		−23.80	−71.40	1699.32
140–144	142	1		−28.80	−28.80	829.44
		N = 50			502.00	7978.00

TABLE 8—(Continued)

Mean = 170.80 (from Table 5)

$N/4 = 12.5$ and $3N/4 = 37.5$

$$Q_1 = 159.5 + \frac{5(12.5 - 10)}{4} = 162.62 \tag{8}$$

$$Q_3 = 174.5 + \frac{5(37.5 - 30)}{8} = 179.19 \tag{9}$$

$$Q = \frac{Q_3 - Q_1}{2} = \frac{179.19 - 162.62}{2} = 8.28 \tag{7}$$

$$AD = \frac{\Sigma \mid fx \mid}{N} = \frac{502.00}{50} = 10.04 \tag{11}$$

$$SD = \sqrt{\frac{\Sigma fx^2}{N}} = \sqrt{\frac{7978.00}{50}} = 12.63 \tag{13}$$

2. Data from Table 3, 200 cancellation scores

(1) Intervals (Scores)	(2) Midpoint X	(3) f		(4) x	(5) fx	(6) fx²
135.5–139.5	137.5	3	4	18.06	54.18	978.49
131.5–135.5	133.5	5	3	14.06	70.30	988.42
127.5–131.5	129.5	16	2	10.06	160.96	1619.26
123.5–127.5	125.5	23	1	6.06	139.38	844.64
119.5–123.5	121.5	52	0	2.06	107.12	220.67
115.5–119.5	117.5	49 101	-1	−1.94	−95.06	184.42
111.5–115.5	113.5	27	-2	−5.94	−160.38	952.66
107.5–111.5	109.5	18 25	3	−9.94	−178.92	1778.46
103.5–107.5	105.5	7	-4	−13.94	−97.58	1360.27
		$N = 200$			1063.88	8927.29

Mean = 119.44 (from Table 6)

$N/4 = 50$ and $3N/4 = 150$

$$Q_1 = 111.5 + \frac{4(50 - 25)}{27} = 115.20 \tag{8}$$

$$Q_3 = 119.5 + \frac{4(150 - 101)}{52} = 123.27 \tag{9}$$

$$Q = \frac{Q_3 - Q_1}{2} = \frac{123.27 - 115.20}{2} = 4.03 \tag{7}$$

$$AD = \frac{\Sigma \mid fx \mid}{N} = \frac{1063.88}{200} = 5.32 \tag{11}$$

$$SD = \sqrt{\frac{\Sigma fx^2}{N}} = \sqrt{\frac{8927.29}{200}} = 6.68 \tag{13}$$

A second illustration of the calculation of Q from a frequency distribution is given in Table 8 (2). To find Q_1, we count off 1/4 of N (200) or 50 scores from the low-score end of the distribution. The intervals 103.5–107.5 and 107.5–111.5, taken together, include 25 scores. Q_1, therefore, must fall on the next interval, 111.5–115.5, which contains 27 scores. These 27 scores when added to the 25 counted off total 52—just 2 more than the 50 wanted. From Table 8 we find that

$l = 111.5$, exact lower limit of the interval containing Q_1
$1/4\,N = 50$
$cum\ f_l = 25$, sum of the scores up to the interval upon which Q_1 falls
$f_q = 27$, number of scores on the interval containing Q_1
$i = 4$

Substituting in formula (8)

$$Q_1 = 111.5 + \frac{4(50 - 25)}{27} = 115.20$$

To find Q_3 we count off 3/4 of N or 150 from the low-score end of the distribution. The first 4 intervals include 101 scores and Q_3 falls on the next interval 119.5–123.5, which contains 52 scores. Data from Table 8 are

$l = 119.5$, exact lower limit of interval containing Q_3
$3/4\,N = 150$
$cum\ f_l = 101$, sum of scores up to interval which contains Q_3
$f_q = 52$, f on the interval on which Q_3 falls
$i = 4$

Substituting in formula (9)

$$Q_3 = 119.5 + \frac{4(150 - 101)}{52} = 123.27$$

Substituting for Q_3 and Q_1 in (7) we get a Q of 4.03 (see Table 8).

The quartiles Q_1 and Q_3 mark off the limits of the middle 50% of scores in the distribution, and the distance between these two points is called the *interquartile range*. Q is 1/2 the range of the middle 50% or the *semi-interquartile range*. Since Q measures the average distance of the quartile points from the median, it is a good index of score density at the middle of the distribution. If the scores in the distribution are packed closely together, the quartiles will be near one another and Q will be small. If scores are widely scattered, the quartiles will be relatively far apart and Q will be large (see Fig. 7).

When the distribution is symmetrical around the mean—or when it is normal—Q marks off exactly the 25% of cases just above, and the 25% of cases just below, the median. The median then lies just halfway between the two quartiles Q_3 and Q_1. In a normal distribution (p. 99) Q is called the *probable error* or *PE*. The terms Q and *PE* are sometimes used interchangeably, but it is best to restrict the term *PE* to the normal probability curve (p. 99).

3. The average deviation or AD

(1) COMPUTATION OF THE AD FROM UNGROUPED SCORES

The average deviation or *AD* (also written mean deviation or *MD*) is the mean of the deviations of *all* of the separate scores in a series taken from their mean (occasionally from the median or mode). In averaging deviations to find the *AD*, no account is taken of signs, and all deviations whether plus or minus are treated as positive.

An example will make the definition clear. The mean of the 5 scores, 6, 8, 10, 12 and 14 is 10. And the deviations of the separate scores from this mean are $6 - 10$ or -4; $8 - 10$ or -2; $10 - 10$ or 0; $12 - 10$ or 2; $14 - 10$ or 4. The sum of these 5 deviations, disregarding signs, is 12; and dividing 12 by 5 (N) we get 2.4 as the mean of these 5 deviations from their mean, or the *AD*. The formula for the *AD* when scores are ungrouped is

$$AD = \frac{\Sigma \,|\, x \,|}{N} \tag{10}$$

(average deviation when scores are ungrouped)

in which the bars $|\ \ |$ enclosing the x indicate that signs are disregarded in arriving at the sum. As always, x is a deviation of a score from the mean, .i.e., $X - M = x$.

(2) CALCULATION OF THE AD FROM GROUPED DATA

The *AD* is rarely used in modern statistics, but it is often found in the older experimental literature. Should the student find it necessary to compute the *AD* from grouped data, the method shown in Table 8 may be followed. In column (4) are entered the deviations (x) of each interval midpoint from the mean of 170.80. The deviation of 197, midpoint of 195–199, from 170.80 is $197 - 170.80$ or 26.20; and all deviations down to 170–174 are plus, as the midpoints in all cases are numerically higher than 170.80. From interval 165–169 on down to the beginning of the distribution, the x's are minus, as the midpoints are all numerically smaller than 170.80.

Each x deviation in column (4) is now "weighted" by the frequency which it represents to give the fx entries in column (5). The first x of 26.20 is multiplied by 1; the second x of 21.20 by 2, and so on to the end of the column. The sum of the fx column is divided by N to give the AD. The formula is

$$AD = \frac{\Sigma \mid fx \mid}{N} \tag{11}$$

(*average deviation or* AD *found from grouped scores*)

Substituting for $\frac{\Sigma \mid fx \mid}{N}$ in the formula, the AD is $\frac{502.00}{50}$ or 10.04.

In the second problem in Table 8, the sum of the fx column—col (5)— is 1063.88 and N is 200. Hence, by formula (11), the $AD = \frac{1063.88}{200}$ or 5.32.

In figuring deviations from the mean, it is helpful to remember that the mean is always subtracted from the midpoint. That is, X (midpoint) minus M (mean) equals x (the deviation). The computation is algebraic: plus and minus signs are recorded. Hence, when the midpoint is numerically greater than the mean, the x will be plus; when numerically less than the mean, the x will be minus.

In the normal distribution (see p. 89), the AD when measured off on the scale above and below the mean includes the middle 57.5% of the cases. The AD is, therefore, always somewhat larger than the Q which includes the middle 50% of cases.

4. The standard deviation or SD

The standard deviation or SD is the most stable index of variability and is customarily employed in experimental work and in research studies. The SD differs from the AD in several respects. In computing the AD, we disregard signs and treat all deviations as positive, whereas in finding the SD we avoid the difficulty of signs by squaring the separate deviations. Again, the squared deviations used in computing the SD are always taken from the mean, never from the median or mode. The conventional symbol for the SD is the Greek letter sigma (σ).

(1) CALCULATION OF THE SD FROM UNGROUPED SCORES

We may illustrate the calculation of the SD for an ungrouped set of data with the same 5 scores used on page 48 to demonstrate the computation of the AD. The mean of the 5 scores 6, 8, 10, 12 and 14 is 10 and the deviations of the separate scores from the mean are −4, −2, 0, 2 and 4, respectively. When each of these 5 deviations is squared, we get 16, 4, 0, 4 and 16; the sum is 40 and N, of course, is 5. The formula for σ when scores are ungrouped is

$$\sigma = \sqrt{\frac{\Sigma x^2}{N}} \qquad (12)$$

(standard deviation calculated from ungrouped data)

and in our example $\sigma = \sqrt{\dfrac{40}{5}}$ or 2.83.

(2) CALCULATION OF *SD* FROM GROUPED DATA

Table 8 illustrates the calculation of σ when scores are grouped into a frequency distribution. The process is identical with that used for ungrouped items, except that, in addition to squaring the x of each midpoint from the mean, we weight each of these squared deviations by the frequency which it represents—that is, by the frequency opposite it. This multiplication gives the fx^2 column. By simple algebra, $x \times fx = fx^2$; and accordingly the easiest way to obtain the entries in column fx^2 [col (6)] is to multiply the corresponding x's and fx's in columns (4) and (5). The first fx^2 entry, for example, is 686.44, the product of 26.20 times 26.20; the second entry is 898.88, the product of 42.40 times 21.20; and so on to the end of the column. All of the fx^2 are necessarily positive since each negative x is matched by a negative fx. The sum of the fx^2 column (7978.00) divided by N (50) gives the mean of the squared deviations as 159.56; and the square root of this result is 12.63, the *SD*. The formula for σ when data are grouped into a frequency distribution is:

$$\sigma = \sqrt{\frac{\Sigma fx^2}{N}} \qquad (13)$$

(SD or σ for data grouped into a frequency distribution)

Problem 2 of Table 8 furnishes another illustration of the calculation of σ from grouped data. In column (6), the fx^2 entries have been obtained, as in the previous problem, by multiplying each x by its corresponding fx. The sum of the fx^2 column is 8927.29; and N is 200. Hence, applying formula (13) we get 6.68 as the *SD*.

The standard deviation is less affected by *sampling errors* (p. 196) than is the Q or the *AD* and is a more stable measure of dispersion. In a normal distribution the σ, when measured off above and below the mean, marks the limits of the middle 68.26% (roughly the middle two-thirds) of the distribution.* This is approximately true also of the σ in less symmetrical distributions. For example, in the first distribution in Table 8 approximately the middle 65% of the scores fall between 183 (170.80 + 12.63) and 158 (170.80 − 12.63).† The SD is larger than the AD which is, in turn, larger than Q. These relationships supply a rough check upon the accuracy of the measures of variability.

II. CALCULATION OF THE SD BY THE SHORT METHOD

1. Calculation of σ from grouped data

On page 35, the Short Method of calculating the mean was outlined. This method consisted essentially in "guessing" or assuming a mean, and later applying a correction to give the actual mean. The Short Method may also be used to advantage in calculating the SD.‡ It is a decided

TABLE 9   The calculation of the SD by the short method.§ Data from Table 1. Calculations by the long method given for comparison

		1. SHORT METHOD			
(1)	(2)	(3)	(4)	(5)	(6)
Scores	Midpoint X	f	x'	fx'	fx'^2
195–199	197	1	5	5	25
190–194	192	2	4	8	32
185–189	187	4	3	12	36
180–184	182	5	2	10	20
175–179	177	8	1	8 (+43)	8
170–174	172	10	0	—	
165–169	167	6	−1	−6	6
160–164	162	4	−2	−8	16
155–159	157	4	−3	−12	36
150–154	152	2	−4	−8	32
145–149	147	3	−5	−15	75
140–144	142	1	−6	−6 (−55)	36
		$N = 50$		98	322

* See p. 35.
† See p. 109 for method of calculating the percent of scores falling between two points in a frequency distribution.
‡ The AD may also be calculated by the assumed mean or Short Method. The AD is used so seldom, however, that a Short Method of calculation (which is neither very short nor very satisfactory) is not given.
§ The calculation of the mean is repeated from Table 7.

TABLE 9—(Continued)

---

1. $AM = 172.00$ $\qquad c = -\dfrac{12}{50} = -.240 \qquad ci = -.240 \times 5 = -1.20$

   $ci = -1.20 \qquad c^2 = .0576$

   $M = 170.80$

2. $SD = i\sqrt{\dfrac{\Sigma fx'^2}{N} - c^2} = 5\sqrt{\dfrac{322}{50} - .0576}$

   $= 12.63$

2. Long Method

(1) Scores	(2) Midpoint X	(3) f	(4) fX	(5) x	(6) fx	(7) fx²
195–199	197	1	197	26.20	26.20	686.44
190–194	192	2	384	21.20	42.40	898.88
185–189	187	4	748	16.20	64.80	1049.76
180–184	182	5	910	11.20	56.00	627.20
175–179	177	8	1416	6.20	49.60	307.52
170–174	172	10	1720	1.20	12.00	14.40
165–169	167	6	1002	−3.80	−22.80	86.64
160–164	162	4	648	−8.80	−35.20	309.76
155–159	157	4	628	−13.80	−55.20	761.76
150–154	152	2	304	−18.80	−37.60	706.88
145–149	147	3	441	−23.80	−71.40	1699.32
140–144	142	1	142	−28.80	−28.80	829.44
		$N = 50$	8540		502.00	7978.00

1. $M = \dfrac{\Sigma fX}{N} = \dfrac{8540}{50} = 170.80$

2. $SD = \sqrt{\dfrac{\Sigma fx^2}{N}} = \sqrt{\dfrac{7978.00}{50}} = 12.63$

---

time and labor saver in dealing with grouped data; and is well-nigh indispensable in the calculation of σ's in a correlation table (p. 135).

The Short Method of calculating σ is illustrated in Table 9. The computation of the mean is repeated in the table, as is also the calculation of the mean and σ by the direct or Long Method. This affords a readier comparison of the two techniques.

The formula for σ by the Short Method is

$$\sigma = i\sqrt{\frac{\Sigma fx'^2}{N} - c^2} \qquad (14)$$

(SD *from a frequency distribution when deviations are taken from an assumed mean*) in which $\Sigma fx'^2$ is the sum of the squared deviations in units of class interval, taken from the assumed mean, c^2 is the squared correction in units of class interval, and i is the class interval.

The calculation of σ by the Short Method may be followed in detail from Table 9. Deviations are taken from the assumed mean (172.0) in units of class interval and entered in column (4) as x'. In column (5) each x' is weighted or multiplied by its f to give the fx'; and in column (6) the fx'^2's are found by multiplying each x' in column (4) by the corresponding fx' in column (5). The process is identical with that used in the Long Method except that the x''s are all expressed in units of class interval. This considerably simplifies the multiplication. The calculation of c has already been described on page 37: c is the algebraic sum of column (5) divided by N. The sum of the fx'^2 column is 322, and c^2 is .0576. Applying formula (14) we get 2.526×5 (interval) or 12.63 as the σ of the distribution. Formula (14) for the calculation of σ by the Short Method holds good no matter what the size of c, the correction in units of class interval, or where the mean has beeen assumed.

2. Calculation of σ from the original measures or scores

It will often save time and computation to apply the Short Method directly to the ungrouped scores. The method is illustrated in Table 10. Note that the 10 scores are ungrouped, and that it is not necessary even to arrange them in order of size. The assumed mean is taken at zero, and each score becomes at once a deviation (x') from this AM, that is, each score (X) is unchanged. The correction, c, is the difference between the actual mean (M) and the assumed mean (0), i.e., $c = M - 0$; hence c is simply M itself. The mean is calculated, as before, by summing the scores and dividing by N. To find σ, square the x''s (or the X's i.e., the scores), sum to get $\Sigma(x')^2$ or ΣX^2, divide by N, and subtract M^2, the correction squared. The square root of the result gives σ. A convenient formula is

$$\sigma = \sqrt{\frac{\Sigma X^2}{N} - M^2} \qquad (15)$$

or replacing the M^2 by $\left(\frac{\Sigma X}{N}\right)^2$,

$$\sigma = \frac{\sqrt{N\Sigma X^2 - (\Sigma X)^2}}{N} \qquad (16)$$

(σ calculated from original scores by the Short Method)

This method of calculating σ is especially useful when there are relatively few scores, say 50 or less, and when the scores are expressed in not

TABLE 10 To illustrate the calculation of the SD from original scores when the assumed mean is taken at zero, and data are ungrouped

Scores (X)	x' (or X)	$(x')^2$ or (X^2)
18	18	324
25	25	625
21	21	441
19	19	361
27	27	729
31	31	961
22	22	484
25	25	625
28	28	784
20	20	400
236	236	5734

$$AM = 0$$

$$M = \frac{236}{10} = 23.6 \qquad N = 10$$

$$c = 23.6 - 0$$
$$= 23.6$$
$$c^2 = 556.96$$

$$\sigma = \sqrt{\frac{5734}{10} - (23.6)^2}$$
$$= \sqrt{16.44}$$
$$= 4.05$$

more than two digits,* so that the squares do not become unwieldy. A calculating machine and a table of squares will greatly facilitate computation. Simply sum the scores as they stand and divide by N to get M. Then enter the squares of the scores in the machine in order, sum, and substitute the result in formula (15) or formula (16).

3. Effect upon σ of (a) adding a constant to each score, or (b) multiplying each score by the same number

(a) If each score in a frequency distribution is increased by the same amount, say 5, the σ is unchanged. The table below provides a simple illustration. The mean of the original scores is 7 and σ is 1.41. When each

* For the application of this method to the calculation of coefficients of corrrelation, and a scheme for reducing the size of the original scores so as to eliminate the need for handling large numbers, see page 144.

score is increased by 5, the mean is 12 $(7+5)$, but σ is still 1.41. Adding a constant (e.g., 5, 10, 15) to each score simply moves the whole distribution up the scale 5, 10, or 15 points. The mean is increased by the amount of the constant added, but the variability (σ) is not affected. If a constant is subtracted from each score, the distribution is moved down the scale by that amount; the mean is decreased by the amount of the constant, and σ, again, is unchanged.

Original scores (X)	x	x^2	Original scores X + 5	x	x^2
9	2	4	14	2	4
8	1	1	13	1	1
7	0	0	12	0	0
6	−1	1	11	−1	1
5	−2	4	10	−2	4
5⟌35		10	5⟌60		10
M = 7			M = 12		

$$\sigma = \sqrt{\frac{10}{5}} = 1.41 \qquad\qquad \sigma = \sqrt{\frac{10}{5}} = 1.41$$

(b) What happens to the mean and σ when each score is multiplied by a constant is shown in the table below:

Original scores (X)	Original scores X × 10	x	x^2
9	90	20	400
8	80	10	100
7	70	0	0
6	60	−10	100
5	50	−20	400
5⟌35	5⟌350		1000
M = 7	M = 70		

$$\sigma = 1.41 \qquad\qquad \sigma = \sqrt{\frac{1000}{5}} = \sqrt{200} = 14.14$$

Each score in the list of five, shown above, has been multiplied by 10; and the net effect of this operation is to multiply the mean *and* the σ by 10.

4. The σ from combined distributions

When two sets of scores have been combined into a single lot, it is possible to calculate the σ of the total distribution from the σ's of the two component distributions. The formula is

$$\sigma_{comb} = \sqrt{\frac{N_1(\sigma^2_1 + d^2_1) + N_2(\sigma^2_2 + d^2_2)}{N}} \qquad (17)$$

(SD *of a distribution obtained by combining two frequency distributions*)

in which

$$\sigma_1 = SD \text{ of distribution 1}$$
$$\sigma_2 = SD \text{ of distribution 2}$$
$$d_1 = (M_1 - M_{comb})$$
$$d_2 = (M_2 - M_{comb})$$

N_1 and N_2 are the numbers of cases in component distributions 1 and 2, respectively, and $N = (N_1 + N_2)$. The M_{comb} is the mean of the combined distribution got from formula (3), p. 30.

An example will illustrate the use of the formula. Suppose we are given the means and SD's on an Achievement Test for two classes differing in size, and are asked to find the σ of the combined group. Data are as follows:

	N	M	SD
Class A	25	80	15
Class B	75	70	25

First, we find that

$$M_{comb} = \frac{25 \times 80 + 75 \times 70}{100} \text{ or } 72.50 \text{ (see p. 30)}$$

We then have that $d_1 = (80 - 72.50)$ and $d^2_1 = 56.25$; that $d_2 = (70 - 72.50)$ and that $d^2_2 = 6.25$. Substituting in formula (17) for σ^2_1, σ^2_2, d^2_1, d^2_2, N_1 and N_2 we have that

$$\sigma_{comb} = \sqrt{\frac{25(225 + 56.25) + 75(625 + 6.25)}{100}}$$

$$= 23.32$$

Formula (17) may easily be extended to include more than two component distributions, by adding N_3, σ_3, d_3, and so on.

5. Correcting σ for grouping error

When σ is computed from a frequency distribution, the scores in each interval are represented by the midpoint of that interval (p. 50). The scores on an interval are not always distributed symmetrically about the midpoint. In intervals above the mean of the distribution, for example, frequencies tend to lie *below* the midpoint more often than above,

whereas in intervals below the mean, the scores tend to lie *above* the midpoint. These opposing tendencies cancel each other out when the mean is computed from all of the intervals. But the "grouping error" introduced will inflate the σ and the more so when intervals are wide and N is small. To adjust for grouping, a correction—called Sheppard's correction—is often used. The formula is

$$\sigma_c = \sqrt{\sigma^2 - \frac{i^2}{12}} \qquad (18)$$

$$= \sqrt{\sigma^2 - .083i^2}$$

(*Sheppard's correction for grouping error*)

in which

$\sigma =$ the SD computed from the frequency distribution

$i =$ the interval length

Sheppard's correction provides a close approximation to the σ which would be obtained with ungrouped scores. The correction is negligible when the intervals are fairly numerous (e.g., 10 or more). But the correction may be considerable when the intervals are broad and few in number. To take an example, suppose that in a group the $\sigma = 10$ and $i = 3$. Then $\sigma_c = \sqrt{100 - .75}$ or 9.96. But if $i = 18$, $\sigma_c = \sqrt{100 - 27} = 8.54$, and the difference is fairly large. An interval of 18 is, of course, quite broad.

III. THE COEFFICIENT OF VARIATION, V

Measures of variability, for example Q or SD, are of necessity expressed in terms of the units of the test or measuring scale. The SD of a set of I.Q.'s is—like the M—in terms of I.Q. units, and the SD of a set of heights is usually in inches or centimeters. When two groups have achieved approximately the same mean score on a test, their σ's can be compared directly. If, for example, on a science aptitude test 10-year-old boys have a $M = 62$ and $\sigma = 10$ and 10-year-old girls have a $M = 61$ and $\sigma = 6$, it is clear that the boys are considerably more variable than the girls.

It is often desirable to compare variabilities when (*a*) means are unequal or when (*b*) units of measurement from test to test are incommensurable. A statistic useful in making such comparisons is the coefficient of variation or V, sometimes called the coefficient of relative variability. The formula is

$$V = \frac{100\sigma}{M} \qquad (19)$$

(*coefficient of variation or coefficient of relative variability*)

V gives the percentage which σ is of the test mean. It is thus a *ratio* which is independent of the units of measurement.

V is restricted in its use owing to certain ambiguities in its interpretation. It is defensible when used with ratio scales—scales in which the units are equal and there is a true zero or reference point (p. 1). For example, V may be used without hesitation with physical scales—those concerned with linear magnitudes, weight and time (p. 2). Two cases arise in the use of V with ratio scales: (1) when units are dissimilar and (2) when M's are unequal, the units of the scale being the same.

(1) WHEN UNITS ARE UNLIKE

Suppose that a group of 7-year-old boys has a mean height of 45 inches with a σ of 2.5 inches; and a mean weight of 50 pounds with a σ of 6 pounds. In which trait is the group more variable? Obviously, we cannot compare inches and pounds directly, but we can compare the relative variability of the two distributions in terms of V. Thus,

$$V_{ht} = \frac{100 \times 2.5}{45} = 5.6$$

and

$$V_{wt} = \frac{100 \times 6}{50} = 12$$

from which it appears that these boys are about twice as variable $(12/5.6 = 2.1)$ in weight as in height.

(2) WHEN MEANS ARE UNEQUAL, BUT SCALE UNITS ARE THE SAME

Suppose we have the following data on height for a group of boys and a group of men:

Group	M	σ	V
Boys	50 lbs	6	12
Men	160 lbs	16	10

In terms of their σ's, the men are 3 times as variable as the boys; but relative to their means, the men and boys are about equally variable. This last result is the more valuable and informative.

(3) CRITICISMS OF V

Objection has been raised to the use of V when employed to compare groups on mental and educational tests. Most standard tests are interval scales, i.e., are scaled in equal units (p. 2). But mental tests are never ratio scales—the zero or reference point is unknown—and many are not

scaled in equal units. How the lack of a true zero affects V may be seen in the following example. Suppose we have administered a vocabulary test to a group of school children, and have obtained a mean of 25.0 and a σ of 5.0. V is 20. Now suppose further that we add 10 very easy items to our vocabulary test. It is likely that all of the children will know the new words. Hence, the mean score will be increased by 10, whereas the σ remains unchanged. An increase in the mean from 25 to 35 with no corresponding increase in σ drops V from 20 to 14; and since we could have added 20 or 200 items to the test, V is clearly a very unstable statistic.

The instability of V should cause us to exercise caution in its use rather than discard it entirely. V shows what percent the σ is of the mean. If the range of difficulty in the test is altered, or the units changed, not only V but M will change. Accordingly, V is, in a sense, no more arbitrary than M and the objections urged against V could be directed with equal force against M. V is useful in comparing the variabilities of a group upon the same test administered under different conditions, as, for example, when a group works at a task with and without distraction. Or V may be used to compare two groups on the same test when the groups do not differ greatly in mean.

It is perhaps most difficult to interpret V when the comparative variability of a group upon *different* mental tests is of interest. If a high school class is compared for variability upon tests of paragraph reading and arithmetic reasoning, it should be made plain that the V's refer only to the specific tests. Other tests of reading and arithmetic may—and probably will—give different results owing to differences in range of difficulty, in size of units, and in the reference point. If we restrict V to the specific tests used, the coefficient of variation will provide information not otherwise obtainable.

IV. WHEN TO USE THE VARIOUS MEASURES OF VARIABILITY

The following rules will serve as useful guides.

I. Use the range

(1) when the data are too scant or too scattered to justify the computation of a more precise measure of variability
(2) when a knowledge of extreme scores or of total spread is all that is wanted.

2. Use the Q

(1) when the median is the measure of central tendency
(2) when there are scattered or extreme scores which would influence the SD disproportionately
(3) when the concentration around the median—the middle 50% of cases—is of primary interest.

3. Use the AD

(1) when it is desired to weight all deviations from the mean according to their size
(2) when extreme deviations would influence SD unduly.

4. Use the SD

(1) when the statistic having the greatest stability is sought (p. 196)
(2) when extreme deviations should exercise a proportionally greater effect upon the variability
(3) when coefficients of correlation and other statistics are subsequently to be computed.

PROBLEMS

1. (a) Calculate the Q and σ for each of the four frequency distributions given on page 39 under problem 1, Chapter 2.
   (b) Compute σ for the first two distributions using Sheppard's correction.
2. Calculate the σ of the 25 ungrouped scores given on page 23, problem 5(a), taking the AM at zero. Compare your result with the σ's calculated from the frequency distributions of the same scores which you tabulated in class intervals of three and five units.
3. For the following list of test scores,

$$52, \quad 50, \quad 56, \quad 68, \quad 65, \quad 62, \quad 57, \quad 70$$

   (a) Find the M and σ by method on page 54.
   (b) Add 6 to each score and recalculate M and σ.
   (c) Subtract 50 from each score, and calculate M and σ.
   (d) Multiply each score by 5 and compute M and σ.
4. (a) In Sample A $(N = 150)$, $M = 120$ and $\sigma = 20$; in Sample B $(N = 75)$, $M = 126$ and $\sigma = 22$. What are the mean and SD of A and B when combined into one distribution of 225 cases?
   (b) What are the mean and SD obtained by combining the following three distributions?

Distribution	N	M	σ
I	20	60	8
II	120	50	20
III	60	40	12

5. Calculate coefficients of variation for the following traits:

Trait	Unit of measurement	Group	M	σ
Length of Head	mms.	802 males	190.52	5.90
Body Weight	pounds	868,445 males	141.54	17.82
Tapping Speed	M of 5 trials 30″ each	68 adults, male and female	196.91	26.83
Memory Span	No. repeated correctly	263 males	6.60	1.13
General Intelligence (Otis Group Intell. Scale)	Points scored	1101 adults	153.3	23.6

Rank these traits in order for relative variability. Judged by their V's which trait is the most variable? which the least variable? which traits have true zeros?

6. (a) Why is the Q the best measure of variability when there are scattered or extreme scores?

(b) Why does the σ weight extreme deviations more than does the AD?

ANSWERS

1. (a) (1) $Q = 3.37$ (2) $Q = 8.12$
   $\sigma = 4.99$ $\sigma = 11.33$
   (3) $Q = 4.50$ (4) $Q = 16.41$
   $\sigma = 7.23$ $\sigma = 24.13$
   (b) (1) $\sigma_c = 4.96$ (2) $\sigma_c = 11.24$

2. σ of ungrouped scores $= 6.72$
   σ of scores grouped in 3-unit intervals $= 6.71$
   σ of scores grouped in 5-unit intervals $= 6.78$

3. (a) $M = 60$ (b) $M = 66$ (c) $M = 10$ (d) $M = 300$
   $\sigma = 6.91$ $\sigma = 6.91$ $\sigma = 6.91$ $\sigma = 34.55$

4. (a) $M = 122.0$; $\sigma = 20.88$
   (b) $M = 48.00$; $\sigma = 18.05$

5. V's in order are 3.10; 12.59; 13.63; 17.12; 15.39. Ranked for relative variability from most to least: Memory Span; General Intelligence; Tapping Speed; Weight; Head Length. Last two traits have true zeros.

CHAPTER 4

CUMULATIVE DISTRIBUTIONS, GRAPHIC METHODS AND PERCENTILES

◇◇

In Chapter 1 we learned how to represent the frequency distribution by means of the polygon and histogram. In the present chapter, two other descriptive methods will be considered—the *cumulative frequency graph* and the *cumulative percentage curve* or *ogive*, as well as several simple graphical devices. Also, a technique will be outlined for computing percentiles * and percentile ranks from frequency distributions and directly from graphs.

I. THE CUMULATIVE FREQUENCY GRAPH

1. Construction of the cumulative frequency graph

The cumulative frequency graph is another way of representing a frequency distribution by means of a diagram. Before we can plot a cumulative frequency graph, the scores of the distribution must be added serially or cumulated, as shown in Table 11, for the two distributions taken from Table 5. These two sets of scores have already been used to illustrate the frequency polygon and histogram in Figures 2, 4, and 5. The first two columns for each of the distributions in Table 11 repeat Table 5 exactly; but in the third column (Cum. f) scores have been accumulated progressively from the bottom of the distribution upward. To illustrate, in the distribution of Alpha scores the first cumulative frequency is 1; $1 + 3$, from the low end of the distribution, gives 4 as the next entry; $4 + 2 = 6$; $6 + 4 = 10$, etc. The last cumulative f is equal, of course, to 50 or N, the total frequency.

* The term "centile" is sometimes used for percentile.

TABLE 11 Cumulative frequencies for the two distributions given in Table 5

Alpha Scores	f	Cum. f	Cancellation Scores	f	Cum. f
195–199	1	50	135.5–139.5	3	200
190–194	2	49	131.5–135.5	5	197
185–189	4	47	127.5–131.5	16	192
180–184	5	43	123.5–127.5	23	176
175–179	8	38	119.5–123.5	52	153
170–174	10	30	115.5–119.5	49	101
165–169	6	20	111.5–115.5	27	52
160–164	4	14	107.5–111.5	18	25
155–159	4	10	103.5–107.5	7	7
150–154	2	6		$N = 200$	
145–149	3	4			
140–144	1	1			
	$N = 50$				

The two cumulative frequency graphs which represent the distributions of Table 11 are shown in Figures 8 and 9. Consider first the graph of the 50 Alpha scores in Figure 8. The class intervals of the distribution have been laid off along the X axis. There are 12 intervals, and by the "75%

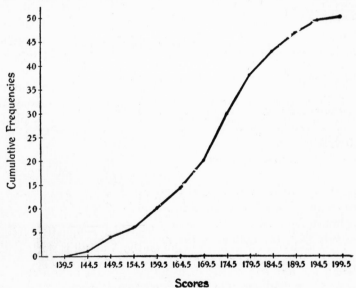

FIG. 8 Cumulative frequency graph
(Data from Table 11)

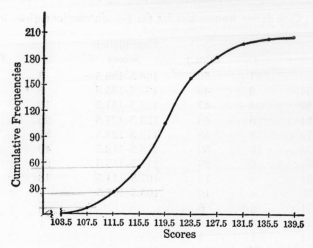

FIG. 9   Cumulative frequency graph
(Data from Table 11)

rule" given on page 11 there should be about 9 unit distances (each equal to one class interval) laid off on the Y axis. Since the largest cumulative frequency is 50, each of these Y units should represent 50/9 or 6 scores (approximately). Instead of dividing up the total Y distance into 9 units each representing 6 scores, however, we have, for convenience in plotting, divided the total Y distance into 10 units of 5 scores each. This does not change significantly the 3:4 relationship of height to width in the figure.

In plotting the frequency polygon the frequency on each interval is taken at the *midpoint* of the class interval (p. 11). But in constructing a cumulative frequency curve each cumulative frequency is plotted at the exact *upper limit* of the interval upon which it falls. This is because in adding progressively from the bottom up each cumulative frequency carries through to the exact upper limit of the interval. The first point on the curve is one Y unit (the cumulative frequency on 140–144) above 144.5; the second point is 4 Y units above 149.5; the third, 6 Y units above 154.5, and so on to the last point which is 50 Y units above 199.5. The plotted points are joined to give the S-shaped cumulative frequency graph. In order to have the curve begin on the X axis it is started at 139.5 (exact upper limit of 134.5–139.5), the cumulative frequency of which is 0.

The cumulative frequency curve in Figure 9 has been plotted from the second distribution in Table 11 by the method just described. The curve

ʼ ᴇɴs at 103.5, the exact lower limit of the first class interval,* and ends at 139.5, the exact upper limit of the last interval; and cumulative frequencies, 7, 25, 52, etc., are all plotted at the exact *upper limits* of their respective class intervals. The height of this graph was determined by the "75% rule" as in the case of the curve in Figure 8. There are 9 class intervals laid off on the X axis; hence, since 75% of 9 is 7 (approximately), the height of the figure should be about 7 class interval units. To determine the score value of each Y unit divide 200 (the largest cumulative frequency) by 7 to give 30 (approximately). Each of the 7 Y units has been taken to represent 30 scores.

II. PERCENTILES AND PERCENTILE RANKS

1. Calculation of percentiles in a frequency distribution

We have learned (p. 30) that the median is that point in a frequency distribution below which lie 50% of the measures or scores; and that Q_1 and Q_3 mark points in the distribution below which lie, respectively, 25% and 75% of the measures or scores. Using the same method by which the median and the quartiles were found, we may compute points below which lie 10%, 43%, 85%, or any percent of the scores. These points are called *percentiles*, and are designated, in general, by the symbol P_p, the p referring to the percentages of cases *below* the given value. P_{10}, for example, is the point below which lie 10% of the scores; P_{78}, the point below which lie 78% of the scores. It is evident that the median, expressed as a percentile, is P_{50}; also Q_1 is P_{25}, and Q_3 is P_{75}.

The method of calculating percentiles is essentially the same as that employed in finding the median. The formula is

$$P_p = l + \left(\frac{pN - F}{f_p}\right) \times i \qquad (20)$$

(*percentiles in a frequency distribution, counting from below up*)

where

p = percentage of the distribution wanted, e.g., 10%, 33%, etc.
l = exact lower limit of the class interval upon which P_p lies
pN = part of N to be counted off in order to reach P_p
F = sum of all scores upon intervals below l
f_p = number of scores within the interval upon which P_p falls
i = length of the class interval

* Or the exact upper limit of the interval just below, i.e., 99.5–103.5.

TABLE 12 Calculation of certain percentiles in a frequency distribution

(Data from Table 1, 50 Army Alpha scores)

Scores	f	Cum. f	Percentiles
195–199	1	50	$P_{100} = 199.5$
190–194	2	49	
185–189	4	47	$P_{90} = 187.0$
180–184	5	43	$P_{80} = 181.5$
175–179	8	38	$P_{70} = 177.6$
170–174	10	30	$P_{60} = 174.5$
165–169	6	20	$P_{50} = 172.0$
160–164	4	14	$P_{40} = 169.5$
155–159	4	10	$P_{30} = 165.3$
150–154	2	6	$P_{20} = 159.5$
145–149	3	4	$P_{10} = 152.0$
140–144	1	1	
$N = 50$			$P_0 = 139.5$

CALCULATION OF PERCENTILE POINTS

10% of 50 = 5 $\qquad 149.5 + \left(\dfrac{5 - 4}{2}\right) \times 5 = 152.0$

20% of 50 = 10 $\qquad 159.5 + \left(\dfrac{10 - 10}{4}\right) \times 5 = 159.5$

30% of 50 = 15 $\qquad 164.5 + \left(\dfrac{15 - 14}{6}\right) \times 5 = 165.3$

40% of 50 = 20 $\qquad 169.5 + \left(\dfrac{20 - 20}{10}\right) \times 5 = 169.5$

50% of 50 = 25 $\qquad 169.5 + \left(\dfrac{25 - 20}{10}\right) \times 5 = 172.0 \ (Mdn)$

60% of 50 = 30 $\qquad 174.5 + \left(\dfrac{30 - 30}{8}\right) \times 5 = 174.5$

70% of 50 = 35 $\qquad 174.5 + \left(\dfrac{35 - 30}{8}\right) \times 5 = 177.6$

80% of 50 = 40 $\qquad 179.5 + \left(\dfrac{40 - 38}{5}\right) \times 5 = 181.5$

90% of 50 = 45 $\qquad 184.5 + \left(\dfrac{45 - 43}{4}\right) \times 5 = 187.0$

In Table 12, the percentile points, P_{10} to P_{90}, have been computed by formula (20) for the distribution of scores made by the fifty college students upon Army Alpha, shown in Table 1. The details of calculation are given in Table 12. We may illustrate the method with P_{70}. Here $pN = 35$ (70% of $50 = 35$), and from the Cum. f we find that 30 scores take us through 170–174 up to 174.5, the exact *lower* limit of the interval next above. Hence, P_{70} falls upon 175–179, and, substituting $pN = 35$, $F = 30$, $f_p = 8$ (frequency upon 175–179), and $i = 5$ (class interval) in formula (20), we find that $P_{70} = 177.6$ (for detailed calculation, see Table 12). This result means that 70% of the 50 students scored *below* 177.6 in the distribution of Alpha scores. The other percentile values are found in exactly the same way as P_{70}. The reader should verify the calculations of the P_p in Table 12 in order to become thoroughly familiar with the method.

It should be noted that P_0, which marks the exact lower limit of the first interval (namely, 139.5) lies at the beginning of the distribution. P_{100} marks the exact *upper limit* of the last interval, and lies at the end of the distribution. These two percentiles represent *limiting points*. Their principal value is to indicate the boundaries of the percentile scale.

2. Calculation of percentile ranks in a frequency distribution

We have seen in the last section how percentiles, e.g., P_{15} or P_{62}, may be calculated directly from a frequency distribution. To repeat what has been said above, percentiles are *points* in a continuous distribution below which lie given percentages of N. We shall now consider the problem of finding an individual's *percentile rank* (PR); or the position on a scale of 100 to which the subject's score entitles him. The distinction between *percentile* and *percentile rank* will be clear if the reader remembers that in calculating percentiles he *starts* with a certain percent of N, say 15% or 62%. He then counts into the distribution the given percent and the point reached is the required percentile, e.g., P_{15} or P_{62}. The procedure followed in computing percentile ranks is the reverse of this process. Here we begin with an individual *score*, and determine the percentage of scores which lies below it. If this percentage is 62, say, the score has a percentile rank or PR of 62 on a scale of 100.

We shall illustrate with Table 12. What is the PR of a man who scores 163? Score 163 falls on interval 160–164. There are 10 scores up to 159.5, exact lower limit of this interval (see column Cum. f), and 4 scores spread over this interval. Dividing 4 by 5 (interval length) gives us .8 score *per unit of interval*. The score of 163, which we are seeking, is 3.5 score units from 159.5, exact lower limit of the interval within which the score of 163 lies. Multiplying 3.5 by .8 we get 2.8 as the score distance of 163 from 159.5; and adding 2.8 to 10 (number of scores below 159.5) we get 12.8 as the part of N lying *below* 163. Dividing 12.8 by 50 gives us 25.6 % as that proportion of N below 163; hence the percentile rank of score 163 is 26. The diagram below will clarify the calculation:

$$f = 4$$

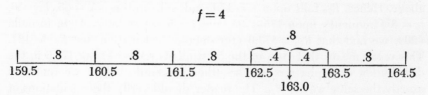

Ten scores lie below 159.5. Prorating the 4 scores on 160–164 over the interval of 5, we have .8 score per unit of interval. Score 163 is just $.8 + .8 + .8 + .4$ or 2.8 scores from 159.5; or score 163 lies 12.8 scores (i.e., $10 + 2.8$) or 25.6% (12.8/50) into the distribution.

The PR of any score may be found in the same way. For example, the percentile rank of 181 is 79 (verify it). The reader should note that a score of 163 is taken as 163.0, midpoint of the score interval 162.5–163.5. This means simply that the midpoint is assumed to be the most representative value in a score interval. The percentile ranks for several scores may be read directly from Table 12. For instance, 152 has a PR of 10, 172 (median) a PR of 50, and 187 a PR of 90. If we take the percentile points as representing *approximately* the score intervals upon which they lie, the PR of 160 (upon which 159.5 lies) is approximately 20 (see Table 12); the PR of 165 (upon which 165.3 lies) is approximately 30; the PR of 170 is approximately 40; of 175, 60; of 178, 70; of 182, 80. These PR's are not strictly accurate, to be sure, but the error is slight.

3. Calculating PR's from ordered data

In many instances, individuals and things can be put in 1-2-3 order with respect to some trait or characteristic (p. 328) when they cannot be measured directly, or measured conveniently. Suppose, for example, that 15 salesmen have been ranked from 1 to 15 for selling ability by the sales manager. It is possible to convert this order of merit into percentile ranks or "scores" on a scale of 100. The formula is

$$PR = 100 - \frac{(100R - 50)}{N} \tag{21}$$

(percentile ranks for persons or objects put in order of merit)

in which R is the rank position, counting #1 as highest and N as lowest. In our example, the salesman who ranks #1 or highest has a $PR = 100 - \dfrac{(100 \times 1 - 50)}{15}$ or 97. The salesman who ranks 5th has a $PR = 100 - \dfrac{(100 \times 5 - 50)}{15}$ or 70; and the salesman who ranks 15th has a PR of 3.

If 100 students are ranked for average grade earned throughout the school year, each student will occupy one division on the percentile scale. Hence, the PR of the best student is 99.5 (midpoint of interval 99–100); and the PR of the poorest student is .5 (midpoint of the lowest interval 0–1). The PR of the 50th student is $100 - \dfrac{(100 \times 50 - 50)}{100}$ or 50.5, midpoint of interval 50–51. As a PR is always the midpoint of an interval, it follows that no one can have a PR of 0 or 100. These two points constitute the boundaries or limits of the percentile scale.

PR's are useful when we wish to compare the standing of an individual in one test with his standing in another: the N's do not have to be the same. For example, suppose that Mary ranks 8th in a class of 22 in English and 18th in a class of 42 in history. How do these two "standings" compare? In English, Mary's PR is $100 - \dfrac{(100 \times 8 - 50)}{22}$ or 66; and in history, her PR is $100 - \dfrac{(100 \times 18 - 50)}{42}$ or 58. It is evident that relative to the members of her class, Mary is better in English than she is in history. In many schools, grades in the various subjects are converted into PR's, so that a student's standing in classes of different sizes may be compared directly.

III. THE CUMULATIVE PERCENTAGE CURVE OR OGIVE

1. Construction of the ogive

The cumulative percentage curve or ogive differs from the cumulative frequency graph in that frequencies are expressed as cumulative *percents* of N on the Y axis instead of as cumulative frequencies. Table 13 shows how cumulative frequencies can be turned into percentages of N. The distribution consists of scores made on a reading test by 125 seventh-grade pupils. In columns (1) and (2) class intervals and frequencies are listed; and in column (3) the f's have been cumulated from the low end of the distribution upward as described before on page 62. These

TABLE 13　Calculation of cumulative percentages to upper limits of class intervals in a frequency distribution

(The data represent scores on a reading test achieved
by 125 seventh-grade children.)

(1) Scores	(2) f	(3) Cum. f	(4) Cum. Percent f
74.5–79.5	1	125	100.0
69.5–74.5	3	124	99.2
64.5–69.5	6	121	96.8
59.5–64.5	12	115	92.0
54.5–59.5	20	103	82.4
49.5–54.5	36	83	66.4
44.5–49.5	20	47	37.6
39.5–44.5	15	27	21.6
34.5–39.5	6	12	9.6
29.5–34.5	4	6	4.8
24.5–29.5	2	2	1.6
$N = 125$			

$$\text{Rate} = \frac{1}{N} = \frac{1}{125} = .008$$

Cum. fs are expressed as percentages of N (125) in column (4). The conversion of Cum. fs into cumulative percents can be carried out by dividing each cumulative f by N; e.g., $2 \div 125 = .016$, $6 \div 125 = .048$, and so on. A better method—especially when a calculating machine is available—is to determine first the reciprocal, $1/N$, called the *Rate*, and multiply each cumulative f in order by this fraction. As shown in Table 13, the *Rate* is $1/125$ or .008. Hence, multiplying 2 by .008, we get .016 or 1.6%; $6 \times .008 = .048$ or 4.8%; $12 \times .008 = .096$ or 9.6%, etc.

The curve in Figure 10 represents an ogive plotted from the data in column (4), Table 13. Exact interval limits have been laid off on the X axis, and a scale consisting of 10 equal distances, each representing 10% of the distribution, has been marked off on the Y axis. The first point on the ogive is placed 1.6 Y units just above 29.5; the second point is 4.8 Y units just above 34.5, etc. The last point is 100 Y units above 79.5, exact upper limit of the highest class interval.

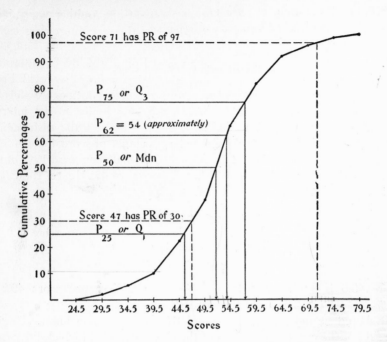

FIG. 10 Cumulative percentage curve or ogive plotted from the data of Table 13

2. Computing percentiles and percentile ranks

(a) *From the cumulative percentage distribution.* Percentiles may be readily determined by direct interpolation in column (4), Table 13. We may illustrate by calculating the 71st percentile. Direct interpolation between the percentages in column (4) gives the following:

$$
\begin{array}{ll}
& 66.4\% \text{ of the distribution up to } 54.5 \\
71.0\% \dashrightarrow & \dashrightarrow 55.9 \\
\text{(given)} & \underline{82.4\% \text{ of the distribution up to } 59.5} \\
& 16.0\% \qquad\qquad\qquad\qquad\qquad 5.0
\end{array}
$$

The 71st percentile lies 4.6% above 66.4%. By simple proportion,

$\dfrac{4.6}{16.0} = \dfrac{x}{5}$ or $x = \dfrac{4.6}{16.0} \times 5 = 1.4$ (x is the distance of the 71st percentile

from 54.5). The 71st percentile, therefore, is $54.5 + 1.4$, or 55.9.

Certain percentiles can be read directly from column (4). We know, for instance, that the 5th percentile is approximately 34.5; that the 22nd percentile is approximately 44.5; that the 38th percentile is approximately

49.5; and that the 92nd percentile is exactly 64.5. Another way of expressing the same facts is to say that 21.6% of the seventh-graders scored below 44.5, that 92% scored below 64.5, etc.

Percentile ranks may also be determined from Table 13 by interpolation. Suppose, for example, we wish to calculate the PR of score 43. From column (4) we find that 9.6% of the scores are *below* 39.5. Score 43 is 3.5 (43.0 − 39.5) from this point. There are 5 score units on the interval 39.5–44.5 which correspond to 12.0% (21.6 − 9.6) of the distribution; hence, 3.5/5 × 12.0 or 8.4 is the percentage distance of score 43 from 39.5. Since 9.6% (up to 39.5) + 8.4% (from 39.5 to 43.0) comprise 18% of the distribution, this percentage of N lies *below* score 43. Hence, the PR of 43 is 18. See detailed calculation below.

$$9.6\% \text{ of distribution up to } 39.5$$
$$18.0\% \longleftarrow\text{-----------------------}\longleftarrow\text{-----}\cdot \text{ score } 43.0$$
$$\underline{21.6\%} \text{ of distribution up to } \underline{44.5} \qquad \text{(given)}$$
$$\underline{12.0\%} \qquad\qquad\qquad\qquad \underline{5.0}$$

Score 43.0 is 3.5/5 × 12.0% or 8.4% from 39.5; hence score 43.0 is 9.6% + 8.4% or 18.0% into the distribution.

It should be noted that the cumulative percents in column (4) give the PR's of the exact *upper* limits of the class intervals in which the scores have been tabulated. The PR of 74.5, for example, is 99.2; of 64.5, 92.0; of 44.5, 21.6, etc. These PR's are the ranks of given points in the distribution, and are not the PR's of scores.

(*b*) *From the ogive.* Percentiles and percentile ranks may be determined quickly and fairly accurately from the ogive of the frequency distribution plotted in Figure 10. To obtain P_{50}, the median, for example, draw a line from 50 on the Y scale parallel to the X axis and where this line cuts the curve drop a perpendicular to the X axis. This operation will locate the median at 51.5, approximately. The exact median, calculated from Table 13, is 51.65. Q_1 and Q_3 are found in the same way as the median. P_{25} or Q_1 falls approximately at 45.0 on the X axis, and P_{75} or Q_3 falls at 57.0. These values should be compared with the calculated Q_1 and Q_3, which are 45.56 and 57.19, respectively. Other percentiles are read in the same way. To find P_{62}, for instance, begin with 62 on the Y axis, go horizontally over to the curve, and drop a perpendicular to locate P_{62} approximately at 54.

In order to read the percentile rank of a given score from the ogive, we reverse the process followed in determining percentiles. Score 71, for example, has a PR of 97, approximately (see Fig. 10). Here we start with score 71 on the X axis, go vertically up to the ogive, and horizontally across to the Y axis to locate the PR at 97 on the cumulative percentage scale. The PR of score 47 is found in the same way to be approximately 30.

Percentiles and percentile ranks will often be slightly in error when read from an ogive. This error, however, can be made very small. When the curve is carefully drawn, the diagram fairly large, and the scale divisions precisely marked, percentiles and PR's can be read to a degree of accuracy sufficient for most purposes.

3. Other uses of the ogive

(1) COMPARISON OF GROUPS

A useful over-all comparison of two or more groups is provided when ogives representing their scores on a given test are plotted upon the same coördinate axes. An illustration is given in Figure 11, which shows the ogives of the scores earned by two groups of children—200 ten-year-old boys and 200 ten-year-old girls—upon an arithmetic reasoning test of 60 items. Data from which these ogives were constructed are given in Table 14.

TABLE 14 Frequency distributions of the scores made by 200 ten-year-old boys and 200 ten-year-old girls on an arithmetic reasoning test

Scores	Boys f	Cum. f	Cum. % f	Smoothed Cum. Percentage f	Girls f	Cum. f	Cum. % f	Smoothed Cum. Percentage f
60–64	0	200	100.0	100.0	0	200	100.0	100.0
55–59	2	200	100.0	99.7	1	200	100.0	99.8
50–54	25	198	99.0	95.2	0	199	99.5	99.7
45–49	48	173	86.5	82.7	9	199	99.5	98.0
40–44	47	125	62.5	62.7	27	190	95.0	92.0
35–39	19	78	39.0	43.7	44	163	81.5	78.7
30–34	26	59	29.5	28.3	43	119	59.5	59.7
25–29	15	33	16.5	18.3	40	76	38.0	38.5
20–24	9	18	9.0	10.0	10	36	18.0	23.0
15–19	7	9	4.5	4.8	20	26	13.0	11.3
10–14	2	2	1.0	1.8	1	6	3.0	6.2
5–9	0	0	0	.3	2	5	2.5	2.3
0–4	0	0	0	0	3	3	1.5	1.3
	200				200			

$$\text{Rate} = \frac{1}{200} = .005$$

Several interesting conclusions can be drawn from Figure 11. The boys' ogive lies to the right of the girls' over the entire range, showing that the boys score consistently higher than the girls. Differences in achievement as between the two groups are shown by the distances separating the two curves at various levels. It is clear that differences at the extremes—between the very high-scoring and the very low-scoring boys and girls—are not so great as are differences over the middle range. This is brought out in a comparison of certain points in the distributions. The boys' median is approximately 42, the girls' 32; and the difference between these measures is represented in Figure 11 by the line AB. The difference between the boys' Q_1 and the girls' Q_1 is represented by the line CD; and the difference between the two Q_3's is shown by the line EF. It is clear that the groups differ more at the median than at either quartile, and are farther separated at Q_3 than at Q_1.

The extent to which one distribution overlaps another, whether at the median or at other designated points, can be determined quite readily from their ogives. By extending the vertical line through B (the boys' median) up to the ogive of the girls' scores, it is clear that approxi-

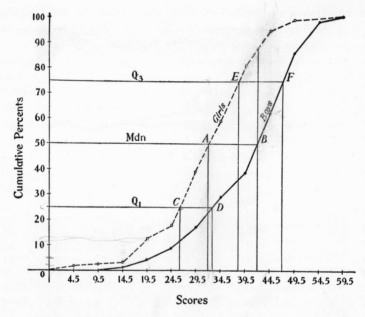

FIG. 11 Ogives representing scores made by 200 boys and 200 girls on an arithmetic reasoning test

(See Table 14)

mately 88% of the girls fall below the boys' median. This means that only 12% of the girls exceed the median of the boys in arithmetic reasoning. Computing overlap from boys to girls, we find that approximately 76% of the boys exceed the girls' median. The vertical line through A (girls' median) cuts the boys' ogive at approximately the 24th percentile. Therefore 24% of the boys fall below the girls' median, and 76% are above this point. Still another illustration may be helpful. Suppose the problem is to determine what percentage of the girls score at or above the boys' 60th percentile. The answer is found by locating first the point where the horizontal line through 60 cuts the boys' ogive. We then find the point on the girls' ogive directly above this value, and from here proceed across to locate the percentile rank of this point at 93. If 93% of the girls fall below the boys' 60th percentile, about 7% score above this point.

(2) PERCENTILE NORMS

Norms are measures of achievement which represent the typical performance of some designated group or groups. The norm for 10-year-old boys in height, and the norm for seventh-grade pupils in City X in arithmetic is usually the mean or the median derived from some large reference group. But norms may be much more detailed and may be reported for other points in the distribution as, for example, Q_1, Q_3, and various percentiles.

Percentile norms are especially useful in dealing with educational achievement examinations, when one wishes to evaluate and compare the achievement of a given student in a number of subject-matter tests. If the student earns a score of 63 on an achievement test in arithmetic, and a score of 143 on an achievement test in English, we have no way of knowing from the scores alone whether his achievement is good, medium, or poor, or how his standing in arithmetic and in English compare. If, however, we know that a score of 63 in arithmetic has a *PR* of 52, and a score of 143 in English a *PR* of 68, we may say at once that this student is average in arithmetic (52% of the students score lower than he) and good in English (68% score below him).

Percentile norms may be determined directly from smoothed ogives. Figure 12 represents the smoothed ogives of the two distributions of scores in arithmetic reasoning given in Table 14. Vertical lines drawn to the base line from points on the ogive locate the various percentile points. In Table 15, selected percentile norms in the arithmetic reasoning test have been tabulated for boys and girls separately. This table of norms may, of course, be extended by the addition of other intermediate

TABLE 15 Percentile norms for arithmetic reasoning test (Table i   ined
from smoothed ogives in Figure 12

| | GIRLS | | BOYS | |
Cum. %'s	Ogive	Calculated	Ogive	Calculated
99	52.0	49.0	57.5	54.5
95	46.5	44.5	54.5	52.9
90	43.5	42.7	52.5	50.9
80	40.0	39.2	49.0	48.1
70	37.0	36.9	46.5	46.1
60	35.0	34.6	44.0	44.0
50	32.5	32.5	41.5	41.8
40	30.0	30.0	39.0	39.7
30	27.0	27.5	35.0	34.8
20	23.5	25.0	30.0	30.9
10	18.5	18.0	24.5	25.2
5	14.0	15.5	19.5	20.1
1	3.5	3.3	6.5	14.5

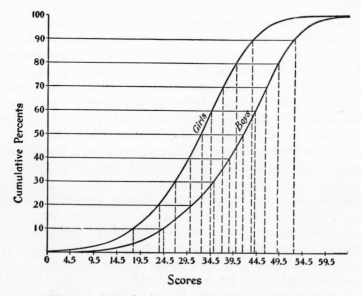

FIG. 12 Smoothed ogives of the scores in Table 14

values. Calculated percentiles are included in the table for comparison with percentiles read from the smoothed ogives. These calculated values are useful as a check on the graphically determined points, but ordinarily need not be found.

It is evident that percentile norms read from an ogive are not strictly accurate, but the error is slight except at the top and bottom of the distribution. Estimates of these extreme percentiles from smoothed ogives are probably more nearly true values than are the calculated points, since the smoothed curve represents what we might expect to get from larger groups or in additional samplings.

The ogives in Figure 12 were smoothed in order to iron out minor kinks and irregularities in the curves. Owing to the smoothing process, these curves are more regular and continuous than are the original ogives in Figure 11. The only difference between the process of smoothing an ogive and smoothing a frequency polygon (p. 13) is that we average cumulative percentage frequencies in the ogive instead of actual frequencies. Smoothed percentage frequencies are given in Table 14. The smoothed cumulative percentage frequency to be plotted above 24.5, boys' distribution, is $\frac{16.5 + 9.0 + 4.5}{3}$ or 10.0; for the same point, girls' distribution, it is $\frac{38.0 + 18.0 + 13.0}{3}$ or 23.0. Care must be taken at the extremes of the distribution where the procedure is slightly different. In the boys' distribution, for example, the smoothed cumulative percent frequency at 9.5 is $\frac{1.0 + 0.0 + 0.0}{3}$ or .3%, and at 59.5, it is $\frac{99.0 + 100.0 + 100.0}{3}$ or 99.7. At 64.5 and 4.5, respectively, both of which lie outside the boys' distribution, the cumulative percentage frequencies are $\left[\frac{100 + 100 + 100}{3}\right]$ and $\left[\frac{0 + 0 + 0}{3}\right]$, respectively. Note that the smoothed ogive extends one interval beyond the original at both extremes of the distribution.

There is little justification for smoothing an ogive which is already quite regular or an ogive which is very jagged and irregular. In the first instance, smoothing accomplishes little; in the second, it may seriously mislead. A smoothed curve shows what we might expect to get if the test or sampling, or both, were different (and perhaps better) than they actually were. Smoothing should never be a substitute for additional data or for an improved test. It should certainly be avoided when the group is small and the ogive very irregular. Smoothing is perhaps most useful when the ogives show small irregularities here and there (see Figure 11) which may reasonably be assumed to have arisen from minor and not very important factors.

IV. SEVERAL GRAPHIC METHODS

Data showing the changes attributable to growth, practice, learning, and fatigue may often be most clearly presented by graphical methods. Widely used devices are the *line graph*, the *bar diagram* and the *pie diagram*. These are illustrated in this section.

1. The line graph

Figure 13 shows an age-progress curve or trend line. The graph represents changes in "logical memory" for a connected passage of prose found for boys and girls from 8 to 18 years old. Norms for adults are also included at the extremes of the diagram. Age is represented on the hori-

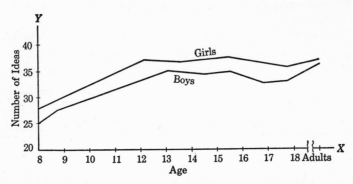

FIG. 13 Logical memory. Age is represented on X axis (horizontal); score, i.e., number of ideas remembered, on Y axis (vertical).

zontal or X axis and mean number of "ideas" reproduced at each age level is marked off on the vertical or Y axis. Memory ability as measured by this test rises to a peak at year 15 for both groups, after which there is a slight decline followed by a rise at the adult levels. There is a small but consistent sex difference, the girls being higher than the boys over the entire age range.

Figure 14 illustrates a learning or practice graph. These trend "lines" show the improvement—in sending and receiving telegraphic messages—resulting from successive trials at the same task over a period of 48 weeks. Improvement is measured by number of letters sent or received, and is indicated along the Y axis. Weeks of practice at the designated tasks are represented by equal intervals laid off on the X axis.

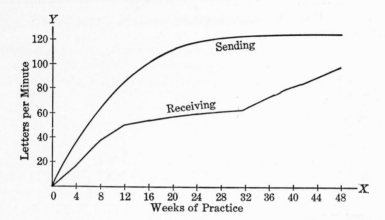

FIG. 14　Improvement in telegraphy. Weeks of practice on X axis; number of letters per minute on Y axis.

Figure 15 shows performance or practice "curve." It represents 25 successive trials with a hand dynamometer made by a man and a woman. A marked sex difference in strength of grip is apparent throughout the practice period. Also, as the experiment progresses, fatigue is noticeable in both subjects.

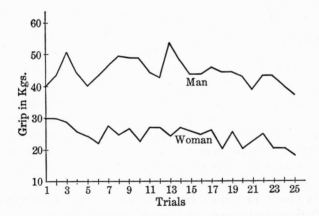

FIG. 15　Hand dynamometer readings in kilograms for 25 successive grips at intervals of ten seconds. Two subjects, a man and a woman.

Figure 16 is the famous Ebbinghaus "curve of retention." It represents memory retention of nonsense syllables as measured by the percentage of the original material retained after the passage of different time intervals. Time between learnings and relearnings is shown on the X axis. Percent retained is laid off on the Y axis.

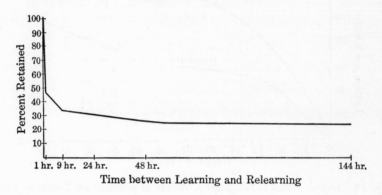

FIG. 16   Curve of retention. The numbers on the base line give hours elapsed from time of learning; numbers along Y axis give percent retained.

2. The bar diagram

The bar diagram is often used in psychology to compare the relative amounts of some trait (height, intelligence, educational achievement) possessed by two or more groups. In education, the bar graph is used to compare several different variables. Examples are cost of instruction in schools of the same system, distribution of students' time in and out of school, teachers' salaries by states or districts, and relative expenditures for educational purposes. A common form of the bar graph is that in which the lengths of the bars are proportional to the amounts of the variable possessed. For emphasis, spaces are often left between the bars, which may be drawn side by side in the vertical or horizontal direction.

A horizontal bar graph is shown in Figure 17. These bars represent the percentage of officers in the various branches of the military service who received grades of A and B or C upon Army Alpha, a test given during World War I. Bars are drawn in order, the service receiving the highest percent of A's and B's being placed at the top. The engineers, who ranked first, received 95% A's and B's and about 5% C's. The veterinarians, who ranked last, received only 60% A's and B's and 40% C's.

Figure 18 shows the percentages of World War II Air Force candidates who were eliminated from pilot training, classified according to the

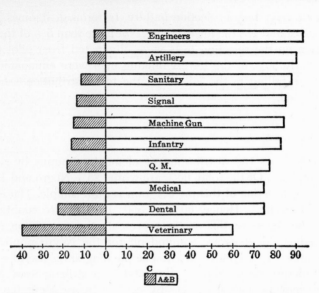

FIG. 17 Comparative bar graphs. The bars represent the percentage in each division of the military service receiving A's and B's or C's.

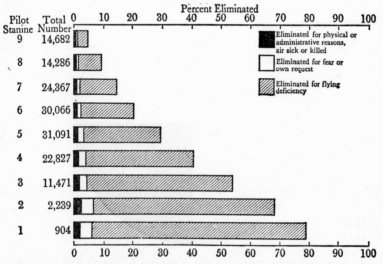

FIG. 18 Percentage of candidates eliminated from primary pilot training classified according to stanine scores on selection battery

(Reproduced from "Psychological Activities in the Training Command, Army Air Forces" by the Staff, Psychological Section, Fort Worth, Texas, in the *Psychological Bulletin*, 1945, Washington, D. C., American Psychological Association, Inc.)

scores they received on a selection battery. In terms of stanines (p. 318) 9 is the highest and 1 is the lowest score. Not more than 5% of the highest ranking men on the selection tests were eliminated from pilot training; whereas nearly 80% of the lowest ranking men were eliminated. About 30% of those falling in the middle of the test distribution (stanine 5) were eliminated.

3. The pie diagram

Figure 19 shows the distribution of elementary pupils by race in a large western city. Of the total, 60% are white, 25% Negro and 15% Oriental. The construction of this pie diagram is quite simple. There are 360 degrees in the circle. Hence, 60% of 360° or 216° are counted off as shown in the diagram; this sector represents the proportion of white students. Ninety degrees are counted off for the Negro pupils (25%) and 54 degrees for Orientals (15%). The pie diagram is useful when one wishes to picture proportions of the total in a striking way. Numbers of degrees may be measured off "by eye" or more accurately with a protractor.

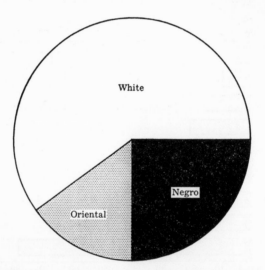

FIG. 19   Distribution by race of pupils in grades 3 through 8 of public schools in a large western city

PROBLEMS

1. The following distributions represent the achievement of two groups, A and B, upon a memory test.
   (a) Plot cumulative frequency graphs of Group A's and of Group B's scores, observing the 75% rule.
   (b) Plot ogives of the two distributions A and B upon the same axes.
   (c) Determine P_{30}, P_{60} and P_{90} graphically from each of the ogives and compare graphically determined with calculated values.
   (d) What is the percentile rank of score 55 in Group A's distribution? In Group B's distribution?
   (e) A percentile rank of 70 in Group A corresponds to what percentile rank in Group B?
   (f) What percent of Group A exceeds the median of Group B?

Scores	Group A		Group B
79–83	6	125	8
74–78	7	122	8
69–73	8	115	9
64–68	10	107	16
59–63	12	97	20
54–58	15	85	18
49–53	23	70	19
44–48	16	47	11
39–43	10	31	13
34–38	12	21	8
29–33	6	9	7
24–28	3	3	2
	$N = 128$		$N = 139$

2. Construct an ogive for the following distribution of scores:

Scores	f	
159.5–169.5	1	285
149.5–159.5	5	284
139.5–149.5	13	279
129.5–139.5	45	266
119.5–129.5	40	221
109.5–119.5	30	181
99.5–109.5	51	151
89.5– 99.5	48	100
79.5– 89.5	36	52
69.5– 79.5	10	16
59.5– 69.5	5	6 .06
49.5– 59.5	1	1 .02
	$N = 285$	

Read off percentile norms for the following cumulative percentages: 99, 95, 90, 80, 70, 60, 50, 40, 30, 20, 10, 5, and 1.

3. Given the following data for 5 cities in the United States, represent the facts by means of a bar graph.

Proportion of Population Which Is

City	Native White	Foreign Born	Negro
A	.65	.30	.05
B	.60	.10	.30
C	.50	.45	.05
D	.50	.10	.40
E	.30	.10	.60

4. (a) Twenty children are put in order of merit for scores on a learning test. Compute the PR for each child.
   (b) If 60 children are put in order of merit for grades in history, what are the PR's of the 1st, 10th, 45th and 60th?
5. (a) John ranks 6th in a class of 30 in mathematics and 6th in a class of 50 in English. Compare his PR's in the two subjects.
   (b) What would John's rank in mathematics need to be in order for his PR in mathematics to equal his PR in English?
6. In the operation of a school system in a certain city, 70% of the money spent goes for instruction, 12% for operation and maintenance, and 18% for auxiliary agencies, fixed charges and incidentals. Construct a pie diagram to show the relations of these expenditures.

ANSWERS

	Group A		Group B	
	Ogive	Cal.	Ogive	Cal.
1. (c) P_{30}	46.0	45.81	48.5	48.69
P_{60}	56.0	55.77	59.75	59.85
P_{90}	74.0	73.64	75.5	74.81

(d) 58; 47
(e) 62   (f) 39–40% of Group A exceed the median of Group B.

2. Read from ogive:

Cum. Percents:	99	95	90	80	70	60	50	40	30
Percentiles:	159	142.5	137.5	131.5	124.5	116.5	107	102	96.5
	20	10	5	1					
	91	82.5	79	64.5					

4. (a) PR's in order are: 97.5, 92.5, 87.5, 82.5, 77.5, 72.5, 67.5, 62.5, 57.5, 52.5, 47.5, 42.5, 37.5, 32.5, 27.5, 22.5, 17.5, 12.5, 7.5, 2.5.
   (b) PR's are 1st, 99.17; 10th 84.17; 45th, 25.83; 60th, .83.
5. (a) John's PR in mathematics, 81.67 or 82. His PR in English is 89.
   (b) John's rank must be 4, approximately.

ADDITIONAL PROBLEMS AND QUESTIONS ON CHAPTERS 1–4

1. Describe the characteristics of those distributions for which the mean is not an adequate measure of central tendency.
2. When is it not advisable to use the coefficient of variation?
3. What is a multimodal distribution? a bimodal distribution?
4. A student writes in a theme that through eugenics it would be possible to raise the intelligence of the race, so that more people would be above the median of 100. Comment on this.
5. How can the discrepancy between the median and the mean be used as a measure of the adequacy of a test?
6. A class in French has a median of 70 and a mean of 80 on a standard examination. Is the "average score" of the class 80?
7. Why cannot the SD of one test be compared directly with the SD of another test?
8. Suppose you made a frequency distribution of the ages of all men applying for a marriage license over the course of a year in a large city. What type of distribution would you expect to get?
9. What effect will an increase in N probably have upon Q?
10. What is the difference between a percentile and a percent grade used in school?
11. Does a PR of 65 earned by a pupil mean that 65% of the group made scores above him; that 65% made scores below him; or that 65% made the same score?
12. Compute the SD for the distribution below with and without Sheppard's correction.

Scores	f
60–69	1
50–59	4
40–49	10
30–39	15
20–29	8
10–19	2
	$N = 40$

13. Compute the mean, median, mode, Q and SD for each of the following distributions:

(1) Scores	f	(2) Scores	f	(3) Scores	f
90–99	2	14–15	3	25	1
80–89	12	12–13	8	24	2
70–79	22	10–11	15	23	6
60–69	20	8–9	20	22	8
50–59	14	6–7	10	21	5
40–49	4	4–5	4	20	2
30–39	1		$N = 60$	19	1
	$N = 75$				$N = 25$

14. (a) Plot the distribution in 13 (1) as a frequency polygon and histogram upon the same coördinate axes.

    (b) Plot the distribution in 13 (2) as an ogive. Locate graphically the median, Q_1, and Q_3. Determine the PR of score 9; of score 12.

ANSWERS

12. $\sigma = 11.07$ $\sigma_c = 10.68$

13. (1) Mean = 68.10   (2) Mean = 9.23   (3) Mean = 22.04
         Median = 68.75   Median = 9.10   Median = 22.06
         Mode = 70.05   Mode = 8.84   Mode = 22.10
         Q = 9.01   Q = 1.69   Q = .91
         SD = 12.50   SD = 2.48   SD = 1.34

14. (b) Median = 9.0; $Q_1 = 7.5$; $Q_3 = 11.0$ (Read from ogive)
        PR of 9 = 50; of 12 = 84.5

CHAPTER 5

THE NORMAL DISTRIBUTION

I. THE MEANING AND IMPORTANCE OF THE NORMAL DISTRIBUTION

1. Introduction

In Figure 20 are four diagrams, two polygons and two histograms, which represent frequency distributions of data drawn from anthropometry, psychology and meteorology. It is apparent, even upon superficial examination, that all of these graphs have the same general form— the measures are concentrated closely around the center and taper off from this central high point or crest to the left and right. There are relatively few measures at the "low-score" end of the scale; an increasing number up to a maximum at the middle position; and a progressive falling-off toward the "high-score" end of the scale. If we divide the area

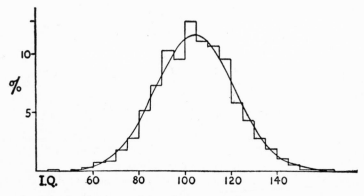

1. Form L. I.Q. distribution and best-fitting normal curve, ages 2½ to 18 (*from* McNemar, Quinn, *The Revision of the Stanford-Binet Scale*, 1942, p. 19)

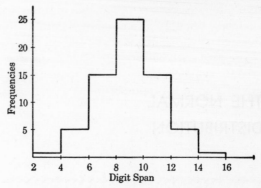

2. Memory span for digits, 123 adult women students (after Thorndike)

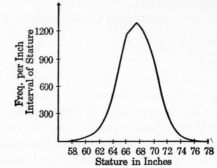

3. Statures of 8585 adult males born in the British Isles (after Yule)

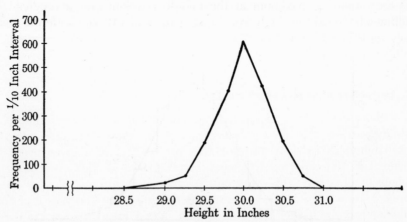

4. Frequency distribution of barometer heights at Southampton: 4748 observations (after Yule)

FIG. 20   Frequency distributions drawn from different fields

under each curve (the area between the curve and the X axis) by a line drawn perpendicularly through the central high point to the base line, the two parts thus formed will be similar in shape and very nearly equal in area. It is clear, therefore, that each figure exhibits almost perfect bilateral symmetry. The perfectly symmetrical curve, or frequency surface, to which all of the graphs in Figure 20 approximate, is shown in Figure 21. This

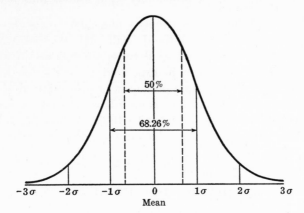

FIG. 21 Normal probability curve

bell-shaped figure is called the *normal probability curve,* or simply the *normal curve,* and is of great value in mental measurement. An understanding of the characteristics of the frequency distribution represented by the normal curve is essential to the student of experimental psychology and mental measurement. This chapter, therefore, will be concerned with the normal distribution, and its frequency polygon, the normal probability curve.

2. Elementary principles of probability

Perhaps the simplest approach to an understanding of the normal probability curve is through a consideration of the elementary principles of probability. As used in statistics, the "probability" of a given event is defined as the expected frequency of occurrence of this event among events of a like sort. This expected frequency of occurrence may be based upon a knowledge of the conditions determining the occurrence of the phenomenon, as in dice-throwing or coin-tossing, or upon empirical data, as in mental and social measurements.

The probability of an event may be stated mathematically as a ratio. The probability of an unbiased coin falling heads is 1/2, and the probability of a die showing a two-spot is 1/6. These ratios, called *probability ratios*, are defined by that fraction, the numerator of which equals the desired outcome or outcomes, and the denominator of which equals the total possible outcomes. More simply put, the probability of the appearance of *any* face on a 6-faced cube (e.g., 4 spots) is 1/6 or the $\frac{\text{desired outcome}}{\text{total number of outcomes}}$. A probability ratio always falls between the limits .00 (impossibility of occurrence) and 1.00 (certainty of occurrence). Thus the probability that the sky will fall is .00; that an individual now living will some day die is 1.00. Between these limits are all possible degrees of likelihood which may be expressed by appropriate ratios.

Let us now apply these simple principles of probability to the specific case of what happens when we toss coins.* If we toss one coin, obviously it must fall either heads (H) or tails (T) 100% of the time; and furthermore, since there are only two possible outcomes in a given throw, a head or a tail is *equally probable*. Expressed as a ratio, therefore, the probability of H is 1/2; of T 1/2; and

$$(H + T) = 1/2 + 1/2 = 1.00$$

If we toss two coins, (a) and (b), at the same time, there are four possible arrangements which the coins may take:

(1)		(2)		(3)		(4)	
a	b	a	b	a	b	a	b
H	H	H	T	T	H	T	T

Both coins (a) and (b) may fall H; (a) may fall H and (b) T; (b) may fall H and (a) T; or both coins may fall T. Expressed as ratios, the probability of *two* heads is 1/4 and the probability of *two* tails 1/4. Also, the probability of an HT combination is 1/4, and of a TH combination 1/4. And since it ordinarily makes no difference which coin falls H or which falls T, we may add these two ratios (or double the one) to obtain 1/2 as the probability of an HT combination. The sum of our probability ratios is $1/4 + 1/2 + 1/4$ or 1.00.

Suppose we go a step further and increase the number of coins to three. If we toss three coins (a), (b), and (c) simultaneously, there are eight possible outcomes:

(1)	(2)	(3)	(4)	(5)	(6)	(7)	(8)
a b c	a b c	a b c	a b c	a b c	a b c	a b c	a b c
H H H	H H T	H T H	T H H	H T T	T H T	T T H	T T T

* Coin-tossing and dice-throwing furnish easily understood and often used illustrations of the so-called "laws of chance."

Expressed as ratios, the probability of *three* heads is 1/8 (combination 1); of *two* heads and *one* tail 3/8 (combinations 2, 3 and 4); of *one* head and *two* tails 3/8 (combinations 5, 6 and 7); and of *three* tails 1/8 (combination 8). The sum of these probability ratios is $1/8 + 3/8 + 3/8 + 1/8$, or 1.00.

By exactly the same method used above for two and for three coins, we can determine the probability of different combinations of heads and tails when we have four, five or any number of coins. These various outcomes may be obtained in a more direct way, however, than by writing down all of the different combinations which may occur. If there are n independent factors, the probability of the presence or absence of each being the same, the "compound" probabilities of various combinations will be expressed by expansion of the binomial $(p + q)^n$. In this expression p equals the probability that a given event will happen, q the probability that the event will not happen, and the exponent n indicates the number of factors (e.g., coins) operating to produce the final result.* If we substitute H for p and T for q (tails = nonheads), we have for two coins $(H + T)^2$; and squaring, the binomial $(H + T)^2 = H^2 + 2HT + T^2$. This expansion may be written,

1 H^2 1 chance in 4 of 2 heads; *probability ratio*   = 1/4
2 HT 2 chances in 4 of 1 head and 1 tail; *probability ratio* = 1/2
$\underline{1}$ T^2 1 chance in 4 of two tails; *probability ratio*   = 1/4
Total $= \overline{4}$

These outcomes are identical with those obtained above by listing the three different combinations possible when two coins are tossed.

If we have three independent factors operating, the expression $(p + q)^n$ becomes for three coins $(H + T)^3$. Expanding this binomial, we get $H^3 + 3H^2T + 3HT^2 + T^3$, which may be written,

1 H^3 1 chance in 8 of 3 heads; *probability ratio*   = 1/8
3 H^2T 3 chances in 8 of 2 heads and 1 tail; *probability ratio* = 3/8
3 HT^2 3 chances in 8 of 1 head and 2 tails; *probability ratio* = 3/8
$\underline{1}$ T^3 1 chance in 8 of 3 tails; *probability ratio*   = 1/8
Total $= \overline{8}$

Again these results are identical with those got by listing the four different combinations possible when three coins are tossed.

The binomial expansion may be applied more usefully to those cases

---

* We may, for example, consider our coins to be independent factors, the occurrence of a head to be the *presence* of a factor and the occurrence of a tail the *absence* of a factor. Factors will then be "present" or "absent" in the various heads-tails combinations.

in which there is a larger number of independent factors operating. If we toss ten coins simultaneously, for instance, we have, by analogy with the above, $(p + q)^{10}$. This expression may be written $(H + T)^{10}$, H standing for the probability of a head, T for the probability of a nonhead (tail), and 10 for the number of coins tossed. When the binomial $(H + T)^{10}$ is expanded, the terms are

$$H^{10} + 10H^9T + 45H^8T^2 + 120H^7T^3 + 210H^6T^4 + 252H^5T^5 + 210H^4T^6$$
$$+ 120H^3T^7 + 45H^2T^8 + 10HT^9 + T^{10}$$

which may be summarized as follows:

			Probability Ratio
1	H^{10}	1 chance in 1024 of all coins falling heads	$\dfrac{1}{1024}$
10	H^9T^1	10 chances in 1024 of 9 heads and 1 tail...	$\dfrac{10}{1024}$
45	H^8T^2	45 chances in 1024 of 8 heads and 2 tails..	$\dfrac{45}{1024}$
120	H^7T^3	120 chances in 1024 of 7 heads and 3 tails..	$\dfrac{120}{1024}$
210	H^6T^4	210 chances in 1024 of 6 heads and 4 tails..	$\dfrac{210}{1024}$
252	H^5T^5	252 chances in 1024 of 5 heads and 5 tails..	$\dfrac{252}{1024}$
210	H^4T^6	210 chances in 1024 of 4 heads and 6 tails..	$\dfrac{210}{1024}$
120	H^3T^7	120 chances in 1024 of 3 heads and 7 tails..	$\dfrac{120}{1024}$
45	H^2T^8	45 chances in 1024 of 2 heads and 8 tails..	$\dfrac{45}{1024}$
10	HT^9	10 chances in 1024 of 1 head and 9 tails...	$\dfrac{10}{1024}$
1	T^{10}	1 chance in 1024 of all coins falling tails..	$\dfrac{1}{1024}$

Total = $\overline{1024}$

These data are represented graphically in Figure 22 by a histogram and frequency polygon plotted on the same axes. The eleven terms of the expansion have been laid off at equal distances along the X axis, and the "chances" of the occurrence of each combination of H's and T's are plotted as frequencies on the Y axis. The result is a symmetrical frequency polygon with the greatest concentration in the center and the "scores" falling away by corresponding decrements above and below the central high point. Figure 22 represents the results to be expected *theoretically* when ten coins are tossed 1024 times.

Many experiments have been conducted in which coins were tossed or dice thrown a great many times, with the idea of checking theoretical against actual results. In one well-known experiment,* twelve dice were

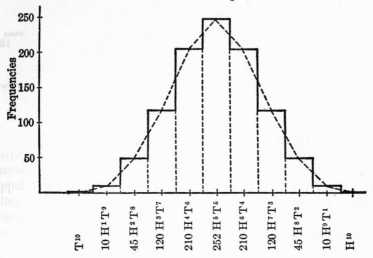

FIG. 22   Probability surface obtained from the expansion of $(H + T)^{10}$

thrown 4096 times. Each four-, five- and six-spot combination was taken as a "success" and each one-, two-, and three-spot combination as a "failure." Hence the probability of success and the probability of failure were the same. In a throw showing the faces 3, 1, 2, 6, 4, 6, 3, 4, 1, 5, 2 and 3, there would be five successes and seven failures. The *observed* frequency of the different numbers of successes and the *theoretical* outcomes obtained from the expansion of the binomial expression $(p + q)^{12}$ have been plotted on the same axes in Figure 23. The student will note that the observed frequencies correspond quite closely to the theoretical except for a tendency to shift slightly to the right. If, as an experiment, the reader will toss ten coins 1024 times his results will be in close agreement with the theoretical outcomes shown in Figure 22.

Throughout the discussion in this section, we have taken the prob-

* Weldon's experiment; see Yule, G. U., *An Introduction to the Theory of Statistics* (London: C. Griffin and Co., 1932), 10th ed., p. 258.

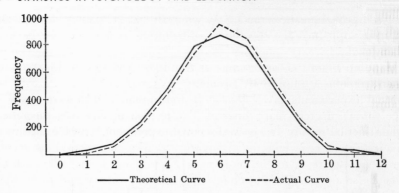

FIG. 23 Comparison of observed and theoretical results in throwing twelve dice 4096 times

(After Yule)

ability of occurrence (e.g., H) and the probability of nonoccurrence (non-H or T) of a given factor to be the same. This is not a necessary condition, however. For instance, the probability of an event's happening may be only 1/5; of its not happening, 4/5. Any probability ratio is is possible as long as $(p + q) = 1.00$. But distributions obtained from the expansion of $(p + q)^n$ when p is not equal to q are "skewed" or asymmetrical and are not normal (p. 99).

3. Use of the probability curve in mental measurement

The frequency curve plotted in Figure 22 from the expansion of the expression $(H + T)^{10}$ is a symmetrical many-sided polygon. If the number of factors (e.g., coins) determining this polygon were increased from 10 to 20, to 30, and then to 100, say (the base line extent remaining the same), the lines which constitute the sides of the polygon would increase regularly in number, becoming progressively shorter. With each increase in the number of factors the points on the frequency surface would move closer together. Finally, when the number of factors became very large—when n in the expression $(p + q)^n$ became infinite—the polygon would exhibit a perfectly smooth surface like that of the curve in Figure 21. This "ideal" polygon represents the frequency of occurrence of various combinations of a very large number of *equal, similar*, and *independent* factors (e.g., coins), when the probability of the appearance (e.g., H) or nonappearance (e.g., T) of each factor is the same. The normal distribution is not an actual distribution of test scores, but is, instead, a mathematical model. As we shall see, frequency distributions of scores *approach* the theoretical distribution as a limit, but the fit is rarely perfect.

If we compare the four graphs plotted from measures of height, intelligence, memory span, and barometric readings in Figure 20 with the normal probability curve in Figure 21, the similarity of these diagrams to the normal curve is clearly evident. The resemblance of these and many other distributions to the normal seems to express a general tendency of quantitative data to take the symmetrical bell-shaped form. This general tendency may be stated in the form of a "principle" as follows: measurements of many natural phenomena and of many mental and social traits under certain conditions *tend* to be distributed symmetrically about their means in proportions which approximate those of the normal probability distribution.

Much evidence has accumulated to show that the normal distribution serves to describe the frequency of occurrence of many variable facts with a relatively high degree of accuracy. Phenomena which follow the normal probability curve (at least approximately) may be classified as follows:

1. *Biological statistics:* the proportion of male to female births for the same country or community over a period of years; the proportion of different types of plants and animals in cross-fertilization (the Mendelian ratios).

2. *Anthropometrical data:* height, weight, cephalic index, etc., for large groups of the same age and sex.

3. *Social and economic data:* rates of birth, marriage or death under certain constant conditions; wages and output of large numbers of workers in the same occupation under comparable conditions.

4. *Psychological measurements:* * intelligence as measured by standard tests; speed of association, perception span, reaction time; educational test scores, e.g., in spelling, arithmetic, reading.

5. *Errors of observation:* measures of height, speed of movement, linear magnitudes, physical and mental traits, and the like contain errors which are as likely to cause them to deviate above as below their true values. Chance errors of this sort vary in magnitude and sign and occur in frequencies which follow closely the normal probability curve.†

It is an interesting speculation that many frequency distributions are similar to those obtained by tossing coins or throwing dice because the former, like the latter, are actually probability distributions. The sym-

* See p. 87.
† This topic is treated in Chapter 8.

metrical normal distribution, as we have seen, represents the probability of occurrence of the various possible combinations of a great many factors (e.g., coins). In a normal distribution all of the *n* factors are taken to be *similar, independent,* and *equal in strength*; and the probability that each will be present (e.g., show an H) or absent (e.g., show a T) is the same. The appearance on a coin of a head or a tail is undoubtedly determined by a large number of small (or "chance") influences as likely to work one way as another. The twist with which the coin is spun may be important, as well as the height from which it is thrown, the weight of the coin, the kind of surface upon which it falls, and many other circumstances of a like sort. By analogy, the presence or absence of each one of the large number of genetic factors which determine the shape of a man's head, or his intelligence, or his personality may depend upon a host of influences whose net effect we call "chance."

The striking similarity of obtained and probability distributions does not warrant the conclusion that *all* distributions of mental and physical traits which exhibit the bell-shaped form have *necessarily* arisen through the operation of those principles which govern the appearance of dice or coin combinations. The factors which determine musical ability, let us say, or mechanical skill are too little known to justify the assumption, *a priori,* that they combine in the same proportions as do the head and tail combinations in "chance" distributions of coins. Moreover, the psychologist usually constructs his tests with the normal hypothesis definitely in mind. The resulting symmetrical distribution is to be taken, then, as evidence of the success of his efforts rather than as conclusive proof of the "normality" of the trait being measured.

The selection of the normal rather than some other type curve is sufficiently warranted by the fact that this distribution generally does fit the data better, and is more useful. But the "theoretical justification and the empirical use of the normal curve are two quite different matters." *

II. PROPERTIES OF THE NORMAL PROBABILITY DISTRIBUTION

1. The equation of the normal curve

The equation of the normal probability curve reads

$$y = \frac{N}{\sigma\sqrt{2\pi}}e^{-\frac{x^2}{2\sigma^2}} \tag{22}$$

(equation of the normal probability curve)

* Jones, D. C., *A First Course in Statistics* (London: G. Bell and Sons, 1921), p. 233.

in which

$x =$ scores (expressed as deviations from the mean) laid off along the base line or X axis.

$y =$ the height of the curve above the X axis, i.e., the frequency of a given x-value.

The other terms in the equation are constants:

$N =$ number of cases
$\sigma =$ standard deviation of the distribution
$\pi = 3.1416$ (the ratio of the circumference of a circle to its diameter)
$e = 2.7183$ (base of the Napierian system of logarithms).

When N and σ are known, it is possible from equation (22) to compute (1) the frequency (or y) of a given value x; and (2) the number, or percentage between two points, or above or below a given point in the distribution. But these calculations are rarely necessary, as tables are available from which this information may be readily obtained. A knowledge of these tables (Table A), is indispensable in the solution of a number of problems. For this reason it is very desirable that the construction and use of Table A be clearly understood.

2. Table of areas under the normal curve

Table A* gives the fractional parts of the total area under the normal curve found between the mean and ordinates (y's) erected at various distances from the mean. The total area under the curve is taken arbitrarily to be 10,000, because of the greater ease with which fractional parts of the total area may then be calculated.

The first column of the table, x/σ, gives distances in tenths of σ measured off on the base line of the normal curve from the mean as origin. We have already learned that $x = X - M$, i.e., that x measures the deviation of a score X from M. If x is divided by σ, deviation from the mean is expressed in σ units. Such σ deviation scores are often called sigma-scores or z scores ($z = x/\sigma$).† Distances from the mean in hundredths of σ are given by the headings of the columns. To find the number of cases in the normal distribution between the mean and the ordinate erected at a distance of 1σ from the mean, go down the x/σ column until 1.0 is reached, and in the next column under .00 take the entry opposite 1.0, viz., 3413. This figure means that 3413 cases in 10,000, or 34.13% of the entire area of the curve, lies between the mean and 1σ. Put more exactly, 34.13% of the cases in

* Tables A to K appear in the Appendix.
† See p. 312,

a normal distribution fall within the area bounded by the base line of the curve, the ordinate erected at the mean, the ordinate erected at a distance of 1σ from the mean, and the curve itself (see Fig. 21). To find the percentage of the distribution between the mean and 1.57σ, say, go down the x/σ column to 1.5, then across horizontally to the column headed .07, and take the entry 4418. This means that in a normal distribution, 44.18% of the area (N) lies between the mean and 1.57σ.

We have so far considered only σ distances measured in the *positive* direction from the mean; that is, we have taken account only of the *right* half of the normal curve. Since the curve is bilaterally symmetrical, the entries in Table A apply to σ distances measured in the *negative* direction (to the *left*) as well as to those measured in the positive direction. To find the percentage of the distribution between the mean and -1.26σ, for instance, take the entry in the column headed .06, opposite 1.2 in the x/σ column. This entry (3962) means that 39.62% of the cases in the normal distribution fall between the mean and -1.26σ. The percentage of cases between the mean and -1σ is 34.13; and the student will now be able to verify the statement made on page 50 that between the mean and $\pm 1\sigma$ are 68.26% of the cases in a normal distribution (see also Fig. 21).

While the normal curve does not actually meet the base line until we are at infinite distances to the right and left of the mean, for practical purposes the curve may be taken to end at points -3σ and $+3\sigma$ distant from the mean. Table A shows that 4986.5 cases in the total 10,000 fall between the mean and $+3\sigma$; and 4986.5 cases will, of course, fall between the mean and -3σ. Therefore, 9973 cases in 10,000, or 99.73% of the entire distribution, lie within the limits -3σ and $+3\sigma$. By cutting off the curve at these two points, we disregard .27 of 1% of the distribution, a negligible amount except in very large samples.

3. Relationships among the constants of the normal probability curve

In the normal probability curve, the mean, the median, and the mode all fall exactly at the midpoint of the distribution and are numerically equal. Since the normal curve is bilaterally symmetrical, all of the measures of central tendency must coincide at the center of the distribution.

The measures of variability include certain constant fractions of the total area of the normal curve, which may be read from Table A. Between the mean and $\pm 1\sigma$ lie the middle two-thirds (68.26% exactly) of the cases in the normal distribution. Between the mean and $\pm 2\sigma$ are found 95% (approximately) of the distribution; and between the mean and $\pm 3\sigma$

68,26

99.7

are found 99.7% or very close to 100% of the distribution. There are about 68 chances in 100 that a case will lie within ±1σ from the mean in the normal distribution; there are 95 chances in 100 that it will lie within ±2σ from the mean; and 99.7 chances in 100 that it will lie within ±3σ from the mean.

Instead of σ the Q may be used as the unit of measurement in determining areas within given parts of the normal curve. In the normal curve the Q (p. 43) is generally called the probable error or PE. The relationships between PE and σ are given in the following equations:

$$PE = .6745\sigma$$
$$\sigma = 1.4826\,PE$$

from which it is seen that σ is always about 50% larger than the PE (p. 48).

By interpolation in Table A we find that ±.6745σ or ±1 PE includes the 25% just above and the 25% just below the mean. This part of the curve, sometimes called the "middle 50," is important because it defines the range of "normal" performance. The upper 25% is somewhat better, and the lowest 25% somewhat poorer than the typical middle or average group. From Table A we find also that ±2 PE (or ±1.3490σ) from the mean includes 82.26% of the measures in the normal curve; that ±3 PE (or ±2.0235σ) includes 97.70%; and that ±4 PE (or ±2.6980σ) includes 99.30%.

III. MEASURING DIVERGENCE FROM NORMALITY

1. Skewness

In a frequency polygon or histogram of test scores, usually the first thing which strikes the eye is the symmetry or lack of it in the figure. In the normal curve model the mean, the median, and the mode all coincide and there is perfect balance between the right and left halves of the fig-

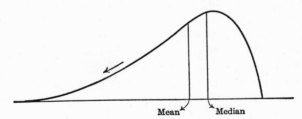

FIG. 24   Negative skewness: to the left

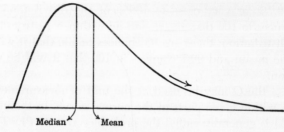

Median   Mean

FIG. 25   Positive skewness: to the right

ure. A distribution is said to be "skewed" when the mean and the median fall at different points in the distribution, and the balance (or center of gravity) is shifted to one side or the other—to left or right. In a normal distribution, the mean equals the median exactly and the skewness is, of course, zero. The more nearly the distribution approaches the normal form, the closer together are the mean and median, and the less the skewness. Distributions are said to be skewed *negatively* or to the *left* when scores are massed at the high end of the scale (the right end) and are spread out more gradually toward the low end (or left) as shown in Figure 24. Distributions are skewed *positively* or to the *right* when scores are massed at the low (or left) end of the scale, and are spread out gradually toward the high or right end as shown in Figure 25.

Note that the mean is pulled more toward the skewed end of the distribution than is the median. In fact, the greater the gap between mean and median, the greater the skewness. Moreover, when skewness is negative, the mean lies to the *left* of the median; and when skewness is positive, the mean lies to the *right* of the median.

A useful index of skewness is given by the formula

$$Sk = \frac{3(mean - median)}{\sigma} \tag{23}$$

(a measure of skewness in a frequency distribution)

If we apply formula (23) to the distribution of 50 Alpha scores in Table 9, $Sk = -.28$. This slight negative skewness in the data may be seen by reference to Figure 2. The skewness for the distribution of 200 cancellation scores in Table 9 is .009. This negligible degree of positive skewness shows how closely this distribution approaches the normal form. The symmetry of the frequency polygon may be verified from Figure 5.

A simple measure of skewness in terms of percentiles is

$$Sk = \frac{(P_{90} + P_{10})}{2} - P_{50} \tag{24}$$

(a measure of skewness in terms of percentiles)

Applying this formula to the distribution of 50 Alpha scores and 200 cancellation scores, we obtain for the first $Sk = -2.50$, and for the second $Sk = .02$. These results are numerically different from those obtained by formula (23), as the two indices are computed from different reference points and are not directly comparable. Both formulas agree, however, in indicating some negative skewness for the Alpha scores and near-normality for the 200 cancellation scores. In comparing the skewness of two distributions, we should, of course, stick to one formula or the other. The more nearly normal a distribution, the closer to zero are the indices of skewness given by both formulas.

The question of how much skewness a distribution must exhibit before it can be called *significantly* skewed cannot be answered until we have a standard error for our index of skewness. Standard errors for formulas (23) and (24) are not very satisfactory and will not be given. The measures of skewness, as they stand, are often sufficient for many problems in psychology and education. When more precise indices of skewness are required, the student should use those based upon the moments of the distribution. Such will be found in more advanced books dealing with mathematical statistics.

2. Kurtosis

The term "kurtosis" refers to the "peakedness" or flatness of a frequency distribution as compared with the normal. A frequency distribution more peaked than the normal is said to be *leptokurtic*; one flatter than the normal, *platykurtic*. Figure 26 shows a leptokurtic distribution and a platykurtic distribution plotted on the same diagram around the same

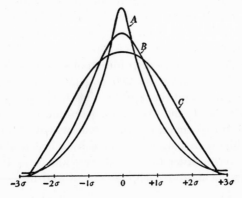

FIG. 26 Leptokurtic (A), normal or mesokurtic (B), and platykurtic (C) curves

mean. A normal curve (called *mesokurtic*) also has been drawn in on the diagram to bring out the contrast in the figures, and to make comparison easier. A formula for measuring kurtosis is

$$Ku = \frac{Q}{(P_{90} - P_{10})} \qquad (25)$$

(*a measure of kurtosis in terms of percentiles*)

For the normal curve, formula (25) gives $Ku = .263$.* If Ku is *greater*

$$Ku = \frac{.6745}{[1.28 - (-1.28)]} = .263$$

than .263 the distribution is platykurtic; if *less* than .263 the distribution is leptokurtic. Calculating the kurtosis of the distributions of 50 Alpha scores and 200 cancellation scores (Table 8), we obtain $Ku = .237$ for the first distribution and $Ku = .223$ for the second. Both distributions, therefore, are slightly leptokurtic.

3. Comparing a given histogram or frequency polygon with a normal curve of the same area, M and σ

In this section methods will be described for superimposing on a given histogram or frequency polygon a normal curve of the same N, M, and σ as the actual distribution. Such a model curve is the "best fitting" normal distribution for the given data. The research worker often wishes to compare his distribution "by eye" with that normal curve which "best fits" the data, and such a comparison may profitably be made even if no measures of divergence from normality are computed. In fact, the direction and extent of asymmetry often strike us more convincingly when seen in a graph than when expressed by measures of skewness and kurtosis. It may be noted that a normal curve can always be readily constructed by following the procedures given here, provided the area (N) and variability (σ) are known.

Table 16 shows the frequency distribution of scores made on the Thorndike Intelligence Examination by 206 college freshmen. The mean is 81.59, the median 81.00, and the σ 12.14. This frequency distribution has been plotted in Figure 27, and over it, on the same axes, has been drawn in the best-fitting normal curve, i.e., the model which best describes these data. The Thorndike scores are represented by a histogram instead of by a frequency polygon in order to prevent coincidence of the surface outlines and to bring out more clearly agreement and disagreement at dif-

---

* From Table A, $PE(Q) = .6745\sigma$, $P_{90} = 1.28\sigma$, and $P_{10} = -1.28\sigma$. Hence by formula (25)

TABLE 16 Frequency distribution of the scores made by 206 freshmen on the Thorndike Intelligence Examination

Scores	f	
115–119	1	
110–114	2	
105–109	4	
100–104	10	Mean = 81.59
95–99	13	Median = 81.00
90–94	18	$\sigma = 12.14$
85–89	34	
80–84	30	
75–79	37	
70–74	27	
65–69	15	
60–64	10	
55–59	2	
50–54	2	
45–49	1	
	$N = 206$	

ferent points. To plot a normal curve over this histogram, we first compute the height of the maximum ordinate (y_o) or the frequency at the middle of the distribution. The maximum ordinate (y_o) can be determined from the equation of the normal curve given on page 96. When x in this equation is put equal to zero (the x at the mean of the normal curve is 0), the term $e^{\frac{-x^2}{2\sigma^2}}$ equals 1.00, and $y_o = \dfrac{N}{\sigma\sqrt{2\pi}}$. In the present problem, $N = 206$; $\sigma = 2.43$ * (in units of class interval), and $\sqrt{2\pi} = 2.51$; hence $y_o = 33.8$ (see Fig. 27 for calculations). Knowing y_o, we are able to compute from Table B the heights of ordinates at given distances from

NORMAL CURVE ORDINATES AT MEAN, $\pm 1\sigma$, $\pm 2\sigma$, $\pm 3\sigma$

$$y_o = \frac{N}{\sigma\sqrt{2\pi}} = \frac{206}{2.43 \times 2.51} = 33.8$$
$$\pm 1\sigma = .60653 \times 33.8 = 20.5$$
$$\pm 2\sigma = .13534 \times 33.8 = 4.6$$
$$\pm 3\sigma = .01111 \times 33.8 = .4$$

* $\sigma = 2.43 \times 5$ (interval). The σ in interval units is used in the equation, since the units on the X axis are in terms of class intervals.

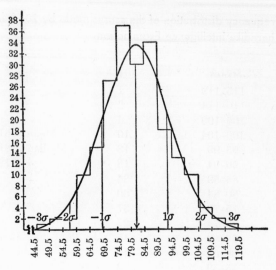

FIG. 27 Frequency distribution of the scores of 206 freshmen on the Thorn-dike Intelligence Examination, compared with best-fitting normal curve for same data

(For data, see Table 16.)

the mean. The entries in Table B give the heights of the ordinates in the normal probability curve, at various σ distances from the mean, expressed as fractions of the maximum or middle ordinate taken equal to 1.00000. To find, for example, the height of the ordinate at $\pm 1\sigma$, we take the entry .60653 from the table opposite $x/\sigma = 1.0$. This means that when the maximum central ordinate (y_0) is 1.00000, the ordinate (i.e., frequency) $\pm 1\sigma$ removed from M is .60653; or the frequency at $\pm 1\sigma$ is about 61% of the maximum frequency at the middle of the distribution. In Figure 27 the ordinates $\pm 1\sigma$ from M are .60653 $\times$ 33.8 (y_0) or 20.5. The ordinates $\pm 2\sigma$ from M are .13534 $\times$ 33.8 or 4.6; and the ordinates $\pm 3\sigma$ from M are .01111 $\times$ 33.8 or .4.

The normal curve may be sketched in without much difficulty through the ordinates at these seven points. Somewhat greater accuracy will be obtained if various intermediate ordinates, for example, at $\pm.5\sigma$, $\pm 1.5\sigma$, etc., are also plotted. The ordinates for the curve in Figure 27 at $\pm.5\sigma$ are .88250 $\times$ 33.8 or 29.8; at $\pm 1.5\sigma$, .32465 $\times$ 33.8 or 11.0, etc.

From formula (24) the skewness of our distribution of 206 scores is found to be 1.24. This small value indicates a low degree of positive skew-ness in the data. The kurtosis of the distribution by formula (25) is .244, and the distribution is slightly leptokurtic (this is shown by the "peak" rising above the model curve). Neither measure of divergence, however, is significant of a "real" discrepancy between our data and those of the normal distribution (see p. 104). On the whole, the normal curve plotted in Figure 27 fits the obtained distribution well enough to warrant our treating these data as sensibly normal.

IV. APPLICATIONS OF THE NORMAL PROBABILITY CURVE

This section will consider a number of problems which may readily be solved if we can assume that our obtained distributions can be treated as normal, or as approximately normal. Each general problem will be illustrated by several examples. These examples are intended to present the issues concretely, and should be carefully worked through by the student. Constant reference will be made to Table A; and a knowledge of how to use this table is essential.

I. To determine the percentage of cases in a normal distribution within given limits

Example (1) Given a distribution of scores with a mean of 12, and a σ of 4. Assuming normality, (a) What percentage of the cases fall between 8 and 16? (b) What percentage of the cases lie above score 18? (c) Below score 6?

(a) A score of 16 * is 4 points above the mean, and a score of 8 is 4 points below the mean. If we divide this scale distance of 4 score units by the σ of the distribution (i.e., by 4) it is clear that 16 is 1σ above the mean, and that 8 is 1σ below the mean (see Fig. 28). There are 68.26% of the cases in a normal distribution between the mean and $\pm 1\sigma$ (Table A). Hence, 68.26% of the scores in our distribution, or approximately the middle two-thirds, fall between 8 and 16. This result may also be stated in terms of "chances." Since 68.26% of the cases in the given distribution fall between 8 and 16, the chances are about 68 in 100 that any score in the distribution will be found between these points.

(b) The *upper limit* of a score of 18, namely, 18.5, is 6.5 score units or 1.625σ above the mean $(6.5/4 = 1.625)$. From Table A we find that 44.79% of the cases in the entire distribution fall between the mean and 1.625σ. Accordingly, 5.21% of the cases $(50.00 - 44.79)$ must lie *above* the upper limit of 18 (viz., 18.5) in order to fill out the 50% of cases in

* A score of 16 is the midpoint of the interval 15.5–16.5.

the upper half of the normal curve (Fig. 28). In terms of chances, there are about 5 chances in 100 that any score in the distribution will be larger than 18.

(c) The *lower limit* of a score of 6, namely, 5.5, is -1.625σ from the mean. Between the mean and 5.5 (-1.625σ) are 44.79% of the cases

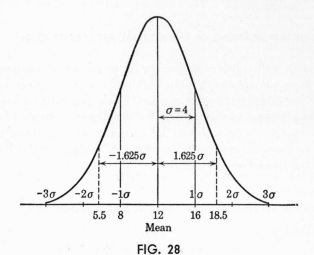

FIG. 28

in the whole distribution. Hence, about 5% of the cases in the distribution lie below 5.5—fill out the 50% below the mean—and the chances are about 5 in 100 that any score in the distribution will be less than 6, i.e., below the lower limit of score 6.

> *Example* (2) Given a distribution with a mean of 29.75 and a σ of 6.75. Assuming normality, what percentage of the distribution will lie between 22 and 26? What are the chances that a score will be between these two points?

A score of 22 * is 7.75 score units or -1.15σ (7.75/6.75 = 1.15) from the mean; and a score of 26 is 3.75 or $-.56\sigma$ from the mean (Fig. 29). We know from Table A that 37.49% of the cases in a normal distribution lie between the mean and -1.15σ; and that 21.23% of the cases lie between the mean and $-.56\sigma$. By simple subtraction, therefore, 16.26% of the cases fall between -1.15σ and $-.56\sigma$ or between the scores 22 and 26. The chances are 16 in 100 that any score in the distribution will lie between these two points.

* A score of 22 is the midpoint of the interval 21.5–22.5.

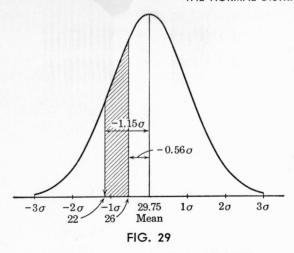

FIG. 29

2. To find the limits in any normal distribution which include a given percentage of the cases

Example (3) Given a distribution of scores with a mean of 16.00 and a σ of 4.00. If we may assume normality, what limits will include the middle 75% of the cases?

The middle 75% of the cases in a normal distribution include the 37.5% just above, and the 37.5% just below the mean. From Table A we find that 3749 cases in 10,000, or 37.5% of the distribution, fall between the mean and 1.15σ; and, of course, 37.5% of the distribution also falls between the mean and −1.15σ. The middle 75% of the cases, therefore, lie between the mean and ±1.15σ; or, since σ = 4.00, between the mean and ±4.60 score units. Adding ±4.60 to the mean (to 16.00), we find that the middle 75% of the scores in the given distribution lie between 20.60 and 11.40 (see Fig. 30).

Example (4) Given a distribution with a median of 150.00 and a *PE(Q)* of 17. Assuming normality, what limits will include the *highest* 20% of the distribution? the *lowest* 10%?

We know from page 99 that σ = 1.4826 *PE*; hence the σ of this distribution is 25.20 (1.4826 × 17). The highest 20% of a normally distributed group will have 30% of the cases between its lower limit and the median, since 50% of the cases lie in the right half of the distribution. From Table A we know that 2995 cases in 10,000, or 30% of the distribution, are between the median and .84σ. Since the σ of the given distribution is 25.20, .84σ will be .84 × 25.20 or 21.17 score units *above*

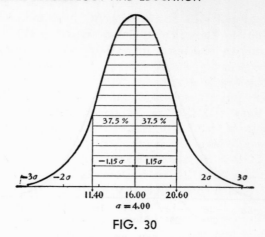

FIG. 30

the median, or at 171.17. The lower limit of the highest 20% of the given group, therefore, is 171.17; and the upper limit is the highest score in the distribution, whatever that may be.

The lowest 10% of a normally distributed group will have 40% of the cases between the median and its upper limit. Almost exactly 40% of the distribution falls between the median and -1.28σ. Hence, since $\sigma = 25.20$, -1.28σ must lie at -1.28×25.20 or 32.26 score units *below* the median, that is, at 117.74. The upper limit of the lowest 10% of scores in the group, accordingly, is 117.74; and the lower limit is the lowest score in the distribution.

3. To compare two distributions in terms of "overlapping"

Example (5) Given the distributions of the scores made on a logical memory test by 300 boys and 250 girls (Table 17). The boys' mean score is 21.49 with a σ of 3.63. The girls' mean score is 23.68 with a σ of 5.12. The medians are: boys, 21.41, and girls, 23.66. What percentage of boys exceed the median of the girls' distribution?

On the assumption that these distributions are normal, we may solve this problem by means of Table A. The girls' *median* is $23.66 - 21.49$ or 2.17 score units above the boys' *mean*. Dividing 2.17 by 3.63 (the σ of the boys' distribution), we find that the girls' median is $.60\sigma$ above the mean of the boys' distribution. Table A shows that 23% of a normal distribution lies between the mean and $.60\sigma$; hence 27% of the boys $(50\% - 23\%)$ exceed the girls' median.

This problem may also be solved by direct calculation from the distributions of boys' and girls' scores without any assumption as to normality of distribution. The calculations are shown in Table 17; and it is interesting to compare the result found by direct calculation with that obtained by use of the probability tables. The problem is to find the *number* of boys whose scores exceed 23.66, the girls' median, and then turn this number into a percentage. There are 217 boys who score up to 23.5 (lower limit of 23.5–27.5). The class interval 23.5–27.5 contains 68 scores; hence there are 68/4 or 17 scores *per scale unit* on this interval. We wish to reach 23.66 in the boys' distribution. This point is .16 of a score (23.66 − 23.50 = .16) above 23.5, or 2.72 (i.e., 17 × .16) score units above 23.5. Adding 2.72 to 217, we find that 219.72 of the boys' scores fall *below* 23.66, the girls' median. Since 300 − 219.72 = 80.28, it is clear that

TABLE 17 To illustrate the method of determining overlapping by direct calculation from the distribution

BOYS		GIRLS	
Scores	f	Scores	f
27.5–31.5	15	31.5–35.5	20
23.5–27.5	68	27.5–31.5	35
19.5–23.5	128	23.5–27.5	73
15.5–19.5	79	19.5–23.5	68
11.5–15.5	10	15.5–19.5	41
	$N = 300$	11.5–15.5	13
	$N/2 = 150$		$N = 250$
			$N/2 = 125$

$$Mdn = 19.5 + \frac{61}{128} \times 4 \qquad\qquad Mdn = 23.5 + \frac{3}{73} \times 4$$

$$= 21.41 \qquad\qquad\qquad = 23.66$$

$$M = 21.49 \qquad\qquad\qquad M = 23.68$$

$$\sigma = 3.63 \qquad\qquad\qquad \sigma = 5.12$$

What percent of the boys exceed 23.66, the median of the girls? First, 217 boys makes scores *below* 23.5. The class interval 23.5–27.5 contains 68 scores; hence, there are 68/4 or 17 scores *per scale unit* on this interval.

The girls' median, 23.66, is .16 *above* 23.5, lower limit of interval 23.5–27.5. If we multiply 17 (number of scores per scale unit) by .16 we obtain 2.72 which is the distance we must go into interval 23.5–27.5 to reach 23.66.

Adding 217 and 2.72, we obtain 219.72 as that part of the boys' distribution which falls *below* the point 23.66 (girls' median). N is 300; hence 300 − 219.72 gives 80.28 as that part of the boys' distribution which lies *above* 23.66. Dividing 80.28 by 300, we find that .2676, or approximately 27%, of the boys exceed the girls' median.

80.28 ÷ 300 or 26.76% (approximately 27%) of the boys exceed the girls' median. This result is in almost perfect agreement with that obtained above. Apparently the assumption of normality of distribution for the boys' scores was justified.

The agreement between the percentage of overlapping found by direct calculation from the distribution and that found by use of the probability tables will nearly always be close, especially if the groups are large and the distributions fairly symmetrical. When the overlapping distributions are small and not very regular in outline, it is safer to use the method of direct calculation, since no assumption as to form of distribution need then be made.

4. To determine the relative difficulty of test questions, problems, and other test items

Example (6) Given a test question or problem solved by 10% of a large unselected group; a second problem solved by 20% of the same group; and a third problem solved by 30%. If we assume the capacity measured by the test problems to be distributed normally, what is the relative difficulty of questions 1, 2 and 3?

Our first task is to find for Question 1 a cut in the distribution, such that 10% of the entire group (the percent passing) lies above, and 90% (the percent failing) lies below the given point. The highest 10% in a normally distributed group has 40% of the cases between its lower limit and the mean (see Fig. 31). From Table A we find that 39.97%

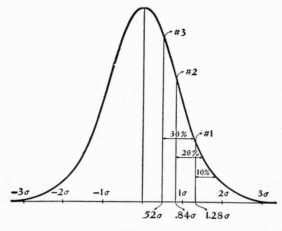

FIG. 31

(i.e., 40%) of a normal distribution falls between the mean and 1.28σ. Hence, Question 1 belongs at a point on the base line of the curve, a distance of 1.28σ from the mean; and, accordingly, 1.28σ may be set down as the difficulty value of this question.

Question 2, passed by 20% of the group, falls at a point in the distribution 30% above the mean. From Table A it is found that 29.95% (i.e., 30%) of the group falls between the mean and .84σ; hence, Question 2 has a difficulty value of .84σ. Question 3, which lies at a point in the distribution 20% above the mean, has a difficulty value of .52σ, since 19.85% of the distribution falls between the mean and .52σ. To summarize our results:

Question	Passed by	σ Value	σ Difference
1	10%	1.28	—
2	20%	.84	.44
3	30%	.52	.32

The σ difference in difficulty between Questions 2 and 3 is .32, which is roughly 3/4 of the σ difference in difficulty between Questions 1 and 2. Since the percentage difference is the same in the two comparisons, it is evident that when ability is assumed to follow the normal curve, σ and not percentage differences are the better indices of differences in difficulty.

Example (7) Given three test items, 1, 2, and 3, passed by 50%, 40%, and 30%, respectively, of a large group. On the assumption of normality of distribution, what percentage of this group must pass test item 4 in order for it to be as much more difficult than 3 as 2 is more difficult than 1?

An item passed by 50% of a group is, of course, failed by 50%; and, accordingly, such an item falls exactly in the middle of a normal distribution of "difficulty." Test item 1, therefore, has a σ value of .00, since it falls exactly at the mean (Fig. 32). Test item 2 lies at a point in the distribution 10% above the mean, since 40% of the group passed and 60% failed this item. Accordingly, the σ value of item 2 is .25, since from Table A we find that 9.87% (roughly 10%) of the cases lie between the mean and .25σ. Test item 3, passed by 30% of the group, lies at a point 20% above the mean, and this item has a difficulty value of .52σ, as 19.85% (20%) of the normal distribution falls between the mean and .52σ.

Since item 2 is .25σ farther along on the difficulty scale (toward the high-score end of the curve) than item 1, it is clear that item 4 must be

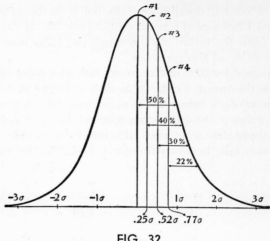

FIG. 32

.25σ above item 3, if it is to be as much harder than item 3 as item 2 is harder than item 1. Item 4, therefore, must have a value of .52σ + .25σ or .77σ; and from Table A we find that 27.94% (28%) of the distribution falls between the mean and this point. This means that 50% − 28% or 22% of the group must *pass* item 4. To summarize:

Test Item	Passed by	σ Value	σ Difference
1	50%	.00	
			.25
2	40%	.25	
3	30%	.52	
			.25
4	22%	.77	

A test item, therefore, must be passed by 22% of the group in order for it to be as much more difficult than an item passed by 30% as an item passed by 40% is more difficult than one passed by 50%. Note again that percentage differences are not reliable indices of differences in difficulty when the capacity measured is distributed normally.

5. To separate a given group into subgroups according to capacity, when the trait is normally distributed

Example (8) Suppose that we have administered an entrance examination to 100 college students. We wish to classify our group into five subgroups A, B, C, D and E according to ability, the *range* of ability to be equal in each subgroup. On the assumption that the trait measured by our examination is normally distributed, how many students should be placed in groups A, B, C, D and E?

Let us first represent the positions of the five subgroups diagrammatically on a normal curve as shown in Figure 33. If the base line of the curve is considered to extend from -3σ to $+3\sigma$, that is, over a range of 6σ, dividing this range by 5 (the number of subgroups) gives 1.2σ as the base line extent to be allotted to each group. These five intervals may be laid off on the base line as shown in the figure, and perpendiculars erected to demarcate the various subgroups. Group A covers the upper 1.2σ; group B the next 1.2σ; group C lies $.6\sigma$ to the *right* and $.6\sigma$ to the *left* of the mean; groups D and E occupy the same relative positions in the lower half of the curve that B and A occupy in the upper half.

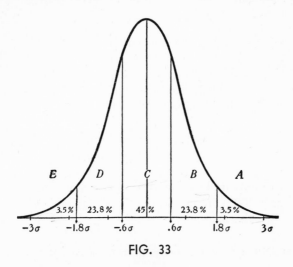

FIG. 33

To find what percentage of the whole group belongs in A we must find what percentage of a normal distribution lies between 3σ (upper limit of the A group) and 1.8σ (lower limit of the A group). From Table A 49.86% of a normal distribution is found to lie between the mean and 3σ; and 46.41% between the mean and 1.8σ. Hence, 3.5% of the total area under the normal curve (49.86% $-$ 46.41%) lies between 3σ and 1.8σ; and, accordingly, group A comprises 3.5% of the whole group.

The percentages in the other groups are calculated in the same way. Thus, 46.41% of the normal distribution falls between the mean and 1.8σ (upper limit of group B) and 22.57% falls between the mean and $.6\sigma$

(lower limit of group B). Subtracting, we find that 46.41% − 22.57% or 23.84% of our distribution belongs in subgroup B. Group C lies from .6σ above to −.6σ below the mean. Between the mean and .6σ is 22.57% of the normal distribution, and the same percent lies between the mean and −.6σ. Group C, therefore, includes 45.14% (22.57 × 2) of the distribution. Finally, subgroup D, which lies between −.6σ and −1.8σ, contains exactly the same percentage of the distribution as subgroup B; and group E, which lies between −1.8σ and −3σ, contains the same percent of the whole distribution as group A. The percentage and number of men in each group are given in the following table:

	Groups				
	A	B	C	D	E
Percentage of total in each group	3.5	23.8	45	23.8	3.5
Number in each group	4 or 3	24	45	24	4 or 3
(100 men in all)					

On the assumption that the capacity measured follows the normal curve, it is clear that 3 to 4 men in our group of 100 should be placed in group A, the "marked" ability group; 24 in group B, the "high average" ability group; 45 in group C, the "average" ability group; 24 in group D, the "low average" ability group; and 3 or 4 in group E, the "very low" or "inferior" group.

The above procedure may be used to determine how many students in a class should be assigned to each of any given number of grade groups. The assumption is always made that performance in the subject upon which the individuals are being marked can be represented by the normal curve. The larger and more unselected the group, and the better the test, the more nearly is this assumption justified.

V. WHY FREQUENCY DISTRIBUTIONS DEVIATE FROM THE NORMAL FORM

It is often important for the research worker to know why his distributions diverge from the normal form, and this is especially true when the deviation from normality is large and significant (p. 100). The reasons why distributions exhibit skewness and kurtosis are numerous and often complex, but a careful analysis of the data will often permit the setting up of hypotheses concerning deviation from normality which may be tested experimentally. Common causes of asymmetry, all of which must be taken into consideration by the careful experimenter, will be summarized in the present section. Further discussion of this topic will be found in Chapter 8.

1. Selection

Selection is a potent cause of skewness. We should hardly expect the distribution of I.Q.'s obtained from a group of 25 superior students to be normal; nor would we look for symmetry in the distribution of I.Q.'s got from a special class of dull-normal 10-year-old boys, even though the group were fairly large. Neither of these groups is an unbiased selection, i.e., a cross section, from some normal group—and in addition, the first group is quite small. A small group is not necessarily selected or atypical, but more often than not it is apt to be (see p. 207).

Selection will produce skewnesss and kurtosis in distributions even when the test has been adequately constructed and carefully administered. For example, a group of elementary school pupils which contains (a) a large number of bilinguals, (b) many children of very low or very high socioeconomic status, and (c) many pupils who are overage for grade or are accelerated will almost surely return skewed distributions even upon standard intelligence and educational achievement examinations.

Scores made by small and homogeneous groups are likely to yield narrow and leptokurtic distributions; scores from large and heterogeneous groups are more likely to be broad and platykurtic in form. A group of eighth-graders, all of I.Q. 100, will differ much less in reading than a group of unselected eighth-graders. The distributions of scores achieved upon an educational test by children throughout the elementary grades will probably be somewhat flattened owing to considerable overlap from grade to grade.

Distributions of physical traits such as height, weight, and strength are measured on ratio scales (p. 2) and are also influenced by selection. Physical traits when measured in large groups of the same sex, age and race will approximate the normal form. But the distribution of height for 14-year-old girls of high socioeconomic status or the distribution of weight for children from slum areas will most likely be skewed, as these groups are subject to selection in various traits related to height and weight.

2. Unsuitable or poorly made tests

If a test is too easy, scores will pile up at the high-score end of the scale, whereas when the test is too hard, scores will pile up at the low-score end of the scale. Imagine, for example, that an examination in arithmetic which requires only addition, subtraction, multiplication, and division has been given to 1000 seventh-graders. The resulting distribution will almost certainly be badly skewed to the left (see Fig. 24). On the other hand, if the examination contains only problems in complex fractions, interest, square root, and the like, the score distribution is likely to be positively skewed—low scores will be more numerous than intermediate or high scores. It is probable also that both distributions will be somewhat more "peaked" (leptokurtic) than the normal.

Asymmetry in cases like these may be explained in terms of those small positive and negative factors which determine the normal distribution. Too easy a test excludes from operation some of the factors which would make for an extension of the curve at the upper end, such as knowledge of more advanced arithmetical processes which the brighter child would know. Too hard a test excludes from operation factors which make for the extension of the distribution at the low end, such as knowledge of those very simple facts which would have permitted the answering of a few at least of the easier questions had these been included. In the first case we have a number of perfect scores and little discrimination; in the second case a number of zero scores and equally poor differentiation. Besides the matter of difficulty in the test, asymmetry may be brought about by ambiguous or poorly made items and by other technical faults.

3. Nonnormal distributions

Skewness or kurtosis or both will appear when there is a real lack of normality in the trait being measured.* Nonnormality of distribution will arise, for instance, when some of the hypothetical factors determining the strength of a trait are dominant or prepotent over the others, and hence are present more often than chance will allow. Illustrations may be found in distributions resulting from the throwing of loaded dice. When off-center or biased dice are cast, the resulting distribution will certainly be skewed and probably peaked, owing to the greater likelihood of combinations of faces yielding certain scores. The same is true of biased coins. Suppose, for example, that the probability of "success" (appearance of H) is four times the probability of failure (nonoccurrence of H, or presence of T), so that $p = 4/5$, $q = 1/5$, and $(p + q) = 1.00$. If we think of the factors making for success or failure as 3 in number,

---

* There is no reason why all distributions should approach the normal form. Thorndike has written: "There is nothing arbitrary or mysterious about variability which makes the so-called normal type of distribution a necessity, or any more rational than any other sort, or even more to be expected on *a priori* grounds. Nature does not abhor irregular distributions." *Theory of Mental and Social Measurement* (New York: Teachers College, 1913), pp. 88–89.

we may expand $(p+q)^3$ to find the incidence of success and failure in varying degree. Thus, $(p+q)^3 = p^3 + 3p^2q + 3pq^2 + q^3$, and substituting $p = 4/5$ and $q = 1/5$, we have

(1) $p^3 = (4/5)^3 = \dfrac{64}{125}$

$3p^2q = 3(4/5)^2 \cdot (1/5) = \dfrac{48}{125}$

$3pq^2 = 3(4/5) \cdot (1/5)^2 = \dfrac{12}{125}$

$q^3 = (1/5)^3 = \dfrac{1}{125}$

(2) Expressed as a frequency distribution:

"Successes"	f
3	64
2	48
1	12
0	1
	$N = 125$

The numerators of the probability ratios (frequency of success) may be plotted in the form of a histogram to give Figure 34.

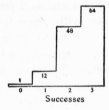

FIG. 34 Histogram of the expansion $(p+q)^3$, where $p = \tfrac{4}{5}$, $q = \tfrac{1}{5}$. p is the probability of success, q the probability of failure

FIG. 35 U-shaped frequency curve

Note that this distribution is negatively skewed (to the *left*); that the incidence of three "successes" is 64, of two 48, of one 12, and of none 1. J-shaped distributions like these are essentially nonnormal. Such curves have been found most often by psychologists to describe certain forms of social behavior. For example, suppose that we tabulate the number of students who appear at a lecture "on time"; and the number who arrive 5, 10 or 15+ minutes late. If frequency of arrival is plotted against time, the distribution will be highest at zero ("on time") on the X axis, and will fall off rapidly as we go to the right, i.e., will be positively skewed in an extreme fashion. Such curves, when plotted as frequency polygons, are called J curves (see Fig. 25). If only the early-comers are tallied, up to the "on time" group, the curve will be negatively skewed like those in Figures 24 and 34. J curves describe behavior which is essentially nonnormal in occurrence because the many causes of the behavior differ greatly in strength. But J curves may represent frequency distributions badly skewed for other reasons.

Nonnormal curves often occur in medical statistics. The likelihood of death due to degenerative disease, for instance, is highest during maturity and old age and minimal during the early years. If the age span from 20 to 80 is laid off on the base line and the probability of death from cancer at each age level plotted on the Y axis, the curve will be negatively skewed and will resemble Figure 24. Factors making for death are pre-potent over those making for survival as age increases, and hence the curve is essentially asymmetrical. In the case of a childhood disease, the probability of death will be positively skewed when plotted against age as the incidence of death becomes less with increase in age.

Another type of nonnormal distribution, which may be briefly de-scribed, is the U-shaped curve shown in Figure 35. U-shaped distributions, like J curves, are rarely encountered in mental and physical measurement. They are sometimes found in the measurement of social and personality traits, if the group is extremely heterogeneous with respect to some attribute, or if the test measures a trait that is likely to be present or absent in an all-or-none manner. Thus, in a group composed about equally of normals and mentally ill persons, the normals will tend to make low scores on a Neurotic Inventory while the abnormals will tend to make high scores. This makes for a dip in the center of the distribution, despite considerable overlap in score. Again, in tests of suggestibility, if a subject yields to suggestion in the first trial he is likely to be suggestible in all trials—thus earning a high score. On the other hand, if he resists sugges-tion on the first trial, he is likely to resist in all subsequent trials—thus earning a zero (or a very low) score.* This all-or-none feature of the score makes for a U-shaped distribution.

4. Errors in the construction and administration of tests

Various factors in addition to those mentioned make for distortions in score distributions. Differences in the size of the units in which test per-formance has been expressed, for example, will lead to irregularities in score distribution. If the items are very easy at the beginning and very hard later on, an increment of one point of score at the upper end of the test scale will be much greater than an increment of one point at the low end of the scale. The effect of such unequal or "rubbery" units jams the distribution and reduces the spread. Scores tend to pile up at some intermediate point and to be stretched out at the low end of the scale.

* See Hull, C. L., *Hypnosis and Suggestibility* (New York: Appleton-Century-Crofts, 1938), p. 68.

Errors in timing or in giving instructions, errors in the use of scoring stencils, large differences in practice or in motivation—all of these factors, if they cause some students to score higher and others to score lower than they normally would, tend to make for skewness in the distribution.

PROBLEMS

1. In two throws of a coin, what is the probability of throwing at least one head?

2. What is the probability of throwing exactly one head in three throws of a coin?

3. Five coins are thrown. What is the probability that exactly two of them will be heads?

4. A box contains 10 red, 20 white and 30 blue marbles. After a thorough shaking, a blindfolded person draws out 1 marble. What is the probability that
   (a) it is blue?
   (b) red or blue?
   (c) neither red nor blue?

5. If the probability of answering a certain question correctly is four times the probability of answering it incorrectly, what is the probability of answering it correctly?

6. (a) If two unbiased dice are thrown, what is the probability that the number of spots showing will total 7?
   (b) Draw up a frequency distribution showing the occurrence of combinations of from 2 to 12 spots when two dice are thrown.

7. (a) In an attitude questionnaire containing 10 statements, each to be marked as True or False, what is the probability of getting a perfect score by sheer guesswork?
   (b) Suppose you know 5 statements to be True and 5 False. What is the probability that you will mark the right ones True (select the right five)?

8. A rat has five choices to make of alternate routes in order to reach the foodbox. If it is true that for each choice the odds are two to one in favor of the correct pathway, what is the probability that the rat will make all of its choices correctly?

9. Assuming that trait X is completely determined by 6 factors—all similar and independent, and each as likely to be present as absent—plot the distribution which one might expect to get from the measurement of trait X in an unselected group of 1000 people.

10. Toss five pennies thirty-two times, and record the number of heads and tails after each throw. Plot frequency polygons of obtained and expected occurrences on the same axes. Compare the M's and σ's of obtained and expected distributions.

11. What percentage of a normal distribution is included between the
    - (a) mean and 1.54σ
    - (b) mean and $-2.7PE$
    - (c) -1.73σ and $.56\sigma$
    - (d) $-3.5PE$ and $1.0PE$
    - (e) $.66\sigma$ and 1.78σ
    - (f) $-1.8PE$ and $-2.5PE$

12. In a normal distribution
    - (a) Determine P_{27}, P_{46}, P_{54}, and P_{81} in σ units.
    - (b) What are the percentile ranks of scores at -1.23σ, $-.50\sigma$, $+.84\sigma$?

13. (a) Compute measures of skewness and of kurtosis for the first two frequency distributions in Chapter 2, problem 1, page 39.
    - (b) Fit normal probability curves to these same distributions, using the method given on page 102.
    - (c) For each distribution, compare the percentage of cases lying between $\pm 1\sigma$ with the 68.26% found in the normal distribution.

14. Suppose that the height of the maximum ordinate (y_o) in a normal curve is 50. What is the height to the nearest integer of the ordinate at the x/σ point which cuts off the top 11% of the distribution? top 30%? bottom 5%? (Use Tables A and B.)

15. In a sample of 1000 cases the mean of a certain test is 14.40 and σ is 2.50. Assuming normality of distribution
    - (a) How many individuals score between 12 and 16?
    - (b) How many score *above* 18? *below* 8?
    - (c) What are the chances that any individual selected at random will score *above* 15?

16. In the Army General Classification Test the distribution is essentially normal with a $M = 100$ and $SD = 20$.
    - (a) What percent of scores lie between 85 and 125?
    - (b) The middle 60% fall between what two points?
    - (c) On what score does Q_3 fall?

17. In a certain achievement test, the seventh-grade mean is 28.00 and SD is 4.80; and the eighth-grade mean is 31.60 and SD is 4.00. What percent of the seventh grade is above the mean of the eighth grade? What percent of the eighth grade is below the mean of the seventh grade?

18. Two years ago a group of 12-year-olds had a reading ability expressed by a mean score of 40.00 and a σ of 3.60; and a composition ability expressed by a mean of 62.00 and a σ of 9.60. Today the group has gained 12 points in reading and 10.8 points in composition. How many times greater is the gain in reading than the gain in composition?

19. In problem 1, Chapter 4, we computed directly from the distribution the percent of group A which exceeds the median of group B. Compare this value with the percentage of overlapping obtained on the assumption of normality in group A.

20. Four problems, A, B, C, and D, have been solved by 50%, 60%, 70%, and 80%, respectively, of a large group. Compare the difference in difficulty between A and B with the difference in difficulty between C and D.

21. In a certain college, ten grades, A+, A, A−; B+, B, B−; C+, C, C−; and

D, are assigned. If ability in mathematics is distributed normally, how many students in a group of 500 freshmen should receive each grade?

22. Assume that the distribution of grades in a class of 500 freshmen is normal with $M = 72$ and $SD = 10$. The instructor wants to give letter grades as follows: 10% A's; 30% B's; 40% C's; 15% D's; and 5% F's. Compute to the closest score the *divisions* between A's and B's; B's and C's; C's and D's; D's and F's.

ANSWERS

1. 3/4   2. 3/8   3. 10/32
4. (a) 1/2
   (b) 2/3
   (c) 1/3
5. 4/5   6. (a) 1/6
7. (a) 1/1024
   (b) 1/252
8. 32/243
10. For expected distribution
    $M = 2.5\ \sigma = 1.12$
11. (a) .4383   (d) .7409
    (b) .4656   (e) .2171
    (c) .6705   (f) .0676
12. (a) $-.61\sigma, -.10\sigma, .10\sigma, .88\sigma$
    (b) 11, 31, 80
13. (a)

	SKEWNESS		KURTOSIS
	By formula (23)	By formula (24)	By formula (25)
(1)	−.018	−.28	.238
(2)	.156	1.03	.276

   (c) 66%, 67%
14. 23, 44, 13
15. (a) 570
    (b) 50; 3
    (c) 33 in 100 or 1 in 3
16. (a) 67%
    (b) 83.2 and 116.8
    (c) 113
17. 23%; 18%
18. Three times as great.
19. 39% as compared with 42%.
20. Difference between A and B is $.25\sigma$; between C and D, $.32\sigma$
21. Grades: A+ A A− B+ B B− C+ C C− D
    Students
    Receiving: 3 14 40 80 113 113 80 40 14 3
22. 85; 75; 64; 56

CHAPTER 6

LINEAR CORRELATION

<<<<<<<<<<<<<<<<<<<<<<<<<<<<<<<<<<<<<<<<<<<<<<<<<<<<<<<<<<<<<<<<<<<<

I. THE MEANING OF CORRELATION

1. Correlation as a measure of relationship

In previous chapters we have been concerned primarily with methods of computing statistical measures designed to represent in a reliable way the performance of an individual or a group in some defined trait. Frequently, however, it is of more importance to examine the *relationship* of one variable to another than to measure performance in either alone. Are certain abilities closely related, and others relatively independent? Is it true that good pitch discrimination accompanies musical achievement; or that bright children tend to be less neurotic than average children? If we know the general intelligence of a child, as measured by a standard test, can we say anything about his probable scholastic achievement as represented by grades? Problems like these and many others which involve the relations among abilities can be studied by the method of correlation.

When the relationship between two sets of measures is "linear," i.e., can be described by a straight line,* the correlation between scores may be expressed by the "product-moment" coefficient of correlation, designated by the letter r. The method of calculating r will be outlined in Section III. Before taking up the details of calculation, let us make clear what correlation means, and how r measures relationship.

Consider, first, a situation in which relationship is fixed and unchanging. The circumference of a circle is always 3.1416 times its diameter ($C = 3.1416D$), and this equation holds no matter how large or how small the circle, or in what part of the world we find it. Each time the diameter of a circle is increased or decreased, the circumference is increased or decreased by just 3.1416 times the same amount. In short,

* See pp. 152–153 for further discussion of "linear" relationship.

the dependence of circumference upon diameter is absolute; the correlation between the two dimensions is said to be perfect, and $r = 1.00$. In theory, at least, the relationship between two abilities, as represented by test scores, may also be perfect. Suppose that a hundred students have exactly the same standing in two tests—the student who scores first in the one test scores first in the other, the student who ranks second in the first test ranks second in the other, and this one-to-one correspondence holds throughout the entire list. The relationship is perfect, since the relative position of each subject is exactly the same in one test as in the other; and the coefficient of correlation is 1.00.

Now let us consider the case in which there is just *no* correlation present. Suppose that we have administered to 100 college seniors the Army General Classification Test and a simple "tapping test" in which the number of separate taps made in thirty seconds is recorded. Let the mean AGCT score for the group be 120, and the mean tapping rate be 185 taps in thirty seconds. Now suppose that when we divide our group into three subgroups in accordance with the size of their AGCT scores, the mean tapping rate of the superior or "high" group (whose mean AGCT score is 130) is 184 taps in thirty seconds; the mean tapping rate of the "middle" group (whose mean AGCT score is 110) is 186 taps in thirty seconds; and the mean tapping rate of the "low" group (whose mean AGCT score is 100) is 185 taps in thirty seconds. Since tapping rate is virtually identical in all three groups, it is clear that from tapping rate alone we should be unable to draw any conclusion as to a student's probable performance upon AGCT. A tapping rate of 185 is as likely to be found with an AGCT score of 100 as with one of 120 or even 160. In other words, there is no correspondence between the scores made by the members of our group upon the two tests, and r, the coefficient of correlation, is zero.*

Perfect relationship, then, is expressed by a coefficient of 1.00, and just no relationship by a coefficient of .00. Between these two limits, increasing degrees of positive relationship are indicated by such coefficients as .33, or .65, or .92. A coefficient of correlation falling between .00 and 1.00 always implies *some* degree of positive association, the degree of correspondence depending upon the size of the coefficient.

Relationship may also be negative; that is, a *high* degree of one trait may be associated with a *low* degree of another. When negative or inverse relationship is perfect, $r = -1.00$. To illustrate, suppose that in a small class of ten schoolboys, the boy who stands first in Latin ranks lowest

* It may be noted that the number of groups (here 3) is unimportant: any convenient set may be used. The important point is that when the correlation is zero, there is no systematic relationship between two sets of scores.

(tenth) in shop work; the boy who stands second in Latin ranks next to the bottom (ninth) in shop work; and that each boy stands just as far from the top of the list in Latin as from the bottom of the list in shop work. Here the correspondence between achievement in Latin and performance in shop work is regular and definite enough, but the *direction* of relationship is inverse and $r = -1.00$. Negative coefficients may range from -1.00 up to .00, just as positive coefficients may range from .00 up to 1.00. Coefficients of $-.20$, $-.50$ or $-.80$ indicate increasing degrees of negative or inverse relationship, just as positive coefficients of .20, .50 and .80 indicate increasing degrees of positive relationship.

2. Correlation expressed as agreement between ranks

The notion underlying correlation can often be most readily comprehended from a simple graphic treatment. Three examples will be given to illustrate values of r of 1.00, -1.00, and approximately .00. Correlation is rarely computed when the number of cases is less than 25, so that the examples here presented must be considered to have illustrative value only.

Suppose that four tests, A, B, C and D, have been administered to a group of five children. The children have been arranged in order of merit on Test A and their scores are then compared separately with Tests B C and D to give the following three cases:

	CASE 1			CASE 2			CASE 3	
Pupil	A	B	Pupil	A	C	Pupil	A	D
a	15	53	a	15	64	a	15	102
b	14	52	b	14	65	b	14	100
c	13	51	c	13	66	c	13	104
d	12	50	d	12	67	d	12	103
e	11	49	e	11	68	e	11	101

Now, if the *second* series of scores under each case (i.e., B, C and D) is arranged in order of merit from the highest score down, and the two scores earned by each child are connected by a straight line, we have the graphs shown on page 125.

The more nearly the lines connecting the paired scores are horizontal and parallel, the higher the positive correlation. The more nearly the connecting lines tend to intersect in one point, the larger the negative correlation. When the connecting lines show no systematic trend, the correlation approaches zero.

CASE 1		CASE 2		CASE 3	
A	B	A	C	A	D
15———53		15 68		15 104	
14———52		14 67		14 103	
13———51		13——66		13 102	
12———50		12 65		12 101	
11———49		11 64		11 100	

All connecting lines are horizontal and parallel, and the correlation is positive and perfect. $r = 1.00$

All connecting lines intersect in one point. The correlation is negative and perfect, and $r = -1.00$

No system is exhibited by the connecting lines, but the resemblance is closer to Case 2 than to Case 1. Correlation low and negative

3. Summary

To summarize our discussion up to this point, coefficients of correlation are indices ranging over a scale which extends from -1.00 through $.00$ to 1.00. A positive correlation indicates that *large* amounts of the one variable tend to accompany *large* amounts of the other; a negative correlation indicates that *small* amounts of the one variable tend to accompany *large* amounts of the other. A zero correlation indicates no consistent relationship. We have illustrated above only perfect positive, perfect negative, and approximately zero relation in order to bring out the meaning of correlation in a striking way. Only rarely, if ever, will a coefficient fall at either extreme of the scale, i.e., at 1.00 or -1.00. In most actual problems, calculated r's fall at intermediate points, such as $.72$, $-.26$, $.50$, etc. Such r's are to be interpreted as "high" or "low" depending in general upon how close they are to ± 1.00. Interpretation of the degree of relationship expressed by r in terms of various criteria will be discussed on pages 176–177.

II. THE COEFFICIENT OF CORRELATION *

1. The coefficient of correlation as a ratio

The product-moment coefficient of correlation may be thought of essentially as that *ratio* which expresses the extent to which changes in one variable are accompanied by—or are dependent upon—changes in a second variable. As an illustration, consider the following simple example which gives the paired heights and weights of five college seniors:

* This section may be taken up after Section III.

(1)	(2)	(3)	(4)	(5)	(6)	(7)	(8)	(9)
STU-DENT	HT. IN INCHES	WT. IN LBS.						
	X	Y	x	y	xy	$\dfrac{x}{\sigma_x}$	$\dfrac{y}{\sigma_y}$	$\left(\dfrac{x}{\sigma_x}\cdot\dfrac{y}{\sigma_y}\right)$
a	72	170	3	0	0	1.34	.00	.00
b	69	165	0	−5	0	.00	−.37	.00
c	66	150	−3	−20	60	−1.34	−1.46	1.96
d	70	180	1	10	10	.45	.73	.33
e	68	185	−1	15	−15	−.45	1.10	−.49
					55			1.80

$M_X = 69$ in. $\sigma_x = 2.24$ in.*

$M_Y = 170$ lbs. $\sigma_y = 13.69$ lbs. correlation $= \dfrac{\Sigma\left(\dfrac{x}{\sigma_x}\cdot\dfrac{y}{\sigma_y}\right)}{N} = \dfrac{1.80}{5} = .36$

From the X and Y columns it is evident that tall students tend to be somewhat heavier than short students, and hence the correlation between height and weight is almost certainly positive. The mean height is 69 inches, the mean weight 170 pounds, and the σ's are 2.24 inches and 13.69 pounds, respectively. In column (4) are given the deviations (x's) of each man's height from the mean height, and in column (5) the deviations (y's) of each man's weight from the mean weight. The product of these paired deviations (xy's) in column (6) is a measure of the agreement between individual heights and weights, and the larger the sum of the xy column the higher the degree of correspondence. When agreement is perfect (and $r = 1.00$) the Σxy column has its maximum value. One may inquire why the sum of $\dfrac{xy's}{N}\left(\text{i.e., }\dfrac{55}{5}\right)$ would not yield a suitable measure of relationship between x and y. The reason is that such an average is *not* a stable measure, as it is not independent of the *units* in which height and weight have been expressed. In consequence, this ratio will vary if centimeters and kilograms (as shown in the example below) are employed instead of inches and pounds. One way to avoid the troublesome matter of differences in units is to divide each x and each y by its own σ, i.e., express each deviation as a σ score. Each x and y deviation is then expressed as a ratio, and is a pure number, independent of the test units. The sum of the products of the σ scores—column (9)—divided by N yields a ratio which, as we shall see later, *is* a stable expression of rela-

* For calculation of σ's see p. 191.

tionship. This ratio is the "product-moment" * coefficient of correlation. In our example, its value of .36 indicates a fairly high positive correlation between height and weight in this small sample. The student should note that our ratio or coefficient is simply the *average product* of the σ scores of corresponding X and Y measures.

Let us now investigate the effect upon our ratio of changing the units in terms of which X and Y have been expressed. In the example below, the heights and weights of the same five students are expressed (to the nearest whole number) in centimeters and kilograms instead of in inches and pounds:

(1) STU-DENT	(2) HT. IN CMS. X	(3) WT. IN KGS. Y	(4) x	(5) y	(6) xy	(7) $\dfrac{x}{\sigma_x}$	(8) $\dfrac{y}{\sigma_y}$	(9) $\left(\dfrac{x}{\sigma_x}\cdot\dfrac{y}{\sigma_y}\right)$
a	183	77	8	0	0	1.43	.00	.00
b	175	75	0	−2	0	.00	−.32	.00
c	168	68	−7	−9	63	−1.25	−1.43	1.79
d	178	82	3	5	15	.53	.79	.42
e	173	84	−2	7	−14	−.36	1.11	−.40
					64			1.81

$M_X = 175$ cms. $\sigma_x = 5.61$ cms.

$M_Y = 77$ kgs. $\sigma_y = 6.30$ kgs.   correlation $= \dfrac{\sum\left(\dfrac{x}{\sigma_x}\cdot\dfrac{y}{\sigma_y}\right)}{N} = \dfrac{1.81}{5} = .36$

The mean height of our group is now 175 cms. and the mean weight 77 kgs.; the σ's are 5.61 cms. and 6.30 kgs., respectively. Note that the sum of the xy column, namely, 64, differs by 9 from the sum of the xy's in the example above, in which inches and pounds were the units of measurement. However, when deviations are expressed as σ scores, the sum of their products $\left(\dfrac{x}{\sigma_x}\cdot\dfrac{y}{\sigma_y}\right)$ divided by N equals .36 as before.

The quotient

$$\frac{\sum\left(\dfrac{x}{\sigma_x}\cdot\dfrac{y}{\sigma_y}\right)}{N}$$

* The sum of the deviations from the mean (raised to some power) and divided by N is called a "moment." When corresponding deviations in x and y are multiplied together, summed, and divided by N $\left(\text{to give }\dfrac{\Sigma xy}{N}\right)$ the term "product-moment" is used.

is a measure of relationship which remains constant for a given set of data, no matter in what units X and Y are expressed. When this ratio is written $\dfrac{\Sigma xy}{N\sigma_x\sigma_y}$ it becomes the well-known expression for r, the prod moment coefficient of correlation.*

2. The scatter diagram and the correlation table

When N is small, the ratio method described in the preceding section may be employed for computing the coefficient of correlation between two sets of data. But when N is large, much time and labor will be saved by arranging the data in the form of a diagram or chart, and then calculating deviations from assumed, instead of from actual, means. Let us con-

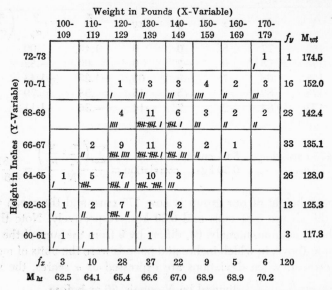

Height in Inches (Y-Variable)	100-109	110-119	120-129	130-139	140-149	150-159	160-169	170-179	f_y	M_{wt}
72-73								1	1	174.5
70-71			1	3	3	4	2	3	16	152.0
68-69			4	11	6	3	2	2	28	142.4
66-67		2	9	11	8	2	1		33	135.1
64-65	1	5	7	10	3				26	128.0
62-63	1	2	7	1	2				13	125.3
60-61	1	1		1					3	117.8
f_x	3	10	28	37	22	9	5	6	120	
M_{ht}	62.5	64.1	65.4	66.6	67.0	68.9	68.9	70.2		

Weight in Pounds (X-Variable)

FIG. 36 A scattergram and correlation table showing the paired heights and weights of 120 students

sider the diagram in Figure 36. This chart, called a "scatter diagram" or "scattergram," represents the paired heights and weights of 120 college students. It is, in fact, a *bivariate distribution,* since it represents the

* The coefficient of correlation, r, is often called the "Pearson r" after Professor Karl Pearson who developed the product-moment method, following the earlier work of Galton and Bravais. See Walker, H. M., *Studies in the History of Statistical Method* (Baltimore: Williams and Wilkins Co., 1929), Chapter 5, pp. 96–111.

SUMMARY

Weight	Mean ht. for given wt. interval	Height	Mean wt. for given ht. interval
170–179	70.2	72–73	174.5
160–169	68.9	70–71	152.0
150–159	68.9	68–69	142.4
140–149	67.0	66–67	135.1
130–139	66.6	64–65	128.0
120–129	65.4	62–63	125.3
110–119	64.1	60–61	117.8
100–109	62.5		

(Weight column — Range 70 Lbs.; Mean ht. column — Range 7.7 In.; Height column — Range 12 In.; Mean wt. column — Range 56.7 Lbs.)

joint distribution of two variables. The construction of a scattergram is relatively simple. Along the left-hand margin from bottom to top are laid off the class intervals of the height distribution, measurement expressed in inches; and along the top of the diagram from left to right are laid off the class intervals of the weight distribution, measurement expressed in pounds. Each of the 120 men is represented on the diagram with respect to height and weight. Suppose that a man weighs 150 pounds and is 69 inches tall. His weight locates him in the sixth column from the left, and his height in the third row from the top. Accordingly, a "tally" is placed in the third cell of the sixth column. There are three tallies in all in this cell, that is, there are three men who weigh from 150 to 159 pounds, and are 68–69 inches tall. Each of the 120 men is represented by a tally in a cell or square of the table in accordance with the two characteristics, height and weight. Along the bottom of the diagram in the f_x row is tabulated the number of men who fall in each weight interval; while along the right-hand margin in the f_y column is tabulated the number of men who fall in each height interval. The f_y column and f_x row must each total 120, the number of men in all. After all of the tallies have been listed, the frequency in each cell is added and entered on the diagram. The scattergram is then a *correlation table*.

Several interesting facts may be gleaned from the correlation table as it stands. For example, all of the men of a given weight interval may be studied with respect to the distribution of their heights. In the third column from the left there are twenty-eight men all of whom weigh 120–129 pounds. One of the twenty-eight is 70–71 inches tall; four are 68–69 inches tall; nine are 66–67 inches tall; seven are 64–65 inches tall; and seven are 62–63 inches tall. In the same way, we may classify all of the men of a given height interval with respect to weight distribution. Thus, in the row next to the bottom, there are thirteen men all of whom are 62–63 inches tall. Of this group one weighs 100–109 pounds; two weigh 110–119 pounds; seven weigh 120–129 pounds; one weighs 130–139 pounds; and two weigh 140–149 pounds. It is fairly clear that the "drift" of paired heights and weights is from the upper right-hand section of the diagram to the lower left-hand section. Even a superficial examination of the diagram reveals a fairly marked tendency for heavy, medium and light men to be tall, medium and short, respectively; and this general relationship holds in spite of the scatter of heights and weights within any given "array" (an array is the distribution of cases within a given column or row). Even before making any calculations, then, we should probably be willing to guess that the correlation between height and weight is positive and fairly high.

Let us now go a step further and calculate the mean height of the three men who weigh 100–109 pounds, the men in column one. The mean height of this group (using the assumed mean method described in Chapter 2, p. 35) is 62.5 inches, and this figure has been written in at the bottom of the correlation table. In the same way, the mean heights of the men who fall in each of the succeeding weight intervals have been written in at the bottom of the diagram. These data have been tabulated in a somewhat more convenient form below the diagram. From this summary, it appears that an actual weight increase of approximately 70 pounds (104.5–174.5) corresponds to an increase in mean height of 7.7 inches; that is, the increase from the lightest to the heaviest man is parallel by an increase of approximately eight inches in height. It seems clear, therefore, that the correlation between height and weight is positive.

Let us now shift from height to weight, and applying the method used above, find the change in *mean weight* which corresponds to the given change in height.* The mean weight of the three men in the bottom row of the diagram is 117.8 pounds. The mean weight of the thirteen men in the next row from the bottom (who are 62–63 inches tall) is 125.3 pounds. The mean weights of the men who fall in the other rows have been written in their appropriate places in the M_{wt} column. In the summary of results we find that in this group of 120 men an increase of about 12 inches in height is accompanied by an increase of about 56.7 pounds in mean weight. Thus it appears that the taller the man the heavier he tends to be, and again the correlation between height and weight is seen to be positive.

* This change corresponds to the *second* regression line in the correlation diagram (see p. 152).

3. The graphic representation of the correlation coefficient

It is often helpful in understanding how the correlation coefficient measures relationship to see how a correlation of .00 or .50, say, looks graphically. Figure 37 (1) pictures a correlation of .50. The data in the

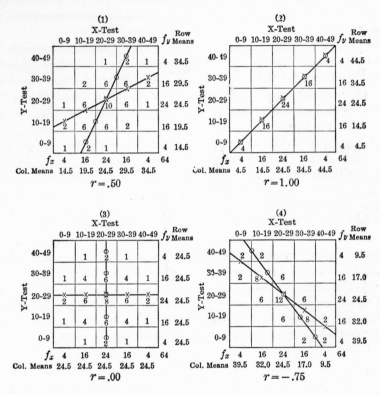

FIG. 37 The graphic representation of the correlation coefficient

table are artificial, and were selected to bring out the relationship in as unequivocal a fashion as possible. The scores laid off along the top of the correlation table from left to right will be referred to simply as the X-test "scores," and the scores laid off at the left of the table from bottom to top as the Y-test "scores." As was done in Figure 36, the mean of each Y row is entered on the chart, and the means of the X columns are entered at the bottom of the diagram.

The means of each Y array, that is, the means of the "scores" falling in each X column, are indicated on the chart by small crosses. Through these crosses a line, called a *regression line,*[*] has been drawn. This line represents the change in the *mean* value of Y over the given range of X. In similar fashion, the means of each X array, i.e., the means of the scores in each Y row, are designated on the chart by small circles, through which another line has been drawn. This second regression line shows the change in the *mean* value of X over the given range of Y. These two lines together represent the linear or straight-line relationship between the variables X and Y.

The closeness of association or degree of correspondence between the X and Y tests is indicated by the relative positions of these two regression lines. When the correlation is positive and perfect, the two regression lines close up like a pair of scissors to form one line. Chart (2) in Figure 37 shows how the two regression lines look when $r = 1.00$, and the correlation is perfect. Note that the entries in Chart (2) are concentrated along the diagonal from the upper right- to the lower left-hand section of the diagram. There is no "scatter" of scores in the successive columns or rows, all of the scores in a given array being concentrated within one cell. If Chart (2) represented a correlation table of height and weight, we should know that the tallest man was the heaviest, the next tallest man the next heaviest, and that throughout the group the correspondence of height and weight was perfect.

A very different picture from that of perfect correlation is presented in Chart (3) where the correlation is .00. Here the two regression lines, through the means of the columns and rows, have spread out until they are perpendicular to each other. There is no change in the *mean* Y score over the whole range of X, and no change in the *mean* X score over the whole range of Y. This is analogous to the situation described on page 123, in which the mean tapping rate of a group of students was the same for those with "high," "middle," and "low" AGCT scores. When the correlation is zero, there is no way of telling from a subject's performance in one test what his performance will be in the other test. The best one can do is to select the *mean* as the most probable value of the unknown score.

Chart (4) in Figure 37 represents a correlation coefficient of −.75. Negative relationship is shown by the fact that the regression lines, through the means of the columns and rows, run from the upper left- to the lower right-hand section of the diagram. The regression lines are closer together than in Chart (1) where the correlation is .50, but are still separated. If this chart represented a correlation table of height and

---

[*] Regression lines have important properties; they will be defined and discussed more fully in Chapter 7.

weight, we should know that the tendency was strong for tall men to be light, and for short men to be heavy.

The charts in Figure 37 represent the linear relationship between sets of artificial test scores. The data were selected so as to be symmetrical around the means of each column and row, and hence the regression lines go through *all* of the crosses and through *all* of the circles in the successive columns and rows. It is rarely if ever true, however, that the regression lines pass through *all* of the means of the columns and rows in a correlation table which represents actual test scores. Figure 38 which

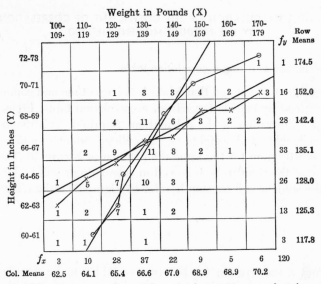

FIG. 38 Graphic representation of the correlation between height and weight in a group of 120 college students (Fig. 36)

reproduces the correlation table of heights and weights given on page 128, shows what happens with real data. The mean heights of the men in the weight (X) columns are indicated by crosses, and the mean weights of the men in the height (Y) rows by circles, as in Figure 37. Note that the series of short lines joining the successive crosses or circles presents a decidedly jagged appearance. Two straight lines have been drawn in to describe the general trend of these irregular lines. These two lines go through, or as close as possible to, the crosses or the circles, more consideration being given to those points near the middle of the chart (because they are based upon more data) than to those at the extremes (which are based upon few scores). Regression lines are called lines of "best fit" because they satisfy certain mathematical criteria to be given later (p. 162). Such lines describe better than any other *straight* lines the "run" or "drift" of the crosses and circles across the chart.

In Chapter 7 we shall develop equations for the "best fitting" lines and show how they may be drawn in to describe the trend of irregular points on a correlation table. For the present, the important fact to get clearly in mind is that when correlation is linear, the means of the columns and rows in a correlation table can be adequately described by two straight lines and the closer together these two lines, the higher the correlation.

III. THE CALCULATION OF THE COEFFICIENT OF CORRELATION BY THE PRODUCT-MOMENT METHOD

1. The calculation of r from a correlation table

On page 128 it was stated that when N is large, time and computational labor are saved by calculating r from a correlation table. Figure 39 will serve as an illustration of the calculations required. This diagram gives the paired heights and weights of 120 college students, and is derived from the scattergram for the same data shown in Figure 36. The following outline of the steps to be followed in calculating r will be best understood if the student will constantly refer to Figure 39 as he reads through each step.

Step 1

Construct a scattergram for the two variables to be correlated, and from it draw up a correlation table as described on page 128.

Step 2

The distribution of heights for the 120 men falls in the f_y column at the right of the diagram. Assume a mean for the height distribution, using the rules given in Chapter 2, page 35, and draw double lines to mark off the *row* in which the assumed mean (ht) falls. The mean for the height distribution has been taken at 66.5 in. (midpoint of interval 66–67) and the y's have been taken from this point. The prime (') of the x's and y's indicates that these deviations are taken from the *assumed* means of the X and Y distributions (see p. 37). Now fill in the fy' and fy'^2 columns. From the first column c_y, the correction in units of interval, is obtained; and this correction together with the sum of the fy'^2 will give the σ of the

Weight in Pounds (X-Variable)

Height in Inches (Y-Variable)	100-109	110-119	120-129	130-139	140-149	150-159	160-169	170-179	f_y	y'	fy'	fy'^2	$\Sigma x'y'$ +	$\Sigma x'y'$ −	$\Sigma x'$	$\Sigma x'y'$
72-73							(6) 2 12	(12) 1 12	1	3	3	9	12		4	12
70-71		(-2) 1 -2	(-1) 4 -4	0 3 0	(2) 3 6	(4) 4 16	(6) 2 12	(8) 3 24	16	2	32	64	58	2	28	56
68-69		(-1) 4 -4	0 11 0	0 11 0	(1) 6 6	(2) 3 6	(3) 2 6	(4) 2 8	28	1	28 (63)	28	26	4	22	22
66-67		0 9 0	0 7 0	0 11 0	0 8 0	0 2 0	0 1 0		33	0	0	0			2	0
64-65	(3) 1 8	(2) 5 10	(1) 7 7	0 10 0	(-1) 3 -3				26	-1	-26	26	20	3	-17	17
62-63	(6) 1 6	(4) 2 8	(2) 7 14	0 1 0	(-2) 2 -4				13	-2	-26	52	28	4	-12	24
60-61	(9) 1 9	(6) 1 6	0 1 0						3	-3	-9 (-61)	27	15		-6	15
									120		2	206	159	-13	22	146

	100-109	110-119	120-129	130-139	140-149	150-159	160-169	170-179	
f_x	3	10	28	37	22	9	5	6	= 120
x'	-3	-2	-1	0	1	2	3	4	
fx'	-9	-20	-28 (-57)	0	22	18	15	24 (79)	= 22
fx'^2	27	40	28	0	22	36	45	96	= 294
$\Sigma y'$	18	-6	-12 -15	0	2	5	11	11	= 2
$\Sigma x'y'$	18	24	16	0	5	22	18	44	= 146

$$\sigma_y = \sqrt{\frac{206}{120} - .0004} \times 2$$
$$= 1.31 \times 2 = 2.62$$

$$\sigma_x = \sqrt{\frac{294}{120} - .0324} \times 10$$
$$= 1.555 \times 10 = 15.55$$

$$c_y = \frac{2}{120} = .02 \qquad c_x = \frac{22}{120} = .18$$
$$c_y^2 = \frac{2}{120} = .0004 \qquad c_x^2 = \frac{22}{120} = .0324$$

$$r = \frac{\frac{146}{120} - .02 \times .18}{1.31 \times 1.55}$$
$$r = .60$$

check → (146) → 159 −13 = 22
check → 24 (79) = 22
check → = 294
check → = 2
check → = 146

FIG. 39 Calculation of the product-moment coefficient of correlation between the heights and weights of 120 college students

$$\sigma = \sqrt{\frac{\Sigma f_i^2}{n} - c^2} \cdot i$$

height distribution, σ_y. As shown by the calculations in Figure 39, the value of σ_y is 2.62 inches.

The distribution of the weights of the 120 men is found in the f_x row at the bottom of the diagram. Assume a mean for the weight distribution, and draw double lines to designate the *column* under the assumed mean (wt). The mean for the weight distribution is taken at 134.5 pounds (midpoint of interval 130–139), and the x''s are taken from this point. Fill in the fx' and the fx'^2 rows; from the first calculate c_x, the correction in units of interval, and from the second calculate σ_x, the σ of the entire weight distribution. In Figure 39, the value of σ_x is found to be 15.55 pounds.

Step 3

The calculations in Step 2 simply repeat the now familiar process of calculating σ by the Assumed Mean method. Our first *new* task is to fill in the $\Sigma x'y'$ column at the right of the chart. Since the entries in this column may be either $+$ or $-$, two columns are provided under $\Sigma x'y'$. Calculation of the entries in the $\Sigma x'y'$ column may be illustrated by considering, first, the single entry in the only occupied cell in the topmost row. The deviation of this cell from the AM of the weight distribution, that is, its x', is four *intervals*, and its deviation from the AM of the height distribution, that is, its y', is three *intervals*. Hence, the product of the deviations of this cell from the two AM's is 4×3 or 12; and a small figure (12) is placed in the upper right-hand corner of the cell.[*] The "product deviation" of the *one* entry in this cell is $1(4 \times 3)$ or 12 also, and hence a figure 12 is placed in the lower left-hand corner of the cell. This figure shows the product of the deviations of this single entry from the AM's of the two distributions. Since there are no other entries in the cells of this row, 12 is placed at once under the $+$ sign in the $\Sigma x'y'$ column.

Consider now the next row from the top, taking the cells in order from right to left. The cell immediately below the one for which we have just found the product deviation also deviates four intervals from the AM (wt) (its x' is 4), but its deviation from the AM (ht) is only two intervals (its y' is 2). The product deviation of this cell, therefore, is 4×2 or 8, as shown by the small figure (8) in the upper right-hand corner of the cell. There are three entries in this cell, and since each has a product devi-

---

[*] We may consider the coördinates of this cell to be $x' = 4$, $y' = 3$. The x' is obtained by counting over four intervals from the *vertical column* containing the AM (wt), and the y' by counting up three intervals from the *horizontal row* containing the AM (ht). The unit of measurement is the class interval.

ation of 8, the final entry in the lower left-hand corner of the cell is $3(4 \times 2)$ or 24. The product deviation of the second cell in this row is 6 (its x' is 3 and its y' is 2) and since there are two entries in the cell, the final entry is $2(3 \times 2)$ or 12. Each of the four entries in the third cell over has a product deviation of 4 (since $x' = 2$ and $y' = 2$) and the final entry is 16. In the fourth cell, each of the three entries has a product deviation of $2(x' = 1$ and $y' = 2)$ and the cell entry is 6. The entry in the fifth cell over, the cell in the AM (wt) column, is 0, since x' is 0, and accordingly $3(2 \times 0)$ must be 0. Note carefully the entry (-2) in the last cell of the row. Since the deviations of this cell are $x' = -1$, and $y' = 2$, the product $1(-1 \times 2) = -2$, and the final entry is negative. Now we may total up the plus and minus entries in this row and enter the results, 58 and -2, in the $\Sigma x'y'$ column under the appropriate signs.

The final entries in the cells for the other rows of the table and the sums of the product deviations of each row are obtained as illustrated for the two rows above. The column and row selected for the two AM's divide the correlation table into 4 quadrants as shown below:

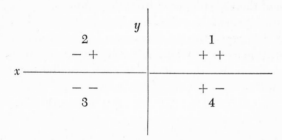

The student should bear in mind in calculating $x'y'$'s that the product deviations of *all* entries in the cells in the *first* and *third* quadrants of the table are positive, while the product deviations of *all* entries in the *second* and *fourth* quadrants are negative (p. 9). It should be remembered, too, that all entries either in the column headed by the AM_X or the row headed by the AM_Y have zero product deviations, since in the one case the x' and in the other the y' equals zero.

All entries in a given row have the same y', so that the arithmetic of calculating $x'y'$'s may often be considerably reduced if each entry in a row cell is first multiplied by its x', and the sum of these deviations $(\Sigma x')$ multiplied once for all by the common y', viz., the y' of the row. The last two columns $\Sigma x'$ and $\Sigma x'y'$ contain the entries for the rows. To illustrate the method of calculation, in the second row from the bottom, taking the cells in order from right to left, and multiplying the entry in each cell by its x', we have $(2 \times 1) + (1 \times 0) + (7 \times -1) + (2 \times -2) + (1 \times -3)$

or -12. If we multiply this "deviation sum" by the y' of the whole row (i.e., by -2) the result is 24 which is the final entry in the $\Sigma x'y'$ column. Note that this entry checks the 28 and -4 entered separately in the $\Sigma x'y'$ column by the longer method. This shorter method is often employed in printed correlation charts and is recommended for use as soon as the student understands fully how the cell entries are obtained.

Step 4 (Checks)

The $\Sigma x'y'$ may be checked by computing the product deviations and summing for columns instead of rows. The two rows at the bottom of the diagram, $\Sigma y'$ and $\Sigma x'y'$, show how this is done. We may illustrate with the first column on the left, taking the cells from top to bottom. Multiplying the entry in each cell by its appropriate y', we have $(1 \times -1) + (1 \times -2) + (1 \times -3)$ or -6. When this entry in the $\Sigma y'$ row is multiplied by the common x' of the column (i.e., by -3) the final entry in the $\Sigma x'y'$ row is 18. The sum of the $x'y'$ computed from the rows should check the sum of the $x'y'$ computed from the columns.

Two other useful checks are shown in Figure 39. The fy' will equal the $\Sigma y'$ and the fx' will equal the $\Sigma x'$ if no error has been made. The fy' and the fx' are the same as the $\Sigma y'$ and $\Sigma x'$; although these columns and rows are designated differently, they denote in each case the sum of deviations around their *AM*.

Step 5

When all of the entries in the $\Sigma x'y'$ column have been made, and the column totaled, the coefficient of correlation may be calculated by the formula

$$r = \frac{\dfrac{\Sigma x'y'}{N} - c_x c_y}{\sigma'_x \sigma'_y} \tag{26}$$

(*coefficient of correlation when deviations are taken from the assumed means of the two distributions*) *

Substituting 146 for $\Sigma x'y'$; .02 for c_y; .18 for c_x; 1.31 for σ'_y; 1.55 for σ'_x; and 120 for N, r is found to be .60 (see Fig. 39).

It is important to remember that c_x, c_y, σ'_x, and σ'_y are *all* in *units of*

* This formula for r differs slightly from the ratio formula developed on page 127. The fact that deviations are taken from assumed rather than from actual means makes it necessary to correct $\Sigma x'y'$ by subtracting the product of the two corrections c_x and c_y.

class interval in formula (26). This is desirable because all product deviations $(x'y's)$ are in interval units, and it is simpler therefore to keep *all* of the terms in the formula in interval units. Leaving the corrections and the two σ's in units of class interval $(\sigma''s)$ facilitates computation, and does not change the result (i.e., the value of the coefficient of correlation).

2. The calculation of r from ungrouped data

(1) THE FORMULA FOR r WHEN DEVIATIONS ARE TAKEN FROM THE MEANS
OF THE TWO DISTRIBUTIONS X AND Y

In formula (26) x' and y' deviations are taken from assumed means; and hence it is necessary to correct $\dfrac{\Sigma x'y'}{N}$ by the product of the two corrections, c_x and c_y (p. 138). When deviations have been taken from the actual means of the two distributions, instead of from assumed means, no correction is needed, as both c_x and c_y are zero. Under these conditions, formula (26) becomes

$$r = \frac{\Sigma xy}{N\sigma_x\sigma_y} \tag{27}$$

*(coefficient of correlation when deviations are taken from
the means of the two distributions)*

which is the ratio for measuring correlation developed on page 127. If we write $\sqrt{\dfrac{\Sigma x^2}{N}}$ for σ_x and $\sqrt{\dfrac{\Sigma y^2}{N}}$ for σ_y, the N's cancel and formula (27) becomes

$$r = \frac{\Sigma xy}{\sqrt{\Sigma x^2 \times \Sigma y^2}} \tag{28}$$

*(coefficient of correlation when deviations are taken from
the means of the two distributions)*

in which x and y are deviations from the actual means as in (27) and Σx^2 and Σy^2 are the sums of the squared deviations in x and y taken from the two means.

When N is fairly large, so that the data can be grouped into a correlation table, formula (26) is always used in preference to formulas (27) or (28) as it entails much less calculation. Formulas (27) and (28) may be used to good advantage, however, in finding the correlation between short, ungrouped series (say, twenty-five cases or so). It is not necessary to tabulate the scores into a frequency distribution. An illustration of the use of formula (28) is given in Table 18. The problem is to find the correlation between the scores made by twelve adults on two tests of controlled association.

The steps in computing r may be outlined as follows:

Step 1

Find the mean of Test 1 (X) and the mean of Test 2 (Y). The means in Table 18 are 62.5 and 30.4, respectively.

Step 2

Find the deviation of each score on Test 1 from its mean, 62.5, and enter it in column x. Next find the deviation of each score in Test 2 from its mean, 30.4, and enter it in column y.

Step 3

Square all of the x's and all of the y's and enter these squares in columns x^2 and y^2, respectively. Total these columns to obtain Σx^2 and Σy^2.

TABLE 18 To illustrate the calculation of r from ungrouped scores when deviations are taken from the means of the series

Subject	TEST 1 X	TEST 2 Y	x	y	x^2	y^2	xy
A	50	22	−12.5	−8.4	156.25	70.56	105.00
B	54	25	−8.5	−5.4	72.25	29.16	45.90
C	56	34	−6.5	3.6	42.25	12.96	−23.40
D	59	28	−3.5	−2.4	12.25	5.76	8.40
E	60	26	−2.5	−4.4	6.25	19.36	11.00
F	62	30	−.5	−.4	.25	.16	.20
G	61	32	−1.5	1.6	2.25	2.56	−2.40
H	65	30	2.5	−.4	6.25	.16	−1.00
I	67	28	4.5	−2.4	20.25	5.76	−10.80
J	71	34	8.5	3.6	72.25	12.96	30.60
K	71	36	8.5	5.6	72.25	31.36	47.60
L	74	40	11.5	9.6	132.25	92.16	110.40
	750	365			595.00 (Σx^2)	282.92 (Σy^2)	321.50 (Σxy)

$$M_X = 62.5 \qquad M_Y = 30.4$$

$$r = \frac{\Sigma xy}{\sqrt{\Sigma x^2 \times \Sigma y^2}} = \frac{321.50}{\sqrt{595 \times 282.92}} = .78 \qquad (28)$$

Step 4

Multiply the x's and y's in the same rows, and enter these products (with due regard for sign) in the xy column. Total the xy column, taking account of sign, to get Σxy.

Step 5

Substitute for Σxy, 321.50; for Σx^2, 595; and for Σy^2, 282.92 in formula (28), as shown in Table 18, and solve for r.

Formula (28) is useful in calculating r directly from two ungrouped series of scores, but it has the same disadvantage as the "long method" of calculating means and σ's described in Chapters 2 and 3. The deviations x and y when taken from actual means are usually decimals and

TABLE 19 To illustrate the calculation of r from ungrouped scores when deviations are taken from the assumed means of the series

	TEST 1	TEST 2					
Subject	X	Y	x'	y'	x'^2	y'^2	$x'y'$
A	50	22	−10	−8	100	64	80
B	54	25	−6	−5	36	25	30
C	56	34	−4	4	16	16	−16
D	59	28	−1	−2	1	4	2
E	60	26	0	−4	0	16	0
F	62	30	2	0	4	0	0
G	61	32	1	2	1	4	2
H	65	30	5	0	25	0	0
I	67	28	7	−2	49	4	−14
J	71	34	11	4	121	16	44
K	71	36	11	6	121	36	66
L	74	40	14	10	196	100	140
	750	365			670	285	334
					($\Sigma x'^2$)	($\Sigma y'^2$)	($\Sigma x'y'$)

$AM_X = 60.0 \qquad AM_Y = 30.0$
$M_X = 62.5 \qquad M_Y = 30.4$
$c_x = 2.5 \qquad c_y = .4$
$c^2_x = 6.25 \qquad c^2_y = .16$

$$r = \frac{\dfrac{334}{12} - 1.00}{7.04 \times 4.86} \qquad (26)$$

$$\sigma_x = \sqrt{\frac{670}{12} - 6.25} \qquad \sigma_y = \sqrt{\frac{285}{12} - .16}$$
$$= 7.04 \qquad\qquad = 4.86 \qquad r = .78$$

the multiplication and squaring of these values is often a tedious task. For this reason—even when working with short ungrouped series—it is often easier to assume means, calculate deviations from these AM's, and apply formula (26). The procedure is illustrated in Table 19 with the same data given in Table 18. Note that the two means, M_X and M_Y, are first calculated. The corrections, c_x and c_y, are found by subtracting AM_X from M_X and AM_Y from M_Y (p. 38). Since deviations are taken from assumed means, fractions are avoided; and the calculations of $\Sigma x'^2$, $\Sigma y'^2$, $\Sigma x'y'$, are readily made. Substitution in formula (26) then gives r.

(2) THE CALCULATION OF r FROM RAW SCORES WHEN DEVIATIONS ARE TAKEN FROM ZERO

The calculation of r may often be carried out most readily—especially when a calculating machine is available—by means of the following formula which is based upon "raw" or obtained scores:

$$r = \frac{\Sigma XY - NM_XM_Y}{\sqrt{[\Sigma X^2 - NM^2{}_X][\Sigma Y^2 - NM^2{}_Y]}} \tag{29}$$

(coefficient of correlation calculated from raw or obtained scores)

In this formula, X and Y are obtained scores, and M_X and M_Y are the means of the X and Y series, respectively. ΣX^2 and ΣY^2 are the sums of the squared X and Y values, and N is the number of cases.

Formula (29) is derived directly from formula (26) by assuming the means of the X and Y tests to be zero. If AM_X and AM_Y are zero, each X and Y score is a deviation from its AM as it stands, and hence we work with the scores themselves. Since the correction, c, always equals $M - AM$, it follows that when the AM equals 0, $c_x = M_X$, $c_y = M_Y$ and $c_xc_y = M_XM_Y$. Furthermore, when $c_x = M_X$, and $c_y = M_Y$ and the "scores" are "deviations," the formula

$$\sigma_x = \sqrt{\frac{\Sigma fx'^2}{N} - c^2{}_x} \times interval$$

(see p. 52) becomes

$$\sigma_x = \sqrt{\frac{\Sigma X^2}{N} - M^2{}_x}$$

and σ_y for the same reason equals $\sqrt{\dfrac{\Sigma Y^2}{N} - M^2{}_Y}$. If we substitute these equivalents for c_xc_y, σ_x, and σ_y in formula (26), the formula for r in terms of raw scores given in (29) is obtained.

An alternate form of (29) is often more useful in practice. This is

$$r = \frac{N\Sigma XY - \Sigma X \times \Sigma Y}{\sqrt{[N\Sigma X^2 - (\Sigma X)^2][N\Sigma Y^2 - (\Sigma Y)^2]}} \qquad (30)$$

(*coefficient of correlation calculated from raw or obtained scores*)

This formula is obtained from (29) by substituting $\dfrac{\Sigma X}{N}$ for M_X, and $\dfrac{\Sigma Y}{N}$

for M_Y in numerator and denominator, and canceling the N's.

The calculation of r from original scores is shown in Table 20. The data are again the two sets of twelve scores obtained on the controlled association tests, the correlation for which was found to be .78 in Table 18. This short example is for the purpose of illustrating the arithmetic and must not be taken as a recommendation that formula (29) be used only with short series. As a matter of fact, formula (29) or (30) is most useful, perhaps, with long series, especially if one is working with a calculating machine.

TABLE 20   To illustrate the calculation of r from ungrouped data when deviations are original scores (AM's $= 0$)

Subject	Test 1 X	Test 2 Y	X^2	Y^2	XY
A	50	22	2500	484	1100
B	54	25	2916	625	1350
C	56	34	3136	1156	1904
D	59	28	3481	784	1652
E	60	26	3600	676	1560
F	62	30	3844	900	1860
G	61	32	3721	1024	1952
H	65	30	4225	900	1950
I	67	28	4489	784	1876
J	71	34	5041	1156	2414
K	71	36	5041	1296	2556
L	74	40	5476	1600	2960
	750	365	47470	11385	23134

$M_X = 62.50$
$M_Y = 30.42$ (means to two decimals)

$$r = \frac{23134 - 12 \times 62.50 \times 30.42}{\sqrt{[47470 - 12 \times (62.50)^2][11385 - 12 \times (30.42)^2]}} \qquad (29)$$

$r = .78$

The computation by formula (30) is straightforward and the method easy to follow, but the calculations become tedious if the scores are expressed in more than two digits. When using formula (30), therefore, it will often greatly lessen the arithmetical work, if we first "reduce" the original scores by subtracting a constant quantity from each of the original X and Y scores. In Table 21, the same two series of twelve scores have been reduced by subtracting 65 from each of the X scores, and 25 from

TABLE 21 To illustrate the calculation of r from ungrouped data when deviations are original scores $(AM's = 0)$

(Scores are "reduced" by the subtraction of 65 from each X, and 25 from each Y to give X' and Y'.)

Sub-ject	TEST 1 X	TEST 2 Y	X'	Y'	X'^2	Y'^2	$X'Y'$
A	50	22	−15	−3	225	9	45
B	54	25	−11	0	121	0	0
C	56	34	−9	9	81	81	−81
D	59	28	−6	3	36	9	−18
E	60	26	−5	1	25	1	−5
F	62	30	−3	5	9	25	−15
G	61	32	−4	7	16	49	−28
H	65	30	0	5	0	25	0
I	67	28	2	3	4	9	6
J	71	34	6	9	36	81	54
K	71	36	6	11	36	121	66
L	74	40	9	15	81	225	135
	750	365	−30($\Sigma X'$)	65($\Sigma Y'$)	670($\Sigma X'^2$)	635($\Sigma Y'^2$)	159($\Sigma X'Y'$)

$$M_X = \frac{\Sigma X'}{N} + 65 \qquad\qquad M_Y = \frac{\Sigma Y'}{N} + 25$$

$$= -\frac{30}{12} + 65 \qquad\qquad\qquad = \frac{65}{12} + 25$$

$$= 62.5 \qquad\qquad\qquad\qquad = 30.4$$

$$r = \frac{(12 \times 159) - (-30 \times 65)}{\sqrt{[12 \times 670 - (-30)^2][12 \times 635 - (65)^2]}} \qquad (30)$$

$$= \frac{3858}{4923}$$

$$= .78$$

each of the Y scores. The reduced scores, entered in the table under X' and Y', are first squared to give $\Sigma X'^2$ and $\Sigma Y'^2$, and then multiplied by rows to give $\Sigma X'Y'$. Substitution of these values in formula (30) gives the coefficient of correlation r. If the means of the two series are wanted, these may readily be found by adding to $\dfrac{\Sigma X'}{N}$ and $\dfrac{\Sigma Y'}{N}$ the amounts by which the X and Y scores were reduced (see computations in Table 21).

The method of computing r by first reducing the scores is usually superior to the method of applying formula (29) or (30) directly to the raw scores. For one thing, we deal with smaller whole numbers, and much of the arithmetic can be done mentally. Again, when raw scores have more than two digits, they are cumbersome to square and multiply unless reduced. Note that instead of 65 and 25 other constants might have been used to reduce the X and Y scores. If the smallest X and Y scores had been subtracted, namely, 50 and 22, all of the X' and Y' would, of course, have been positive. This is an advantage in machine calculation but these reduced scores would have been somewhat larger numerically than are the reduced scores in Table 21. In general, the best plan in reducing scores is to subtract constants which are close to the means. The reduced scores are then both plus and minus, but are numerically about as small as we can make them.

(3) THE CALCULATION OF r BY THE DIFFERENCE FORMULA

It is apparent from the preceding sections that the product-moment formula for r may be written in several ways, depending upon whether deviations are taken from actual or assumed means and upon whether raw scores or deviations are employed. The present section contributes still another formula for calculating r—namely, the difference formula. This formula will complete our list of expressions for r. The student who understands the meaning and use of the correlation formulas given so far will have no difficulty with other variations should he encounter them.

The formula for r by the difference method is

$$r = \frac{\Sigma x^2 + \Sigma y^2 - \Sigma d^2}{2\sqrt{\Sigma x^2 \times \Sigma y^2}} \tag{31}$$

(coefficient of correlation by difference formula, deviations from the means of the distributions)

in which $\Sigma d^2 = \Sigma(x - y)^2$.

The principal advantage of the difference formula is that no cross products (xy's) need be computed. For this reason, this formula is employed in several of the printed correlation charts. Formula (31) is illustrated in Table 22 with the same data used in Table 19 and elsewhere in this chapter. Note that the x, y, x^2, and y^2 columns repeat Table 19. The d or $(x - y)$ column is found by subtracting algebraically each y deviation from its corresponding x deviation. These differences are then squared and entered in the d^2 or $(x - y)^2$ column. Substitution of Σx^2, Σy^2, and Σd^2 in formula (31) gives $r = .78$.

TABLE 22 To illustrate the calculation of r from ungrouped data by the difference formula, deviations from the means

	Test 1	Test 2			d			d^2
Subject	X	Y	x	y	$(x - y)$	x^2	y^2	$(x - y)^2$
A	50	22	−12.5	−8.4	−4.1	156.25	70.56	16.81
B	54	25	−8.5	−5.4	−3.1	72.25	29.16	9.61
C	56	34	−6.5	3.6	−10.1	42.25	12.96	102.01
D	59	28	−3.5	−2.4	−1.1	12.25	5.76	1.21
E	60	26	−2.5	−4.4	1.9	6.25	19.36	3.61
F	62	30	−.5	−.4	−.1	.25	.16	.01
G	61	32	−1.5	1.6	−3.1	2.25	2.56	9.61
H	65	30	2.5	−.4	2.9	6.25	.16	8.41
I	67	28	4.5	−2.4	6.9	20.25	5.76	47.61
J	71	34	8.5	3.6	4.9	72.25	12.96	24.01
K	71	36	8.5	5.6	2.9	72.25	31.36	8.41
L	74	40	11.5	9.6	1.9	132.25	92.16	3.61
						595.00	282.92	234.92

$M_X = 62.5$

$$r = \frac{595.00 + 282.92 - 234.92}{2\sqrt{595 \times 282.92}} \qquad (31)$$

$M_Y = 30.4$

$$= .78$$

Another variation of the difference formula is often useful in machine calculation. This version makes use of raw or obtained scores:

$$r = \frac{N[\Sigma X^2 + \Sigma Y^2 - \Sigma(X - Y)^2] - 2(\Sigma X) \times (\Sigma Y)}{2\sqrt{[N\Sigma X^2 - (\Sigma X)^2][N\Sigma Y^2 - (\Sigma Y)^2]}} \qquad (32)$$

(*coefficient of correlation by difference formula, calculation from raw or obtained scores*)

in which $\Sigma(X - Y)^2$ is the sum of the squared differences between the two sets of scores.

PROBLEMS

1. Find the correlation between the two sets of scores given below, using the ratio method (p. 125).

Subjects	X	Y
a	15	40
b	18	42
c	22	50
d	17	45
e	19	43
f	20	46
g	16	41
h	21	41

2. The scores given below were achieved upon a group intelligence test and typewriting tests by 100 students in a typewriting class. The typewriting scores are in number of words written per minute, with certain penalties. Find the coefficient of correlation. Use an interval of 5 units for Y and an interval of 10 units for X.

Typing (Y)	Test (X)	Typing (Y)	Test (X)	Typing (Y)	Test (X)
46	152	26	164	40	120
31	96	33	127	36	140
46	171	44	144	43	141
40	172	35	160	48	143
42	138	49	106	45	138
41	154	40	95	58	149
39	127	57	146	23	142
46	156	23	175	45	166
34	156	51	126	44	138
48	133	35	120	47	150
48	173	41	154	29	148
38	134	28	146	46	166
26	179	32	154	46	146
37	159	50	159	39	167
34	167	29	175	49	139
51	136	41	164	34	183
47	153	32	111	41	150
39	145	49	164	49	179
32	134	58	119	31	138
37	184	35	160	47	136
26	154	48	149	40	172
40	90	40	149	30	145
53	143	43	143	40	109
46	173	38	159	38	158
39	168	37	157	29	115

Typing (Y)	Test (X)	Typing (Y)	Test (X)	Typing (Y)	Test (X)
52	187	41	153	43	93
47	166	51	149	55	163
31	172	40	163	37	147
33	189	35	175	52	169
22	147	31	133	38	75
46	150	23	178	39	152
44	150	37	168	32	159
37	143	46	156	42	150
31	133				

3. In the correlation table given below compute the coefficient of correlation.

BOYS: AGES 4.5 TO 5.5 YEARS

Weight in Pounds (X)

Height in Inches (Y)	24–28	29–33	34–38	39–43	44–48	49–53	Totals
45–47			1		2		3
42–44			4	35	21	5	65
39–41		5	87	90	7	1	190
36–38	1	18	72	8			99
33–35	5	15	5				25
30–32	2						2
Totals	8	38	169	133	30	6	384

4. In the following correlation table compute the coefficient of correlation.

Group Test I.Q.'s

School Marks	84 and lower	85–89	90–94	95–99	100–104	105–109	110–114	115–119	120–124	125 over	Totals
90 and over				3	3	15	12	9	9	5	56
85–89				8	17	15	24	13	6	6	89
80–84			4	6	22	21	20	10	5	1	89
75–79			7	25	33	23	10	7	4		109
70–74		4	10	18	14	22	12	1	1		82
65–69	1	3	3	12	7	8	8	1			43
60–64			2	5	3	1	1				12
Totals	1	7	26	77	99	105	87	41	25	12	480

5. Compute the coefficient of correlation in the table below:

Arithmetic (X)

	12–13	14–15	16–17	18–19	20–21	22–23	24–25	Totals
35–37					1		1	2
32–34					6	3		9
29–31		1	2	6	8	1		18
26–28		4	4	6	11	4	1	30
23–25	2	1	6	5	4	1		19
20–22	3	2	1	1				7
Totals	5	8	13	18	30	9	2	85

Reading (Y)

6. Compute the coefficient of correlation between the Algebra Test scores and I.Q.'s shown in the table below.

Algebra Test Scores

		30–34	35–39	40–44	45–49	50–54	55–59	60–64	65–69	Totals
	130–139				1		1		1	3
	120–129			1		1	2	1		5
	110–119	1	2	5	6	11	6	3	2	36
I.Q.'s	100–109	3	7	9	17	13	5	1	1	56
	90–99	4	10	16	12	5	1			48
	80–89	4	9	8	2	2				25
	Totals	12	28	39	38	32	15	5	4	173

7. Compute the correlation between the two sets of scores given below
   (a) when deviations are taken from the means of the two series [use formula (28)];
   (b) when the means are taken at zero. First reduce the scores by subtracting 150 from each of the scores in Test 1, and 40 from each of the scores in Test 2.

Test 1	Test 2	Test 1	Test 2
150	60	139	41
126	40	155	43
135	45	147	37
176	50	162	58
138	56	156	48
142	43	146	39
151	57	133	31
163	38	168	46
137	41	153	52
178	55	150	57

8. Find the correlation between the two sets of memory-span scores given below (the first series is arranged in order of size) (a) when deviations are taken from assumed means [formula (26)], (b) by the difference method given on page 145.

Test 1 (digit span)	Test 2 (letter span)
15	12
14	14
13	10
12	8
11	12
11	9
11	12
10	8
10	10
10	9
9	8
9	7
8	7
7	8
7	6

ANSWERS

1. $r = .65$
2. $r = -.05$
3. $r = .71$
4. $r = .46$
5. $r = .54$
6. $r = .52$
7. $r = .41$
8. $r = .78$

PART II

INFERENCE AND PREDICTION

◇◇◇

CHAPTER 7

REGRESSION AND PREDICTION

<><><><><><><><><><><><><><><><><><><><><><><><><><><><><><><><><><><><><><><><>

I. THE REGRESSION EQUATIONS

1. Problem of predicting one variable from another

Suppose that in a group of 120 college students (p. 128), we wish to estimate a certain man's height knowing his weight to be 153 pounds. The best possible "guess" that we can make of this man's height is the mean height of all of the men who fall in the 150–159 weight interval. In Figure 40 the mean height of the nine men in this column is 68.9 inches, which is, therefore, the most *likely* height of a man who weighs 153 pounds. In the same way, the most probable height of a man who weighs 136 pounds is 66.6 inches, the mean height of the thirty-seven men who fall in weight column 130–139 pounds. And, in general, the most probable height of any man in the group is the *mean* of the heights of *all* of the men who weigh the same (or approximately the same) as he, i.e., who fall within the same weight column.

Turning to weight, we can make the same kind of estimates. Thus, the best possible "guess" that we can make of a man's weight knowing his height to be 66.5 inches is 135.1 pounds, viz., the mean weight of the thirty-three men who fall in the height interval 66–67 inches. Again, in general, the most probable weight of any man in the group is the *mean* weight of *all* of the men who are of the same (or approximately the same) height.

Our illustration shows that from the scatter diagram alone it is possible to "predict" one variable from another. But the prediction is rough, and is obviously subject to a large "error of estimate." *

* See p. 160.

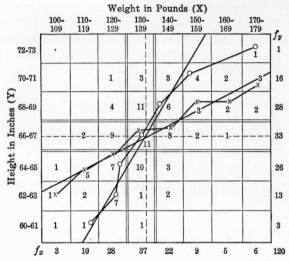

FIG. 40 Illustrating positions of regression lines and calculation of the regression equations (see Fig. 38)

$r = .60$

$M_X = 136.3$ pounds

$M_Y = 66.5$ inches

For plotting on the chart, regression equations are written with σ_x and σ_y in class-interval units, viz.—

$$\overline{y} = .51x \;\} \text{ see}$$
$$\overline{x} = .71y \;\} \text{ p. 157}$$

CALCULATION OF REGRESSION EQUATIONS

I. Deviation Form

$$(1) \qquad \overline{y} = .60 \times \frac{2.62}{15.55}\, x = .10x \qquad (33)$$

$$(2) \qquad \overline{x} = .60 \times \frac{15.55}{2.62}\, y = 3.56y \qquad (34)$$

II. Score Form

(1) $Y - 66.5 = .10(X - 136.3)$ or $\overline{Y} = .10X + 52.9$ (35)

(2) $X - 136.3 = 3.56(Y - 66.5)$ or $\overline{X} = 3.56Y - 100.4$ (36)

CALCULATION OF STANDARD ERRORS OF ESTIMATE

$$\sigma_{(est\ Y)} = 2.62\sqrt{1 - .60^2} = 2.10 \text{ inches} \qquad (37)$$
$$\sigma_{(est\ X)} = 15.55\sqrt{1 - .60^2} = 12.43 \text{ pounds} \qquad (38)$$

Moreover, while we have made use of the fact that the means are the most probable points in our arrays (columns or rows), we have made no use of our knowledge concerning the over-all relationship between the two variables. The two regression lines in Figure 40 are determined by the correlation between height and weight and their degree of separation indicates the size of the correlation coefficient* (p. 131). Consequently, these lines describe more ~ularly, and in, a more generalized fashion than do the series of short straight lines joining the means, the relationship between height and weight *over the whole range* (see also p. 129). A knowledge of the equations of the regression lines is necessary if we are to make a prediction based upon *all* of our data. Given the weight (*X*) of a man comparable to those in our group, for example, if we substitute for *X* in the equation connecting *Y* and *X* we are able to predict this man's height more accurately than if we simply took the mean of his height array. The task of the next section will be to develop equations for the two regression lines by means of which predictions from *X* to *Y* or from *Y* to *X* can be made.

2. The regression equations in deviation form

(1) WHAT THE REGRESSION EQUATIONS DO

The equations of the two regression lines in a correlation table represent the straight lines which "best fit" the means of the successive columns and rows in the table. Using as a definition of "best fit" the criterion of "least squares," † Pearson worked out the equation of the line which goes through, or as close as possible to, more of the column means than any other straight line; and the equation of the line which goes through, or as close as possible to, more of the row means than any other straight line. These two lines are "best fitting" in a mathematical sense, the one to the observations of the columns and the other to the observations of the rows.

The equation of the first regression line, the line drawn to represent the trend of the crosses in Figure 40, is as follows:

$$\bar{y} = r \frac{\sigma_y}{\sigma_x} \times x \qquad (33)$$

(regression equation of y on x, deviations taken from the means of Y and X)

* The term "regression" was first used by Francis Galton with reference to the inheritance of stature. Galton found that children of tall parents tend to be less tall, and children of short parents less short, than their parents. In other words, the heights of the offspring tend to "move back" toward the mean height of the general population. This tendency toward maintaining the "mean height" Galton called the principle of regression, and the line describing the relationship of height in parent and offspring was called a "regression line." The term is still employed, although its original meaning of "stepping back" to some stationary average is not necessarily implied (see p. 174).

† For an elementary mathematical treatment of the method of least squares as applied to the problem of fitting regression lines, see Walker, H. M., *Elementary Statistical Method* (New York: Henry Holt and Co., 1943), pp. 308–310.

The factor $r\dfrac{\sigma_y}{\sigma_x}$ is called the *regression coefficient*, and is often replaced in (33) by the term b_{yx} or b_{12} so that formula (33) may be written $\overline{y} = b_{yx} \times x$, or $\overline{y} = b_{12} \times x$. The bar over the y ($\overline{y}$) means that our estimate is an average value.

If we substitute in formula (33) the values of r, σ_y, and σ_x, obtained from Figure 40, we have

$$\overline{y} = .60 \times \frac{2.62}{15.55}\, x, \quad \text{or}$$

$$\overline{y} = .10x$$

This equation gives the relationship of deviations from mean height to deviations from mean weight. When $x = \pm 1.00$, $\overline{y} = \pm .10$; and a deviation of 1 pound from the mean of the X's (weight) is accompanied by a deviation of .10 inch from the mean of the Y's (height). The man who stands 1 pound *above* the mean weight of the group, therefore, is most probably .10 inch *above* the mean height. Since this man's weight is 137.3 pounds ($136.3 + 1.00$), his height is most probably 66.6 inches ($66.5 + .10$). Again, the man who weighs 120 pounds, i.e., is 16.3 pounds *below* the mean of the group, is most probably 64.9 inches tall—or about 1.6 inches *below* the mean height of the group. To get this last value, substitute $x = -16.3$ in the equation above to get $\overline{y} = -1.63$, and refer this value to its means. The regression equation is a generalized expression of relationship. It tells us that the most probable deviation of an individual in our group from the M_{ht} is just .10 of his deviation from the M_{wt}.

The equation $\overline{y} = r\dfrac{\sigma_y}{\sigma_x} \times x$ gives the relationship between Y and X in *deviation form*. This designation is appropriate since the two variables are expressed as deviations from their respective means (i.e., as x and y); hence, for a given *deviation* from M_X the equation gives the most probable accompanying *deviation* from M_Y.

The equation of the second regression line, the line drawn through the circles (i.e., the means) of the rows in Figure 40, is

$$\overline{x} = r\frac{\sigma_x}{\sigma_y} \times y \tag{34}$$

(*regression equation of x on y, deviations taken from the means of X and Y*)

As in the first regression equation, the regression coefficient $r\dfrac{\sigma_x}{\sigma_y}$ is often replaced by the expression b_{xy} or b_{21} and formula (34) written $\overline{x} = b_{xy} \times y$ or $\overline{x} = b_{21} \times y$.

If we substitute for r, σ_x, and σ_y, in formula (34), we have

$$\bar{x} = .60 \times \frac{15.55}{2.62}\, y \quad \text{or}$$

$$x = 3.56y$$

from which it is evident that a deviation of 1 inch from the M_{ht}, from 66.5 inches, is accompanied by a deviation of 3.56 pounds from the M_{wt}, or from 136.3 pounds. Expressed generally, the most probable deviation of *any man* from the mean weight is just 3.56 times his deviation from the mean height. Accordingly, a man 67 inches tall or .5 inch *above* the mean height ($66.5 + .5 = 67$) most probably weighs 138.1 pounds, or is 1.8 pounds *above* the mean weight ($136.3 + 1.8$). (Substitute $y = .5$ in the equation and $\bar{x} = 1.8$.)

Equation $\bar{x} = r\dfrac{\sigma_x}{\sigma_y} \times y$ gives the relationship between X and Y in *devia-tion form*. That is to say, it gives the most probable *deviation* of an X measure from M_X corresponding to a known *deviation* in the Y measure from M_Y.

(2) WHY THERE ARE TWO REGRESSION LINES

Although both regression equations involve x and y, the two equations cannot be used interchangeably—neither can be employed to predict *both* x and y. This is an important fact which the student must bear in mind constantly. The first regression equation $\bar{y} = r\dfrac{\sigma_y}{\sigma_x} \times x$ can be used *only* when y is to be predicted from a given x (when y is the "dependent" variable).* The second regression equation $\bar{x} = r\dfrac{\sigma_x}{\sigma_y} \times y$ can be used *only* when x is to be predicted from a known y (when x is the dependent variable).

In summary, there are two regression equations in a correlation table, the one through the means of the columns and the other through the means of the rows. This is always true unless the correlation is perfect. When $r = 1.00$, $\bar{y} = r\dfrac{\sigma_y}{\sigma_x}x$ becomes $\bar{y} = \dfrac{\sigma_y}{\sigma_x} \times x$ or $\bar{y}\sigma_x = x\sigma_y$. Moreover, when $r = 1.00$, $\bar{x} = r\dfrac{\sigma_x}{\sigma_y}y$ becomes $\bar{x} = \dfrac{\sigma_x}{\sigma_y} \times y$ or $\bar{x}\sigma_y = y\sigma_x$. In short, when

---

* The dependent variable takes its value from the other or independent variable in the regression equation. For example, in the linear equation $y = 5x - 10$, y depends for its value upon the number assigned x. Hence, y is the dependent variable and x is the independent.

the correlation is perfect, the two equations are identical and the two regression lines coincide. To illustrate this situation, suppose that the correlation between height and weight in Figure 40 were perfect. Then the first regression line would be $\overline{y} = 1.00 \times \dfrac{2.62}{15.55} x$ or $\overline{y} = .17x$; and the second equation, $\overline{x} = 1.00 \times \dfrac{15.55}{2.62} y$, or $\overline{x} = 5.93y$. Algebraically, the equation $x = 5.93y$ equals $y = .17x$. For if we write $x = y/.17$, $x = 5.93y$. When $r = \pm 1.00$ there is only *one* equation and a *single* regression line. Moreover, if $r = \pm 1.00$, and in addition $\sigma_x = \sigma_y$, the single regression line makes an angle of 45° or 135° with the horizontal axis, since $y = \pm x$ (see p. 157).

3. Plotting the regression lines in a correlation table *

In Figure 40, the coördinate axes have been drawn in on the correlation table through the means of the X and Y distributions. The vertical axis is drawn through 136.3 pounds (M_{wt}), and the horizontal axis through 66.5 inches (M_{ht}). These axes intersect close to the center of the

* A brief review of the equation of a straight line, and of the method of plotting a simple linear equation is given here in order to simplify the plotting of the regression equations.

In Figure 41, let X and Y be coördinate axes, or axes of reference. Now suppose that we are given the equation $y = 2x$ and are required to represent the relation between x and y graphically. To do this we assign values to x in the equation and compute the corresponding values of y. When $x = 2$, for example, $y = 2 \times 2$ or 4; when $x = 3$, $y = 2 \times 3$ or 6. In the same way, given any x value we can compute the value of y which will "satisfy" the equation, that is, make the left side equal to the right. If the series of x and y values found from the equation are plotted on the diagram with respect to the X and Y coördinates (as in Fig. 41) they will be found to fall along a straight line. This straight line pictures the relation $y = 2x$. It goes through the origin, since when $x = 0$, $y = 0$. The equation $y = 2x$ represents, then, a straight line which passes through the origin; and the relation of its coördinates (points lying along the line) is such that $\dfrac{y}{x}$, called the *slope* of the line, is always equal to 2.

The general equation of any straight line which passes through the origin may be written $y = mx$, where m is the slope of the line. If we replace m in the general formula by $r \dfrac{\sigma_y}{\sigma_x}$ it is clear that the regression line in *deviation form*, namely,

$\overline{y} = r \dfrac{\sigma_y}{\sigma_x} x$, is simply the equation of a straight line which goes through the origin. For the same reason, when the general equation of a straight line through the origin is written $x = my$, $\overline{x} = r \dfrac{\sigma_x}{\sigma_y} y$ is also seen to be a straight line through the origin, its slope being $r \dfrac{\sigma_x}{\sigma_y}$.

chart. Equations (33) and (34) define straight lines which pass through the origin or point of intersection of these coördinate axes. It is a comparatively simple task to plot in our regression lines on the correlation chart with reference to the given coördinate axes.

Correlation charts are usually laid out with equal distances representing the X and Y class intervals (the printed correlation charts are always so constructed) although the intervals expressed in terms of the variables themselves may be, and often are, unequal and incommensurable. This is true in Figure 40. In this diagram, the intervals in X and Y appear to be equal, although the actual interval for height is 2 inches, and the actual interval for weight is 10 pounds. Because of this difference in interval length it is important that we express σ_x and σ_y in our regression equations in *class-interval units* before plotting the regression lines on the chart. Otherwise we must equate our X and Y intervals by laying out our diagram in such a way as to make the X interval five times the Y interval. This latter method of equating intervals is impractical, and is rarely used, since all we need do in order to use correlation charts drawn up

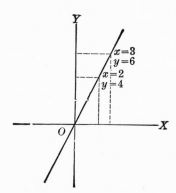

FIG. 41   Plot of the straight line, y = 2x

with equal intervals is to express σ_x and σ_y in formulas (33) and (34) in units of interval. When this is done, and the interval, *not* the score, is the unit, the first regression equation becomes

$$\overline{y} = .60 \frac{1.31}{1.55} x \quad \text{or } \overline{y} = .51x$$

and the second

$$\overline{x} = .60 \frac{1.55}{1.31} y \quad \text{or } \overline{x} = .71y$$

Since each regression line goes through the origin, only one other point (besides the origin) is needed in order to determine its course. In the first regression equation, if $x = 10, \overline{y} = 5.1$; and the two points $(0, 0)$ and $(10, 5.1)$ locate the line. In the second regression equation, if $y = 10$, $\overline{x} = 7.1$; and the two points $(0, 0)$ and $(7.1, 10)$ determine the second line. In plotting points on a diagram any convenient scale may be employed. A millimeter rule is useful.

It is important for the student to remember that when the two σ's are expressed in interval units, regression equations do *not* give the relationship between the X and Y score deviations. These special forms of the regression equation should *not be used* except when plotting the equations on a correlation chart. Whenever the most probable deviation in the one variable corresponding to a known deviation in the other is wanted, formulas (33) and (34), in which the σ's are expressed in *score units*, must be employed.

4. The regression equations in score form

In the preceding sections it was pointed out that formulas (33) and (34) give the equations of the regression lines in deviation form—that values of x and y substituted in these equations are deviations from the means of the X and Y distributions, and are not scores. Regression equations in *deviation form* are actually all that one needs in order to pass from one variable to another, but it is decidedly convenient to be able to estimate an individual's *actual score* in Y, directly from the score in X without first converting the X score into a deviation from M_X. This can be done by using the *score form* of the regression equation. The conversion of deviation form to score form is made as follows: Denoting the mean of the Y's by M_Y and any Y score simply by Y, we may write the deviation of any individual from the mean as $Y - M_Y$ or, in general, $y = Y - M_Y$. In the same way, $x = X - M_X$ when x is the deviation of any X score from the mean X. If we substitute $Y - M_Y$ for y, and $X - M_X$ for x, in formulas (33) and (34), the two regression equations become

$$Y - M_Y = r \frac{\sigma_y}{\sigma_x} (X - M_X)$$

or

$$\overline{Y} = r \frac{\sigma_y}{\sigma_x} (X - M_X) + M_Y \qquad (35)$$

and

$$X - M_X = r \frac{\sigma_x}{\sigma_y} (Y - M_Y)$$

or

$$\overline{X} = r \frac{\sigma_x}{\sigma_y} (Y - M_Y) + M_X \tag{36}$$

(*regression equations of* Y *on* X *and* X *on* Y *in score form*)

These two equations are said to be in *score form*, since the X and Y in both equations represent *actual scores, and not deviations from the means* of the two distributions.

If we substitute in (35) the values of M_Y, r, σ_y, σ_x, and M_X obtained from Figure 40, the regression of height on weight in score form becomes

$$\overline{Y} = .60 \times \frac{2.62}{15.55} (X - 136.3) + 66.5$$

or upon reduction

$$\overline{Y} = .10X + 52.9$$

To illustrate the use of this equation, suppose that a man in our group weighs 160 pounds and we wish to estimate his most probable height. Substituting 160 for X in the equation, $\overline{Y} = 69$ inches; and accordingly, the most probable height of a man who weighs 160 pounds is 69 inches.

If the problem is to predict weight instead of height, we must use the second regression equation, formula (36). Substituting for M_X, r, σ_x, σ_y, and M_Y in (36) we have

$$\overline{X} = .60 \times \frac{15.55}{2.62} (Y - 66.5) + 136.3$$

or

$$\overline{X} = 3.56Y - 100.4$$

Now, if a man is 71 inches tall, we find, on replacing Y by 71 in the equation, that $\overline{X} = 152.4$. Hence the most probable weight of a man who is 71 inches tall is about 152½ pounds.

5. The meaning of a "prediction" from the regression equation

It may seem strange, perhaps, to talk of "predicting" a man's weight from his height, when the heights and weights of the 120 men in our group are already known. When we have measures of both variables it is unnecessary, of course, to estimate one from the other. But suppose that all we know about a given individual is his height and the fact that he falls within the age range of our group of 120 men. Since we know the correlation between height and weight to be .60, it is possible from the regression equation to predict the most probable weight of our subject in lieu of actually measuring him. Furthermore, the regression equation may be employed to estimate the weight of other men in the population from which our group is chosen, provided our sample is an unbiased selection from the larger group. A regression equation holds, of course, only for the population from which the sample group was drawn. We cannot forecast the weights of children from a regression equation which decribes the relationship between height and weight for men aged 30 to 40. Conversely, we cannot expect a regression equation established upon elementary school children to hold for an adult group.

Perhaps height and weight, as both are so easily measured, do not demonstrate the usefulness of prediction *via* the regression equation so clearly as do mental and educational tests. Height and weight were chosen for our "model" problem because they are objective, measurable, and definite in meaning. To consider a problem of more direct psychological interest, suppose that for a group of 300 high school freshmen, the correlation between a battery of achievement tests given at the beginning of the school year and average grade over the first year is .60. Now, if the same battery of tests is administered at the start of the following year, we can forecast the probable scholastic achievement of the *new* class by means of the regression equation established the previous year. Forecasts of this sort are useful in educational guidance and prognosis. The same is true in vocational guidance or in the selection of workers in office and factory. We can often predict from a battery of aptitude tests the probable success of an individual who plans to enter a given trade or profession. Advice on such a basis is measurably better than subjective judgment.

II. THE ACCURACY OF PREDICTIONS FROM REGRESSION EQUATIONS

1. The standard error of estimate (σ_{est})

Values of X and Y predicted by way of the regression equation have been constantly referred to above as being the most probable values of the dependent variable which can be obtained from a given value of the independent variable. It is important that we have clearly in mind what "most probable" means in the present connection. A forecast may well be the best we can make under existing condtions, and at the same time not be precise enough to be of much practical value. In Figure 40, fourth column from the right, there are 22 men all of whom weigh 144.5 pounds (midpoint of the interval 140–149). These same 22 men vary in height from 62.5 to 70.5 inches, but our best forecast of the height of any one of them chosen at random is the $\overline{Y}$ given by the regression line which passes through or close to the mean of the given column (see Fig. 40). It is clear that some men will be shorter and some taller than our $\overline{Y}$ estimate, and the question arises of *how* accurate is our most probable estimate. To answer this query we need some index of the goodness of our forecast, and such a measure is the standard error of estimate (σ_{est}).

The formula for the SE of estimate when $\overline{Y}$ scores are predicted from X scores is

$$\sigma_{(est\ Y)} = \sigma_y\sqrt{1 - r^2} \qquad (37)$$

*(standard error of a Y measure predicted from an X score
in the regression equation)*

in which
$$\sigma_y = \text{the } SD \text{ of the } Y \text{ distribution}$$
and
$$r = \text{the coefficient of correlation between } X \text{ and } Y$$

From the formula for the regression of Y on X (p. 159), we computed the most probable height of a man weighing 160 pounds to be 69 inches. And from the same equation, we predict the height of a man weighing 144.5 pounds to be 67 inches. In order to determine the accuracy of these forecasts, substitute for $\sigma_{ht} = 2.62$ inches and $r = .60$ in formula (37) to get

$$\sigma_{(est\ Y)} = 2.62\sqrt{1 - .60^2}$$

$$= 2.1 \text{ inches}$$

We can now say that the most probable height of a man weighing 160 pounds is 69 inches with a SE of estimate of 2.1 inches. And by the same token, the most probable height of a man weighing 144.5 pounds is 67 inches with a $\sigma_{(est\ Y)}$ of 2.1 inches. The $SE_{(est\ Y)}$ may be interpreted generally to mean that in predicting the heights of 100 men, 68 of our estimates should not miss the man's actual height by more than ± 2.1 inches—i.e., by more than $\pm 1\sigma_{(est\ Y)}$ (see p. 163).

When X scores are predicted from Y scores, the standard error of estimate is

$$\sigma_{(est\ X)} = \sigma_x\sqrt{1 - r^2} \qquad (38)$$

(standard error of an X measure predicted from a regression equation)

in which
$$\sigma_x = \text{the } SD \text{ of the } X \text{ distribution}$$
and
$$r = \text{the coefficient of correlation between } X \text{ and } Y.$$

On page 159 we estimated from the regression equation that the most probable weight (X) of a man 71 inches tall is 152.4 pounds. The $\sigma_{(est\ X)}$ of this forecast is

$$\sigma_{(est\ X)} = 15.55\sqrt{1 - .60^2} = 12.4 \text{ lbs}$$

and our best estimate of the weight of *any* man in our group of 120 has a standard error of 12.4 pounds. The chances are about 2 in 3 (68 in 100) that any given estimate will not miss the man's actual weight by more than about 12 pounds (p. 163).

2. Assumptions made in using the $SE_{(est)}$ formula

Three assumptions are made in predicting *via* the regression equation, and unless these conditions are satisfied the regression equation and the $\sigma_{(est)}$ will not give accurate inforomation. The *first* and most general assumption is that of *linearity*—namely, that the relationship between X and Y can be described by a straight line. Linearity of regression is generally found in mental and educational measurement. But true non-linearity is sometimes encountered in the relations between mental and social-personality variables. In a college class, for example, the B and C students are often more active in extracurricular activities than are either the straight A or the failing students. Hence, the relationship between marks and extracurricular activities in this situation would be curvilinear (see p. 396). Whenever relationship is not clearly curvilinear, straight-line relation is the simplest and often the most reasonable hypothesis.

A *second* assumption made when we use the regression line for prediction is that the distributions in X and Y are normal—or at least not badly skewed (p. 100). Reference to the "ideal" diagrams on page 131 shows that when the X and Y distributions are normal, the subdistributions in the columns or rows (the "arrays") are also normal and spread out symmetrically around a central point. Figure 42 represents schematically the spread of scores in the columns of a correlation table, and shows the regression of Y on X. Note that the distribution in each of the columns is normal, and that the regression line passes through the mean of each of the small column distributions. As we shall see later, the $SE_{(est)}$ is the standard deviation of the distributions in the columns.*

The *third* assumption made in regression-line prediction is that the spread or scatter is the same for each column (or row) in the correlation

---

* The $SE_{(est\ Y)}$ is a standard deviation when it gives the spread of the scores in the individual columns. It is a standard error when used to give the range allowable in a forecast made from the regression equation.

table. This condition is called *homoscedasticity* (the word means "equal scattering"). Equal scatter in the columns, as shown in Figure 42, enables us to substitute one measure of spread [namely, $SE_{(est\ Y)}$] for the SD's of the separate columns. Figure 42 shows how for a given X, we locate the most probable Y ($\overline{Y}$) from the regression line. The range of allowable fluctuation in the prediction of any Y is given by the $SE_{(est\ Y)}$ and is the

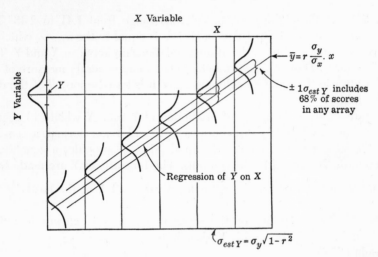

X Variable

$$\overline{y} = r\frac{\sigma_y}{\sigma_x}\cdot x$$

$\pm 1\sigma_{est\ Y}$ includes 68% of scores in any array

Y Variable

Regression of $\overline{Y}$ on X

$$\sigma_{est\ Y} = \sigma_y\sqrt{1-r^2}$$

FIG. 42 How forecasts are made from the regression line. Only the columns of the correlation table and one regression line are represented. Homoscedasticity is shown by the equal spread (SD's) in each column. The SD in any column is $\sigma_{(est\ Y)}$.

same for all columns under the assumption of homoscedasticity. Only the range of $\pm 1\sigma_{(est\ Y)}$ is marked off in Figure 42. The probability is higher, of course, for wider intervals. Thus the chances are about 95 in 100 that a predicted Y will not be in error by more than $\pm 2\sigma_{(est\ Y)}$; and the chances are almost 100% (99.7) that a predicted Y will not miss its actual value by more than $\pm 3\sigma_{(est\ Y)}$.

The requirement that there be equal scatter in the columns (and rows) of a correlation table (i.e., homoscedasticity) often strikes the student as a stringent one, not likely to be realized with real data. To be sure, some variation in the SD's of the columns of a correlation table is nearly always found. But in the correlation of mental and educational tests, especially when N is large, the assumption of equal scatter in columns (or rows) is reasonable. Suppose, for example, that we compute the SD's of the columns in the correlation diagram in Figure 40. These are

X Variable

	100–109	110–119	120–129	130–139	140–149	150–159	160–169	170–179
SD:	1.63	1.79	2.48	2.23	2.30	1.63	1.55	1.41
N:	3	10	28	37	22	9	5	6

The SD's of the eight separate columns range from 1.41 to 2.48. The weighted mean is 2.1 (to 1 decimal), i.e., is equal to the $\sigma_{(est\ Y)}$ which is, of course, computed from the all-over relationship between X and Y. This single figure, SD or $\sigma_{(est\ Y)}$, is a better (i.e., more general) measure of the true scatter in the separate columns, since it is based upon *all* of the data in the table.

Figure 42 gives the range of prediction of Y from X when (1) regression is linear, when (2) distributions in X and Y are normal, and when (3) the scatter in the columns is equal. $SE_{(est\ Y)}$ provides a generalized estimate of the spread in the columns. The forecasts of Y are made from the regression line, $\overline{y} = r\dfrac{\sigma_y}{\sigma_x} \cdot x$, for fixed values of X at the heads of the columns. The variability of the separate columns is *always* less than the variability of the entire Y distribution, except when $r = .00$ [see formula (37)].

3. The accuracy of individual predictions from the regression equation

When the three assumptions described in the preceding section are satisfied, the $SE_{(est)}$ provides an accurate measure of the *range* in an individual forecast—i.e., the error made in taking the predicted measure instead of the actual measure.* The size of the standard error of estimate depends upon the SD of the dependent variable (the variable we are predicting) and upon the extent of correlation between X and Y. If the $r = 1.00$, clearly $\sqrt{1-r^2}$ is $.00$, and the $SE_{(est)}$ is also zero—there is no error of estimate, and each score is predicted exactly (see diagram 2 in Fig. 37). At the other correlational extreme, when $r = .00$, $\sqrt{1-r^2}$ is 1.00, and the error of estimate equals the SD of the distribution into which prediction is made, i.e., the distribution of the dependent variable. When the correlation is zero, the regression equation is, of course, of no value in enabling us to make a better forecast: each individual's most

---

* It can be shown mathematically that when $\overline{Y}$ is the predicted score and Y is the actual score, the SD of the distribution of the differences $(Y - \overline{Y})$ is $SE_{(est\ Y)}$.

probable score (his $\overline{Y}$) is simply M_Y (see diagram 3, Fig. 37). In this situation, all that we can say with assurance is that a person's predicted score will fall *somewhere* in the Y (or X) distribution. The $SE_{(est)}$ equals the SD of the distribution.

If the variability in Y is small and the correlation coefficient is high, Y can be predicted quite adequately from known measures in X. But when the variability of the dependent variable is large or the correlation low, or when both conditions exist, estimates may be so unreliable as to be virtually worthless. Even when r is fairly high, forecasts may have an uncomfortably large $SE_{(est)}$ (see p. 169). We have seen (p. 159) that in spite of an r of .60 between height and weight (Fig. 39) our forecast of a man's weight from his height has a $SE_{(est)}$ of about 12 pounds. Furthermore, heights predicted from weights will in 1/3 of the cases be in error by slightly more than 2 inches, i.e., lie outside of the limits $\pm 1 SE_{(est)}$. In the example in Figure 43, the high correlation offsets to some extent the fairly large SD's, thus permitting reasonably good prediction (p. 170).

When an investigator uses the regression equation for forecasting, he should always give the $SE_{(est)}$. The value of the prediction will depend primarily upon the error of estimate. But it will also depend upon the units in which the test variables are expressed, and the purpose for which the prediction is made (p. 176).

4. The accuracy of group predictions

We have seen in the preceding section that only when $r = 1.00$ and $\sqrt{1-r^2}$ is .00 can the estimate of an individual's score be made without error. The correlation coefficient must be .87 before $\sqrt{1-r^2}$ is .50, i.e., before the $SE_{(est)}$ is reduced 50% below the SD of the whole test. Obviously, then, unless r is large (larger than we often get in practice) the regression equation may offer little aid in enabling us to forecast accurately what a person can be expected to do. This fact has led many to discount unwisely the value of correlation in prediction and to conclude that computation of the regression equation is not worth the trouble. This decision is unfortunate, as even a small reduction (as little as 10%) in the error with which performance in a criterion can be forecast, may represent a distinct saving in time and money, as the experience in industry and the Armed Forces has amply shown.

Correlation makes a better showing in forecasting the probable performance of groups than in predicting the likely achievement of a selected individual. In attempting to predict the success of a youngster entering college or of a new worker in a factory, the psychologist is in much the same position as is the insurance actuary. The actuary cannot tell how long Sam Brown, aged 20, will live. But from his experience tables the actuary can tell quite accurately how many in a group of 10,000 Sam Browns or their counterparts, aged 20, will live to be 30, 40, 50, etc. In the same manner, the psychologist may be quite uncertain [large $SE_{(est)}$] concerning the probable performance of a specific Sam Brown. But knowing the correlation between a battery of tests and a criterion of performance, he can tell with some assurance how many of a given group (whose test scores are known) will be successful in terms of the criterion. The improvement in forecasting depends solely upon the size of the correlation coefficient between test battery and criterion.

To illustrate "actuarial prediction," let us suppose that 280 (i.e., 70%) of a freshman class of 400 students achieve grades in their first year of college above the minimum passing standard, and may, therefore, be considered "satisfactory." Suppose further that the correlation between a standard intelligence test given at the beginning of the term and freshman grades is .50. Now, if we had selected only the *upper* 50% of our entering group (i.e., the 200 who performed best on the intelligence test) at the start of the term, how many of these selected 200 should have proved to be satisfactory in terms of passing grades? From Table 23, it is found that 168 of the 200 "best" freshmen, or 84%, ought to be in the satisfactory group (the upper 70%) with respect to college grades. The entry .84 is found in the column headed .50 (proportion of the test distribution chosen) opposite the correlation coefficient .50. The number, 168, should be compared with the number 140 (i.e., 70%) who can be expected to fall in the satisfactory group when selection is random—or catch-as-catch-can. The entry .70 is in column .50 opposite the r of .00.

The smaller the group of freshmen and the more highly selected with respect to the test battery, the greater the number who should prove to be satisfactory in academic performance. From Table 23, for example, we know that 91% of the best 20% of our 400 students (about 73 in 80) may be expected to prove satisfactory in terms of grades (i.e., being in the upper 70% of the grade distribution). Read the entry .91 in column .20 opposite r = .50. When the correlation between test battery and grades is .60 instead of .50, 87% or 174 in 200 of the best half (according to the test) should meet the criterion. Both of these forecasts are to be compared with 70% or 140, the estimate when r = .00. It is clear that the higher the r, the larger the number likely to meet the standard set by the criterion.

Table 23 is a small segment of a larger table in which "proportions considered satisfactory in achievement," i.e., in the criterion, range from .05

TABLE 23 * Proportion of students considered satisfactory in terms of grades = .70

| | Selection Ratio: Proportion Selected on Basis of Tests | | | | | | | | | |
r	.05	.10	.20	.30	.40	.50	.60	.70	.80	.90	.95
.00	.70	.70	.70	.70	.70	.70	.70	.70	.70	.70	.70
.05	.73	.73	.72	.72	.72	.71	.71	.71	.71	.70	.70
.10	.77	.76	.75	.74	.73	.73	.72	.72	.71	.71	.70
.15	.80	.79	.77	.76	.75	.74	.73	.73	.72	.71	.71
.20	.83	.81	.79	.78	.77	.76	.75	.74	.73	.71	.71
.25	.86	.84	.81	.80	.78	.77	.76	.75	.73	.72	.71
.30	.88	.86	.84	.82	.80	.78	.77	.75	.74	.72	.71
.35	.91	.89	.86	.83	.82	.80	.78	.76	.75	.73	.71
.40	.93	.91	.88	.85	.83	.81	.79	.77	.75	.73	.72
.45	.94	.93	.90	.87	.85	.83	.81	.78	.76	.73	.72
.50	.96	.94	.91	.89	.87	.84	.82	.80	.77	.74	.72
.55	.97	.96	.93	.91	.88	.86	.83	.81	.78	.74	.72
.60	.98	.97	.95	.92	.90	.87	.85	.82	.79	.75	.73
.65	.99	.98	.96	.94	.92	.89	.86	.83	.80	.75	.73
.70	1.00	.99	.97	.96	.93	.91	.88	.84	.80	.76	.73
.75	1.00	1.00	.98	.97	.95	.92	.89	.86	.81	.76	.73
.80	1.00	1.00	.99	.98	.97	.94	.91	.87	.82	.77	.73
.85	1.00	1.00	1.00	.99	.98	.96	.93	.89	.84	.77	.74
.90	1.00	1.00	1.00	1.00	.99	.98	.95	.91	.85	.78	.74
.95	1.00	1.00	1.00	1.00	1.00	.99	.98	.94	.86	.78	.74
1.00	1.00	1.00	1.00	1.00	1.00	1.00	1.00	1.00	.88	.78	.74

to .95. The correlation between test scores and criterion may range from .00 to 1.00. These tables are not strictly accurate unless the distributions are normal for both test battery and criterion. They may be used with considerable confidence, however, when the distributions are not badly skewed provided that N is large.

Forecasting tables like Table 23 are especially useful when the problem is concerned with personnel in industry and in business. First, the proportion of a given group of workers considered "satisfactory" must be

* Taylor, H. C., and Russell, J. T., "The Relationships of Validity Coefficients to the Practical Effectiveness of Tests in Selection: Discussion and Tables," *Jour. of Applied Psychology*, 1939, 23, 565–578.

determined. From this information and the correlation between an aptitude battery and the performance criterion, we can—from their test scores—predict how many of a group of new applicants will meet the criterion of "satisfactoriness." Let us assume, for example, that 70% of a group of factory workers are rated satisfactory, acceptability having been determined from such criteria as ratings by foremen, amount of work done in a given time, excellence of work, experience and personality. Assume further, that the aptitude test battery has a correlation of .45 with worker acceptability. Then, if the best 20 out of 100 applicants are chosen (best according to the aptitude battery), we find from Table 23 that 18 or 90% ought to be satisfactory workers. If we had used no tests and had simply picked the first 20 applicants to appear—or *any* 20—14 of these or 70% should have been acceptable. Use of aptitude tests in this situation improves our forecast by 30%; and the higher the correlation and the more stringent the selection (number to be chosen) the greater the improvement in prediction made by using the test battery.

III. THE SOLUTION OF A SECOND CORRELATION PROBLEM

The solution of a second correlation problem will be found in Figure 43. The purpose of another "model" is to strengthen the student's grasp of correlational techniques by having him work straight through the process of calculating r and the regression equations upon a new set of data. A student often fails to relate the various aspects of a correlational problem when these are presented in piecemeal fashion.

1. Calculation of r

Our first problem in Figure 43 is to find the correlation between the I.Q.'s achieved by 190 children of the same—or approximately the same—chronological age who have taken an intelligence examination upon two occasions separated by a six-month interval. The correlation table has been constructed from a scattergram, as described on page 128. The test given first is the X variable, and the test given second is the Y variable. The calculation of the two means, and of c_x, c_y, σ_x, and σ_y covers familiar ground, is given in detail on the chart, and need not be repeated here.

The product deviations in the $\Sigma x'y'$ column have been taken from column 100–104 (column containing the AM_X) and from row 105–109 (row containing the AM_Y). The entries in the $\Sigma x'y'$ column have been calculated by the shorter method described on page 137; that is, each cell entry in a given row has been multiplied *first* by its x deviation (x') and the

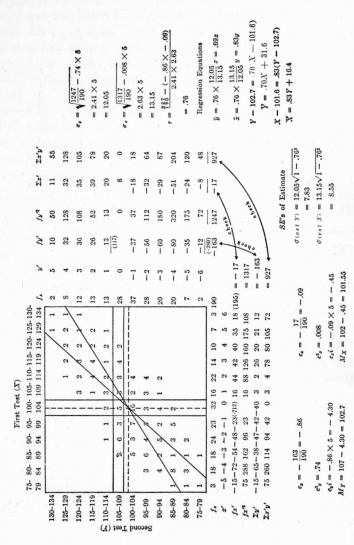

FIG. 43 Calculation of the correlation between the I.Q.'s achieved by 190 children of the same C.A. upon two forms of an individual intelligence examination

sum of these deviations entered in the column $\Sigma x'$. The $\Sigma x'$ entries were then "weighted" once for all by the y' of the whole row. To illustrate, in the first row reading from left to right $(1 \times 5) + (1 \times 6)$ or 11 is the $\Sigma x'$ entry. The x''s are 5 and 6, respectively, and may be read from the x' row at the bottom of the correlation table. Since the common y' is 5, the final $\Sigma x'y'$ entry is 55. Again in the seventh row reading down from the top of the diagram $(5 \times -3) + (3 \times -2) + (7 \times -1) + (16 \times 0) + (2 \times 1) + (4 \times 2)$ or -18 makes up the $\Sigma x'$ entry. The y' of this row is -1, and the final $\Sigma x'y'$ entry is 18. To take still a third example, in the eleventh row from the top of the diagram, $(1 \times -5) + (3 \times -4) + (1 \times -3) + (2 \times -2)$ or -24 is the $\Sigma x'$ entry. The common y' is -5 and the $\Sigma x'y'$ entry is 120.

Three checks of the calculations (see p. 138), upon which r, σ_x and σ_y are based, are given in Figure 43. Note that $fx' = \Sigma x'$; and that, when the $\Sigma x'y'$'s are recalculated, at the bottom of the chart, $fy' = \Sigma y'$, and the two determinations of $\Sigma x'y'$ are equal. When the $\Sigma x'y'$'s have been checked, the calculation of r by formula (26) is a matter of substitution. Note carefully that c_x, c_y, σ_x, σ_y are all left in *units of class interval* in the formula for r (p. 138).

2. Calculation of the regression equations and the SE's of estimate

The regression equations in deviation form are given on the chart and the two lines which these equations represent have been plotted on the diagram. Note that these equations may be plotted as they stand, since the class interval is the same for X and Y (p. 157). In the routine solution of a correlational problem it is not strictly necessary to plot the regression lines on the chart. These lines are often of value, however, in indicating whether the means of the X and Y arrays can be represented by straight lines, that is, whether regression is linear. If the relationship between X and Y is not linear, other methods of calculating the correlation must be employed (p. 396).

The standard errors of estimate, shown in Figure 43, are 7.83 and 8.55, depending upon whether the prediction is of Y from X or X from Y. All I.Q.'s predicted on the Y test from X may be considered to have the same error of estimate,[*] and similarly for all predictions of X from Y.

Errors of estimate are most often used to give the reliability of specific predicted measures. But they also have a more general interpretation.

[*] See, however, Terman, L. M., and Merrill, M. A., *Measuring Intelligence* (Boston: Houghton Mifflin Co., 1937), pp. 44–47, where the SE's of estimate have been computed for various I.Q. levels.

Thus a $\sigma_{(est\ Y)}$ of 7.83 points means that 68% of the I.Q.'s predicted on Test Y from Test X may be expected to differ from their actual values by not more than ± 7.83 points, while the remaining 32% may be expected to differ from their actual values by more than ± 7.83 points.

IV. FACTORS AFFECTING THE INTERPRETATION OF r

I. Range of talent

The size of a correlation coefficient will vary with the heterogeneity, i.e., the degree of scatter, in the group; and the more restricted the spread of test scores, the lower the correlation. The correlation between an arithmetic test and a reading test, for example, will be lower in a group of 50 sixth-grade children than in a group of 250 children drawn from Grades 5, 6 and 7. Curtailment in the range of intelligence test scores in college freshmen is one reason for the lower correlation between intelligence tests and school grades in college as compared with high school. The less able students fail to reach college, selection for intelligence becomes more stringent, the range of scores narrows, and r decreases. Suppose that we know the distribution of intelligence test scores in an unrestricted group composed of both college and noncollege men. Then from the SD of the curtailed distribution of intelligence test scores in the college group, and the r between intelligence and grades in this group, we can estimate the correlation between intelligence and grades in the unrestricted group of greater range. Two assumptions must be made: (1) regression must be linear and (2) the arrays (columns or rows) in the uncurtailed distribution must be homoscedastic (p. 163). Neither of these conditions is unreasonable, provided the sample is large.

A formula for predicting r in the group uncurtailed in Y is

$$r'_{xy} = \frac{r_{xy}(\sigma'_y/\sigma_y)}{\sqrt{1 - r^2_{xy} + r^2_{xy}(\sigma'_y/\sigma_y)^2}} \tag{39}$$

(formula for estimating the correlation in an uncurtailed range from the r in the curtailed range)

in which

$\sigma_y = $ SD of the group curtailed in Y
$\sigma'_y = $ SD of the group uncurtailed in Y
$r_{xy} = $ correlation between X and Y in the group curtailed in Y
$r'_{xy} = $ correlation between X and Y in the group uncurtailed in Y

To illustrate the application of formula (39), suppose that the correlation between an aptitude test for selling and a criterion of sales performance in a small group of highly experienced men is .40. Suppose further that the *SD* of the criterion (sales performance) in this selected (curtailed) group is 6.0; and that the *SD* of the criterion in a larger group of more varied experience (uncurtailed) is 9.0. What correlation would we expect to find between criterion and aptitude tests in the group in which experience is less restricted, i.e., has greater range? Substituting $\sigma_y = 6.0$, $\sigma'_y = 9.0$, and $r_{xy} = .40$ in formula (39), we have

$$r'_{xy} = \frac{.40(3/2)}{\sqrt{1 - .16 + .16(9/4)}}$$

$$= .55$$

The correlation of .55 is the relationship to be anticipated when selection with respect to the sales criterion has been broadened to include those of less experience.

Slight changes in formula (39) make it possible for us to estimate *r* in a group restricted in *Y*, say, when we know the correlation in a group unrestricted with respect to *Y*. The formula is

$$r_{xy} = \frac{r'_{xy}(\sigma_y/\sigma'_y)}{\sqrt{1 - r'^2_{xy} + r'^2_{xy}(\sigma_y/\sigma'_y)^2}} \tag{40}$$

(formula for estimating the correlation in a curtailed range from the r *in an uncurtailed range)*

in which the subscripts have the same meaning as in (39).

If the correlation between I.Q. and grades in a large group of school children is .60 and the *SD* of the I.Q. distribution is 15, what is the *r* to be expected in a group in which the *SD* of the I.Q. distribution is only 10 points? Substituting now for $\sigma_y = 10$, $\sigma'_y = 15$ and $r' = .60$ in (40), we get an estimated *r* of .45 in the more narrow or curtailed group.

The considerable effect which differences in range have upon the correlation coefficient renders it imperative that *SD*'s always be reported whenever *r*'s are given. The correlation coefficient is never an absolute index of relationship, but is always relative to the variability of the measures being correlated (p. 176).

2. Averaging *r*'s

It has been fairly common practice to average *r*'s obtained from comparable samples in the hope of getting a better (i.e., more stable) measure of the relationship between the two variables. The averaging of *r*'s is often dubious, however, and may be an incorrect procedure. Correlation coefficients do not vary along a linear scale, so that an increase from .40 to .50 does not imply the same change in relationship as does an increase from .80 to .90. Again, if $+r$'s and $-r$'s are combined as they stand, they tend to cancel each other out. When r's do not differ greatly in size, their arithmetic mean will yield a useful result; but this is not true when r's differ widely in size and differ in sign. Thus averaging r's of .60 and .70 to obtain .65 is permissible, whereas averaging r's of .10 and .90 to obtain .50 is not.

Perhaps the safest plan is not to average r's at all. But when for various reasons averaging is demanded by the problem, the best method is to transform the r's into Fisher's z function and take the arithmetic mean of the z's. This mean z can then be converted into an equivalent r. Some of the advantages of the z function are given on page 199. Suffice it to say here that z is more stable than r (its distribution is nearly normal) and that z is not limited in range—as is r—between ± 1.00. An example will show the procedure to be followed in transforming r's to z's, and back to a mean r.

> *Example* (1) In 5 parallel experiments, the following r's were obtained between the same two variables: .50, .90, .40, .30, and .70. The N's in the 5 experiments were in order: 33, 27, 63, 74 and 26. What is the mean correlation, i.e., the weighted average, of these 5 r's?

r	z	N	$(N-3)$	$z(N-3)$
.50	.55	33	30	16.50
.90	1.47	27	24	35.28
.40	.42	63	60	25.20
.30	.31	74	71	22.01
.70	.87	26	23	20.01
		223	208	119.00

The mean $z = 119.00/208$ or .57. The equivalent r (Table C) is .51.

By means of Table C we can convert these 5 r's into equivalent z's as follows: .55, 1.47, .42, .31 and .87. Each z is then weighted by $(N-3)$, as 3 degrees of freedom are lost in computing each z (see p. 199). The sum of the weighted z's (119.00) is divided by the sum of the $(N-3)$ or 208 to give the mean z of .57. This value is now converted back into an r of .51 by means of Table C. Comparison of the "derived" r of .51 with the average of the unweighted r's (i.e., .56), gives an idea of the correction effected in using the z-transformation. When N's differ widely, the correction may be considerable; but when N's are equal or nearly equal, the correction is negligible.

3. The "regression effect" in prediction

Predicted scores tend to "move in" toward the mean of the distribution into which prediction is made (p. 153). This so-called regression effect has often been noted by investigators and is always present when correlation is less than ±1.00.[*] The regression phenomenon can be clearly seen in the following illustrations: From the regression equation $\overline{Y} = .70X + 31.6$ (Fig. 43) it is clear that a child who earns an I.Q. of 130 on the first test (X) will most probably earn an I.Q. of 123 on the second test (Y); while a child who earns an I.Q. of 120 in X will most probably score 116 in Y. In both of these illustrations the predicted Y-test I.Q. is lower than the first or X-test I.Q. Put differently, the second I.Q. has *regressed* or moved down toward the mean of test Y, i.e., toward 102.7. The opposite effect occurs when the I.Q. on the X test is *below* its mean: the tendency now is for the predicted score in Y to move *up* toward its mean. Thus from the equation $\overline{Y} = .70X + 31.6$, we find that if a child earns an I.Q. of 70 on the X test his most likely score on the second test (Y) is 81; while an I.Q. of 80 on the first test forecasts an I.Q. of 88 on the second. Both of these predicted I.Q.'s have moved nearer to 102.7 (i.e., M_y).

The tendency for all scores predicted from a regression equation to converge toward the mean can be seen as a general phenomenon if the regression equation is written in σ-score form. Given

$$\overline{y} = r \frac{\sigma_y}{\sigma_x} \times x \qquad \text{(33) (p. 153)}$$

if we divide both side of this equation by σ_y and write σ_x under x, we have

$$\frac{\overline{y}}{\sigma_y} = r \frac{x}{\sigma_x} \text{ or } z_y = rz_x \qquad (41)$$

(regression equation when scores in X and Y are expressed as z or σ scores)

In the problem in Figure 43, $z_y = .76z_x$. If z_x is ±1.00σ, or ±2.00σ, or ±3.00σ from M_x, z_y will be ±.76σ, ±1.52σ, or ±2.28σ from M_y. That is to say, *any* score above or below the mean of X forecasts a Y score somewhat *closer* to the mean of Y.

In studying the relation of height in parent and offspring, Galton (p. 153) interpreted the phenomenon of regression to the mean to be a

[*] Thorndike, R. L., "Regression Fallacies in the Matched Groups Experiment," *Psychometrika*, 1942, 7, 85–102.

provision of nature designed to protect the race from extremes. This same effect occurs, however, in *any* correlation table in which *r* is less than ±1.00, and need not be explained in biological terms. The I.Q.'s of a group of very bright children, for instance, will tend upon retest to move *downward* toward 100, the mean of the group; while the I.Q.'s of a group of dull children will tend upon retest to move *upward* toward 100.

V. THE INTERPRETATION OF THE COEFFICIENT OF CORRELATION

When should a coefficient of correlation be called "high," when "medium," and when "low"? Does an *r* of .40 between two tests indicate "marked" or "low" relationship? How high should an *r* be in order to permit accurate prediction from one variable to another? Can an *r* of .50, say, be interpreted with respect to "overlap" of determining factors in the two variables correlated? Questions like these, all of which are concerned with the *significance* or *meaning* of the relationship expressed by a correlation coefficient constantly arise in problems involving mental measurement, and their implications must be understoood before we can effectively employ the correlational method.

The value of *r* as a measure of correspondence may be profitably considered from two points of view. In the first place, *r*'s are computed in order to determine whether there is *any* correlation (over and above chance) between two variables; and in the second place, *r*'s are computed in order to determine the *degree* or closeness of relationship when some association is known, or is assumed, to exist. The question "Is there *any* correlation between brain weight and intelligence?" voices the first objective. And the question *"How significant* is the correlation between high-school grades and first-year performance in college?" expresses the second. The problem of when an obtained *r* denotes significant relationship will be considered later, on page 198. This section is concerned mainly with the second problem, namely, the evaluation—with respect to degree of relationship—of an obtained coefficient. The questions at the beginning of the paragraph above all bear upon this topic.

1. The interpretation of *r* in terms of verbal description

It is customary in mental measurement to describe the correlation between two tests in a general way as high, marked or substantial, low or negligible. While the descriptive label applied will vary somewhat in meaning with the author using it, there is fairly good agreement among workers with psychological and educational tests that an

r from   .00 to ± .20 denotes indifferent or negligible relationship;
r from ±.20 to ± .40 denotes low correlation; present but slight;
r from ±.40 to ± .70 denotes substantial or marked relationship;
r from ±.70 to ±1.00 denotes high to very high relationship.

This classification is broad and somewhat tentative, and can only be accepted as a general guide with certain reservations. Thus a coefficient of correlation must always be judged with regard to

(1) the nature of variables with which we are dealing;
(2) the significance of the coefficient;
(3) the variability of the group (p. 171);
(4) the reliability coefficients of the tests used (p. 358);
(5) the purpose for which the *r* was computed.

To consider, first, the matter of the variables being correlated, an *r* of .30 between height and intelligence, or between head measurements and mechanical ability would be regarded as important although rather low, since correlations between physical and mental functions are usually much lower—often zero. On the other hand, the correlation must be .70 or more between measures of general intelligence and school grades or between achievement in English and in history to be considered high, since *r*'s in this field usually run from .40 to .60. Resemblances of parents and offspring with respect to physical and mental traits are expressed by *r*'s of .35 to .55; and, accordingly, an *r* of .60 would be high. By contrast, the reliability of a standard intelligence test is ordinarily much higher than .60, and the self-correlation of such a test must be .85 to .95 to be regarded as satisfactory. In the field of vocational testing, the *r*'s between test batteries and measures of aptitude represented by various criteria rarely rise above .50. Correlations above this figure would be considered exceptionally promising, and smaller *r*'s are often serviceable (p. 359).

Correlation coefficients must always be evaluated with due regard to the reliabilities of the tests concerned (p. 352). Owing in part to chance errors, an obtained *r* is always less than its "corrected" value (p. 358) and hence, in a sense, is a minimum index of the relationship present. The effect upon *r* of range of talent in the group has been treated elsewhere (p. 171) and a formula for estimating such effects provided. The purpose for which the correlation has been computed is always important. The *r* to be used for predicting the standing of individuals, for instance, must be a great deal higher than the *r* to be used in forecasting the likely achievement of groups (p. 165).

In summary, a correlation coefficient is always to be judged with reference to the conditions under which it was obtained, and the objectives of the experiment. There is no such thing as *the* correlation between mechanical aptitude and job performance, for example, but only *a* correlation between certain tests of mechanical aptitude and certain criteria of performance on the job.

2. The interpretation of r in terms of $\sigma_{(est)}$ and the coefficient of alienation

One of the most useful ways of evaluating the effectiveness of r is through the $SE_{(est)}$. We have found on page 160 that $SE_{(est)}$—which equals $\sqrt{1-r^2}$—enables us to tell how well the regression equation is able to predict scores in Y, say, when we know the scores in X. As r changes from ± 1.00 to $.00$, the $SE_{(est)}$ increases markedly, so that predictions from the regression equation will range all of the way from certainty to what is virtually a "guess." * The effectiveness of an r, therefore, with respect to predictive value, depends on the extent to which prediction is improved over sheer guess.

The following will serve as an illustration. Suppose that the r between two tests X and Y is .60 and that σ_y is 5.00. Then $\sigma_{(est\ Y)} = 5\sqrt{1 - .60^2}$ or 4.00. This $SE_{(est)}$ is 20% less than 5.00, which is the $SE_{(est\ Y)}$ when r is .00, i.e., has minimum predictive value. The reduction in $\sigma_{(est\ Y)}$ as r varies from .00 to 1.00 is given by the expression $\sqrt{1-r^2}$, and hence it is possible to gauge from $\sqrt{1-r^2}$ alone the predictive strength of an r. The $\sqrt{1-r^2}$ is called the *coefficient of alienation* and is denoted by the letter k.

$$k = \sqrt{1-r^2} \qquad (42)$$

(coefficient of alienation for determining the predictive value of r)

We may think of k as measuring the *absence* of relationship between two variables X and Y in the same sense that r measures the presence of relation. When $k = 1.00$, $r = .00$, and when $k = .00$, $r = 1.00$. The *larger* the coefficient of alienation, the *smaller* the extent of relationship and the less precise the forecast from X to Y. The k's for certain values of r are given in Table 24.

The student should note that r must be .87 (.866 exactly) before k lies halfway between ± 1.00 and .00, i.e., between 100% accuracy and the minimum of accuracy. At $k = .87$, the $SE_{(est)}$ is reduced one-half of its maximum value at $k = 1.00$. For r's of .80 or less, the k's are so large that

---

* The term "guess" as here used does not mean an estimate which is based upon no information whatever—a shot in the dark, so to speak. When $r = .00$, the most probable Y score, forecast for every person in the Y distribution, is M_y; and the $SE_{(est)}$ equals SD_y exactly. Our Y's are guesses in the sense that they may lie anywhere in the Y distribution—but not anywhere at all!

TABLE 24   Coefficients of alienation (k) for values of r from .00 to 1.00

r	$k = \sqrt{1 - r^2}$	r	$k = \sqrt{1 - r^2}$
.0000	1.0000	.8000	.6000
.1000	.9950	(.8660)	(.5000)
.2000	.9798	.9000	.4359
.3000	.9539	.9500	.3122
.4000	.9165	.9800	.1990
.5000	.8660	.9900	.1411
.6000	.8000	1.0000	.0000
.7000	.7141		
(.7071)	(.7071)		

prediction of individual scores *via* the regression equation may take a wide range of values. When $r = .99$, for example, the standard error of estimate is still 1/7 of its maximum value, i.e., the value it would take when $k = 1.00$. It seems clear that in order to forecast an individual's score with high accuracy the r must be at least .90.

3. The interpretation of r in terms of E, the coefficient of forecasting efficiency

The coefficient E given below is often used to provide a quick estimate of the predictive efficiency of an obtained r. E is called the *coefficient of forecasting efficiency* or coefficient of dependability. It is derived from k as follows:

$$E = 1 - \sqrt{1 - r^2}$$

or   (43)

$$E = 1 - k$$

(coefficient of forecasting efficiency or of dependability)

If the correlation between an aptitude test battery and a criterion is .50, from formula (43), $E = 1 - .87$ or .13: and the test's forecasting efficiency is 13%. When $r = .90$, $E = .56$ and the test is 56% efficient; when r is .98, E is .80 and the test is 80% efficient, and so on. Clearly the correlation must be .87 and above in order for the test's forecasting efficiency to be greater than 50%.

E provides essentially the same information as does k or $\sigma_{(est)}$.

4. Interpretation of r in terms of the coefficient of determination

The interpretation of r in terms of "overlapping" factors in the tests being correlated may be generalized through an analysis of the *variance*

(σ^2) of the dependent variable—usually the Y test. In studying the variability among individuals upon a given test, the variance of the test scores is often a more useful measure of "spread" than is the standard deviation. The object in analyzing the variance of Test Y is to determine from the correlation between Y and X what part of Test Y's variance is associated with, or dependent upon, the variance of Test X, and what part is determined by the variance of factors not in Test X.

When we have computed the correlation between Tests X and Y, σ^2_y provides a measure of the *total* variance of the Y scores and $\sigma^2_{(est\ Y)}$ which equals $\sigma^2_y (1 - r^2)$ gives a measure of the variance *left* in Test Y when that part of the variance associated with Test X has been ruled out (see p. 152). Instead of $\sigma_{(est\ Y)}$ the designation $\sigma_{y.x}$ is often used to show that the variability in X—in so far as it affects Y—has been held constant. As we have seen (p. 163), $\sigma_{(est\ Y)}$ or $\sigma_{y.x}$ is the *SD* of the columns in a correlation table. In Figure 40, for example, X has a constant value for each column and accordingly $\sigma_{y.x}$ is a measure of the variability in Y for a fixed value of X.

The relationship between σ_y and $\sigma_{y.x}$ can be seen more clearly in the following illustration. If we have the correlation between height and weight in a group of fifth-grade boys, σ^2_{ht} will be reduced to $\sigma^2_{ht.wt}$ when the variance in weight is zero—when *all* of the children in the group have the same weight. Clearly, if $\sigma^2_{y.x}$ is subtracted from σ^2_y there remains that part of the variance of Test Y which is associated with variation in X. If this last is divided by σ^2_y we have, finally, that fraction of the variance of Y which is attributable to or associated with X. Carrying out the designated operations, we find that

$$\frac{\sigma^2_y - \sigma^2_{y.x}}{\sigma^2_y} = \frac{\sigma^2_y - \sigma^2_y + \sigma^2_y r^2_{xy}}{\sigma^2_y} = r^2_{xy}$$

from which it is apparent that r^2_{xy} gives the *proportion* of the variance of Y which is accounted for by X. When used in this way, r^2 is sometimes called the *coefficient of determination*. When the r between Y and X is .71, r^2 is .50. Hence, an r of .71 means that 50% of the variance of Y is associated with variability in X. Also, since $r^2 + k^2 = 1.00$, the proportion of the variance of Y which is *not* accounted for by X is given by k^2. When $r^2 = .50$, $k^2 = .50$ also.

When this analysis of the dependence of Y upon X is taken a step further, certain interesting relationships appear. Suppose we write:

$$\sigma^2_y - \sigma^2_{y.x} = \sigma^2_{y(x)}$$

the $\sigma^2_{y(x)}$ becomes that part of the variance of Y which *is* dependent upon

X, just as $\sigma^2_{y.x}$ is that part of the variance of Y which is *not* dependent upon X. If we substitute $\sigma^2_y(1 - r^2)$ for $\sigma^2_{y.x}$, we find that

$$\sigma^2_y - \sigma^2_y + \sigma^2_y r^2_{xy} = \sigma^2_{y(x)}$$

and

$$r_{xy} = \sigma_{y(x)}/\sigma_y$$

This means that r_{xy} is the *ratio* found by dividing that part of the SD of Y which is dependent upon X by the SD of the whole Y test. Thus, it becomes clear that r is a measure of the extent to which variability in X accounts for variability in Y.

Inspection of the coefficients of determination for small r's emphasizes the very slight degree of association which these r's disclose. An r of .10, for instance, or .20 or even .30 between two tests X and Y indicates only 1%, 4% and 9%, respectively, of the variance of Y to be associated with X. At the other extreme, when $r = .95$, about 90% of the variance of Y is accounted for by variability in X, only about 10% being independent of X. For further treatment of this type of analysis see, later, analysis of variance (p. 277) and partial and multiple correlations (p. 419).

5. Correlation and causation

A correlation coefficient gives us, to be sure, a quantitative determination of the degree of relationship between two variables X and Y. But r alone gives us *no* information as to the *character* of the association, and we cannot assume a causal sequence unless we have evidence beyond the correlation coefficient itself. Causation implies an invariable sequence—A always leads to B—whereas correlation is simply a measure of mutual association between two variables. Two cases arise in which the direction of the cause-effect relation may be inferred. In the correlation between X and Y, (1) X may be in part at least a cause of Y; and (2) X and Y may have the same basic cause or causes. Athletic prowess is known to depend upon physical strength, dexterity and muscular coördination. The r between sensorimotor tests and athletic performance will be positive and high, and the direction of the cause-effect relation is clear. Again, the correlation between tests in English and history, or intelligence and school grades probably arises from the same basic traits; whereas the r between executive ability and emotional stability is determined (besides selection) by overlapping personality dimensions. Causal relations are sometimes revealed or suggested by the technique of partial correlation (p. 403). Through the application of this method, the influence of a given variable, for example, age, can be controlled and its effects upon variability in other traits held constant. The r between intelligence and educational achievement over a wide age range is often drastically reduced when the effect of the age variable is removed.

PROBLEMS

1. Write out the regression equations in score form for the correlation table in example 3, page 148.
   (a) Compute $\sigma_{(est\ Y)}$ and $\sigma_{(est\ X)}$.
   (b) What is the most probable height of a boy who weighs 30 pounds? 45 pounds? What is the most probable weight of a boy who is 36 inches tall? 40 inches tall?
2. In example 4, page 148, find the most probable grade made by a child whose I.Q. is 120. What is the $\sigma_{(est)}$ of this grade?
3. What is the most probable algebra grade of a child whose I.Q. is 100 (data from example 6, p. 149)? What is the $\sigma_{(est)}$ of this grade?
4. Given the following data for two tests:

History (X)	English (Y)
$M_X = 75.00$	$M_Y = 70.00$
$\sigma_x = 6.00$	$\sigma_y = 8.00$

$$r_{xy} = .72$$

   (a) Work out the regression equations in score form.
   (b) Predict the probable grade in English of a student whose history mark is 65. Find the $\sigma_{(est)}$ of this prediction.
   (c) If r_{xy} had been .84 (σ's and means remaining the same) how much would $\sigma_{(est\ Y)}$ be reduced?
5. The correlation of a test battery with worker efficiency in a large factory is .40, and 70% of the workers are regarded as "satisfactory."
   (a) From 75 applicants you select the best 25 in terms of test score. How many of these should be satisfactory workers?
   (b) How many of the best ten should be satisfactory?
   (c) How many in the two groups should be satisfactory if selected at random, i.e., without using the test battery?
6. Plot the regression lines in on the correlation diagram given in example 6, page 149. Calculate the means of the Y arrays (successive Y columns), plot as points on the diagram, and join these points with straight lines. Plot, also, the means of the X arrays and join them with straight lines. Compare these two "lines-through-means" with the two fitted regression lines (see Fig. 40, p. 152).
7. In a group of 115 freshmen, the r between reaction time to light and substitution learning is .30. The σ of the reaction times is 20 ms. (a) What would you estimate the correlation between these two tests to be in a group in which the SD of the reaction times is 25 ms.? (b) In which the SD of reaction times is 10 ms.?

8. Show the regression effect in example 4, p. 148, by calculating the regression equation in standard-score form. For X's of $\pm 1.00\sigma$ and $\pm 2.00\sigma$ from the mean in arithmetic, find the corresponding reading scores in σ-score form.

9. Basing your answer upon your experience and general knowledge of psychology, decide whether the correlation between the following pairs of variables is most probably (1) positive or negative; (2) high, medium, or low.

(a) Intelligence of husbands and wives.
(b) Brain weight and intelligence.
(c) High-school grades in history and physics.
(d) Age and radicalism.
(e) Extroversion and college grades.

10. How much more will an r of .80 reduce a given $\sigma_{(est)}$ than an r of .40? An r of .90 than an r of .40?

11. (a) Determine k and E for the following r's: .35; $-.50$; .70; .95. Interpret your results.

(b) What is the "forecasting efficiency" of an r of .45? an r of .99?

12. The correlation of a criterion with a test battery is .75. What percent of the variance of the criterion is associated with variability in the battery? What percent is independent of the battery?

13. In 4 experiments, the correlations between X and Y were as follows: .60, .20, .70 and .40. The N's were 26, 31, 42 and 35. What is the mean r: the weighted average of these 4 r's?

14. What is the direction of the cause-effect relationship in the following cases:

(a) intelligence tests and school grades
(b) personality measures and neurotic behavior
(c) eye tests and scores in marksmanship
(d) aptitude tests and vocational success
(e) alcoholism and delinquency.

ANSWERS

1. $\bar{Y} = .40X + 24.12$; $\bar{X} = 1.26Y - 11.52$
   (a) $\sigma_{(est\ Y)} = 1.78$; $\sigma_{(est\ X)} = 3.16$
   (b) 36.12 inches; 42.12 inches; 33.84 pounds; 38.88 pounds
2. 85.2; $\sigma_{(est\ Y)} = 7.0$
3. $\bar{X} = .37Y + 8.16$. When Y (I.Q.) is 100, $\bar{X}$ (algebra) is 45.2. $\sigma_{(est\ X)} = 6.8$
4. (a) $\bar{Y} = .96X - 2$; $\bar{X} = .54Y + 37.2$
   (b) 60.4; $\sigma_{(est\ Y)} = 5.5$.
   (c) 22%
5. (a) 21
   (b) 9
   (c) 17.5 and 7 (i.e., 70%)

7. (a) $r = .37$ (b) $r = .16$
8. $\pm.54$ and ±1.08

10. Five times as much; seven times as much.
11. (a)

r	k	E
.35	.94	.06
−.50	.87	.13
.70	.71	.29
.95	.31	.69

    (b) 11%; 86%
12. 56%; 44%
13. Mean $r = .51$

CHAPTER 8

THE SIGNIFICANCE OF THE MEAN
AND OF OTHER STATISTICS

◇◇◇

I. THE MEANING OF STATISTICAL INFERENCE

The primary objective of *statistical inference* is to enable us to general-ize from a sample to some larger *population* of which the sample is a part. Suppose, for example, that for a group of 166 eighth-grade boys in the schools of City A, the mean and the σ for a test of Numerical Reason-ing are known. Can we from the data on this relatively small group say anything regarding the mean peformance of *all* of the eighth-grade boys in City A? The answer to this and to other questions like it is "Yes"—under certain conditions to be specified later. And the method of obtain-ing an answer involves inductive reasoning and probability theory—viz., statistical inference.

It is rarely if ever possible to measure *all* of the members of a given population, and hence we must usually be content with samples drawn from this population. Furthermore, owing to differences in the composi-tion of our samples, means and σ's computed from such groups will tend to be sometimes larger and sometimes smaller than their population values. Ordinarily, we have only the *single* sample; and our problem becomes one of determining how well we can *infer* or estimate the M_{pop}, for example, from the one sample mean. Means and other measures com-puted from samples are called *statistics*, and are subject to what are called "fluctuations of sampling." Measures descriptive of a population, on the other hand, are called *parameters* and are to be thought of as fixed refer-ence values.

We do not know, of course, the parameters of a given population. But we can—under specified conditions—forecast the parameters from our sample statistics with known degrees of accuracy. The degree to which a sample mean represents its parameter is an index of the *significance* or trust-

184

worthiness of the computed sample mean. When we have calculated a statistic, therefore, we may ask ourselves this question: "How good an estimate is this statistic of the parameter based upon the entire population from which my sample was drawn?" The purpose of this chapter is to provide methods which will enable us to answer this question for the mean, the median, and for other statistics.

II. THE SIGNIFICANCE OF THE MEAN AND OF THE MEDIAN

1. The standard error of the mean (σ_M) in large samples

The need for a standard error of a sample mean can best be understood when we have examined the factors upon which the stability of this statistic depends. Suppose that we wish to measure the ability of college freshmen in Ohio colleges by means of the American Council Psychological Examination. To measure the performance of Ohio college freshmen *in general* would require in strict logic that we test *all* of the first-year students in the state. This would be a stupendous if not an impossible task, and we must of necessity be satisfied with a sample. This sample—in order for it adequately to represent all freshmen—should be as large and as *randomly* drawn as possible. The definition of a random sample is given later on page 203. Suffice it to say here that in drawing a random sample we cannot take freshmen from only a single institution or from only one section of the state; and we must guard against selecting only those with high, or only those with low, scholastic records. The more nearly successful we are in obtaining an "unselected" group, the more nearly representative this group will be of all freshmen in Ohio. It seems clear, then, that the degree to which a sample mean approximates its parameter depends for one thing upon how impartially we have drawn our sample.

Given a random sample—that is to say, a cross section of the population—the representativeness of a sample mean can be shown to depend mathematically upon two characteristics of the distribution: (1) N, the number of cases, and (2) σ, the variability or spread of scores around the mean. The formula for the standard error of the mean is

$$SE_M \quad \text{or} \quad \sigma_M = \frac{\sigma}{\sqrt{N}} \qquad (44)$$

(standard error of an arithmetic mean)

where

σ = the standard deviation of the population

and

N = the number of cases in the sample.

In this formula for the SE_M, the σ in the numerator is actually the population and *not* the sample SD. As we rarely have the SD of a population, we must of necessity use a substitute for it in the formula, and the best estimate we have is the SD of the sample in hand. Modern writers on mathematical statistics make a distinction between the SD of the population and the SD of a sample, designating the population SD by σ and the sample SD by s. It can be shown mathematically that the SD of a random sample *underestimates* (is smaller than) the corresponding population σ, although the negative bias is not large unless the sample is quite small. To correct this tendency toward underestimation, and thus to get a better approximation to the population σ, we should compute the SD of a sample by the formula $s = \sqrt{\dfrac{\Sigma x^2}{(N-1)}}$ instead of by the usual formula $SD = \sqrt{\dfrac{\Sigma x^2}{N}}$.

In the social sciences we may generally omit this correction, as our samples are usually so large that the subtraction of 1 from N makes no appreciable difference in the computed SD. Whenever N is "large" (it is conventional to call any sample greater than 30 large), it is not worthwhile making the correction. But when N is "small" (less than 30), it is advisable to use $(N-1)$, and it is imperative when N is quite small—say, less than about 10. The student must remember (1) that theoretically $(N-1)$ should always be used when the SD is to be an estimate of the population σ; and that (2) the distinction between "large sample statistics" and "small sample statistics" in terms of a cutting point of $N = 30$ is arbitrary, and is in part a matter of convenience (p. 194).

The SE_M varies directly with the size of the sample SD (or s) and inversely with the size of N. As it is difficult to influence the size of the sample SD, our best chance of decreasing the σ_M lies in increasing the size of N. SE_M measures the degree to which the M is affected by (1) errors of measurement (p. 346) as well as by (2) errors of sampling—i.e., inevitable fluctuations from sample to sample. SE_M is an important and much-used formula.

(1) APPLICATION OF SE_M IN LARGE SAMPLES

A problem will serve to illustrate the computation and interpretation of the SE of the mean in large samples.

Example (1) The mean on a test of abstract reasoning for 225 boys in the tenth grade of City F was 27.26 with a SD of 11.20. How dependable is this mean? Specifically, how good an estimate is it of the mean which could be expected if *all* of the tenth-grade boys in City F were tested?

From formula (44), we find that the SE_M is

$$SE_M = \sigma_M = \frac{11.20}{\sqrt{225}} = .75 \text{ (to two significant figures)}$$

Note that the SD of 11.20 is taken as our estimate of the population σ without correction, and that the computation of σ_M is rounded to two decimals (p. 20). The SE_M can be thought of as the standard deviation of a distribution of sample M's (like our M of 27.26) around the fixed population mean. The normal curve in Figure 44 pictures this *sampling distribu-*

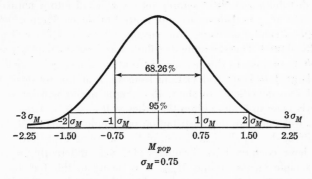

M_{pop}

$\sigma_M = 0.75$

FIG. 44 Sampling distribution of means, showing variability of obtained means around population M in terms of σ_M.

tion: it is centered at the (unknown) population mean, and its SD is .75 (i.e., σ_M). Note that the sample means fall equally often on the $+$ and $-$ sides of the population mean. About 2/3 of the sample means (exactly 68.26%) lie within $\pm 1.00\sigma_M$ of the population M, i.e., within a range of $\pm .75$. Furthermore, 95 in 100 sample means lie within $\pm 2.00\sigma_M$ (more exactly $\pm 1.96\sigma_M$) of the population mean—miss the population mean by $\pm 1.96 \times .75$ or ± 1.47.

Our mean of 27.26 is, of course, only *one* of the sample means represented in the sampling distribution of Figure 44. Hence the expectation is high (the probability is .95) that 27.26 or *any* sample mean for that matter, will not miss the M_{pop} by more than ± 1.47. Conversely, the probability is low ($P = .05$) that 27.26 *does* miss the parameter (the population mean) by more than ± 1.47. Both of these statements express the dependability of the sample mean in terms of the degree to which it estimates accurately the population parameter. Larger deviations from M_{pop} which are less likely of occurrence may be computed by taking into account more of the sampling distribution in Fig. 44.

Discussion

How the standard error measures the stability or trustworthiness of a sample mean may be shown more clearly perhaps in the following way. Suppose that we have calculated the mean on our test of Abstract Reasoning for each of 100 samples of tenth-grade boys; that each sample contains 225 boys; and that the samples are drawn at random from the population of tenth-grade boys in cities like City F. The 100 means computed from the 100 samples will tend to differ more or less from each other owing to fluctuations of sampling. Accordingly, not all samples will represent with equal fidelity the population from which they have all been drawn. It can be shown mathematically that the frequency distribution of these sample means will fall into a normal distribution around the M_{pop} as their measure of central tendency. Even when the samples themselves exhibit skewness, the *means* of these samples will tend to be normally distributed. This sampling distribution reflects the fluctuations in mean from sample to sample. In this normal distribution of means, we shall find relatively few large + or large − deviations from M_{pop}; and many small plus, small minus, and zero deviations. In short, the sample means will hit very near to M_{pop} or fairly close to it more often than they will miss it by large amounts.

The mean of our sampling distribution of sample means is M_{pop}. And our best estimate of the standard deviation of the sampling distribution is the SE_M which we have computed by formula (44). Said differently, σ_M shows the spread of sample means around M_{pop}. It is owing to this fact that the SE_M becomes a measure of the amount by which the sample means diverge from the over-all population mean.

The results of our hypothetical experiment are represented graphically in Figure 44. The 100 sample means fall into a normal distribution around the M_{pop} and σ_M is equal to .75. The *SD* of a normal distribution when measured off in the + and − directions from the mean includes the middle 68.26% of the cases (Table A). About 68 of our 100 sample means, therefore, will fall within $\pm 1.00\sigma_M$ or within $\pm.75$ of the M_{pop}; and about 95 of our 100 sample means will fall within $\pm 1.96\sigma_M$ or within ± 1.47 of the M_{pop}. The probability (P) is .95, therefore, that our sample mean of 27.26 does *not* miss the M_{pop} by more than ± 1.47; and the probability is .05 that 27.26 does miss the M_{pop} by more than ± 1.47. The size of the probable deviation of a sample mean from its M_{pop} is a measure of the efficiency with which we have been able—from the sample mean—to estimate the population mean.

(2) SETTING UP CONFIDENCE INTERVALS FOR THE POPULATION MEAN

Description of the stability of a sample mean in terms of "probable divergence of statistic from parameter" is straightforward and reasonable, as it is evident that confidence can be placed in a sample mean if there is small likelihood of its having missed its population value by a large amount. An obvious difficulty with probability statements of this sort, however, arises from our inability to say how far a sample mean should miss M_{pop} before the expected deviation is to be judged as "large." The size of the range $(M - M_{pop})$—i.e., the sampling error allowable in a mean will always depend upon the purpose of the experiment, the standards of accuracy demanded, the units of measurement employed, and upon other factors. In short, the experimenter can never say categorically that a sample mean is—or is not—a dependable estimate of M_{pop}: he can only give the probability of a given divergence.

A better approach to the problem of estimating the M_{pop} is through the setting up of limits which, for a given degree of confidence, will embrace the population mean. Such limits are said to define *confidence intervals*. The method of establishing confidence intervals is as follows. It is clear from Figure 44 that in a sampling distribution of means, $M_{pop} \pm 3\sigma_M$ provides limits within which nearly *all* (actually 99.73%) of the sample means may be expected to fall. As the M_{pop} itself is unknown, all that we can infer with respect to this parameter is that it could be any one of a range of values—one of which will be our sample mean. Suppose that we take $\pm 3.00\sigma_M$ as our quite inclusive working range. Then if our M falls at the tentative *upper* limit of the sampling distribution, $M_{pop} = M - 3\sigma_M$; whereas, if M falls at the tentative *lower* limit of the sampling distribution, $M_{pop} = M + 3\sigma_M$. These relations are shown in Figure 45. Since $\pm 3.00\sigma_M$ in a normal distribution includes 99.73% of the cases, the limits

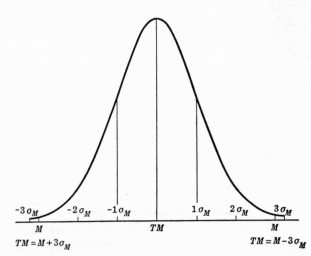

FIG. 45   When M falls at $+3\sigma_M$, $TM = M - 3\sigma_M$; when M falls at $-3\sigma_M$, $TM = M + 3\sigma_M$

specified by $M \pm 3\sigma_M$ may be said to define the 99.73% confidence interval. The degree of faith placed in these limits is represented by a $P = .9973$. Evidently, we may be confident to a degree approaching certainty that M_{pop} lies within this range.

Intervals which deserve lesser degrees of assurance can be set up in the same way. Two confidence intervals are in general use and are now accepted as standard by most statisticians. We know that 95% of the cases in a normal distribution fall within the limits $\pm 1.96\sigma_M$, and that 99% fall within the limits $\pm 2.58\sigma_M$ (see Table A). If we take the limits specified by $M \pm 1.96\sigma_M$, we define an interval for which the level of confidence is .95. Basing our judgment as to the size of M_{pop} on these limits, we stand to be right 95% of the time and wrong 5%. For greater assurance, we may take the interval defined by the limits $M \pm 2.58\sigma_M$. The level of confidence for this interval is expressed by a $P = .99$; or stated differently, the limits $M \pm 2.58\sigma_M$ define the .99 confidence interval.

By way of illustration, let us apply the concept of confidence intervals to the problem on page 188. Taking as our limits $M \pm 1.96\sigma_M$, we have $27.26 \pm 1.96 \times .75$ or a confidence interval marked off by the limits 25.79 and 28.73. Our assurance that this interval contains M_{pop} is expressed by a P of .95. If we desire a higher degree of assurance, we can take the .99 level of confidence, for which the limits are $M \pm 2.58\sigma_M$. In our problem, these limits become $27.26 \pm 2.58 \times .75$ or 25.33 and 29.19. We may be quite confident that M_{pop} is not lower than 25.33 nor higher than 29.19. The width of a confidence interval becomes a direct measure of the adequacy of the inference, and hence of the trustworthiness of our sample mean.

It may seem to the student that use of the confidence interval is an exceedingly roundabout way of making an inference concerning the population mean. It would appear to be much more straightforward to say that "the chances are 95 in 100 that the M_{pop} lies between 25.79 and 28.73." Such probability statements concerning M_{pop} are often made and lead to what appears to be virtually the same result as that given in terms of confidence intervals. Theoretically, however, such inferences regarding the M_{pop} are incorrect, as this parameter is *not* a variable which can take several values but is a fixed point. The M_{pop} has only *one* value and the probability that it equals some given figure is always either 100% or 0%— right or wrong. Our probability figures (e.g., .95 or .99) do not relate to our confidence that M_{pop} itself could take one of several values within a specified range. Rather, the probability used in specifying a confidence interval is an expression of our confidence in the *inference,* namely, of our confidence that the given interval does in fact include M_{pop}. This is a subtle point but a valid one.

The limits of the confidence interval of a parameter have been called by R. A. Fisher * *fiduciary limits* and the confidence placed in the interval defined by the limits as containing the parameter is called the *fiduciary probability*. In terms of fiduciary probability, the .95 confidence interval would be described as follows: "The fiduciary probability is .95 that M_{pop} lies within the interval $M \pm 1.96\sigma_M$, and .05 that it falls outside of these limits."

2. The standard error of the mean in small samples

Whenever N is less than about 30 (see p. 186) the formula for the σ_M should read:

$$s_M = \frac{s}{\sqrt{N}} \qquad (45)$$

(standard error of the mean in small samples)

in which $s = \sqrt{\dfrac{\Sigma x^2}{(N-1)}}$ and N is the size of the sample.† In addition to the use of $(N-1)$ in the computation of s in small sample statistics, there is a still more important difference between the treatment of large and small samples. This has to do with the sampling distribution of means computed from small samples. Figure 46 shows how the appropriate sampling distribution—called the t distribution—compares with the normal. When N is small, the t distribution lies under the normal curve, but the tails or ends of the curve are higher than the corresponding parts of the normal curve. Note that the t distribution does not differ greatly from the normal unless N is quite small; and that as N increases in size the t distribution approaches more and more closely to the normal form. The units along the baseline of the t distribution are actually σ scores, i.e.,

$$t = \frac{(M - M_{pop})}{s_M} \cdot \ddagger$$

* Fisher, R. A., *The Design of Experiments* (London: Oliver and Boyd, 1935), pp. 200 f.

† If the *SD* has been computed with N in the denominator, the same correction shown in (45) can be accomplished by using the formula $SE_M = \dfrac{\sigma}{\sqrt{N-1}}$.

‡ For a mathematical treatment of the t distribution, see Walker, H. M., and Lev, J., *Statistical Inference* (New York: Henry Holt and Co., 1953), pp. 145 f.

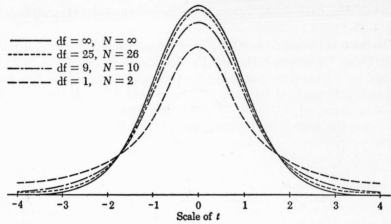

FIG. 46 Distribution of *t* for degrees of freedom from 1 to ∞. When *df* is very large, the distribution of *t* is virtually normal.

[After Lewis, D., *Quantitative Methods in Psychology* (Iowa City, 1948), p. 188]

Selected points in the *t* distribution are given in Table D. For *N*'s over a wide range, this table gives the *t*-distances *beyond* which—to the right and left—certain percents of the sampling distribution fall. These percent points are .10, .05, .02, and .01. An illustration will make clear the use of Table D in small samples and will introduce the concept of "degrees of freedom" (see p. 194).

> *Example* (2)   Ten measures of reaction time to light are taken from a practiced observer. The mean is 175.50 ms (milliseconds) and the *s* is 5.82 ms. Determine the .95 confidence interval for the M_{pop}; the .99 confidence interval.

From formula (45), we compute s_M to be $\dfrac{5.82}{\sqrt{10}}$ or 1.84 ms. We do not, of course, know the value of the population mean, but if we have the proper number of degrees of freedom we can determine the vaue of *t* at selected points in the sampling distribution. The *df* (degrees of freedom) available for determining *t* are $(N - 1)$ or 9. Entering Table D with 9 *df*, we read that $t = 2.26$ at the .05 point and 3.25 at the .01 point. From the first *t*, we know that 95% of sample means like 175.50 (the mean of our sample) lie between the M_{pop} and $\pm 2.26 s_M$ and that 5% fall outside of these limits. From the second *t*, we know that 99% of sample means lie between M_{pop} and $\pm 3.25 s_M$, and that 1% fall beyond these limits (see Fig. 47).

Confidence intervals may be established for the population mean in this problem by the methods of page 188. Taking as our limits, $M \pm 2.26 s_M$

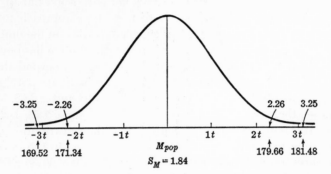

FIG. 47 Confidence intervals for the M_{pop} in the t distribution when $df = 9$

we have $175.50 \pm 2.26 \times 1.84$ or 171.34 and 179.66 as the limits of the .95 confidence interval. Or taking the limits $M \pm 3.25 s_M$, we have 175.50 ± 5.98 or 169.52 and 181.48 as the limits of the .99 confidence interval. The P is .99 that the M_{pop} is not less than 169.52 nor greater than 181.48. If we infer that M_{pop} lies within the latter interval, over a long series of experiments we should be right 99% of the time and wrong 1%. The width of the .99 confidence interval (i.e., $181.48 - 169.52$ or 11.96) shows the marked instability present when an inference is based upon a small N. Small samples should be avoided if possible in the social sciences. Inferences drawn from small groups are usually unsatisfactory owing to great variability from sample to sample. It is difficult, too, to be sure that a small sample adequately represents (is a random sample of) the parent population.

(1) INFERENCES FROM LARGE AND SMALL SAMPLES

Several points in the solution of this problem deserve further comment as they bring out clearly the difference in accuracy between inferences from large and small samples. Had we used formula (44) instead of (45) in the problem above, the SE of our mean would have been 1.75 ms instead of 1.84 ms—about 5% too small. Again the .05 and .01 points in the unit normal curve are ± 1.96 and ± 2.58 (Table A). These limits are 13% and 21% smaller than the correct t limits of ± 2.26 and ± 3.25 read from Table D for 9 df. It is obvious, then, that when N is small, use of formula (44) and the normal curve as sampling distribution will cause a computed mean to appear to be more trustworthy than it actually is.

The SE of the mean in the problem on page 187 was .75. Had formula (44) and Table A been used in evaluating the stability of our sample mean of 27.26, results would not have differed appreciably from those obtained with formula (45) and Table D. From Table D, for example. we find that for 224 df (225 − 1) the .05 point is 1.97 and the .01 point is 2.60. As N increases, Table D shows that t entries approach more and more closely to the corresponding normal curve entries. In the unit normal curve, for instance (see Table A), 10% of the distribution lies beyond the limits ±1.65, 5% beyond the σ-limits ±1.96 and 1% beyond the limits ±2.58. In Table D, the corresponding t limits for 50 df are ±1.68, ±2.01 and ±2.68. For 100 df the t limits are ±1.66, ±1.98 and ±2.63. When N is very large, the t distribution becomes a normal curve (see last line in Table D). It is only when N is quite small that the t distribution diverges markedly from the normal form. As research workers in the mental and social sciences rarely work with groups smaller than 30, small sample statistics are not generally as useful in psychology and education as they are in biology and agriculture.

(2) DEGREES OF FREEDOM

The concept of degrees of freedom which we encountered on page 192 is highly important in small sample statistics. It is crucial, too, in analysis of variance and in other procedures which will appear in later chapters. When a statistic is used to estimate a parameter, the number of degrees of freedom (df) available depends upon the restrictions placed upon the observations. One df is lost for each restriction imposed. If we have 5 scores, 5, 6, 7, 8, and 9, the mean is 7; and the deviations of our scores from 7 are −2, −1, 0, 1 and 2. The sum of these deviations is zero. Of the 5 deviations, only 4 ($N − 1$) can be selected "freely" (i.e., are independent) as the condition that the sum equal zero immediately restricts the value of (fixes) the 5th deviate. The SD is, of course, based upon the squares of the deviations taken around the mean. There are N df for computing the mean, but only ($N − 1$) available for the s (the SD) as one df is lost in calculating the mean. In example (2) the df available for estimating the M_{pop} were given as 9 or ($N − 1$)—one less than the number of observations, namely, 10. One df was lost in computing the M and accordingly only 9 are left for estimating the M_{pop} by way of s and the t distribution.

Whenever a statistic is used to estimate a parameter, the rule is that the df available equals N minus the number of parameters already estimated from the sample. The M is an estimate of M_{pop} and in computing it we lose 1 df. In example (2) the only parameter estimated is M_{pop} and the number of degrees of freedom is $(N-1)$ or 9. The degrees of free-dom are not always $(N-1)$ however, but will vary with the problem and the restrictions imposed. In estimating the dependability of an r, for exam-ple (which depends upon the deviations from *two* means), the df are $(N-2)$. Rules for determining the df available in the chi-square test (p. 254) and in analysis of variance tables will be given in appropriate places in later chapters.

3. The standard error of a median

In terms of σ and Q, the SE's of the median for large samples (e.g., as large as 100) are

$$\sigma_{Mdn} = \frac{1.253\sigma}{\sqrt{N}} \tag{46}$$

and

$$\sigma_{Mdn} = \frac{1.858Q}{\sqrt{N}} \tag{47}$$

(standard error of the median in terms of σ and Q)

The fact that the SE_{Mdn} is roughly $1\frac{1}{4}$ times the σ_M shows the mean to be in general more dependable (less subject to sampling fluctuations) than the median (p. 185). An example will illustrate the use and interpretation of formula (47):

> *Example* (3) On the Trabue Language Scale A, 801 twelve-year-old boys made the following record: $Mdn = 21.40$ and $Q = 4.90$. How well does this median represent the median of the population from which this sample was drawn?

By formula (47), the $\sigma_{Mdn} = \dfrac{1.858 \times 4.90}{\sqrt{801}}$ or .32 (to two decimals). Since N is large, the sampling distribution may be taken to be normal and the confidence interval found from the last line in Table D. The .99 confidence interval for the Mdn_{pop} is $21.40 \pm 2.58 \times .32$ or $21.40 \pm .83$. We may be confident that the median of the population is not less than 20.57 nor more than 22.23. This narrow range shows a high degree of trust-worthiness in the sample median.

III. THE SIGNIFICANCE OF MEASURES OF VARIABILITY

1. The *SE* of the standard deviation

The SE of a standard deviation, like the SE_M, is found by computing the probable divergence of the sample SD from its parameter (population SD). The formula for SE_σ is

$$SE_\sigma \quad \text{or} \quad \sigma_\sigma = \frac{.71\sigma}{\sqrt{N}} \qquad (48)$$

(standard error of a standard deviation)

The sampling distribution of σ is skewed for small samples (N less than about 25). But when samples are large and drawn at random from their population, formula (48) may be applied and interpreted in the same way as SE_M. To illustrate, it was stated on page 187 that for 225 tenth-grade boys, the SD around the mean of 27.26 on the Abstract Reasoning Test was 11.20. By formula (48)

$$SE_\sigma = \frac{11.20 \times .71}{\sqrt{225}} = .53$$

Since N is large, the .99 confidence interval for the SD_{pop} can safely be taken at the limits $\pm 2.58\sigma_\sigma$. Substituting for σ_σ we have $11.20 \pm 2.58 \times .53$. If we assume that the SD_{pop} lies between the limits 9.83 and 12.57, we should be right 99% of the time and wrong 1%.

The SE of a standard deviation is always smaller than SE_M. The σ_σ may be written $\dfrac{\sigma}{\sqrt{2N}}$.

2. The SE of the quartile deviation or Q

The SE_Q may be found from the formulas

$$\sigma_Q = \frac{.786\sigma}{\sqrt{N}} \qquad (49)$$

$$\sigma_Q = \frac{1.17Q}{\sqrt{N}} \qquad (50)$$

(standard errors of Q in terms of σ and Q)

These formulas may be applied and interpreted as are the other SE formulas. Thus, in the problem on page 195, the median for 801 boys on the Trabue Scale was 21.40 and the Q was 4.90. The SE of this Q by (50) is

$$\sigma_Q = \frac{1.17 \times 4.90}{\sqrt{801}} = .203 \text{ (to 3 decimals)}$$

The .99 confidence interval for the population Q is from 4.38 to 5.42, i.e., $4.90 \pm 2.58 \times .203$. This narrow range shows that the sample Q is a highly dependable statistic.

IV. SIGNIFICANCE OF PERCENTAGES AND OF THE CORRELATION COEFFICIENT

1. The stability of a percentage

It is often feasible to find the percentage of a given sample which exhibits a certain behavior or possesses a definite attitude or other characteristic when it is difficult or impossible to measure these attributes directly. Given the percentage occurrence of a behavior, the question often arises of how much confidence we can place in the figure. How reliable an index is our percentage of the incidence of the behavior in which we are interested? To answer this question, we must compute the SE of a percentage by the equation:

$$\sigma_\% = \sqrt{\frac{PQ}{N}} \qquad (51)$$

(SE *of a percentage*)

in which

$P =$ the percentage occurrence of the behavior
$Q = (1 - P)$
$N =$ number of cases

To illustrate formula (51) with a problem:

Example (4)   In a study of cheating among elementary-school children, 144 or 41.4% of the 348 children from homes of high socioeconomic status were found to have cheated on various tests. Assuming our sample to be representative of children from good homes, how much confidence can we place in this percentage? How well does it represent the population percentage?

Applying formula (51), we get that

$$\sigma_\% = \sqrt{\frac{41.4\% \times 58.6\%}{348}} = 2.6\%$$

The sampling distribution of percentages can be taken as normal when N is large (larger than about 50) and when P is less than 95% and greater than 5%. The $SE_\%$ is interpreted like the σ_M. In the present problem, the .99 confidence interval for the population percentage is 41.4% ± 2.58 × 2.6% or from 34.7% to 48.1%. We may feel sure that the percentage of children in general who cheat on tests of the sort used in this study will be at least 34.7% and will not be larger than 48.1%.

2. The significance of the coefficient of correlation

(1) THE SE OF r

The classical formula for the SE of r is

$$\sigma_r = \frac{(1 - r^2)}{\sqrt{N}} \qquad (52)$$

(SE of a coefficient of correlation r when N is large)

In the height-weight problem on page 135, $r = .60$ and $N = 120$. The SE_r by formula (52), therefore, is $\dfrac{(1 - .60^2)}{\sqrt{120}}$ or .06 (to two decimals). To test the dependability of r in terms of its SE, we assume the sampling distribution of r to be normal, place the "true or population r" at the center (Fig. 48) of the distribution, and take .06 (i.e., SE_r) to be the

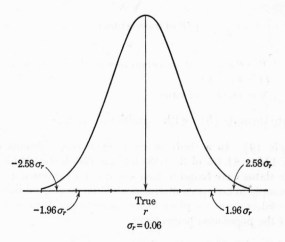

FIG. 48 There are 95 chances in 100 that the obtained r does not miss the true r by more than ±.12 (±1.96σr). The .99 confidence interval for the true r is r ± 2.58σr or .60 ± .15, i.e., .45 to .75.

SD of this sampling distribution of r's. Since the probability is .05 of an r exceeding ±1.96σr, there is only one chance in 20 that an error of ±.12 or more is present in our r. Again, the .99 confidence interval for the population r can be taken as r ±2.58σr. Substituting for r and SE_r, we get .45 and .75 as the limits of our .99 confidence interval. We can feel quite certain, therefore, that r is at least as large as .45 and is no larger than .75.

There are two serious objections to the use of formula (52). In the *first* place, the r in the formula is really the true or population r. Since we do not have the true r, we must substitute the calculated r in the formula in order to get an estimate of the standard error of r. If the obtained r is in error, our estimate also will be in error; and at best it is an approximation.

In the *second* place, the sampling distribution of r is not normal except when the population $r = .00$ and N is large. When r is high (.80 or more) and N is small, the sampling distribution of r is skewed and the SE_r from (52) is quite misleading. This is true also when r is low (e.g., .20 or less). Skewness in the sampling distribution of high r's results from the fact that the range of r is from $+1.00$ to -1.00. If $r = .80$ and $N = 20$, the probability of an r less than .80 in a new sample of 20 cases is much greater than the probability of an r greater than .80 because of the sample r's nearness to unity. The distribution of r's obtained from successive samples of 20 cases will be skewed negatively (p. 99) and the skewness increases as r increases. For values of r close to $\pm.50$, and for N's of 100 or more, the distribution of r in successive samples will conform closely to the normal curve, and formula (52) will yield a useful estimate of significance. But unless SE_r is used with care it is likely to be misinterpreted.

(2) CONVERTING r'S INTO FISHER'S z FUNCTION

A mathematically more defensible method of testing the significance of an r, especially when the coefficient is very high or very low, is to convert r into R. A. Fisher's z function * and find the SE of z. The function z has two advantages over r: (1) its sampling distribution is approximately normal and (2) its SE depends only upon the size of the sample N, and is independent of the size of r. The formula for σ_z is

$$\sigma_z = \frac{1}{\sqrt{N-3}} \tag{53}$$

(SE *of Fisher's z function*)

Suppose that $r = .85$, and $N = 52$. First, from Table C we read that an r of .85 corresponds to a z of 1.26. SE_z from (53) is $\dfrac{1}{\sqrt{52-3}}$ or .14. The .95 confidence interval for the true z is now .99 to 1.53 (i.e., $1.26 \pm 1.96 \times$ .14 or $1.26 \pm .27$). Converting these z's back into r's we get a confidence interval of from .76 to .91. The fiduciary probability is .95 that this interval contains the true r (p. 191).

*Fisher, R. A., *Statistical Methods for Research Workers* (8th ed.; London: Oliver and Boyd, 1941), pp. 190–203.

The coefficient of correlation .60 in the height-weight problem (p. 135) is not large enough for the conversion into z to make much difference in our significance estimate, namely, $.45 - .75$. An r of .60 is equivalent to a z of .69 (Table C), and the SE_z is $\dfrac{1}{\sqrt{120-3}}$ or .09 (to two decimals). The .99 confidence interval for the true z, therefore, is .46 to .92 (i.e., $.69 \pm 2.58 \times .09$ or $.69 \pm .23$). When we convert these z's back into r's the .99 confidence interval for the population r becomes .43 to .73. This range is almost identical with that on page 198 obtained when we used r and SE_r.

(3) TESTING r AGAINST THE NULL HYPOTHESIS

The significance of an obtained r may be tested also against the hypothesis that the population r is in fact zero.* If the computed r is large enough to invalidate or cast serious doubt upon this null hypothesis we accept r as indicating the presence of at least some degree of correlation. To make the test, enter Table 25 with $(N - 2)$ degrees of freedom and compare the obtained r with the tabulated entries. Two significance levels, .05 and .01, are given in Table 25, which is read as follows when, for example, $r = .60$ and $N = 120$. For 118 df the entries at .05 and .01 are by linear interpolation .18 and .24, respectively (to two decimals). This means that only 5 times in 100 trials would an r as large as $\pm.18$ arise from fluctuations of sampling alone *if* the population r were actually

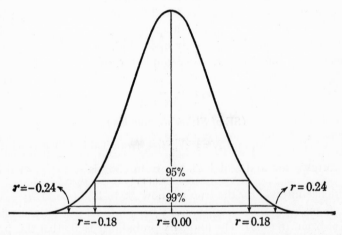

FIG. 49 When the population r is zero, and $df = 118$, 5% of the sample r's exceed $\pm.18$, and 1% exceeds $\pm.24$

* See page 247 for further definition of the null hypothesis.

TABLE 25   Correlation coefficients at the 5% and 1% levels of significance

Example: When N is 52 and *df* is 50, an *r* must be .273 to be significant at .05 level, and .354 to be significant at .01 level.

Degrees of freedom $(N-2)$	.05	.01	Degrees of freedom $(N-2)$	.05	.01
1	.997	1.000	24	.388	.496
2	.950	.990	25	.381	.487
3	.878	.959	26	.374	.478
4	.811	.917	27	.367	.470
5	.754	.874	28	.361	.463
6	.707	.834	29	.355	.456
7	.666	.798	30	.349	.449
8	.632	.765	35	.325	.418
9	.602	.735	40	.304	.393
10	.576	.708	45	.288	.372
11	.553	.684	50	.273	.354
12	.532	.661	60	.250	.325
13	.514	.641	70	.232	.302
14	.497	.623	80	.217	.283
15	.482	.606	90	.205	.267
16	.468	.590	100	.195	.254
17	.456	.575	125	.174	.228
18	.444	.561	150	.159	.208
19	.433	.549	200	.138	.181
20	.423	.537	300	.113	.148
21	.413	.526	400	.098	.128
22	.404	.515	500	.088	.115
23	.396	.505	1000	.062	.081

.00; and only once in 100 trials would an *r* as large as ±.24 appear if the population *r* were .00 (Fig. 49). It is clear that the obtained *r* of .60, since it is much larger than .24, is highly significant, i.e., at the .01 level.

Table 25 takes account of *both* ends of the sampling distribution—does not consider the sign of *r*. When $N = 120$, the probability $(P/2)$ of an *r* of .18 or more arising on the null hypothesis is .025; and the probability of an *r* of −.18 or less is, of course, .025 also. For a $P/2$ of .01 (or P of .02) the *r* by linear interpolation between .05 (.18) and .01 (.24) is .22. On the hypothesis of a population *r* of zero, therefore, only once in 100 trials would a *positive r* of .22 or larger arise through accidents of sampling.

The .05 and .01 levels in Table 25 are the only ones needed ordinarily in evaluating the significance of an obtained r. Several illustrations of the use of Table 25 in determining significance are given below:

Size of Sample (N)	Degrees of Freedom (N − 2)	Calculated r	Interpretation
10	8	.70	significant at .05, not at .01 level
152	150	−.12	not significant
27	25	.50	significant at .05, barely at .01 level
500	498	.20	very significant
100	98	−.30	very significant

It is clear from these examples that even a small r may be significant if computed from a very large sample, and that an r as high as .70 may not be significant if N is quite small. Table 25 is especially useful when N is small. Suppose that we have found an r of .55 from a sample of 12 cases. Entering Table 25 with $(N − 2)$ or 10 df we find that r must be .71 to be significant at the .01 level and .58 to be significant at the .05 level. In this small sample, therefore, even an r as high as .55 cannot be taken as indicative of any real correlation.

V. SAMPLING AND THE USE OF STANDARD ERROR FORMULAS

All of the SE formulas given in this chapter depend upon N, the size of the sample, and most of them require some measure of variability (usually σ). It is unfortunate, perhaps, that there is nothing in the *statement* of a SE formula which might deter the uncritical worker from applying it to the statistics calculated from any set of test scores. But the general and indiscriminate computation of SE's will inevitably lead to erroneous conclusions and false interpretations. Hence, it is highly important that the research worker in experimental psychology and in educational research have clearly in mind (1) the conditions under which SE formulas are (and are not) applicable; and that he know (2) what his formulas may be reasonably expected to do. Some of the limitations to the use of SE's have been given in this chapter. These statements will now be amplified and further cautions to be observed in the use of SE's will be indicated.

'I. Methods of sampling

Various techniques have been devised for obtaining a sample which will be representative of its population. The adequacy of a sample (i.e., its lack of bias) will depend upon our knowledge of the population or supply * as well as upon the method used in drawing the sample. Commonly used sampling methods will be described in this section under four headings: *random, stratified* or *quota, incidental,* and *purposive.*

(1) RANDOM SAMPLING

The descriptive term "random" is often misunderstood. It does not imply that the sample has been chosen in an offhand, careless or haphazard fashion. Instead it means that we rely upon a certain method of selection (called "random") to provide an unbiased cross section of the larger group or population. The criteria for randomness in a sample are met when (1) every individual (or animal or thing) in the population or supply has the same chance of being chosen for the sample; and (2) when the selection of one individual or thing in no way influences the choice of another. Randomness in a sample is assured when we draw similar and well shaken-up slips out of a hat; or numbers in a lottery (provided it is honest); or a hand from a carefully shuffled deck of cards. In each of these cases selection is made in terms of some mechanical process and is not subject to the whims or biases (if any) of the experimenter.

A clear distinction should be made between representative and random samples. A representative sample is one in which the distribution of scores in the sample closely parallels that of the population. Experience has shown that if one is asked to get representative samples from a population he will for various reasons (some not recognized) often draw samples which exhibit consistent biases of one sort or another. The most trustworthy way of securing representativeness, therefore, is to make sure that the sampling is random. If we draw samples at random from the population we know at least that (*a*) there will be no *consistent* biases; (*b*) *on the average* these samples will be representative; (*c*) the degree of discrepancy likely to occur in any given sample can be determined by probability methods. The *SE* formulas given in this chapter apply *only* to random samples.

In research problems in psychology and in education three situations arise in connection with the drawing of a random sample: (*a*) the members of the population or supply are on file or have been catalogued in

---

* A supply usually means a population of objects or things.

some way; (b) the form of the distribution of the trait in the population is known to be (or can reasonably be assumed to be) normal; (c) the population is known only in general terms. These situations will be discussed in order.

(a) *Members of population are on file or are catalogued.* If the population has been accurately listed, a type of systematic selection will provide what is approximately a random sample. Thus we may take every fifth or tenth name (depending upon the size of the sample wanted) in a long list, provided names have been put in alphabetical order and are not arranged with respect to some differential factor, such as age, income or education. (A better plan in such cases is to assign numbers to the members of the population and draw a sample as described below.) By this method an approximately random sample of telephone users may be obtained by reference to the telephone directory; of sixth-grade children from attendance rolls; of automobile owners from the licensing bureau; of workers in a factory from payroll lists. Random samples of the population with respect to a variety of characteristics may be drawn in the same way from census data.

Systematic selection from a catalogued population is often used in determining the acceptance rate of industrial products. Thus in sampling machine-produced articles for defectives, a random sample may be obtained by taking every tenth article, say, as it comes from the machine. Sampling of this sort is justified if the manufactured articles are taken just as they come from the machine, so that systematic selection provides an approximately random sample from the supply.

When the subjects in a group are to be assigned at random to one or more experimental and control subgroups, tables of random numbers may be used to good purpose.[*] In such tables, numbers arranged by a chance procedure are printed in sequence. The tenth block of 25 numbers, taken from Fisher and Yates' table and reproduced here will serve as an example:

34	50	57	74	37
85	22	04	39	43
09	79	13	77	48
88	75	80	18	14
90	96	23	70	00

The Fisher-Yates table is made up of 300 similar blocks of 25 numbers, printed on 6 pages of 10 rows and 5 columns each. To read from the table

[*] Fisher, R. A., and Yates, F., *Statistical Tables* (New York: Hafner Publishing Co., 1948), Table 33.

one may begin at any point on any page and read in any direction, up or down, right or left. When all of the individuals in the entire group or population have been numbered in 1, 2, 3 order, a random sample of any size can be drawn by following in order the numbers read from the table. Suppose, for example, that a random sample of 25 is to be drawn from a larger "population" of 100. Then, if we have decided beforehand to start with the second column in the block above and read down, individuals numbered 50, 22, 79, 75 and 96 will be included. Other blocks chosen in advance may be used to provide the additional 20 subjects. If the same number occurs twice, the second draw is disregarded.

(b) *Distribution of trait in the population is known.* As a result of much research in individual differences, many physical and mental traits are believed to be normally distributed—or approximately so—in the general population. If a trait or ability in which we are interested is known to be normally distributed in the population, a sample drawn at random from this population will also be normally distributed. Hence, under the stipulated conditions, normality of distribution becomes a good criterion of sample adequacy.

(c) *Population known only in general terms.* In many problems in psychology and in education the population is (1) not clearly defined, (2) not readily accessible for sampling (for example, the population of a state), and (3) very expensive to sample extensively. Under conditions such as these a useful test of the adequacy of a sample consists in drawing several samples at random and in succession from the population, such samples to be of approximately the same size as the sample with which we are working. Random samples of ten-year-old school boys in a large school system, for instance, must be drawn without bias as to able, mediocre or poor individuals; they cannot be drawn exclusively from poor neighborhoods, from expensive private schools, or from any larger group in which special factors are likely to make for systematic differences.

When the means and SD's of our presumably random samples match closely, we may feel reasonably sure that our samples are all representing the same thing. If the correspondence among samples is not close we should reëxamine each sample for bias. This test can be criticized on the grounds that (1) the correspondence of two or more samples may reflect nothing more than a common bias and (2) that consistency is not a sufficient criterion of representativeness. Both of these objections are valid. At the same time, consistency among samples is a necessary, if not a sufficient, condition of randomness. When successively drawn samples are consistent in mean and SD, they may be taken to be random unless subsequent examination reveals a common bias. When samples differ widely, we cannot be sure that any one of them is representative of the population.

(2) STRATIFIED OR QUOTA SAMPLING

Stratified or quota sampling (also called "controlled" sampling) is a technique designed to ensure representativeness and avoid bias by use of a modified random sampling method. This scheme is applicable when the population is composed of subgroups or *strata* of different sizes, so that a representative sample must contain individuals drawn from each category or stratum in accordance with the sizes of the subgroups. Within each stratum or subgroup the sampling is random—or as nearly so as possible. Stratified sampling is illustrated in the standardization of the 1937 Stanford-Binet Scale in the course of which approximately 3000 children were tested. To ensure an adequate selection of American youth, the occupational levels of the parents of the children in the standard group were checked against the six occupational levels of employed males in the general population as shown by the U.S. Census of 1930. Differing proportions of men were found in the groups classified as professionals, semi-professionals, businessmen, farmers, skilled laborer, slightly skilled and unskilled laborers. Only 4% of employed males were found in the professional group, while 31% were in the skilled labor group. Accordingly, only 4% of the children in the Stanford-Binet standardization group could have fathers in the professional category, while 31% could have fathers in the skilled labor group. In public opinion polling, the investigator must see that his sample takes account of various strata or criteria such as age, sex, political affiliation, urban and rural residence, etc.

When sampling is stratified, the SE formula for the mean differs slightly from the SE_M formula when sampling is strictly random. The new formula is

$$\sigma_M = \sqrt{\frac{\sigma^2 - \sigma^2{}_s}{N}} \tag{54}$$

(SE *of* M *when sampling has been stratified*)

in which $\sigma = SD$ of the entire sample

$\sigma_s = SD$ of the means of the various strata around the mean of the entire sample.

A convenient formula for σ_s is

$$\sigma_s = \sqrt{\frac{[N_1(M_1 - M)^2 + N_2(M_2 - M)^2 + \cdots + N_k(M_k - M)^2]}{N}} \tag{55}$$

(*standard deviation of the means of strata around the mean of the entire group*) in which $N_1, N_2 \ldots N_k$ = number of cases in strata 1 to k; and N and M are the size and mean of the whole sample.

To illustrate formula (54), suppose that in a sample of 400 cases, there are 8 subgroups or strata which vary in size from 70 to 25. The M of the whole sample is 80 and σ is 15. The SD of the means of the 8 strata [by (55)] around the general mean of 80 is known to be 5. Substituting in (54) we have

$$\sigma_M = \sqrt{\frac{225 - 25}{400}} = \sqrt{\frac{200}{400}} = .71$$

Had no account been taken of the variation in the subgroups, σ_M would have been $\sqrt{\frac{225}{400}}$ or .75. Unless the various strata introduce considerable variation, it is obvious that the correction got by using (54) instead of (44) is fairly small.

(3) INCIDENTAL SAMPLING

The term "incidental sampling" (also called "accidental" sampling) should be applied to those groups which are used chiefly because they are easily or readily obtainable. School children, college sophomores enrolled in psychology classes, and laboratory animals are available at times, in numbers, and under conditions none of which may be of the experimenter's choosing. Such casual groups rarely constitute random samples of any definable population. SE formulas apply with a high degree of approximation—if at all—to incidental samples. And generalizations based upon such data are often misleading.

(4) PURPOSIVE SAMPLING

A sample may be expressly chosen because, in the light of available evidence, it mirrors some larger group with reference to a given characteristic. Newspaper editors are believed to reflect accurately public opinion upon various social and economic questions in their sections of the country. A sample of housewives may represent accurately the buyers of canned goods; a sample of brokers, the opinion of financiers on a new stock issue. If the saying "As Maine goes, so goes the Nation" is accepted as correct, then Maine becomes an important barometer (a purposive sample) of political thinking. Random sampling formulas apply more or less accurately to purposive samples.

2. Size of sample

The dependability of a M or σ is contingent upon the *size* of the sample upon which the SE is based. SE's vary inversely as the square root of sample size so that the larger the N in general the smaller the SE. A small sample is often satisfactory in an intensive laboratory study in which many measurements are taken upon each subject. But if N is less than 25, say, there is often little reason for believing such a small group of persons to be adequately descriptive of *any* population (see p. 188).

The larger the N the larger the SD of the sample and the more inclusive (and presumably representative) our sample becomes of the general population. The range covered by samples of different sizes—when all are drawn from a normal population—will be approximately as follows:

$N = 10$	Range $\pm 2.0\sigma$
$N = 50$	Range $\pm 2.5\sigma$
$N = 200$	Range $\pm 3.0\sigma$
$N = 1000$	Range $\pm 3.5\sigma$

A range of $\pm 3.5\sigma$ from the mean includes 9995 cases in 10,000 in a normally distributed population. In a sample of 10,000 only 5 cases lie outside of this range; in a sample of 100 cases none lies outside of this range. The more extreme the score, large or small, the less the probability of its occurrence in a small sample. In fact, in very small samples widely deviant scores can hardly appear in a random sample drawn from a normal group.

A fairly simple and practical method of deciding when a sample is "sufficiently large" is to increase N until the addition of extra cases, drawn at random, fails to produce any appreciable change (more than $\pm 1SE_M$, say) in the M and σ. When this point is reached, the sample is probably large enough to be taken as adequately descriptive of its population. But the corollary must be recognized that mere numbers in and of themselves do not guarantee a random sample (see also p. 203).

3. Sampling fluctuations and errors of measurement

SE's measure (1) errors of sampling *and* (2) errors of measurement. We have already considered the question of sampling errors on page 185. The investigator in establishing generalizations from his data regarding individual differences, say, must perforce make his observations upon limited groups or samples drawn at random from the population. Owing to differences among individuals and groups, plus chance factors (errors of measurement), neither the sample in hand nor another similarly drawn and approximately of the same size will describe the population exactly. Hence it is unlikely that M's and σ's from successive samples will equal each other. Fluctuations from sample to sample—the so-called "errors" of sampling—are not to be thought of as mistakes, failures and the like, but as variations arising from the fact that no two samples are ever exactly alike. Means and σ's from random samples are *estimates* of their parameters, and the *SE* formulas measure the goodness of this estimate.

The term "errors of measurement" includes all of those variable factors which affect test scores, sometimes in the plus and sometimes in the minus direction. If the SE_M is large, it does not follow *necessarily* that the mean is affected by a large sampling error, as much of the variation may be due to errors of measurement. When errors of measurement are low, however (reliability of tests high, see p. 345), a large SE_M indicates considerable sampling error.

4. Bias in sampling and constant errors

Errors which arise from inadequate sampling or from bias of any sort are neither detected nor measured by *SE* formulas. The mean score on an aptitude test achieved by 200 male college freshmen in a college of high admission standards will not be representative of the aptitude of the general male population between the ages of 18 and 21, say, and for this reason the SE_M for this group is not an adequate measure of sampling fluctuations. College freshmen usually constitute an incidental—and often a highly biased—sample. In consequence, other samples of young men 18–25, drawn at random from the male population, will return very different means and σ's from those in our group. Differences like these are not sampling fluctuations but are errors due to inadequate or biased selection. *SE* formulas do not apply.

SE's do not detect constant errors. Such errors work in only one directions and are always plus or minus. They arise from many sources—familiarity with test materials prior to examination, cheating, fatigue, faulty techniques in administering and in scoring tests, in fact from a consistent bias of any sort. *SE*'s are of doubtful value when computed from scores subject to large constant errors. The careful study of successive samples, rechecks when possible, care in controlling conditions, and the use of objective tests will reduce many of these troublesome sources of error. The research worker cannot learn too early that even the best statistical techniques are unable to make bad data yield valid results.

PROBLEMS

1. Given $M = 26.40$; $\sigma = 5.20$; $N = 100$

   (a) Compute the .95 confidence interval for the true σ.
   (b)   "   "   .99   "   "   "   "   " mean.

2. The mean of 16 independent observations of a certain magnitude is 100 and the *SD* is 24.

(a) At the .05 confidence level what are the fiduciary limits of the true mean? (p. 191)

(b) Taking the .99 confidence interval as our standard, we may be assured that the true mean is at least as large as what value?

3. For a given group of 500 soldiers the mean AGCT score is 95.00 and the SD is 25.

(a) Determine the .99 confidence interval for the true mean.

(b) It is unlikely that the true mean is larger than what value?

4. The mean of a large sample is K and σ_K is 2.50. What are the chances that the sample mean misses the true mean by more than (a) ±1.00; (b) ±3.00; (c) ±10.00?

5. The following measures of perception span for unrelated words are obtained from 5 children: 5   6   4   7   5

(a) Find the .99 confidence interval for the true mean of these scores.

(b) Compare the fiduciary limits (.99 confidence interval) when calculated by large sample methods with the result in (a).

6. Suppose it is known that the SD of the scores in a certain population is 20. How many cases would we need in a sample in order that the SE

(a) of the sample M be 2?

(b) of the sample SD be 1?

7. In a sample of 400 voters, 50% favor the Democratic candidate for president. How often can we expect polls based on random samples of 400 to return percents of 55 or more in favor of the Democrats?

8. Opinion upon an issue seems about equally divided. How large a sample (N) would you need to be sure (at .01 level) that a deviation of 3% in a sample is not accidental (due to chance)?

9. Given an r of .45 based upon 60 cases,

(a) Using formula (52), p. 198, find the SE_r. Determine the limits of the .99 confidence interval for the population r.

(b) Convert the given r into z, and find σ_z by formula (53). Check the limits of the .99 confidence interval determined from σ_z against those found in (a) above.

(c) Is the given r significant at the .01 level? (Use Table 25.)

10. An r of .81 is obtained from a random sample of 37 cases.

(a) Establish the fiduciary limits of the true r at the .01 level, using the z-conversion.

(b) Check the significance of r from Table 25.

11. Given a sample of 500 cases in which there are six subgroups or strata. The means of the six subgroups are 50 ($N = 100$), 54 ($N = 50$), 46 ($N = 100$), 50 ($N = 120$), 58 ($N = 80$), 42 ($N = 50$). The SD for the entire sample is 12.

(a) Find the mean of the whole sample of 500 (p. 30).

(b) Compute the σ_M by formula (54) (p. 206).

(c) Compare σ_M by formula (44) with the result found in (b).

12. Fill out the following table:

	Size of sample (N)	df (N − 2)	r	Significance
(a)	15	13	−.68	
(b)	30	28	.22	
(c)	82	80	−.40	
(d)	225	223	.05	

ANSWERS

1. (a) 4.48 to 5.92   (b) 25.06 to 27.74
2. (a) 87.22 to 112.78   (b) 82.3
3. (a) 92.11 to 97.89   (b) 97.89
4. 69 in 100; 23 in 100; less than 1 in 100
5. (a) 3.05 to 7.75   (b) By large sampling methods the fiduciary limits at the .99 confidence level are 4.21 to 6.59
6. (a) 100   (b) 202
7. About once in 50 trials
8. 1850
9. (a) .18 to .72   (b) .15 to .67   (c) Yes
10. (a) .60 to .92   (b) Significant at the .01 level
11. (a) 50.08   (b) .495   (c) .495 vs. .537
12. (a) Significant at the .01 level
    (b) Not significant
    (c) Significant at the .01 level
    (d) Not significant

CHAPTER 9

THE SIGNIFICANCE OF THE DIFFERENCE BETWEEN MEANS AND OTHER STATISTICS

◇◇

I. THE SIGNIFICANCE OF THE DIFFERENCE BETWEEN MEANS

Suppose that we wish to discover whether 10-year-old boys and 10-year-old girls differ in linguistic ability. *First*, we would assemble as large and as random a sample of boys and girls as possible. *Next*, we would administer a battery of verbal tests, compute the means of the two groups, and find the difference between them. A large difference in favor of the girls would offer strong evidence that girls of 10 are in general more able linguistically than are boys of 10. And contrariwise, a small difference (1 or 2 points, for example) would clearly be unimpressive, and would suggest strongly that further comparative tests might well show no difference at all between 10-year-old boys and 10-year-old girls.

When can we feel reasonably sure that a difference between two means is large enough to be taken as real and dependable? This question involves the SE's of the two means being compared, and cannot be answered categorically. We have already found an obtained mean is subject to sampling fluctuations or "errors of sampling" (p. 184); and it is reasonable to expect that the difference between two means will also be subject to sampling errors. Even when $M_{pop\ 1} = M_{pop\ 2}$, the means of two samples drawn, the one from population #1, and the other from population #2, may—and usually will—differ in some degree owing to sampling errors. In order to test the significance of an obtained difference, we must first have a SE of the difference. Then from the difference between the sample means and the SE_D we can determine whether a difference probably exists between the population means. A difference is called *significant* when the probability is high that it cannot be attributed to chance (i.e., temporary and accidental factors) and hence represents a true difference between population means. And a difference is *nonsignificant* or chance when it appears reasonably certain that it could easily have arisen from sampling fluctuations, and hence implies no real or true difference between the population means.

1. The null hypothesis

Experimenters have found the *null hypothesis* a useful tool in testing the significance of differences. In its simplest form (see p. 247), this hypothesis asserts that there is no true difference between two population means, and that the difference found between sample means is, therefore, accidental and unimportant. The null hypothesis is akin to the legal principle that a man is innocent until he is proved guilty. It constitutes a challenge; and the function of an experiment is to give the facts a chance to refute (or fail to refute) this challenge. To illustrate, suppose it is claimed that Eskimos have keener vision than Americans. This hypothesis is vaguely stated and cannot be tested precisely as we do not know how *much* better the Eskimo's vision must be before it can be adjudged "keener." If, however, we assert that Eskimos do not possess keener vision than Americans, or that the differences are trifling and as often in favor of one group as the other (the true difference being zero), this null hypothesis is *exact* and can be tested. If our null hypothesis is untenable, it must be rejected. And in discarding our null hypothesis, what we are saying is that—as far as our tests go—differences in visual acuity as between Eskimos and Americans cannot be fully explained as temporary and occasional.

2. The SE of the difference between two independent means

To discover whether two groups differ sufficiently in mean performance to enable us to say with confidence that there is a difference between the means of the populations from which the samples were drawn, we need to know the standard error of the difference between the two sample means. Two situations arise with respect to differences between means: (1) those in which the means are *uncorrelated* and (2) those in which the means are *correlated*. Means are uncorrelated or independent when computed from different samples or from uncorrelated tests administered to the same sample.

(1) THE SE OF THE DIFFERENCE (σ_D) WHEN MEANS ARE UNCORRELATED AND SAMPLES ARE LARGE

The formula for the SE of the difference between uncorrelated or independent means is

$$\sigma_D = \sigma_{(M1-M2)} = \sqrt{\sigma^2_{M1} + \sigma^2_{M2}} \qquad (56a)$$

$$\sigma_D = \sqrt{\frac{\sigma^2_1}{N_1} + \frac{\sigma^2_2}{N_2}} \qquad (56b)$$

(standard error of the difference between uncorrelated means)

in which

σ_{M1} = the SE of the mean of the first sample
σ_{M2} = the SE of the mean of the second sample
σ_D = the SE of the difference between the two sample means
N_1 and N_2 = sizes of the two samples

From formula (56) it is clear that one way to find the SE of the difference between two means is to compute, first, the SE's of the two means themselves. Another way is to compute σ_D directly, and this is done when σ_{M_1} and σ_{M_2} are not wanted.

Application of these formulas to a problem is shown in the following example:

Example (1) In a study of abstract reasoning, a sample of 83 twelfth-grade boys and a sample of 95 twelfth-grade girls scored as shown below on a test of abstract reasoning:

Sex	N	Mean	σ
Girls	95	29.21	11.56
Boys	83	30.92	7.81

Assuming that our samples are *random*, would further testing of similar groups of boys and girls give virtually the same result: or would the difference in means be reduced to zero or even reversed in favor of the girls?

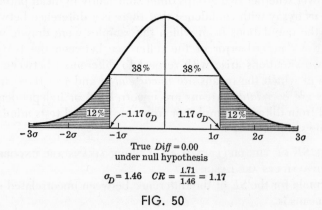

$$\sigma_D = 1.46 \quad CR = \frac{1.71}{1.46} = 1.17$$

FIG. 50

To answer these questions, we must compute the SE of the difference between the two means. By formula (56b):

$$\sigma_D = \sqrt{\frac{(7.81)^2}{83} + \frac{(11.56)^2}{95}}$$

$$= \sqrt{2.1415}$$

$$= 1.46 \text{ (to two decimals)}$$

The obtained difference between the means of the boys and girls is 1.71 (i.e., 30.92 − 29.21); and the SE of this difference (σ_D) is 1.46. As a first step in determining whether twelfth-grade boys and girls actually differ in mean ability, we shall set up a null hypothesis. This hypothesis asserts that the difference between the population means of boys and girls is zero and that—except for sampling accidents—mean differences from sample to sample will *all* be zero. Is the obtained mean difference of 1.71—in view of its SE—large enough to cast serious doubt on this null hypothesis?

To answer this question, we must compute a critical ratio or CR found by dividing the difference between the sample means by its standard error ($CR = D/\sigma_D$).* This operation reduces the obtained difference to a σ score, and enables us to measure it off along the base line of the sampling distribution of differences. In the present problem, $CR = 1.71/1.46$ or 1.17. When the N's of the samples are large (30 or more is "large"), the distribution of CR's is known to be normal around the true difference between the population means. In testing the null hypothesis, we set up a normal sampling distribution like that shown in Figure 50. The mean difference is set at zero (true difference) and the SD of this distribution of differences is 1.46(σ_D). In the figure, our CR falls at 1.17 on the base line to the *right* of the mean of 0, and also at −1.17 to the *left* of this mean. We need to measure in *both* directions (see p. 217) since under the null hypothesis (true difference of zero) differences between sample means are as likely to be plus as minus—to fall above as below the mean difference of zero.

From Table A we know that 38% × 2 or 76% of the cases in a normal distribution fall between the mean and ±1.17σ_D; and 24% of the cases fall outside these limits. This means that under the null hypothesis we can expect CR's as large as or larger than ±1.17 to occur "by chance" 24 times in 100 comparisons of the means of samples of twelfth-grade

* CR really equals $\dfrac{(M_1 - M_2) - 0}{\sigma_D}$ or $\dfrac{(D - 0)}{\sigma_D}$: the difference ($D$) between the two sample means is taken from .00 in terms of σ_D (see Fig. 50).

boys and girls on this test. A mean difference of ±1.71 (i.e., a CR of ±1.17), therefore, might easily arise as a sampling fluctuation from zero, and is clearly *not* significant. Accordingly, we retain the null hypothesis since—as far as our tests go—there is no reason to believe twelfth-grade boys and girls actually differ in mean performance on abstract reasoning tests. With respect to reasoning as represented by our test, the two groups could well have been random samples from the same population.

(2) LEVELS OF SIGNIFICANCE

Whether a difference is to be taken as statistically significant or not depends upon the probability that the given difference could have arisen "by chance." It also depends upon the purposes of the experiment (p. 189). Usually, a difference is marked "significant" when the gap between two sample means points to or signifies a real difference between the parameters of the populations from which our samples were drawn. Before a judgment of significant or nonsignificant is made, some critical point or points must be designated along the probability scale which will serve to separate these two judgment categories. At the same time, it must be stressed that judgments concerning differences are never absolute, but on the contrary range over a scale of probability, our confidence increasing as the chances of a wrong judgment decrease.

Experimenters and research workers have for convenience chosen several arbitrary standards—called *levels of significance*—of which the .05 and .01 levels are most often used. The confidence with which an experimenter rejects—or retains—a null hypothesis depends upon the level of significance adopted. From Table A we read that ±1.96σ mark off points along the base line of a normal distribution to the left and right of which lie 5% (2½% at each end of the curve) of the cases. When a CR is 1.96 or more, we may reject a null hypothesis at the .05 level of significance, on the grounds that not more than once in 20 repetitions of the same experiment would a difference as large as or larger than that found arise—*if* the true difference were zero. The CR of 1.17 in our problem (p. 214) falls short of 1.96 (does not reach the .05 level) and accordingly the null hypothesis is retained. Generally speaking, the level of significance which he will accept is set by an experimenter *before* he collects his data. It is not good practice to shift from a higher to a lower standard after the data are in.

The .01 level of significance is more exacting than the .05 level. From Table A we know that ±2.58σ mark off points to the left and right of which lie 1% of the cases in a normal distribution. If the CR is 2.58 or larger, then, we reject the null hypothesis at the 01 level, on the grounds that not more than once in 100 trials would a difference of this size arise if the true difference were zero (i.e., if $M_{pop_1} - M_{pop_2} = 0.00$).

The significance of a difference may also be evaluated by setting up confidence intervals for the population difference as was done for the M_{pop} on page 188. The limits specified by $D \pm 1.96\sigma_D$ define the .95 confidence interval for the population difference; and $D \pm 2.58\sigma_D$ define the .99 confidence interval for the true difference. To illustrate, let us return to the problem of whether twelfth-grade boys and girls differ in reasoning (p. 214). The difference between the sample means was 1.71 and the σ_D was 1.46. Hence, the .99 confidence interval for the true difference is $1.71 \pm 2.58 \times 1.46$, or it runs from -2.06 to 5.48. This is a fairly wide range, and the fact that it extends from minus to plus through zero shows clearly that the true D could well be zero. Acceptance of a null hypothesis always means that zero lies within the confidence interval with which we are working.

An example will serve to clarify further the use of significance levels.

> *Example* (2)   In the problem of the twelfth-grade boys and girls on page 214, suppose that the mean difference had been 3.40 in favor of the boys instead of 1.71, the N's and SD's remaining the same. Is this D significant at the .05 level?

The CR is $3.40/1.46$ or 2.33, which is clearly significant at the .05 level. This CR does not reach 2.58 and hence is not significant at the .01 level. From Table A or from Table D last line we find that 2% of a normal distribution falls beyond $\pm 2.33\sigma$: 1% at each end of the curve. The given difference is significant at the .02 level, therefore, and would be accepted at this level, had it been so stipulated at the start of the experiment.

(3) TWO-TAILED AND ONE-TAILED TESTS OF SIGNIFICANCE

Under the null hypothesis, differences between obtained means (i.e., $M_1 - M_2$) may be either plus or minus and as often in one direction as in the other from the true (population) difference of zero, so that in determining probabilities we take *both* tails of the sampling distribution (Fig. 50). This *two-tailed* test, as it is sometimes called, is generally used when we wish to discover whether two groups have conceivably been drawn from the same population with respect to the trait being measured [see example (1)].

In many experiments our primary concern is with the *direction* of the difference rather than with its existence in absolute terms. This situation arises when negative differences, if found, are of no importance practically; or when a difference if it exists at all must of necessity be positive. Suppose, for example, that we wish to determine the gain in vocabulary resulting from additional weekly reading assignments or want to evaluate the gain in numerical computation brought about by an extra hour of drill per day. It is unlikely that additional reading will lead to an actual loss in vocabulary. Moreover, if drill decreases arithmetic skill it would be the same as though it had no effect—in either event we would drop the drill. Only an increase as a result of drill, therefore, is of any practical interest.

In cases like these the *one-tailed* test of significance is appropriate. We may illustrate with example (3).

> *Example (3)* We know from experience that intensive coaching increases reading skill. Therefore, if a class has been coached, our hypothesis is that it will gain in reading comprehension—failure to gain or a loss in score is of no interest. At the end of a school year, Class A, which had received special coaching, averaged 5 points higher on a reading test than Class B, which had received no coaching. The standard error of this difference was 3. Is the gain significant?

To evaluate the 5 points gained, i.e., determine its significance, we must use the one-tailed and not the two-tailed test. The critical ratio is 5/3 or 1.67, and from Table D we find that 10% of the cases in a normal distribution lie to the left and right of 1.65σ, so that 5% $(P/2)$ lie to the right of 1.65σ. Our critical ratio of 1.67 just exceeds 1.65 and is significant at the .05 level through barely so (see Fig. 51). We reject the null hypothesis,

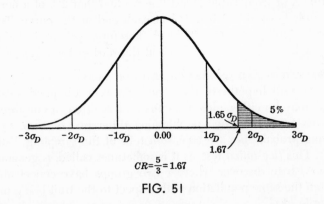

$$CR = \frac{5}{3} = 1.67$$

FIG. 51

therefore, since only once in 20 trials would a gain as large as or larger than 5 occur by chance. When a critical ratio is 2.33 $(P = .02$ and $P/2 = .01)$ we mark a positive difference significant at the .01 level.

It may be noted that in using the one-tailed test the experimenter sets up the hypothesis he wishes to test *before* he takes his data. This means that the experiment is designed at the outset to test the hypothesis; an hypothesis cannot be proposed to fit the data after they are in. If in example (3) we had been interested simply in whether Class A and Class B were significantly different in reading score, the two-tailed test would have been appropriate. As we have seen, the two-tailed test gives us the probability of a mean positive difference of 5 points (A ahead of B), together with the probability of a mean negative difference (loss) of 5 points (B ahead of A). This is true since under the null hypothesis fluctuations of sampling alone will tend to show A samples better than B samples, and B better than A, about equally often. A difference in favor of either A or B, therefore, is possible and equally acceptable.

The one-tailed test should be used when we wish to determine the probability of a score occurring beyond a stated value. An illustration is given in example (4).

> *Example* (4) In certain studies of deception among school children the scores achieved on tests given under conditions in which cheating was possible were compared with scores achieved by comparable groups under strictly supervised conditions. In a certain test given under "honest" conditions the mean is 62 and the σ is 10. Several children who took the test under nonsupervised conditions turned in scores of 87 and above. Is it probable that these children cheated?

The mean of 62 is 24.5 score units from 86.5, the lower limit of score 87. Dividing 24.5 by 10 we find that scores of 87 and above lie at the point 2.45σ above the mean of 62. On the assumption of normality of distribution, there is less than one chance in 100 that a score of 87 or more will appear in the "honest" distribution. While scores of 87 and above might, of course, be "honest," examinees who make such scores under nonsupervised conditions are certainly open to suspicion of having cheated. The one-tailed test is appropriate here as we are concerned only with the positive end of the distribution—the probability of scores of 87 and above.

(4) ERRORS IN MAKING INFERENCES

In testing hypotheses, two types of wrong inference can be drawn and must be reckoned with by the research worker. What are called Type I and Type II errors may be described as follows:

Type I errors are made when we *reject* a null hypothesis by marking a difference *significant,* although no true difference exists.

Type II errors are made when we *accept* a null hypothesis by marking a difference *not* significant, when a true difference actually exists.

The distinction between these two kinds of error can perhaps be made clear in the following way. Suppose that the difference between two population means $(M_{pop_1} - M_{pop_2})$ * is actually zero. If our test of significance when applied to the two sample means leads us to believe that the difference in population means is significant, we make a Type I error. On the other hand, suppose there *is* a true difference between the two population means. Now if our test of significance leads to the judgment "not significant," we commit a Type II error.

(*a*) *Example of a Type I error.* Various precautions can be taken to avoid both sorts of erroneous inference. If we set up a *low* level of significance (*P* greater than .05), we *increase* the likelihood of Type I errors; whereas, if we set up a *high* level of significance (*P* less than .05), we render such erroneous inferences less likely. How this works out in practice may best be shown by an example. Suppose that a silver dollar, known to us to be a good coin, is suspected by a numismatist of a bias in favor of heads.† When our numismatist tosses this coin 10 times, it turns up 8 heads and 2 tails. The theoretical expectation for a good coin is, of course, 5 heads and 5 tails; and the specific question for the numismatist to decide is whether the occurrence of 8 heads represents a "heads" bias— a significant deviation from the expected 5 heads. The distribution of heads and tails obtained when a single coin is tossed 10 times is given by expansion of the binomial $(p + q)^{10}$, where p = the probability of a head and q = the probability of a tail (non-head). Both p and q are $\frac{1}{2}$. The mean of $(p + q)^n$ is np and the SD is $\sqrt{npq}$; hence in our example the mean is 5 and the SD is $\sqrt{10 \cdot 1/2 \cdot 1/2}$ or 1.58. A "score" of 8 extends over the interval 7.5–8.5, so that to determine the probability of 8 or *more* heads the CR we wish is $\dfrac{7.5 - 5}{1.58}$ or 1.58 (see Fig. 52). (A problem similar to this will be found on p. 252). From Table A we know that 8 or *more* heads, that is, a CR of 1.58, may be expected on the null hypothesis approximately 6 times in 100 trials.‡ If our experimenter is willing to accept $P = .06$ as significant (i.e., set his standards low), he will *reject* the null hypothesis—although it is true. That is, he will report the coin to be biased in favor of heads, although it is in fact a good coin.

If our experimenter had set his significance level higher (say .01 or

* When $M_{pop_1} - M_{pop_2} = 0$, the two populations are the same with respect to the trait or characteristic being measured. For example, boys and girls may be thought of as constituting the *same* population with respect to most mental tests.

† If a coin is "leaded" or weighted on the tails side, the heads side, being lighter, will tend to appear more often than tails.

‡ This is a one-tailed test (p. 217) because our experimenter's hypothesis is that the coin is biased in favor of heads.

even .05) he would have avoided this erroneous inference. Furthermore, had he increased the number of tosses of the coin from 10 to 100 or even 500, he might have avoided his wrong inference, as heads and tails in a good coin will *tend* to occur equally often. Increasing the experimental data gives the null hypothesis a chance to assert itself (if true) and guards against freak results. We should not be willing to reject a null hypothesis too quickly, as in so doing we must assume the existence of a true difference—often a heavy responsibility.

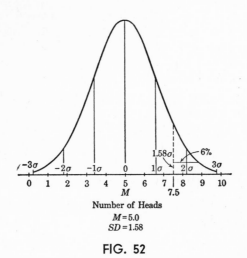

Number of Heads

M = 5.0

SD = 1.58

FIG. 52

(*b*) *Example of a Type II error.* In contrast to what happens in the case of Type I errors, the possibility of drawing erroneous inferences of the Type II sort (namely, accepting the null hypothesis when false) is *enhanced* when we set a very high level of significance. This may be shown by reference to the coin example above—with a change in conditions. Suppose that a silver dollar known to us to be biased in favor of heads is tested by a numismatist who believes it to be a good coin. Again the coin is tossed 10 times and shows, as did the coin before, 8 heads and 2 tails. From the data given on page 220, we know that in a good coin 8 or more heads can be expected by chance 6 in 100 throws—that is, $P = .06$. Now, if our numismatist sets .01 as his level of significance (or even .05), he will accept the null hypothesis and mark his result "not significant." The coin is now rated as "good" although it is actually biased, and our numismatist has committed a Type II error.

(*c*) *Avoiding errors in drawing inferences.* How can we guard against both types of erroneous inference? Perhaps the wisest first course—when significance is doubtful or uncertain—is to demand more evidence. This gives the data a chance to refute (or fail to refute) the null hypothesis. Additional data, repetition of the experiment, and better controls will often make possible a correct judgment. If a coin is biased toward heads, this bias will continue to cause more heads than tails to appear in further tosses. For example, if the ratio of 8 heads to 2 tails in the 10 tosses described in the last paragraph holds consistently, we shall get 80 heads and 20 tails in 100 throws. The critical ratio for 100 tosses will be 5.9 * (as compared with 1.58 for 10 tosses), and the probability is far less than .01 that 80 heads is a random fluctuation from the expected 50 heads. Our experimenter would correctly mark this result very significant—i.e., significant beyond the .01 level.

Setting a high level of significance will tend, then, to prevent Type I errors but will encourage the appearance of Type II errors. Hence it appears that an experimenter must decide which kind of wrong inference he would rather avoid, as apparently he can prevent one type of error only at the risk of making the other more likely. In the long run, errors of Type I (rejecting a null hypothesis when true, by marking a non-significant difference significant) are perhaps more likely to prove serious in a research program in the social sciences than are errors of Type II. If an experimenter claims a significant finding erroneously, for instance, the fact that it is a *positive* result is likely to terminate the research, so that the error persists. When a high level of significance is demanded (.01, say) we may feel assured that significance will be claimed incorrectly not more than once in 100 trials.

Errors of Type II (accepting the null hypothesis when false, i.e., when a true difference exists) must be watched for carefully when the experimental factor or factors are potentially dangerous. Thus, if one is studying the psychological effects of a drug suspected of inducing rather drastic emotional and temperamental changes, an error of Type II might well prove to be disastrous. Fortunately, the fact that a negative finding is inconclusive and often unsatisfactory may lead to further experimental work, and thus obviate somewhat the harm done by Type II errors. Especially is this true when the problem is important enough further to challenge investigators.

For many years it was customary for research workers in experimental

---

* When $n = 100$, $p = .50$, $q = .50$:

$$M = np = 50$$
$$\sigma = \sqrt{npq} = \sqrt{100 \times 1/2 \times 1/2} = 5$$
$$CR = \frac{79.5 - 50}{5} = 5.9$$

psychology to demand critical ratios of 3.00 or more before marking a difference significant. This extremely high standard almost certainly caused the null hypothesis to be accepted more often than it should have been—a Type II error on the side of conservatism. As a general rule it is probably wise to demand a significance level of at least .01 in most experimental research, i.e., to risk Type II errors by preventing those of Type I. But the .05 level is often satisfactory, especially in preliminary work.

3. The SE of the difference between M's in small independent samples

When the N's of two independent samples are small (less than 30), the SE of the difference between two means should depend upon the SD's computed by the formula $SD = \sqrt{\dfrac{\Sigma x^2}{(N-1)}}$, and the degrees of freedom in the two groups must be taken into account. Table D may be used conveniently to test the significance of t,[*] which is the appropriate critical ratio for use with small samples. An example will illustrate the procedures.

Example (5) An Interest Test is administered to 6 boys in a Vocational Training class and to 10 boys in a Latin class. Is the mean difference between the two groups significant at the .05 level?

Scores are as follows:

VOCATIONAL CLASS				LATIN CLASS			
$N_1 = 6$				$N_2 = 10$			
Scores	(X_1)	x_1	x_1^2	Scores	(X_2)	x_2	x_2^2
28		−2	4	20		−4	16
35		5	25	16		−8	64
32		2	4	25		1	1
24		−6	36	34		10	100
26		−4	16	20		−4	16
35		5	25	28		4	16
6 | 180			110	31		7	49
$M_1 = 30$				24		0	0
				27		3	9
				15		−9	81
				10 | 240			352
				$M_2 = 24$			

$$N_1 - 1 = 5$$
$$N_2 - 1 = \underline{9}$$
$$14$$

[*] t is a critical ratio in which a more exact estimate of the σ_D is used. The sampling distribution of t is not normal when N is small (less than 30, say). t is a CR; but all CR's are not t's (see p. 215).

$$SD(\text{or } s) = \sqrt{\frac{110 + 352}{14}} = 5.74 \qquad \text{by (57)}$$

$$SE_D = 5.74 \sqrt{\frac{6 + 10}{60}} = 5.74 \times .5164 = 2.96 \qquad \text{by (58)}$$

$$t = \frac{(30 - 24) - 0}{2.96} = 2.03$$

For 14 df, the .05 level (Table D) is 2.14; and the .01 level is 2.98.

The mean of the interest scores made by the 6 boys in the Vocational class is 30 and the mean of the interest scores made by the 10 boys in the Latin class is 24. The mean difference of 6 is to be tested for significance. When two samples are small, as here, we get a better estimate of the "true" SD (σ in the population) by pooling the sums of squares of the deviations taken around the means of the two groups and computing a single SD.* The justification for pooling is that under the null hypothesis no real mean difference exists as between the two samples, which are assumed to have been drawn from the same parent population with respect to the trait being measured. We have, therefore, only *one* σ (that of the common population) to estimate. Furthermore, by increasing N we get a more stable SD based upon *all* of our cases. The formula for computing this "pooled" SD and the formula for the SE of the difference are as follows:

$$SD = \sqrt{\frac{\Sigma(X_1 - M_1)^2 + \Sigma(X_2 - M_2)^2}{(N_1 - 1) + (N_2 - 1)}} \qquad (57)$$

(SD *when two small independent samples are pooled*)

$$SE_D = SD\sqrt{\frac{N_1 + N_2}{N_1 N_2}} \qquad (58)$$

(SE *of the difference between means in small independent samples*)

In formula (57), $\Sigma(X_1 - M_1)^2 = x^2_1$ is the sum of the square deviations around the mean of Group 1; and $\Sigma(X_2 - M_2)^2 = \Sigma x_2^2$ is the sum of the squared deviations around the mean of Group 2. These sums of squares are combined to give a single SD. In example (5) the sum of squares in the Vocational class around the mean of 30 is 110; and in the Latin class the sum of squares around the mean of 24 is 352. The df are $(N_1 - 1) = 5$, and $(N_2 - 1) = 9$.† By formula (57), therefore, the

---

* The SD so computed is subject to a slight negative bias, which is negligible when $N > 20$. See Holtzman, W. H., "The Unbiased Estimate of the Population Variance and Standard Deviation," *Amer. Jour. Psychol.*, 1950, 63, 615–617.

† 1 df is "used up" in computing each mean (p. 194).

$SD = \sqrt{\dfrac{110 + 352}{14}}$ or 5.74. This SD serves as a measure of variability for

each of the two groups. Thus the $SE_{M_1} = \dfrac{5.74}{\sqrt{6}}$ and the $SE_{M_2} = \dfrac{5.74}{\sqrt{10}}$ [by

formula (44), p. 185]. Combining these two SE's by formula (56) we

find that $SE_D = \sqrt{\dfrac{(5.74)^2}{6} + \dfrac{(5.74)^2}{10}} = 5.74\sqrt{\dfrac{16}{60}}$ or 2.96. Formula (58)

combines the two SE_M's enabling us to calculate SE_D in one operation.

$t = \dfrac{6}{2.96}$ or 2.03; and the df in the two groups (namely, 5 and 9) are

combined to give 14 df for use in inferring the significance of the mean
difference. Entering Table D with 14 df, we get the entries 2.14 at the .05
and 2.98 at the .01 levels. Since our t does not reach the .05 level, the
obtained mean difference of 6 must be marked "not significant."

An example will illustrate further the use of levels of significance when
samples are small.

Example (6)   On an arithmetic reasoning test 31 ten-year-old
boys and 42 ten-year-old girls made the following scores:

	Mean	SD	N	df
Boys:	40.39	8.69	31	30
Girls:	35.81	8.33	42	41

Is the mean difference of 4.58 in favor of the boys significant at the
.05 level?

By formula (57) we find

$$SD^* = \sqrt{\dfrac{(8.69)^2 \times 30 + (8.33)^2 \times 41}{71}} \text{ or } 8.48.$$

And by formula (58),

$$SE_D = 8.48\sqrt{\dfrac{31 + 42}{31 \times 42}} = 2.01.$$

t is 4.58/2.01 or 2.28 and the degrees of freedom for use in testing the
significance of the mean difference are $30 + 41$ or 71. Entering Table D
with 71 df we find t entries of 2.00 at the .05 and of 2.65 at the .01 levels.
The obtained t of 2.28 is significant at the .05 but not at the .01 level.
Only once in 20 comparisons of boys and girls on this test would we
expect to find a difference as large as or larger than 4.58 under our null
hypothesis. We may be reasonably confident, therefore, that in general
10-year-old boys do better than 10-year-old girls on this test.

* $SD^2 = \dfrac{\Sigma x^2}{(N-1)}$; hence $\Sigma x^2 = SD^2 \times (N-1)$.

4. The significance of the difference between two correlated means

(1) THE SINGLE GROUP METHOD

The preceding section dealt with the problem of determining whether the difference between two means is significant when these means represent the performance of *independent* groups—boys and girls, Latin and non-Latin students, and the like. A closely related problem is concerned with the significance of the difference between correlated means obtained from the *same* test administered to the *same* group upon two occasions. This experimental design is called the "single group" method. Suppose that we have administered a test to a group of children and two weeks later have repeated the test. We wish to measure the effect of practice or of special training upon the second set of scores; or to estimate the effects of some activity interpolated between test and retest. In order to determine the significance of the difference between the means obtained in the initial and final testing, we must use the formula

$$SE_D = \sqrt{\sigma^2{}_{M_1} + \sigma^2{}_{M_2} - 2r_{12}\sigma_{M_1}\sigma_{M_2}}$$
(59)

(SE *of the difference between correlated means*)

in which σ_{M_1} and σ_{M_2} are the SE's of the initial and final test means, and r_{12} is the coefficient of correlation between scores made on initial and final tests.* An illustration will bring out the difference between formula (56) and formula (59).

> *Example* (7)   At the beginning of the school year, the mean score of a group of 64 sixth-grade children upon an educational achievement test in reading was 45.00 with a σ of 6.00. At the end of the school year, the mean score on an equivalent form of the same test was 50.00 with a σ of 5.00. The correlation between scores made on the initial and final testing was .60. Has the class made significant progress in reading during the year?

We may tabulate our data as follows:

	Initial Test		Final Test
No. of children:	64		64
Mean score:	45.00(M_1)		50.00(M_2)
Standard Deviations:	6.00(σ_1)		5.00(σ_2)
Standard errors of means:	.75(σ_{M_1})		.63(σ_{M_2})
Difference between means:		5.00	
Correlation between initial and final tests:		.60	

* The correlation between the means of successive samples drawn from a given population equals the correlation between test scores, the means of which are being compared.

Since we are concerned only with progress or *gain*, this is a one-tailed test (p. 217). Substituting in formula (59) we get

$$SE_D = \sqrt{(.75)^2 + (.63)^2 - 2 \times .60 \times .75 \times .63} = .63$$

The t ratio is 5.00/.63 or 7.9. Since there are 64 children, there are 64 pairs of scores and 64 differences,* so that the df becomes $64 - 1$ or 63. From Table D, the t for 63 df is 2.39 at the .02 level. (The table gives 2.39 for the two-tailed test which is .01 for the one-tailed test.) The obtained t of 7.9 is far greater than 2.39 and hence can be marked "very significant." It seems certain that the class made substantial progress in reading over the school year.

When groups are small, a procedure called the "difference method" is often to be preferred to that given above. The following example will serve as an illustration:

Example (8)   Twelve subjects are given 5 successive trials upon a digit-symbol test of which only the scores for trials 1 and 5 are shown. Is the mean gain from initial to final trial significant?

Trial 1	Trial 5	Difference (5 − 1)	x	x^2
50	62	12	4	16
42	40	−2	−10	100
51	61	10	2	4
26	35	9	1	1
35	30	−5	−13	169
42	52	10	2	4
60	68	8	0	0
41	51	10	2	4
70	84	14	6	36
55	63	8	0	0
62	72	10	2	4
38	50	12	4	16
$\overline{572}$	$\overline{668}$	12|96		$\overline{354}$
		8		

$Mean_D = 8.0$

$$SD_D = \sqrt{\frac{354}{11}} = 5.67$$

$$SE_{M_D} = \frac{5.67}{\sqrt{12}} = 1.64$$

$$t = \frac{8 - 0}{1.64} = 4.88$$

* 1 df is lost since SE_D is computed around the mean of the distribution of differences (p. 194).

From the column of differences between pairs of scores, the mean difference is found to be 8, and the SD around this mean (SD_D) by the formula $SD = \sqrt{\dfrac{\Sigma x^2}{(N-1)}}$ is 5.67. On our null hypothesis the true difference between the means of Trials 5 and 1 is 0, so that we must test our obtained mean difference of 8 against this hypothetical zero gain. The SE of the mean difference $\left(SE_{M_D} = \dfrac{SD}{\sqrt{N}}\right)$ is 1.64 and $t\left(\dfrac{D-0}{SE_{M_D}}\right)$ is 4.88. Entering Table D with 11 $(12-1)$ degrees of freedom, we find t entries of 2.20 and 3.11 at the .05 and at the .01 levels. Our t of 4.88 is far above the .01 level and the mean difference of 8 is obviously very significant.

If our hypothesis initially had been that practice *increases* test score, we would have used the *one-tailed test*. The probability of a positive difference (gain) of 8 or more on the null hypothesis is quite remote. In the one-tailed test, for 11 df the .05 level is read from the .10 column $(P/2 = .05)$ to be 1.80 and the .01 level from the .02 column $(P/2 = .01)$ is 2.72. Our t of 4.88 is much larger than the .01 level of 2.72 and there is little doubt that the *gain* from Trial 1 to Trial 5 is significant.

The result found in example (8) may be checked by the single group method. By use of formula (31), p. 145, the r between Trials 1 and 5 is found to be .944. Substituting for r_{12} (viz., .944), for σ_{M_1} (3.65) and for σ_{M_2} (4.55) in formula (59) we get a σ_D of 1.63 which checks SE_{M_D} within the error of computation. The "difference method" is quicker and easier to apply than is the longer method of calculating SE's for each mean and the SE of the difference, and is to be preferred unless the correlation between initial and final scores is wanted.

(2) THE METHOD OF EQUIVALENT GROUPS: MATCHING BY PAIRS

Formula (59) is applicable in those experiments which make use of *equivalent groups* as well as in those using a single group. In the method of equivalent groups the matching is done initially by *pairs* so that each person in the first group has a match in the second group. This procedure enables us to set off the effects of one or more experimentally varied conditions (experimental factors) against the absence of these same variables (control). The following problem is typical of many in which the equivalent group technique is useful.

Example (9)   Two groups, X and Y, of seventh-grade children, 72 in each group, are paired child for child for age and score on Form A of the Otis Group Intelligence Scale. Three weeks later, both groups are given Form B of the same test. Before the second test, Group X, the experimental group, is praised for its performance on the first test and urged to try to better its score. Group Y, the control group, is given the second test without comment. Will the incentive (praise) cause the final scores of Group X and Group Y to differ significantly?

This is a two-tailed test, since the incentive (praise) could conceivably raise or lower the mean of the experimental group. The relevant data may be tabulated as follows:

	Experimental Group X	Control Group Y
No. of children in each group:	72	72
Mean scores on Form A, initial test:	80.42	80.51
SD on Form A, initial test:	23.61	23.46
Mean scores on Form B, final test:	88.63(M_1)	83.24(M_2)
SD on Form B, final test:	24.36(σ_1)	21.62(σ_2)
Gain, $M_1 - M_2$:	5.39	
Standard errors of means, final tests:	2.89	2.57

Correlation between final scores (experimental and control groups) = .65

The means and σ's of the control and experimental groups in Form A (initial test) are almost identical, showing the original pairing of scores to have been quite satisfactory. The correlation between the final scores on Form B of the Otis Test is calculated from the paired scores of children who were matched originally in terms of initial score.*

The difference between the means on the final test is 5.39 (88.63 − 83.24). the SE of this difference, σ_D, is found from formula (59) to be

$$\sigma_D = \sqrt{(2.89)^2 + (2.57)^2 - 2 \times .65 \times 2.89 \times 2.57} = 2.30$$

The t ratio is 5.39/2.30 or 2.34; and since there are 72 pairs, there are (72 − 1) or 71 degrees of freedom. Entering Table D with 71 df we find the t's at .05 and .01 to be 2.00 and 2.65, respectively. The given difference is significant at the .05 but not at the .01 level; and we may feel reasonably certain that praise will have a significant effect in stimulating the performance of seventh-grade children.

It is worth noting that had no account been taken of the correlation between final scores on Form B [if formula (56) had been used instead of (59)], σ_D would have been 3.87 instead of 2.30. t would then have been 1.39 instead of 2.34 and would have fallen considerably below the .05 level of 2.00. In other words, a significant finding would have been marked

* Note that the correlation between final scores in the equivalent groups method is analogous to the correlation between initial and final scores in the single group method. In equivalent groups one group is the experimental and the other the control. In the single group method, the initial scores furnish the control.

"not significant." Evidently, it is important that we take account of the correlation between final scores—especially if it is high.

When $r = .00$, formula (59) reduces to (56) since group means are then independent or uncorrelated. Also, when r is positive, the σ_D from formula (59) is smaller than the σ_D from (56) and the larger the plus r the greater the reduction in σ_D by use of (59). For a given difference between means, the smaller the σ_D the larger the t and the more significant the obtained difference. The relative efficiency obtained by using a single group or equivalent groups as compared with independent groups can be determined by the *size* of the r between final scores, or between initial and final scores. The correlation coefficient, therefore, gives a measure of the advantage to be gained by matching.

If r is negative, formula (59) gives a larger σ_D than that given by formula (56). In this case, the failure to take account of the correlation will lead to a smaller σ_D and a t larger and apparently more significant than it should be.

One further point may be mentioned. If the difference between the means of two groups is significant by formula (56) it will, of course, be even more significant by formula (59) if r is positive. Formula (56) may be used in a preliminary test, therefore, if we can be sure that the correlation is positive. The correlation between initial and final score is usually positive, though rarely as high as that found in example (9).

(3) GROUPS MATCHED FOR MEAN AND SD

When it is impracticable or impossible to set up groups in which subjects have been matched person for person, investigators often resort to the matching of groups in terms of mean and σ. The matching variable is usually different from the variable under study but is, in general, related to it and sometimes highly related. No attempt is made to pair off individuals and the two groups are not necessarily of the same size, although a large difference in N is not advisable.

In comparing final score means of matched groups the procedure is somewhat different from that used with equivalent groups. Suppose that X is the variable under study, and Y is the function or variable in terms of which our two groups have been equated as to mean and SD. Then if r_{xy} is the correlation between X and Y *in the population* from which our samples have been drawn, the SE of the difference between means in X is

$$SE_{D_{M_1-M_2}} = \sigma_D = \sqrt{\left(\sigma^2_{M_{x_1}} + \sigma^2_{M_{x_2}}\right)\left(1 - r^2_{xy}\right)} \tag{60}$$

(SE *of the difference between the* X *means of groups matched for mean and for* SD *in* Y)

An example will illustrate the procedure.

Example (10) The achievement of two groups of first-year high-school boys, the one from an academic and the other from a technical high school, is compared on a Mechanical Aptitude Test. The two groups are matched for mean and *SD* upon a general intelligence test so that the experiment becomes one of comparing the mechanical aptitude scores of two groups of boys of "equal" general intelligence enrolled in different courses of study. Do the two groups differ in mean ability?

	Academic	Technical
No. of boys in each group:	125	137
Means on Intelligence Test (Y):	102.50	102.80
σ's on Intelligence Test (Y):	33.65	31.62
Means on Mechanical Ability Test (X):	51.42	54.38
σ's on Mechanical Ability Test (X):	6.24	7.14

Correlation between the General Intelligence Test and the Mechanical Ability Test for first-year high-school boys is .30.

$$M_{x_1} - M_{x_2} = 54.38 - 51.42 = 2.96$$

$$\text{By (60) } \sigma_D = \sqrt{\left(\frac{(6.24)^2}{125} + \frac{(7.14)^2}{137}\right)(1 - .30^2)}$$

$$= .79$$

$$t = \frac{2.96}{.79} = 3.75$$

Again this is a two-tailed test. The difference between the mean scores in the Mechanical Ability Test of the academic and technical high-school boys is 2.96 and the σ_D is .79. The t is 2.96/.79 or 3.75; and the degrees of freedom to be used in testing this t are $(125 - 1) + (137 - 1) - 1$, or 259.* We must subtract the one additional df to allow for the fact that our groups were matched in variable Y. The general rule (p. 194) is that 1 df is subtracted for *each* restriction imposed upon the observations, i.e., for each matching variable.

Entering Table D with 259 df, we find that our t of 3.75 is larger than the entry of 2.59 at the .01 level. The observed difference in mechanical aptitude, therefore, though small, is highly significant. In rejecting the null hypothesis in this problem we are asserting that in general boys in the technical high school are higher in mechanical aptitude than are boys of "equal general intelligence" in the academic high school.

* When $df = 259$ little is gained by using t as the CR.

The correlation term must be introduced into formula (60) because when two groups have been matched in some test or tests their variability is restricted in *all* functions correlated with the matching variables. Height and weight, for instance, are highly correlated in 9-year-old boys. Hence, if a group of 9-year-old boys of the same or nearly the same height is selected, the variability in weight of these children will be substantially reduced as compared with 9-year-old boys in general. When groups are matched for several variables, e.g., age, intelligence, socioeconomic status, and the like, and compared with respect to some correlated variable, the correlation coefficient in formula (60) becomes a multiple coefficient of correlation (p. 404). When $r_{xy} = .00$, (60) reduces to (56)—our groups are independent and unrestricted by the matching variable.

Groups matched for mean and σ and equivalent groups in which individuals are paired as to score have been widely used in a variety of psychological and educational studies. Illustrations are found in experiments designed to evaluate the relative merits of two methods of teaching, the effects of drugs, e.g., tobacco or caffeine, upon efficiency, transfer effects of special training, and the like. Other techniques useful in assessing the role of experimental factors are described in Chapter 10.

5. The SE of the difference between uncorrelated medians

The significance of the difference between two medians obtained from independent samples may be found from the formula

$$\sigma_{D_{Mdn}} \text{ or } \sigma_{Mdn_1 - Mdn_2} = \sqrt{\sigma^2_{Mdn_1} + \sigma^2_{Mdn_2}} \tag{61}$$

(SE *of the difference between two uncorrelated medians*)

When medians are correlated, the value of r_{12} cannot be determined accurately and the reliability of the median cannot be readily computed. When samples are not independent, therefore, it is better procedure to use means instead of medians.

II. THE SIGNIFICANCE OF THE DIFFERENCE BETWEEN σ's

I. SE of the difference between standard deviations

(1) THE SE OF A DIFFERENCE WHEN σ'S ARE UNCORRELATED

In many studies in psychology and education, the differences in variability among groups is a matter of considerable importance. The student of individual and of experimentally induced differences is oftentimes more interested in knowing whether his groups differ significantly in SD than in knowing whether they differ in mean achievement. And the educational psychologist who is investigating a new method of teaching arithmetic may want to know whether the changed procedures have led to greater variability in score than that present under the older method.

When samples are independent, i.e., when different groups are studied or when tests given to the same groups are uncorrelated, the significance of a difference between two σ's may be found from the formula:

$$\sigma_{D_\sigma} \text{ or } \sigma_{\sigma_1 - \sigma_2} = \sqrt{\sigma^2_{\sigma_1} + \sigma^2_{\sigma_2}} \qquad (62)$$

(SE *of the difference between two uncorrelated σ's when N's are large*)

in which σ_{σ_1} is the SE of the first σ and σ_{σ_2} is the SE of the second σ.

By way of illustration, let us apply our formula to the data obtained from twelfth-grade boys and girls on the Abstract Reasoning Test (p. 214). The σ of the boys' scores is 7.81; of the girls' scores 11.56. Is this difference of 3.75 significant at the .01 level? Calling the σ of the boys' scores σ_1 and the σ of the girls' scores σ_2, we have

$$\sigma_{\sigma_1} = \frac{.71 \times 7.81}{\sqrt{83}} = .61$$

$$\sigma_{\sigma_2} = \frac{.71 \times 11.56}{\sqrt{95}} = .84$$

and $\sigma_{D_\sigma} = \sqrt{(.61)^2 + (.84)^2} = 1.04$ (to two decimals)

The CR is 3.75/1.04 or 3.61. On the null hypothesis ($\sigma_1 - \sigma_2 = 0$), this CR (Table D, last line) is considerably larger than 2.58 the .01 point. Hence, the obtained difference is significant beyond the .01 level; and we may feel quite confident that on our reasoning test the girls are more variable in general than are the boys.

Formula (62) is adequate for testing the significance of the difference between two uncorrelated SD's when N's are large (greater than 30). For a method of testing the significance of the difference between two σ's computed from small samples, see page 303.

(2) SE OF A DIFFERENCE WHEN σ'S ARE CORRELATED

When we compare the σ's of the same group upon two occasions or the σ's of equivalent groups on a final test, we must take into account possible correlation between the σ's in the two groups being compared. The formula for testing the significance of an obtained difference in variability when SD's are correlated is

$$\sigma_{D_\sigma} = \sqrt{\sigma^2_{\sigma_1} + \sigma^2_{\sigma_2} - 2r^2_{12}\sigma_{\sigma_1}\sigma_{\sigma_2}} \qquad (63)$$

(SE *of the difference between correlated σ's when N's are large*) where σ_{σ_1} and σ_{σ_2} are the SE's of the two SD's and $r^2{}_{12}$ is the square of the coefficient of correlation between scores in initial and final tests or between final scores of equivalent groups.*

Formula (63) may be applied to the problems on page 226 by way of illustration. In the first problem, the SD of 64 sixth-grade children was 6.0 on the initial and 5.0 on the final test. Is there a significant drop in variability in reading after a year's schooling? Putting $\sigma_1 = 6.0$ and $\sigma_2 = 5.0$, we have

$$\sigma_{\sigma_1} = \frac{.71 \times 6.0}{\sqrt{64}} = .53 \qquad \text{by (48)}$$

$$\sigma_{\sigma_2} = \frac{.71 \times 5.0}{\sqrt{64}} = .44$$

The coefficient of correlation between initial and final scores is .60, so that $r^2{}_{12} = .36$. Substituting for r^2 and the σ_σ's in formula (63) we have

$$\sigma_{D_\sigma} = \sqrt{(.53)^2 + (.44)^2 - 2 \times .36 \times .53 \times .44} = .55$$

The difference between the two σ's is 1.0 and the SE of this difference is .55. Therefore, on the null hypothesis of equal σ's, $t = \dfrac{(6-5) - 0}{.55}$ or 1.82. Entering Table D with 63 df, we find t at the .05 level to be 2.00. The obtained t does not quite reach this point, and there is no reason to suspect a true difference in variability between initial and final reading scores.

In the equivalent groups problem on page 228, the SD of the experimental group on the final test was 24.36 and the SD of the control group on the final test was 21.62. The difference between these SD's is 2.74 and the number of children in each group is 72. Did the incentive (praise) produce significantly greater variability in the experimental group as compared with the control? Putting $\sigma_1 = 24.36$, and $\sigma_2 = 21.62$, we have

$$\sigma_{\sigma_1} = \frac{.71 \times 24.36}{\sqrt{72}} = 2.04 \qquad \text{by (48)}$$

$$\sigma_{\sigma_2} = \frac{.71 \times 21.62}{\sqrt{72}} = 1.81$$

The r between final test scores in the experimental and control groups is .65 and $r^2{}_{12}$, therefore, is .42. Substituting for r^2 and the two SE's in formula (63) we have

* The correlation between the SD's of samples drawn from a given population equals the square of the coefficient of correlation between the test scores, the SD's of which are being compared.

$$\sigma_{D_\sigma} = \sqrt{(2.04)^2 + (1.81)^2 - 2 \times .42 \times 2.04 \times 1.81}$$

$$= 2.08$$

Dividing 2.74 by 2.08, our t is 1.32; and for 71 degrees of freedom this t falls well below the .05 level of 2.00. There is no evidence, therefore, that the incentive increased variability of response to the test.

III. THE SIGNIFICANCE OF THE DIFFERENCE BETWEEN PERCENTAGES AND CORRELATION COEFFICIENTS

1. The significance of the difference between two percents

(1) SE OF THE DIFFERENCE WHEN PERCENTS ARE UNCORRELATED

On page 197, the formula for the SE of a percentage was given as $SE_{\%} = \sqrt{\dfrac{PQ}{N}}$ where $P =$ percent occurrence of the observed behavior, $Q = (1 - P)$, and N is the size of the sample. One of the most useful applications of the SE formula is in determining the significance of the difference between two percents. In much experimental work, especially in social and abnormal psychology, we are able to get the percent occurrence of a given behavior in two or more independent samples. We then want to know whether the incidence of this behavior is reliably different in the two groups. The following problem which repeats part of example (4), will provide an illustration.

> *Example (11)* In a study of cheating * among elementary-school children, 144 or 41.4% of 348 children from homes of good socio-economic status were found to have cheated on various tests. In the same study, 133 or 50.2% of 265 children from homes of poor socio-economic status also cheated on the same tests. Is there a true difference in the incidence of cheating in these two groups?

Let us set up the hypothesis that no true difference exists as between the percentages cheating in the two groups and that, with respect to cheating, both samples have been randomly drawn from the same population. A useful procedure in testing this null hypothesis is to consider P_1 (41.4%) and P_2 (50.2%) as being independent determinations of the common population parameter, P; and to estimate P by pooling P_1 and P_2 (see p. 30). A pooled estimate of P is obtained from the equation:

$$P = \frac{N_1 P_1 + N_2 P_2}{N_1 + N_2}$$

Q being, of course, $(1 - P)$.

* Data from Hartshorne, H., and May, M. A., *Studies in Deceit* (New York: Macmillan, 1928), Book II, p. 161.

The estimated percentages, P and Q, may now be put in formula (64) to give the SE of the difference between P_1 and P_2.

$$\sigma_{D_\%} = \sigma_{P_1 - P_2} = \sqrt{\sigma^2_{P_1} + \sigma^2_{P_2}} \qquad (64)$$

or

$$= \sqrt{PQ\left[\frac{1}{N_1} + \frac{1}{N_2}\right]}$$

(SE *of the difference between two uncorrelated percentages*)

In the present example, $P = \dfrac{348 \times 41.4 + 265 \times 50.2}{348 + 265}$ or 45.2% and $Q = (1 - P)$ or 54.8%. Substituting these two values in (64) we get

$$\sigma_{P_1 - P_2} = \sqrt{45.2 \times 54.8 \left[\frac{1}{348} + \frac{1}{265}\right]} = 4.06\%$$

The difference between the two percents P_1 and P_2 is 8.8% $(50.2 - 41.4)$; and dividing by 4.06 $\left(CR = \dfrac{(P_1 - P_2) - 0}{\sigma_{P_1 - P_2}}\right)$ we get a CR of 2.17. Entering Table D we find that our CR exceeds 1.96 (.05 level) but does not reach 2.58 (.01 level).

The obtained difference is significant, therefore, at the .05 level of confidence. We may feel reasonably sure that our two samples do not come from a common population with respect to deception, and that there is a true difference in the incidence of cheating in these two socioeconomic groups.

The .95 confidence interval for the difference between the means in the two populations is 8.8 ± 1.96 × 4.06 or 8.8% ± 8.0%. The lower limit of this interval is .8%—evidence that our assurance is not so great as it would have been had our CR reached the .01 level.

(2) *SE* OF THE DIFFERENCE WHEN PERCENTS ARE CORRELATED

Responses recorded in percentages may be, and usually are, correlated when individuals have been paired or matched in some attribute; or when the same group gives answers (e.g., "Yes"–"No") to the same questions or items. To illustrate with an example:

> *Example (12)* A large group of veterans (250°) answered as follows the two questions below. Is the difference between the percents answering the two questions "Yes" significant?
> 1. Do you have a great many bad headaches?   Yes 150   No 100
> 2. Are you troubled with fears of being crushed
>   in a crowd?   Yes 125   No 125

° The data have been simplified for illustrative purposes.

	#1					#1		
	No	Yes				No	Yes	
Yes	25	100	125		Yes	(b) 10%	(a) 40%	50%
#2					#2			
No	75	50	125		No	(d) 30%	(c) 20%	50%
	100	150	250			40%	60%	100%

The data in the 2×2 table on the left show the number who answered "Yes" to both questions, "No" to both questions, "Yes" to one and "No" to the other. In the second diagram (on the right) frequencies are expressed as percents of 250. The letters a, b, c, and d are to designate the four cells (p. 137). We find that a total of 60% answered "Yes" to Question 1, and that a total of 50% answered "Yes" to Question 2. Is this difference significant?

The general formula for the significance of the difference between two correlated percents is

$$\sigma_{P_1-P_2} = \sqrt{\sigma^2_{P_1} + \sigma^2_{P_2} - 2r_{P_1P_2}\sigma_{P_1}\sigma_{P_2}} \qquad (65)$$

(SE *of difference between two correlated percents*)

in which r between the two percents is given by the phi coefficient (p. 388), a ratio equivalent to the correlation coefficient in 2×2 tables. If P_1 and P_2 have been averaged in order to provide an estimate of P, the population parameter, formula (65) becomes

$$\sigma_{P_1-P_2} = \sqrt{2\sigma^2_P (1 - r_{P_1P_2})} \qquad (66)$$

(SE *of the difference between two correlated percents when*
P *is estimated from* P_1 *and* P_2)

In example (12), $P_1 = 60\%$ and $P_2 = 50\%$, so that $P = 55\%$ and $Q = 45\%$. Substituting in (66) we have that

$$\sigma_{P_1-P_2} = \sqrt{\frac{2 \times .55 \times .45}{250} (1 - .41)}°$$

$$= .034$$

The obtained difference of .10 (.60 − .50) divided by .034 gives a CR of 2.94. From Table D, we find that this critical ratio exceeds 2.58, the .01 level. We abandon the null hypothesis, therefore, and conclude that our groups differed significantly in their answers to the two questions.

° The phi coefficient of .41 was found from formula (99), page 389.

A simpler formula than (66) which avoids the calculation of the correlation coefficient may be used when P has been estimated from P_1 and P_2 under the null hypothesis. This formula * is

$$\sigma_{D_\%} = \sqrt{\frac{(b+c)}{N}} \qquad (67)$$

(SE *of the difference between two correlated percentages*)

In example (12) we read from the second diagram that $c = 20\%$ and $b = 10\%$, N being 250. Substituting in (67) we have

$$\sigma_{D_\%} = \sqrt{\frac{.10 + .20}{250}} = .035$$

which checks the result obtained from (66).

2. Comparing obtained percents with reference values

In many situations (in polling, for example), the percentage occurrence of a certain response is known from previous work, or is strongly suspected from other evidence. We are then interested in discovering whether a sample percentage deviates significantly from this reference value. The example below illustrates the problem.

> *Example (13)* Opinion upon a certain issue is believed to be split 50–50 in the population. In a sample of 225 voters, it is found that 55% respond affirmatively to the issue. Is this deviation from "chance" (50–50) significant at the .05 level?

If we let the probability of "Yes" or $p = 1/2$, and the probability of "No" or q also be $1/2$, we find the SE of our percentage (p. 197) to be

$$\sigma_p = \sqrt{\frac{.50 \times .50}{225}} = .033$$

We will reject the null hypothesis if p is either .45 or .55—deviates $\pm.05$ from expectation—hence we have a two-tailed test. The critical ratio is

$$CR = \frac{.55 - .50}{.033} = 1.51$$

and from Table D, this CR obviously does not reach 1.96 and hence is not significant at the .05 level. The 55% of "Yes" responses in our sample could well be a sampling fluctuation from 50% and hence attributable to chance.

---

* McNemar, Q., "Note on the Sampling Error of the Difference between Correlated Proportions or Percentages," *Psychometrika*, 1947, 12, 153–157.

Example (14) In a sample of 400 children from "good" homes, 49% are found to have cheated on various tests. If we accept 41% as the "standard percentage" for children in populations of this sort (p. 197), is cheating in our present group significantly greater than expectation?

The $SE_p = \sqrt{\dfrac{.41 \times .59}{400}} = .025$ and the CR is $\dfrac{.49 - .41}{.025} = 3.20$. In this problem, we are concerned to know whether 49% is significantly larger than 41%—we have a one-tailed test. The .05 point for a one-tailed test is 1.65 ($P = .10$, Table D). Our CR is so much larger than 1.65 that we confidently reject the null hypothesis. It appears that cheating in this group is significantly greater than it was in the previous study.

3. Size of N needed to reach a given level of significance

In many public opinion polls, forecasts are often reported as being accurate to within 3% or 5% of the "true" value, and this range is called the "allowable" error. Suppose that opinion on a political issue is known from past records to be split 50–50 in the voting population. How large a sample is needed in order that the odds may be 19:1 that our sample percentage is *not* in error by more than ±3%? Stated differently, how large an N is required in order that we may feel assured that *any* sample percentage between 47% and 53% represents a nonsignificant deviation from 50%?

This question cannot be answered unless we know (1) the percentage occurrence of the behavior in the population with some accuracy and (2) unless we can specify the degree of assurance demanded. First, we begin with the fact that $CR = D/\sigma_p$ where D is the deviation of a sample percentage from the expected (population) value, and σ_p is the SE of the sampling distribution of percents around the true or population percentage. When $D/\sigma_p = 1.96$, a deviation or D is significant at the .05 level, and we have a two-tailed test. Substituting .03 for D, and solving for σ_p we have that $\sigma_p = .03/1.96$ or .0153. Since $\sigma_p = \sqrt{\dfrac{pq}{N}}$ (p. 197), squaring and solving for N, we have that

$$N = \frac{pq}{\sigma_p{}^2} \qquad (67a)$$

(N *needed to reach a given level of significance*)

and substituting $(.0153)^2$ for σ_p and $.50 \times .50$ for pq, we have that

$$N = \frac{.50 \times .50}{(.0153)} = 1068$$

We now are able to say that when N is 1068, any obtained percent within the limits 50% ± 3% (i.e., from 53% to 47%) represents a nonsignificant deviation from the stipulated population value. A sample percentage must be larger than 53% or smaller than 47% in order to represent a significant departure from 50% at the .05 level of significance.

> *Example* (15) In a college population, opinion is believed to favor an issue to the extent of 80%. How large a sample is needed in order that the odds may be 99:1 that a sample percentage between 75% and 85% represents a nonsignificant deviation from the expected 80%? (Here the allowable margin of error is ±5% and we are to test at the .01 level.)

Following the method of the preceding example, $D/\sigma_p = 2.58$, and when $D = .05$, $\sigma_p = .05/2.58$ or .0194. From formula (67a), we have that

$$N = \frac{.80 \times .20}{(.0194)^2} = 425$$

and a sample of 425 should assure that any sample percent between 75% and 85% will represent a nonsignificant departure from 80%.

To check the obtained N, compute $\sigma_p = \sqrt{\dfrac{.80 \times .20}{425}} = .0194$. The .99 confidence interval is .80 ± 2.58 × .0194 or 80% ± 5%, thus checking the allowable error. The odds are 99:1 that when N is 425 the sample percent must be larger than 85% and smaller than 75% to be significant at the .01 level. Any percent between these limits represents a nonsignificant deviation within the stipulated error of 5%.

Decision as to the most economical N to use is difficult when the occurrence of the phenomenon in the population is uncertain. The following problem will illustrate the procedure in such cases.

> *Example* (16) A physical anthropologist wishes to study the members of a primitive tribe. Among other data he wants to know the proportion in the tribe who are "longheaded" (dolichocephalic). He states that his figure must be accurate within 5%, i.e., if his sample shows 40% longheads, the percent for the whole tribe must lie between 35% and 45%. The anthropologist stipulates that he is unwilling to accept more than one chance in 20 of getting a bad sample. He insists that this precaution is necessary since no matter how large the sample N there is always some chance that a single sample will be biased in some way.
>
> This problem cannot be solved unless the anthropologist can supply a probable value for the percent of longheads in the tribe. Suppose he finally says that from previous work with related tribes, he

estimates the incidence of longheadedness in the population to lie between 30% and 60%. Can we compute a satisfactory N under these conditions?

Following the method of preceding examples, $CR = D/\sigma_p = 1.96$ and if D is $\pm 5\%$, $\sigma_p = .05/1.96$ or $.0255$. From formula (67a), setting $p = 30\%$, we have

$$N = \frac{.30 \times .70}{(.0255)^2} = 323$$

and again putting $p = 60\%$, we have that

$$N = \frac{.60 \times .40}{(.0255)^2} = 369$$

Finally, if p is set at 50%, the product pq is at its maximum and equals .2500. When this is true, N is 385 and we might set the desired N at 385 or, to be on the safe side, at 400. A random sample of around 400, then, should provide a group in which the odds are 19:1 that the percent of longheads is within $\pm 5\%$ of the percent in the whole tribe.

To check the above result, put the population $p = 45\%$, i.e., $\left(\frac{30\% + 60\%}{2}\right)$, and $N = 400$. Then $\sigma_p = \sqrt{\frac{.45 \times .55}{400}} = .025$. Any percent in the range $45\% \pm 1.96 \times 2.5\%$ or $45\% \pm 5\%$ represents a nonsignificant deviation from 45%. The interval 40%–50% represents the .95 confidence interval for the population percentage.

4. The significance of the difference between two r's

A useful and mathematically exact method of determining the SE of the difference between two r's requires that we first convert the r's into Fisher's z function. The significance of the difference between two z's is then determined. The formula for the SE of the difference between two z's is

$$\sigma_{D_z} = \sigma_{z_1 - z_2} = \sqrt{\frac{1}{N_1 - 3} + \frac{1}{N_2 - 3}} \qquad (68)$$

(SE *of the difference between two z coefficients*)

where $\sigma_z = \dfrac{1}{\sqrt{(N-3)}}$ * and N_1 and N_2 are the sizes of the two samples.

* The two correlated variables take away 2 degrees of freedom; and the transformation into z adds another restriction. Hence we subtract 3 from each N (p. 194).

The following example will illustrate the procedure.

Example (17) The r between intelligence and achievement in the freshman class of College A is .40, for $N = 400$. And the r between intelligence and achievement in the freshman class of College B is .50 for $N = 600$. Is the relationship between intelligence and achievement higher in College B than in College A?

From Table C we read that r's of .40 and .50 correspond to z's of .42 and .55, respectively. If we put $N_1 = 400$ and $N_2 = 600$, we have on substituting in (68)

$$\sigma_{z_1-z_2} = \sqrt{\frac{1}{(400-3)} + \frac{1}{(600-3)}}$$

$$= .07 \text{ (to 2 decimals)}$$

Dividing .13 (i.e., .55 − .42) by .07, we get a CR of 1.86. This CR is slightly below 1.96 and hence is not significant at the .05 level. Based on the evidence we have, the correlation between intelligence and scholastic achievement does not really differ in the two colleges.

Use of the z transformation for r is especially useful when r's are very high, as the sampling distributions of such r's are known to be skewed— often badly so. To illustrate, suppose that r between two achievement tests is .87 in Grade 6 ($N_1 = 50$) and that the r between the same tests is .72 in Grade 7 ($N_2 = 65$). Is there a significant difference between these two r's?

From Table C we find that r's of .87 and .72 yield z's of 1.33 and .91, respectively; and substituting N_1 and N_2 in formula (68) we have

$$\sigma_{z_1-z_2} = \sqrt{\frac{1}{47} + \frac{1}{62}}$$

$$= .19$$

Dividing .42 (1.33 − .91) by .19 we get a CR of 2.21, well above the .05 level of 1.96 but below the .01 level of 2.58. We may discard the null hypothesis, therefore, and mark the difference between our r's significant at the .05 level.

Measurement of the significance of the difference between two r's obtained from the same sample presents certain complications, as r's from the same group are presumably correlated. Formulas for computing the correlation between two correlated r's are not entirely satisfactory and there is no method of determining the correlation between two z's directly. Fortunately, we may feel sure that *if* the r's are positively correlated in our group, and the CR as determined by the SE from (68) is significant, that the *CR* would be even more significant if the correlation between the *r*'s were known.

The *z* transformation can be usefully employed when *r*'s which differ widely in size are to be averaged or combined (p. 173).

PROBLEMS

1. The difference between two means is 3.60 and $\sigma_D = 3$. Both samples are larger than 100.

    (*a*) Is the obtained difference significant at the .05 level?

    (*b*) What percent is the obtained difference of the difference necessary for significance at the .01 level?

    (*c*) Find the limits of the .99 confidence interval for the true difference.

2. A personality inventory is administered in a private school to 8 boys whose conduct records are exemplary, and to 5 boys whose records are very poor. Data are given below.

    Group 1:   110   112   95   105   111   97   112   102
    "   2:   115   112   109   112   117

    Is the difference between group means significant at the .05 level? at the .01 level?

3. In which of the following experimental problems would it be more important to avoid Type I errors of inference than Type II errors in determining the significance of a difference?

    (*a*) Sex differences in reading rate and comprehension in the fifth grade.

    (*b*) Effects of a new drug upon reaction time—especially when the drugs are potent and probably dangerous.

    (*c*) Comparison of two methods of learning a new skill.

    (*d*) Acceptance of a program which involves much time and money and rejection of a less expensive program.

    (*e*) Comparative efficiency of a speed-up and a normal rate of work in a factory.

4. In the first trial of a practice period, 25 twelve-year-olds have a mean score of 80.00 and a *SD* of 8.00 upon a digit-symbol learning test. On the tenth trial, the mean is 84.00 and the *SD* is 10.00. The *r* between scores on the first and tenth trials is .40. Our hypothesis is that practice leads to gain.

    (*a*) Is the *gain* in score significant at the .05 level? at the .01 level? (p. 217)

    (*b*) What gain would be significant at the .01 level, other conditions remaining the same?

5. Two groups of high-school pupils are matched for initial ability in a biology test. Group 1 is taught by the lecture method, and Group 2 by the lecture-demonstration method. Data are as follows:

	Group 1 (control)	Group 2 (experimental)
N	60	60
Mean initial score on the biology test	42.30	42.50
σ of initial scores on the biology test	5.36	5.38
Mean final score on the biology test	54.54	56.74
σ of final scores on the biology test	6.34	7.25
r (between final scores on the biology test) =	.50	

(a) Is the difference between the final scores made by Groups 1 and 2 upon the biology test significant at the .05 level? at the .01 level?

(b) Determine the limits of the .95 confidence interval for the true difference.

(c) Is the difference in the variability of the final scores made by Groups 1 and 2 significant at the .05 level?

6. Two groups of high-school students are matched for M and σ upon a group intelligence test. There are 58 subjects in Group A and 72 in Group B. The records of these two groups upon a battery of "learning" tests are as follows:

	Group A	Group B
M	48.52	53.61
σ	10.60	15.35
N	58	72

The correlation of the group intelligence test and the learning battery in the entire group from which A and B were drawn is .50. Is the difference between Groups A and B significant at the .05 level? at the .01 level?

7. Opinion on a certain issue in a college community is believed to be split 80% for and 20% against. In a sample of 400, 83% answer affirmatively. Does this result discredit the original hypothesis?

8. The incidence of a certain behavior in a primitive society is known to be between 10% and 20%. How large a sample do we need (a) in order to be accurate within 2% of the true value and (b) to have the odds 19:1 in favor of a good sample?

9. In a school of 500 pupils, 52.3% are girls; and in a second school of 300 pupils, 47.7% are girls. Is there a significant difference between the percentages of girls enrolled in the two schools?

10. Given the following data for an item in Stanford-Binet: of 100 nine-year-olds, 72% pass; of 100 ten-year-olds, 78% pass. Is the item more difficult for nine-year-olds than for ten-year-olds?

11. (a) To the question "Would you like to be an aviator?" 145 fifteen-year-old boys in a high-school class of 205 answered "Yes" and 60 answered "No." To the question "Would you like to be an engineer?" 125 said "Yes" and 80 answered "No." The data in the table below show the number who answered "Yes" to both questions, "No" to both questions, "Yes" to one and "No" to the other. Is desire to be an aviator significantly stronger in this group than desire to be an engineer?

QUES. 1

	No	Yes	
Yes	25 b	100	125
QUES. 2			
No	35	45 c	80
	60	145	205

(b) In a group of 64 seventh-grade children, 32 answered Item 23 correctly and 36 answered Item 26 correctly. From the table below, determine whether the difference in the percentage of correct answers is significant.

ITEM 23

	−	+	
+	10	26	36
ITEM 26			
−	22	6	28
	32	32	64

12. In random samples of 100 cases each from four groups, A, B, C and D, the following results were obtained:

	A	B	C	D
Mean	101.00	104.00	93.00	86.00
σ	10.00	11.00	9.60	8.50

What are the chances that, in general, the mean of

(a) the B's is higher than the mean of the A's
(b) the A's is higher than the mean of the C's
(c) the C's is higher than the mean of the D's

What are the chances that

(a) any B will be better than the mean A
(b) any B will be better than the mean C
(c) any B will be better than the mean D

13. (a) The correlation between height and weight in a sample of 200 ten-year-old boys is .70; and the correlation between height and weight in a sample of 250 ten-year-old girls is .62. Is this difference significant?

(b) In a sample of 150 high-school freshmen the correlation of two educational achievement tests is .65. If from past years the correlation has averaged .60, is the present group atypical? (Does .65 differ significantly from .60?)

ANSWERS

1. (a) No. $CR = 1.20$ (b) 46.5%   (c) −4.14 and 11.34
2. $t = 2.3$; for 11 df, significant at .05, not at .01 level
3. a, c, d and e
4. (a) Significant at .05, not at .01 level. Since $t = 2.00$ there is approximately 1 chance in 50 that a *plus* difference (gain) of 4 would occur under the null hypothesis.
   (b) 4.98
5. (a) $t = 2.49$; difference in M's significant at .05 but not at .01 level
   (b) .43 to 3.97
   (c) No. $t = 1.20$
6. Significant at .05 level ($t = 2.57$) and almost significant at .01 level.
7. No. Deviation is not significant
8. Sample must be between 900 and 1600 to provide significance at the .05 level. A good compromise would be an $N = 1285$ (see p. 239).
9. No. $CR = 1.24$
10. No. $CR = .98$
11. (a) Significant at .05, not at .01 level ($CR = 2.40$)
    (b) Not significant (CR approximately 1.00)
12. (a) 98 in 100
    (b) more than 99 in 100
    (c) more than 99 in 100
    (a) 61 in 100
    (b) 84 in 100
    (c) 95 in 100
13. (a) No. $CR = 1.47$ (b) No. $CR = 1.09$

CHAPTER 10

TESTING EXPERIMENTAL HYPOTHESES

◇◈◇

The hypothesis proposed in a psychological experiment may take the form of a general theory or a specific inquiry. A specific hypothesis is ordinarily to be preferred to a general proposal, as the more definite and exact the query the greater the likelihood of a conclusive answer. In the preceding chapter the significance of an obtained difference was tested against a null hypothesis. In the present chapter, we shall consider further the nature of hypotheses and shall present certain useful procedures and methods for answering the questions raised by an experiment.

I. THE HYPOTHESIS OF "CHANCE"

1. Nature of the null hypothesis

In Chapter 9 the difference between two statistics was tested against a null hypothesis, namely, that the population difference is zero. The null hypothesis is not confined to zero differences nor to the differences between statistics. Other forms of this hypothesis assert that the results found in an experiment do not differ significantly from results to be expected on a probability basis or stipulated in terms of some theory. A null hypothesis is ordinarily more useful than other hypotheses because it is *exact* (p. 212). Hypotheses other than the null can, to be sure, be stated exactly: we may, for example, assert that a group which has received special training will be 5 points on the average ahead of an untrained (control) group. But it is difficult to set up such precise expectations in many experiments. For this reason it is usually advisable to test against a null hypothesis, rather than some other, if this can be done.

It is sometimes not fully understood that the rejection of a null hypothesis does not immediately force acceptance of a contrary view. The extra-sensory perception (ESP) experiments offer a good illustration of what is meant by this statement. In a typical ESP experiment, a pack of 25 cards is used. There are 5 different symbols on these cards, each symbol appearing on 5 cards. In guessing through the pack of 25, the probability of chance success with each card is 1/5. And the number of correct "calls" in a pack of 25 should be 5. If a subject calls the cards correctly much in excess of chance expectation (i.e., in excess of 5), the null (chance) hypothesis is rejected. But rejection of the chance hypothesis does not force acceptance of ESP as the *cause* of the extra-chance result. Before this claim can be made, one must demonstrate in follow-up experiments that extra-chance results are obtained when *all* likely causes, such as runs of cards, visual and other cues, poor shuffling and recording, have been eliminated. If under rigid controls calls in excess of chance are consistently obtained, we may reject the null (chance) hypothesis and accept ESP. But the acceptance of a positive hypothesis—it should be noted—is the end result of a series of careful experiments. And, moreover, it is a logical and not primarily a statistical conclusion.

2. Testing experimentally observed results against the direct determination of probable outcomes

The null hypothesis is useful when we wish to compare observed results with those to be expected by "chance." Several examples will illustrate the methods to be employed.

> *Example (1)* Two tones, differing slightly in pitch, are to be compared in an experiment. The tones are presented in succession, the subject being instructed to report the second as higher or lower than the first. Presentation is in random order. In ten trials a subject is right in his judgment seven times. Is this result significant, i.e., better than chance?

Since the subject is either right or wrong in his judgment, and since judgments are separate and independent, we may test our result against the binomial expansion (p. 89). Ten judgments may be taken as analogous to ten coins; a right judgment corresponds to a head, say, a wrong judgment to a tail. The odds are even that any given judgment will be right; hence in ten trials (since $p = 1/2$) our subject should in general be right five times by chance alone. The question, then, is whether seven "rights" are significantly greater than the expected five. From page 92 we find that upon expanding $(p + q)^{10}$ the probability of 10 right judgments is 1/1024; of 9 right and one wrong, 10/1024; of 8 right and 2 wrong, 45/1024; and of 7 right and 3 wrong, 120/1024. Adding these fractions we get 176/1024, or .172 as the probability of 7 or *more* right judgments by chance alone. The probability of *just* 7 rights is 120/1024, or approximately .12. Neither of these results is significant at the .05 level of confidence (p. 190) and accordingly the null hypothesis must be retained. On the evidence there is no reason to believe that our subject's judgments are really better than chance expectation.

Note that to get 10 right is highly significant (the probability is approximately .001); to get 9 *or* 10 right is also significant (the probability is 1/1024 + 10/1024, or approximately .01). To get 8 or *more* right is almost significant at the .05 level (the probability is .055); but any number right less than 8 fails to reach our standard. The situation described in example (1) occurs in a number of experiments—whenever, for example, objects, weights, lights, test items, or other stimuli are to be compared, the odds being 50:50 that a given judgment is correct.

> *Example* (2) Ten photos, 5 of feeble-minded and 5 of normal children (of the same age and sex), are presented to a subject who claims he can identify the feeble-minded from their photographs. The subject is instructed to designate which five photographs are those of feeble-minded children. How many photos must our subject identify correctly before the null hypothesis is disproved?

Since there are 5 feeble-minded and 5 normal photos, the subject has a 50:50 chance of success with each photo and the method of example (1) could be used. A better test,* however, is to determine the probability that a particular set of 5 photos (namely, the *right* 5) will be selected from all possible sets of 5 which may be drawn from the 10 given photos. To find how many combinations of 5 photos can be drawn from a set of 10, we may use conveniently the formula for the combination of 10 things taken 5 at a time. This formula † is written $C^{10}_5 = \dfrac{10!}{5!\,5!} = 252$. The symbol C^{10}_5 is read "the combinations of ten things taken five at a time"; 10! (read "10 factorial") is $10 \cdot 9 \cdot 8 \cdot 7 \cdot 6 \cdot 5 \cdot 4 \cdot 3 \cdot 2 \cdot 1$; and $5! = 5 \cdot 4 \cdot 3 \cdot 2 \cdot 1$.

It is possible, therefore, to draw 252 combinations of 5 from a set of 10, and accordingly there is one chance in 252 that a judge will select the 5 correct photos out of all possible sets of 5. If he does select the right 5, this result is obviously significant (the probability is approximately .004)

---

* Fisher, R. A., *The Design of Experiments* (London: Oliver and Boyd, 1935), Chapter 2, pp. 26–29 especially.

† The general formula for the combinations of *n* things taken *r* at a time is $C^n_r = \dfrac{n!}{r!\,(n-r)!}$.

and the null hypothesis must be rejected. Suppose that our judge's set of 5 photos contains 4 feeble-minded and one normal picture; or 3 feeble-minded and 2 normal pictures. Is either of these results significant? The probability of 4 right selections and one wrong selection by chance is $\dfrac{C^5_4 \times C^5_1}{C^{10}_5}$, i.e., the product of the number of ways 4 rights can be selected from the 5 feeble-minded pictures times the number of ways one wrong can be selected from the 5 normal pictures divided by the total number of combinations of 5. Calculation shows this result to be 25/252 or 1/10 (approximately) and hence *not* significant at the .05 level. The probability of getting 3 right and 2 wrong is given by $\dfrac{C^5_3 \times C^5_2}{C^{10}_5}$; namely, the product of the number of ways 3 pictures can be selected from 5 (the 5 feeble-minded pictures) times the number of ways 2 pictures can be selected from the 5 normal pictures divided by the total number of combinations of 5. This result is 100/252 or slightly greater than 1/3, and is clearly not significant.

Our subject disproves the null hypothesis, then, *only* when *all* 5 feeble-minded pictures are correctly chosen. The probabilities of various combinations of right and wrong choices are given below—they should be verified by the student:

$$
\begin{array}{rll}
\text{Probability of all } 5R = & 1/252 \\
\text{``} \qquad \text{``} \qquad 4R = & 25/252 \\
\text{``} \qquad \text{``} \qquad 3R = & 100/252 \\
\text{``} \qquad \text{``} \qquad 2R = & 100/252 \\
\text{``} \qquad \text{``} \qquad 1R = & 25/252 \\
\text{``} \qquad \text{``} \qquad 0R = & 1/252 \\
\end{array}
$$

It may be noted that by increasing the number of pictures of feeble-minded and normal from 10 to 20, say, the *sensitiveness* of the experiment can be considerably enhanced. With 20 pictures it is not necessary to get all 10 feeble-minded photos right in order to achieve a significant result. In fact, 8 right is nearly significant at the .01 level as shown below.

$$C^{20}_{10} = \frac{20!}{10!\,10!} = 184{,}756$$

Combinations		Frequency	Prob. ratio (freq. ÷ 184,756)
10R	0W	1	.000005
9R	1W	100	.0005
8R	2W	2025	.011
7R	3W	14400	.078
6R	4W	44100	.239

Combinations		Frequency	Prob. ratio (freq. ÷ 184,756)
5R	5W	63504	.344
4R	6W	44100	.239
3R	7W	14400	.078
2R	8W	2025	.011
1R	9W	100	.0005
0R	10W	1	.000005
		184,756	

3. Testing experimentally observed results against probabilities calculated from the normal curve

When the number of observations or the number of trials is large, direct calculation of expectations by expanding the binomial $(p + q)^n$ becomes highly laborious. Since $(p + q)^n$ yields a distribution (p. 000) which is essentially normal when n is large, in many experiments the normal curve may be usefully employed to provide expected results under the null hypothesis. An example will make the method clear.

> *Example* (3)   In answering a test of 100 true-false items, a subject gets 60 right. Is it likely that the subject merely guessed?

As there are only two possible answers to each item, one of which is right and the other wrong, the probability of a correct answer to any item is 1/2, and our subject should by chance answer 1/2 of 100 or 50 items correctly. Letting p equal the probability of a right answer, and q the probability of a wrong answer, we could, by expanding the binomial $(p + q)^{100}$, calculate the probability of various combinations of rights and wrongs on the null hypothesis. When the exponent of the binomial (here, number of items) is as large as 100, however, the resulting distribution is very close to the normal probability curve (p. 87) and may be so treated with little error.

Figure 53 illustrates the solution of this problem. The mean of the curve is set at 50. The SD of the probability distribution found by expanding $(p + q)^n$ is $\sigma = \sqrt{npq}$; hence, for $(p + q)^{100}$, $\sigma = \sqrt{100 \times 1/2 \times 1/2}$ or 5. A score of 60 covers the interval on the base line from 59.5 up to 60.5. The lower limit of 60 is 1.9σ removed from the mean $\left(\dfrac{59.5 - 50}{5} = 1.9\sigma\right)$ and from Table A we find that 2.87% of the area of a normal curve lies *above* 1.9σ.* There are only three chances in 100 that a score of 60 (or

---

* Note that only one end of the normal curve is used, i.e., this is a one-tailed test (p. 217).

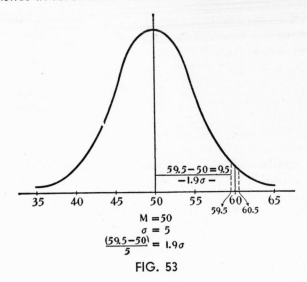

$59.5-50=9.5$
$-1.9\sigma-$

| 35 | 40 | 45 | 50 | 55 | 60 | 65 |

59.5   60.5

M = 50
$\sigma = 5$
$\dfrac{(59.5-50)}{5} = 1.9\sigma$

FIG. 53

more) would be made if the null hypothesis were true. A score of 60, therefore, is significant at the .05 level. We reject the null hypothesis and conclude that our subject could not have been simply guessing.

Note that this problem could have been solved equally well in terms of percentages. We expect our subject to get 50% of the items right by guessing. The SD of this percentage is $\sqrt{\dfrac{50\% \times 50\%}{100}}$ or 5% (see p. 197). A score of 60% (lower limit 59.5%) is 9.5% or 1.9σ distant from the middle of the curve. We interpret this result in exactly the same way as that above.

> *Example* (4)   A multiple-choice test of 60 items provides four possible responses to each item. How many items should a subject answer correctly before we may feel sure that he knows something about the test material?

Since there are four responses to each item, only one of which is correct, the probability of a right answer by guessing is 1/4, of a wrong answer 3/4. The final score to be expected if a subject knows nothing whatever about the test and simply guesses is $1/4 \times 60$ or 15. Our task, therefore, is to determine how much better than 15 a subject must score in order to demonstrate real knowledge of the material.

This problem can be solved by the methods of example (1). By expanding the binomial $(p + q)^n$, for instance, in which $p = 1/4$, $q = 3/4$, and $n = 60$, we can determine the probability of the occurrence of any score from 0 to 60. The direct determination of probabilities from the binomial expansion is straightforward and exact but the calculation is tedious. Fortunately, therefore, a satisfactory approximation to the answer we want can be obtained by using the normal distribution to determine probabilities, as in example (3). The mean of our "chance" distribution is 1/4 of 60 or 15; and the $\sigma = \sqrt{npq} = \sqrt{60 \times 1/4 \times 3/4}$ or 3.35. From Table A we know that 5% of the frequency in a normal distribution lies above 1.65σ. Multiplying our obtained σ (3.35) by 1.65, we get 5.53; and this value when added to 15 gives us 20.5 as the point above which lies 5% of the "chance" distribution of scores. A score of 21 (20.5 to 21.5), therefore, may be regarded as significant, and if a subject achieves such a score we can be reasonably sure that he is not merely guessing.

For a higher level of assurance, we may take that score which would occur by chance only once in 100 trials. From Table A, 1% of the frequency in the normal curve lies above 2.33σ. This point is 7.81 (3.35×2.33) above 15 or at 22.8. A score of 23, therefore, or a higher score is *very* significant; only once in 100 trials would a subject achieve such a score by guessing.

Use of the normal probability curve in the solution of problems like this always involves a degree of approximation. When p differs considerably from 1/2 and n is small, the distribution resulting from the expansion of $(p + q)^n$ is skewed and is not therefore accurately described by the normal curve. When these conditions hold, one must resort to the direct calculation of probabilities as in example (1). When n is large, however, and p not too far from 1/2, the normal distribution may be safely used, as will be seen from the χ^2 tests on page 261.

II. THE χ^2 (CHI-SQUARE) TEST AND THE NULL HYPOTHESIS

The chi-square test represents a useful method of comparing experimentally obtained results with those to be expected theoretically on some hypothesis. The equation for chi square (χ^2) is stated as follows:

$$\chi^2 = \Sigma \left[\frac{(f_o - f_e)^2}{f_e} \right] \qquad (69)$$

(chi-square formula for testing agreement between observed and expected results)

in which f_o = frequency of occurrence of observed or experimentally determined facts;

f_e = expected frequency of occurrence on some hypothesis.

The differences between observed and expected frequencies are squared and divided by the expected number in each case, and the sum of these quotients is χ^2. The more closely the observed results approximate to the expected, the smaller the chi square and the closer the agreement between observed data and the hypothesis being tested. Contrariwise, the larger the chi square the greater the probability of a real divergence of experimentally observed from expected results. To evaluate chi square, we enter Table E with the computed value of chi square and the appropriate number of degrees of freedom. The number of $df = (r-1)(c-1)$ in which r is the number of rows and c the number of columns in which the data are tabulated. From Table E we read P, the probability that the obtained χ^2 is significant. Several illustrations of the chi-square test will clarify the discussion given above.

I. Testing the divergence of observed results from those expected on the hypothesis of equal probability (null hypothesis)

Example (5)   Forty-eight subjects are asked to express their attitude toward the proposition "Should the United States Join an Organization of Nations for the Control of Atomic Power?" by marking F (favorable), I (indifferent) or U (unfavorable). Of the members in the group, 24 marked F, 12 I, and 12 U. Do these results indicate a significant trend of opinion?

The observed data (f_o) are given in the first row of Table 26. In the second row is the distribution of answers to be expected on the null hypothesis (f_e), if each answer is selected equally often. Below the table are entered the differences $(f_o - f_e)$. Each of these differences is squared and divided by its f_e $(64/16 + 16/16 + 16/16)$ to give $\chi^2 = 6$.

TABLE 26

	Answers			
	Favorable	Indifferent	Unfavorable	
Observed (f_o)	24	12	12	48
Expected (f_e)	16	16	16	48
$(f_o - f_e)$	8	4	4	
$(f_o - f_e)^2$	64	16	16	
$\dfrac{(f_o - f_e)^2}{f_e}$	4	1	1	

$$\chi^2 = \Sigma\left[\frac{(f_o - f_e)^2}{f_e}\right] = 6 \qquad df = 2 \qquad P = .05 \text{ (Table E)}$$

The degrees of freedom in the table may be calculated from the formula $df = (r-1)(c-1)$ to be $(3-1)(2-1)$ or 2. Or, the degrees of freedom may be found directly in the following way: Since we know the row totals to be 48, when two entries are made in a row the third is immediately fixed, is not "free." When the first two entries in row 1 are 24 and 12, for example, the third entry must be 12 to make up 48. Since we also know the sums of the columns, only *one* entry in a column is free, the second being fixed as soon as the first is tabulated. There are, then, *two* degrees of freedom for rows and *one* degree of freedom for columns, and $2 \times 1 = 2$ degrees of freedom for the table.

Entering Table E we find in row $df = 2$, a χ^2 of almost 6 (actually, 5.991) in the column headed .05. A P of .05 means that should we repeat this experiment, only once in 20 trials would a χ^2 of 6 (or more) occur if the null hypothesis is true. Our result may be marked "significant at the .05 level," therefore, on the grounds that divergence of observed from expected results is too unlikely of occurrence to be accounted for *solely* by sampling fluctuations. We reject the "equal answer" hypothesis and conclude that our group really favors the proposition. In general, we may safely discard a null hypothesis whenever P is .05 or less.

> *Example* (6)   The items in an attitude scale are answered by underlining one of the following phrases: Strongly approve, approve, indifferent, disapprove, strongly disapprove. The distribution of answers to an item marked by 100 subjects is shown in Table 27. Do these answers diverge significantly from the distribution to be expected if there are no preferences in the group?

TABLE 27

	Strongly Approve	Approve	Indiffer- ent	Disap- prove	Strongly Disap- prove	
Observed (f_o)	23	18	24	17	18	100
Expected (f_e)	20	20	20	20	20	100
$(f_o - f_e)$	3	2	4	3	2	
$(f_o - f_e)^2$	9	4	16	9	4	
$\dfrac{(f_o - f_e)^2}{f_e}$	.45	.20	.80	.45	.20	

$$\chi^2 = 2.10 \qquad df = 4 \qquad P \text{ lies between .70 and .80}$$

On the null hypothesis of "equal probability," 20 subjects may be expected to select each of the 5 possible answers. Squaring the $(f_o - f_e)$, dividing by the expected result (f_e), and summing, we obtain a χ^2 of 2.10. $df = (5 - 1)(2 - 1)$ or 4. From Table E, reading across from row $df = 4$, we locate a χ^2 of 2.195 in column .70. This χ^2 is nearest to our calculated value of 2.10, which lies between the entries in columns .70 and .80. It is sufficiently accurate to describe P as lying between .70 and .80 without interpolation. Since this much divergence from the null hypothesis (p. 255) namely, 2.10, can be expected to occur upon repetition of the experiment in approximately 75% of the trials, χ^2 is clearly *not* significant and we must retain the null hypothesis. There is no evidence of either a strongly favorable or a strongly unfavorable attitude toward the proposition.

A better idea of the meaning of levels of significance can be obtained from Figure 54, which shows the χ^2 distribution for 1, 4, 5 and 10 degrees of freedom. Let us consider the χ^2 curve for 4 df, the number in the problem above. Beginning at zero, this curve (a positively skewed distribution) runs out slightly beyond 14 on the base line. From Table E we read that for 4 df, 5% of the area of our χ^2 curve lies to the *right* of 9.49 and 1% lies to the *right* of 13.28. When $df = 4$, then, a χ^2 of 9.49 or larger is significant at the .05 level; and a χ^2 of 13.28 or larger is significant at the .01 level. Only once in 100 repetitions of the given experiment would we expect to find a χ^2 of 13.28 or larger if the null hypothesis is true. Any χ^2 in the region of the curve at or beyond 13.28, therefore, represents a significant value in the sense of being a very infrequent and

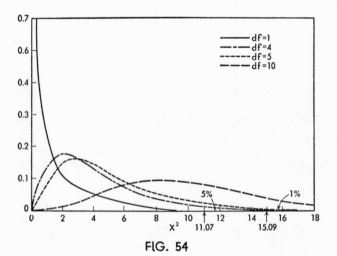

FIG. 54

unusual deviation from 0. Our χ^2 of 2.10 falls far short of 9.49, the .05 point; and hence is nonsignificant. We retain the null hypothesis, since the deviation of observed answers from expectation might easily be a matter of chance.

2. Testing the divergence of observed results from those expected on the hypothesis of a normal distribution

Our hypothesis may assert that the frequencies of an event which we have observed really follow the normal distribution instead of being equally probable. An example illustrates how this hypothesis may be tested by chi square.

> *Example* (7) Forty-two salesman have been classified into 3 groups—very good, satisfactory, and poor—by a consensus of sales managers. Does this distribution of ratings differ significantly from that to be expected if selling ability is normally distributed in our population of salesmen?

TABLE 28

	Good	Satisfactory	Poor	
Observed (f_o)	16	20	6	42
Expected (f_e)	6.7	28.6	6.7	42
$(f_o - f_e)$	9.3	8.6	.7	
$(f_o - f_e)^2$	86.49	73.96	.49	
$\dfrac{(f_o - f_e)^2}{f_e}$	12.90	2.59	.07	

$$\chi^2 = 15.56 \qquad df = 2 \qquad P \text{ is less than } .01$$

The entries in row 1 give the number of men classified in each of the 3 categories. In row 2 the entries show how many of the 42 salesmen may be expected to fall in each category on the hypothesis of a normal distribution. These last entries were found by first dividing the base line of a normal curve (taken to extend over 6σ) into 3 equal segments of 2σ each. From Table A, the proportion of the normal distribution to be found in each of these segments is then as follows:

	Proportion
Between $+3.00\sigma$ and $+1.00\sigma$	.16
" $+1.00\sigma$ and -1.00σ	.68
" -1.00σ and -3.00σ	.16
	1.00

These proportions of 42 have been calculated and are entered in Table 28 opposite (f_e). The χ^2 in the table is 15.56 and $df = (3-1)(2-1)$ or 2. From Table E it is clear that this χ^2 lies beyond the limits of the table, hence P is listed simply as less than .01. The discrepancy between observed and expected values is so great that the hypothesis of a normal distribution of selling ability in this group must be rejected. Too many men are described as good, and too few as satisfactory, to make for agreement with our hypothesis.

3. The chi-square test when table entries are small

When the entries in a table are fairly large, χ^2 gives an estimate of divergence from hypothesis which is close to that obtained by other measures of probability. But χ^2 is not stable when computed from a table in which *any* experimental frequency is less than 5. Moreover, when the table is 2×2 fold (when $df = 1$), χ^2 is subject to considerable error unless a correction for continuity (called Yates' correction) is made. Reasons for making this correction and its effect upon χ^2 can best be seen by working through the examples following.

> *Example* (8) In example (1), an observer gave 7 correct judgments in ten trials. The probability of a right judgment was 1/2 in each instance, so that the expected number of correct judgments was 5. Test our subject's deviation from the null hypothesis by computing chi square and compare the P with that found by direct calculation.

TABLE 29

	Right	Wrong	
Observed (f_o)	7	3	10
Expected (f_e)	5	5	10
$(f_o - f_e)$	2	2	
Correction $(-.5)$	1.5	1.5	
$(f_o - f_e)^2$	2.25	2.25	
$\dfrac{(f_o - f_e)^2}{f_e}$	.45	.45	

$$\chi^2 = .90$$
$$df = 1$$
$$P = .356 \text{ (by interpolation in Table E)}$$
$$1/2P = .178$$

Calculations in Table 29 follow those of previous tables except for the correction which consists in *subtracting* .5 from each $(f_o - f_e)$ difference. In applying the χ^2 test we assume that adjacent frequencies are connected by a continuous and smooth curve (like the normal curve) and are not discrete numbers. But in 2×2 fold tables, especially when entries are small, the χ^2 curve is not continuous. Hence, the deviation of 7 from 5 must be written as 1.5 $(6.5 - 5)$ instead of 2 $(7 - 5)$, as 6.5 is the lower limit of 7 in a continuous series. In like manner the deviation of 3 from 5 must be taken from the upper limit of 3, namely, 3.5 (see Fig. 53). Still another change in procedure must be made in order to have the probability obtained from χ^2 agree with the direct determination of probability. P in the χ^2 table gives the probability of 7 or more right answers *and* of 3 or fewer right answers, i.e., takes account of both ends of the probability curve (see p. 217). We must take 1/2 of P, therefore (make a one-tailed test), if we want the probability of 7 or more right answers. Note that the $P/2$ of .178 is very close to the P of .172 got by the direct method on page 249. If we repeated our test we should expect a score of 7 or better about 17 times in 100 trials. It is clear, therefore, that the obtained score is not significant and does not refute the null hypothesis.

It should be noted that had we omitted the correction for continuity, chi square would have been 1.60 and $P/2$ (by interpolation in Table E), .104. Failure to use the correction causes the probability of a given result to be greatly *underestimated* and the chances of its being called significant considerably increased.

When the expected entries in a 2×2 fold table are the same (as in Tables 29, 30) the formula for chi square may be written in a somewhat shorter form as follows:

$$\chi^2 = \frac{2(f_o - f_e)^2}{f_e} \tag{70}$$

(*short formula for χ^2 in 2×2 fold tables when expected frequencies are equal*)

Applying formula (70) to Table 29 we get a chi square of $\dfrac{2(1.5)^2}{5} = .90$

Example (9)   In example (3) a subject achieved a score of 60 right on a test of 100 true-false items. From the chi-square test, determine whether this subject was merely guessing. Compare your result with that found on page 251 when the normal curve hypothesis was employed.

TABLE 30

	Right	Wrong	
Observed (f_o)	60	40	100
Expected (f_e)	50	50	100
$(f_o - f_e)$	10	10	
Correction $(-.5)$	9.5	9.5	
$(f_o - f_e)^2$	90.25	90.25	
$\dfrac{(f_o - f_e)^2}{f_e}$	1.81	1.81	

$$\chi^2 = 3.62 \qquad\qquad P = .06$$
$$df = 1 \qquad\qquad 1/2P = .03$$

Although the cell entries in Table 30 are large, use of the correction for continuity will be found to yield a result in somewhat closer agreement with that found on page 252 than can be obtained without the correction. As shown in Figure 53, the probability of a deviation of 10 or more from 50 is that part of the curve lying above 59.5. In Table E, the P of .06 gives us the probability of scores of 60 or more *and* of 40 or less. Hence we must take 1/2 of P (i.e., .03) to give us the probability of a score of 60 or more. Agreement between the probability given by the χ^2 test and by direct calculation is very close. Note that when χ^2 is calculated without the correction, we get a $P/2$ of .023, a slight underestimation. In general, the correction for continuity has little effect when table entries are large, 50 or more, say. But failure to use the correction even when numbers are large may lead to some underestimation of the probability; hence it is generally wise to use it.

Example (10) In example (4), given a multiple-choice test of 60 items (four possible answers to each item) we were required to find what score a subject must achieve in order to demonstrate knowledge of the test material. By use of the normal probability distribution, it was shown that a score of 21 is reasonably significant and a score of 23 highly significant. Can these results be verified by the chi-square test?

In Table 31 an obtained score of 21 is tested against an expected score of 15. In the first line of the table the observed values (f_o) are 21 right and 39 wrong; in the second line, the expected or "guess" values are 15

TABLE 31

	R	W	
f_o	21	39	60
f_e	15	45	60
$(f_o - f_e)$	6	6	
Correction $(-.5)$	5.5	5.5	
$(f_o - f_e)^2$	30.25	30.25	
$\dfrac{(f_o - f_e)^2}{f_e}$	2.02	.67	

$\chi^2 = 2.69$ $P = .10$
$df = 1$ $1/2P = .05$

right and 45 wrong. Making the correction for continuity, we obtain a χ^2 of 2.69, a P of .10 and $1/2P$ of .05. Only once in 20 trials would we expect a score of 21 or higher to occur if the subject were merely guessing and had no knowledge of the test material. This result checks that obtained on page 252.

In Table 32 a score of 23 is tested against the expected score of 15. Making the correction for continuity, we obtain a χ^2 of 5.00 which yields a P of .0279 and $1/2P$ of .0139. Again this result closely checks the answer obtained on page 253 by use of the normal probability curve.

TABLE 32

	R	W	
f_o	23	37	60
f_e	15	45	60
$(f_o - f_e)$	8	8	
Correction $(-.5)$	7.5	7.5	
$(f_o - f_e)^2$	56.25	56.25	
$\dfrac{(f_o - f_e)^2}{f_e}$	3.75	1.25	

$\chi^2 = 5.00$ $P = .0279$
$df = 1$ $1/2P = .0139$ or $.01$

4. The chi-square test when table entries are in percentages

The chi-square test should not be used with percentage entries unless a correction for size of sample is made. This follows from the f t that in dealing with probability the significance of an event depends upon its *actual* frequency and is not shown by its percentage occurrence. For a penny to fall heads 8 times in 10 tosses is not as significant as for the penny to fall heads 80 times in 100 tosses, although the percentage occurrence is the same in both cases. If we write the entries in Table 29 as percentages, we have

	R	W	
f_o	70%	30%	100%
f_e	50%	50%	100%
$(f_o - f_e)$	20%	20%	
Correction* (-5%)	15%	15%	
$(f_o - f_e)^2$	225%	225%	

$$\chi^2{}_\% = \frac{2(225)}{50} = 9 \qquad \text{by (70)}$$

$$\chi^2 = 9 \times \frac{10}{100} = .90 \text{ (Table 29)}$$

It is clear that in order to bring χ^2 to its proper vaue in terms of original numbers we must multiply the "percent" χ^2 by 10/100 to give .90. A χ^2 calculated from percentages must always be multiplied by $N/100$ (N = number of observations) in order to adjust it to the actual freqencies in the given sample.

5. The chi-square test of independence in contingency tables

We have seen that χ^2 may be employed to test the agreement between observed results and those expected on some hypothesis. A further useful application of χ^2 can be made when we wish to investigate the relationship between traits or attributes which can be classified into two or more categories. The same persons, for example, may be classified as to hair color (light, brown, black, red) and as to eye color (blue, gray, brown), and the correspondence in these attributes noted. Or fathers and sons may be classified with respect to interests or temperament or achievement and the relationship of the attributes in the two groups studied.

* From Table 29 it is clear that the correction of $-.5$ becomes $-.5/10$ or $-.05$; this is -5% when entries in the table are expressed as percents.

Table 33 is a contingency table, i.e., a double entry or two-way table in which the possession by a group of varying degrees of two characteristics is represented. In the tabulation in Table 33, 413 persons have been classified as to "eyedness" and "handedness." Eyedness, or eye dominance,

TABLE 33 Comparison of eyedness and handedness in 413 persons *

	Left-eyed	Ambiocular	Right-eyed	Totals
Left-handed	(35.4) 34	(58.5) 62	(30.0) 28	124
Ambidextrous	(21.4) 27	(35.4) 28	(18.2) 20	75
Right-handed	(61.1) 57	(101.0) 105	(51.8) 52	214
Totals	118	195	100	413

I. Calculation of independence values (f_e):

$$\frac{118 \times 124}{413} = 35.4 \qquad \frac{195 \times 124}{413} = 58.5 \qquad \frac{100 \times 124}{413} = 30.0$$

$$\frac{118 \times 75}{413} = 21.4 \qquad \frac{195 \times 75}{413} = 35.4 \qquad \frac{100 \times 75}{413} = 18.2$$

$$\frac{118 \times 214}{413} = 61.1 \qquad \frac{195 \times 214}{413} = 101.0 \qquad \frac{100 \times 214}{413} = 51.8$$

II. Calculation of χ^2:

$(-1.4)^2 \div 35.4 = .055$	$(3.5)^2 \div 58.5 = .209$	$(-2.0)^2 \div 30 = .133$
$(5.6)^2 \div 21.4 = 1.465$	$(-7.4)^2 \div 35.4 = 1.547$	$(1.8)^2 \div 18.2 = .178$
$(-4.1)^2 \div 61.1 = .275$	$(4.0)^2 \div 101.0 = .158$	$(.20)^2 \div 51.8 = .001$

$$\chi^2 = 4.02 \qquad df = 4 \qquad P \text{ lies between .30 and .50}$$

is described as left-eyed, ambiocular, or right-eyed; handedness as left-handed, ambidextrous, or right-handed. Reading down the first column we find that of 118 left-eyed persons, 34 are left-handed, 27 ambidextrous and 57 right-handed. Across the first row we find 124 left-handed persons, of whom 34 are left-eyed, 62 ambiocular and 28 right-eyed. The other columns and rows are interpreted in the same way.

* From Woo, T. L., *Biometrika*, 1936, 20A, pp. 79–118.

The hypothesis to be tested is the null hypothesis, namely, that handedness and eyedness are essentially unrelated or independent. In order to compute χ^2 we must first calculate an "independence value" for each cell in the contingency table. Independence values are represented by the figures in parentheses within the different cells; they give the number of people whom we should expect to find possessing the designated eyedness and handedness combinations in the absence of any real association. The method of calculating independence values is shown in Table 33. To illustrate with the first entry, there are 118 left-eyed and 124 left-handed persons. If there were no association between left-eyedness and left-handedness we should expect to find, by chance, $\dfrac{118 \times 124}{413}$ or 35.4 individuals in our group who are left-eyed *and* left-handed. The reason for this may readily be seen. We know that 118/413 of the entire group are left-eyed. This proportion of left-eyed individuals should hold for any subgroup, if there is *no* dependence of eyedness on handedness. Hence, 118/413 or 28.6% of the 124 left-handed individuals, i.e., 35.4, should also be left-eyed. Independence values for all cells are shown in Table 33.

When the expected or independence values have been computed, we find the difference between the observed and expected values for each cell, square each difference and divide in each instance by the independence value. The sum of these quotients by formula (69) gives χ^2. In the present problem $\chi^2 = 4.02$ and $df = (3 - 1)(3 - 1)$ or 4. From Table E we find that P lies between .30 and .50 and hence χ^2 is not significant. The observed results are close to those to be expected on the hypothesis of independence and there is no evidence of any real association between eyedness and handedness within our group.

6. 2 × 2 fold contingency tables

When the contingency table is 2×2 fold, χ^2 may be calculated without first computing the four expected frequencies—the four independence values. Example (11) illustrates the method.

Example (11) All of the sixth-grade children in a public-school system are given a standard achievement test in arithmetic. A sample of 40 boys, drawn at random from the sixth-grade population, showed 23 at or above the national norm in the test and 17 below the national norm. A random sample of 50 sixth-grade girls showed 22 at or above the national norm and 28 below. Are the boys really better than the girls in arithmetic? Data are arranged in a fourtold table as follows.

	below norm	at or above norm	
Boys	(A) 17	(B) 23	(A + B) 40
Girls	(C) 28	(D) 22	(C + D) 50
	(A + C) 45	(B + D) 45	N 90

In a fourfold table, chi square is given by the following formula.*

$$\chi^2 = \frac{N(AD - BC)^2}{(A + B)(C + D)(A + C)(B + D)} \tag{71}$$

(*chi square in a fourfold contingency table*)

Substituting for A, B, C, D, in the formula, we have

$$\chi^2 = \frac{90(374 - 644)^2}{40 \times 50 \times 45 \times 45} = 1.62$$

and for $df = 1$, P is larger than .20. χ^2 is not significant and there is no evidence that the table entries really vary from expectation, i.e., that there is a true sex difference in arithmetic.

When entries in a fourfold table are quite small (for example, 5 or less) Yates' correction for continuity (p. 258) should be applied to formula (71). The corrected formula reads:

$$\chi^2_c = \frac{N(|AD - BC| - N/2)^2}{(A + B)(C + D)(A + C)(B + D)} \tag{72}$$

(χ^2 for 2×2 fold table, corrected for continuity)

The vertical lines $|AD - BC|$ mean that the difference is to be taken as positive. We may illustrate (72) by applying it to the data of the table in example (11). Substituting for N, A, B, C, and D we have

$$\chi^2_c = \frac{90(|374 - 644| - 45)^2}{40 \times 50 \times 45 \times 45}$$

$$= 1.12$$

a value somewhat smaller than the χ^2 of 1.62 obtained without the correction. Yates' correction will always reduce the size of χ^2. It should be used when entries are small, as it is here that its effect may be crucial. If χ^2 is barely significant, χ^2_c may well fall below the level set for significance. However, if χ^2 is *not* significant, χ^2_c will be even less so.

† See page 391 for relation of χ^2 to phi coefficient.

7. The additive property of χ^2

When several χ^2's have been computed from independent experiments (i.e., from tables based upon different samples), these may be summed to give a new chi square with $df =$ the sum of the separate df's. The fact that chi squares may be added to provide an over-all test of a hypothesis is important in many experimental studies. In example (11) we have seen that the boys did slightly better than the girls on the arithmetic achievement test, but the chi square of 1.62 is not large enough to indicate a superiority of boys over girls. Suppose that three repetitions of this experiment are carried out, in each instance groups of boys and girls [of about the same size as in example (11)] being drawn independently and at random from the sixth grade and listed as scoring "at or above" or "below" the national norm. Suppose further that the three chi squares from these tables are 2.71, 5.39, and .15, in each case the boys being somewhat better than the girls. We can now combine these four results to get an over-all test of the significance of this sex difference in arithmetic. Adding the three χ^2's to the 1.62 in example (11) we have a total χ^2 of 9.87 with 4 df's. From Table E this χ^2 is significant at the .05 level, and we may be reasonably sure that sixth-grade boys are, on the average, better than sixth-grade girls in arithmetic. It will be noted that our four experiments taken in aggregate yield a significant result, although only one of the χ^2's (5.39) is itself significant. Combining the data from several experiments will often yield a conclusive result, when separate experiments, taken alone, provide only indications.

III. NONPARAMETRIC METHODS

When making tests of the significance of the difference between two means (in terms of the CR or t, for example), we assume that scores upon which our statistics are based are normally distributed in the population. What we actually do—under the null hypothesis—is to estimate from our sample statistics the probability of a true difference between the two parameters. When N is quite small or the data are badly skewed,* so that the assumption of normality is doubtful, "parametric methods" are of dubious value or are not applicable at all. What we need in such cases are techniques which will enable us to compare samples and to make inferences or tests of significance without having to assume normality in the populations. Such methods are called *nonparametric* or *distribution-free*. Several of these have already been encountered. The χ^2 test, for

* The means of moderately skewed samples are themselves normally distributed.

example (p. 253), is a nonparametric technique. The significance of χ^2 depends only upon the degrees of freedom in the table; no assumption need be made as to *form* of distribution for the variables classified into the categories of the χ^2 table. The problem on page 248 in which observed values were tested against frequencies determined from the binomial expansion illustrates a nonparametric test: a test of observed against expected f's. The rank-difference correlation coefficient (*rho*) is also a nonparametric technique. When ρ is computed from scores ranked in order of merit (p. 371), the distributions from which the scores are taken are liable to be badly skewed and N is nearly always small.

The nonparametric techniques do not have the "power" * of the parametric tests, that is, they are less able to detect a true difference when such is present. Nonparametric tests should not be used, therefore, when other more exact tests are applicable. In general, distribution-free methods are most useful when (1) N is small, (2) when assumptions (e.g., of normality) concerning the population are doubtful, and when (3) data can be expressed only in ranks.

1. The sign test

This is the simplest and most generally applicable of the nonparametric tests. It is illustrated in the example below:

> *Example (12)* S and C represent two tasks, S the spelling of 25 words presented *separately*, and C the spelling of 25 words of equal difficulty presented as an integral part of a sentence (i.e., in *context*). A teacher wants to know which condition is favorable to higher scores. Table 34 shows the scores of 10 seventh-grade children under C and S, the scores being recorded in pairs. Column (3) shows the sign of the difference (C − S) as plus or minus. Under the null hypothesis 1/2 of the differences should be + and 1/2 should be −. Test the hypothesis that C is better than S.

Of the 10 differences, 7 are plus (C higher than S), 2 are minus (S higher than C) and one is zero. Excluding the 0 as being neither + nor −, we have 9 differences of which 7 are plus. Is condition C significantly superior to condition S? To answer this question, we shall first expand the binomial $(p+q)^9$ in which p is the probability of a + and q is the probability of a −:

$$(p + q)^9 = p^9 + 9p^8q + 36p^7q^2 + 84p^6q^3 + 126p^5q^4 + 126p^4q^5$$
$$+84p^3q^6 + 36p^2q^7 + 9pq^8 + q^9$$

* Moses, Lincoln E., "Non-parametric statistics for psychological research," *Psychol. Bull.*, 1952, pp. 122–143.

TABLE 34 Sign test applied to data consisting of 10 pairs of scores obtained under two conditions—in context and in isolation

(1) C°	(2) S†	(3) (C − S)	Signs:	
15	12	+	+	7
18	15	+	−	2
9	10	−	0	1
15	16	−		$\overline{10}$
18	18	0		
12	10	+		
15	12	+		
16	13	+		
14	12	+		
22	19	+		

°C = words in context
†S = words spelled as separates

The total number of combinations is 2^9 or 512. Adding the first 3 terms (namely, $p^9 + 9p^8q + 36p^7q^2$), we have a total of 46 combinations (i.e., 1 of 9, 9 of 8, and 36 of 7) which contain 7 or more plus signs. Some 46 times in 512 trials 7 or more plus signs out of 9 will occur when the mean number of + signs under the null hypothesis is 4.5 (p. 248). The probability of 7 or more + signs, therefore, is 46/512 or .09, and is clearly not significant. This is a one-tailed test, since our hypothesis states that C is better than S. If the hypothesis at the outset had been that C and S *differ* without specifying which is superior, we would have had a 2-tailed test for which $P = .18$.

Tables * are available which give the number of signs necessary for significance at different levels, when N varies in size. When the number of pairs is as large as 20, the normal curve may be used as an approximation to the binomial expansion (p. 93) or the χ^2 test applied.

2. The median test

The median test is used to compare the performance of two independent groups as for example an experimental group and a control group. First, the two groups are thrown together and a common median found. If the two groups have been drawn at random from the same population, 1/2 of the scores in each group should lie above and 1/2 below

* Dixon, W. J., and Massey, F. J., *Introduction to Statistical Analysis* (New York: McGraw-Hill Co., 1951), Table 10, p. 324.

the common median. In order to test this null hypothesis, we need to draw up a 2×2 table and calculate χ^2. *Above* vs. *below* the common median constitutes one category in this table, and *experimental group* vs. *control group* the other. The method is shown in example (13):

Example (13)   A clinical psychologist wants to investigate the effects of a tranquilizing drug upon hand tremor. Fourteen psychiatric patients are given the drug, and 18 other patients matched for age and sex are given a placebo (i.e., a harmless dose). Since the medication is in pill form the patients do not know whether they are getting the drug or not. The first group is the experimental, the second the control group.

Tremor is measured by a steadiness tester. Table 35 gives the scores of the two groups: a + sign indicates a score above the common median, a − sign a score below the common median. Does the drug increase steadiness—as shown by *lower* scores in the experimental group? As we are concerned only if the drug *reduces* tremor, this is a one-tailed test.

TABLE 35   Median test applied to experimental and control groups. Plus signs indicate scores above the common median, minus signs scores below the common median

$N = 14$ Experimental	Sign	$N = 18$ Control	Sign
53	+	48	−
39	−	65	+
63	+	66	+
36	−	38	−
47	−	36	−
58	+	45	−
44	−	59	+
38	−	53	+
59	+	58	+
36	−	42	−
42	−	70	+
43	−	71	+
46	−	65	+
46	−	46	−
		55	+
		61	+
		62	+
		53	+

Common median = 49.5

The common median is 49.5. In the experimental group 4 scores are above and 10 below the common median instead of the 7 above and 7 below to be expected by chance. In the control group, 12 scores are above and 6 below the common median instead of the expected 9 in each category. These frequencies are entered in Table 36 and χ^2 is computed by formula (72) with correction for continuity.

TABLE 36

	Below Median	Above Median	Total
Experimental	10	4	14
Control	6	12	18
	16	16	32

The χ^2 is, when corrected,

$$\chi^2_c = \frac{32(|120 - 24| - 32/2)^2}{16 \times 16 \times 18 \times 14}$$

$$= 3.17$$

A χ^2_c of 3.17 with 1 degree of freedom yields a P which lies at .08, about midway between .05 and .10. We wanted to know whether the median of the experimental group was significantly lower than that of the control (thus indicating more steadiness and less tremor). For this hypothesis, a one-tailed test, $P/2$, is approximately .04 and χ^2_c is significant at the .05 level. Had our hypothesis been that the two groups differ without specifying the direction, we would have had a two-tailed test and χ^2 would have been marked not significant. Our conclusion, made somewhat tentatively, is that the drug produces some reduction in tremor. But owing to the small samples and lack of a highly significant finding, the clinical psychologist would almost certainly repeat the experiment—perhaps several times.

χ^2 is generally applicable in the median test. However, when N_1 and N_2 are small (e.g., less than about 10) the χ^2 test is not accurate and the exact method of computing probabilities should be used.[*]

[*] Walker, H. M., and Lev, J., *Statistical Inference* (New York: Henry Holt, 1953), pp. 103 ff.

3. The sum-of-ranks test

The sum-of-ranks test is used to test the hypothesis that two independent groups of observations (e.g., scores or other data) have been drawn at random from the same population—and hence that there is no real difference between them. This general hypothesis requires that we make a two-tailed test. A one-tailed test is appropriate when the hypothesis asserts that one group is higher or lower than the other group. Application of the "ranks" test is made in example (14):

> *Example (14)* In order to find the effects upon school achievement of additional assignments in English composition, a teacher divided her class into two sections of 10 pupils each. Children were assigned at random to Section 1 or to Section 2. The first group (the experimental) was given additional assignments, while the second group (the control) was excused from extra work. At the end of 3 months a subject matter test was administered to both groups with the results shown in Table 37. The control group was reduced from 10 to 8 owing to absence and illness. Do the two groups differ on the final test?

TABLE 37 Sum-of-ranks test applied to experimental and control groups. Ranks from lowest to highest have been assigned to each score in the entire group of 18 pupils

Experimental Group Scores	$(N_1 = 10)$ Ranks	Control Group Scores	$(N_2 = 8)$ Ranks
42	9	41	8
53	15	36	4
47	13	33	2
38	5	55	16
46	12	44	10
51	14	35	3
62	18	32	1
60	17	40	7
45	11		$R_2 = \overline{51}$
39	6		
	$R_1 = \overline{120}$		

First, the entire set of 18 scores is ranked in 1-2-3 order from smallest to largest. The sum of the ranks is obtained separately for each group. As a check, note that $R_1 + R_2$ must equal $\dfrac{N(N+1)}{2}$. In our problem,

$R_1 = 120$ and $R_2 = 51$, the sum being 171. Since $N = 18$, $\dfrac{N(N+1)}{2} =$ $\dfrac{18 \times 19}{2}$ or 171, which checks the sum $R_1 + R_2$. When N_1 and N_2 are equal to or larger than 8, we may compute a σ score for each rank total by the following formula:

Sample 1:

$$z_1 = \frac{2R_1 - N_1(N+1)}{\sqrt{\dfrac{N_1 N_2 (N+1)}{3}}}$$

Sample 2:

$$z_2 = \frac{2R_2 - N_2(N+1)}{\sqrt{\dfrac{N_1 N_2 (N+1)}{3}}}$$

These z's may be referred to the normal distribution, and their probability of occurrence determined. The two z's should equal each other with opposite sign. In the problem above,

$$z_1 = \frac{2 \times 120 - 10 \times 19}{\sqrt{\dfrac{10 \times 8 \times 19}{3}}} = \frac{50}{22.5} = 2.22$$

$$z_2 = \frac{2 \times 51 - 8 \times 19}{\sqrt{\dfrac{10 \times 8 \times 19}{3}}} = \frac{-50}{22.5} = -2.22$$

From Table A we read that 1.3% of the normal curve lies to the right of 2.22σ; and of course, 1.3% lies to the left of -2.22σ. The P, therefore, is .03 and the null hypothesis must be rejected. On the present evidence our two groups differ in mean achievement. If the hypothesis had been that the experimental group is *superior* to the control (one-tailed test), P would be .013 and the result significant, almost at the .01 level.

The nonparametric methods are applicable to a number of problems involving small groups. They are especially useful when few assumptions can be made or are tenable under the conditions of the problem. Nonparametric methods should not be substituted for the parametric methods where the latter are applicable.

PROBLEMS

1. Two sharp clicking sounds are presented in succession, the second being always more intense or less intense than the first. Presentation is in

random order. In eight trials an observer is right six times. Is this result significant?

(a) Calculat. P directly (p. 249).
(b) Check P found in (a) by χ^2 test (p. 258). Compare P's found with and without correction for continuity.

2. A multiple-choice test of fifty items provides five responses to each item. How many items must a subject answer correctly.

(a) to reach the .05 level?
(b) to reach the .01 level?
(Use normal curve)

3. A multiple-choice test of thirty items provides three responses for each item. How many items must a subject answer correctly before the chances are only one in fifty that he is merely guessing?

4. A pack of fifty-two playing cards contains four suits (diamonds, clubs, spades and hearts). A subject "guesses" through the pack of cards, naming only suits, and is right eighteen times.

(a) Is this result better than "chance"? (Hint: In using the probability curve, compute area to 17.5, lower limit of 18.0, rather than to 18.0.)
(b) Check your answer by the χ^2 test (p. 260).

5. Twelve samples of handwriting, six from normal and six from insane adults, are presented to a graphologist who claims he can identify the writing of the insane. How many "insane" specimens must he recognize correctly in order to prove his contention? (Assume that the graphologist knows that there are 6 specimens from normal and 6 from insane.)

6. The following judgments were classified into six categories taken to represent a continuum of opinion:

	Categories						
	I	II	III	IV	V	VI	Total
Judgments:	48	61	82	91	57	45	384

(a) Test given distribution versus "equal probability" hypothesis.
(b) Test given distribution versus normal distribution hypothesis.

7. In 120 throws of a single die, the following distribution of faces was obtained:

	Faces						
	1	2	3	4	5	6	Total
Observed frequencies:	30	25	18	10	22	15	120

Do these results constitute a refutation of the "equal probability" (null) hypothesis?

8. The following table represents the number of boys and the number of girls who chose each of the five possible answers to an item in an attitude scale.

	Approve Strongly	Approve	Indiffer-ent	Dis-approve	Strongly Dis-approve	Total
Boys	25	30	10	25	10	100
Girls	10	15	5	15	15	60

Do these data indicate a significant sex difference in attitude toward this question? [Note: Test the independence (null) hypothesis.]

9. The table below shows the number of normals and abnormals who chose each of the three possible answers to an item on a neurosis questionnaire.

	Yes	No	?	Total
Normals	14	66	10	90
Abnormals	27	66	7	100
	41	132	17	190

Does this item differentiate between the two groups? Test the independence hypothesis.

10. From the table below, determine whether Item 27 differentiates between two groups of high and low general ability.

Numbers of Two Groups Differing in General
Ability Who Pass Item 27 in a Test

	Passed	Failed	Total
High Ability	31	19	50
Low Ability	24	26	50
	55	45	100

11. Five χ^2's computed from fourfold tables in independent replications of an experiment are .50, 4.10, 1.20, 2.79 and 5.41. Does the aggregate of these tests yield a significant χ^2?

12. In a group of 15 identical twin pairs, one member of each pair is given special training, the other member of the pair acting as a control. In a final test, 10 of the trained twins were superior to their twin controls, 4 were inferior, and in one pair the scores were the same. Were the trained twins superior to the untrained? Apply the sign test. (Hint: take $(p + q)^{14}$.)

13. In answering a questionnaire the following scores were achieved by 10 men and 20 women:
Men: 22, 31, 38, 47, 48, 48, 49, 50, 52, 61
Women: 22, 23, 25, 25, 31, 33, 34, 34, 35, 37, 40, 41, 42, 43, 44, 44, 46, 48, 53, 54
Do men and women differ significantly in their answers to this questionnaire? Apply the median test (take the median = 41.5).

14. The Attitude toward the Church scale is administered to a group of 78 sophomores. Of the 78, 57 had had a course in religious education and 21 had not. Suppose that 37 of the 57 are above the common median of the whole group of 78, and that only 15 of the 21 are above the common median. Are the two groups significantly different? Apply the median test.

15. Two groups of graduate students, 8 in each group, earn the following scores:
   A: 19, 28, 14, 23, 14, 17, 12, 15
   B: 25, 23, 29, 15, 27, 21, 24, 20
   Do the two groups differ significantly? Apply the sum-of-ranks test.

ANSWERS

1. (a) $P = .145$; not significant
   (b) $P = .145$ when corrected; .083 uncorrected
2. (a) 15
   (b) 17
3. 16
4. Probability of 18 or better is about .08; not significant
5. 5 or 6 (Probability of 5 or 6 = 37/924 = .04)
6. (a) $\chi^2 = 27$; P less than .01 and hypothesis of "equal probability" must be discarded.
   (b) $\chi^2 = 346$; P is less than .01, and the deviation from the normal hypothesis is significant.
7. Yes. $\chi^2 = 12.90$, $df = 5$, and P is between .02 and .05
8. No. $\chi^2 = 7.03$, $df = 4$, and P is between .20 and .10
9. No. $\chi^2 = 4.14$, $df = 2$, and P is between .20 and .10
10. No. $\chi^2 = 1.98$, $df = 1$, and P lies between .20 and .10
11. Yes. $\chi^2 = 14.00$, $df = 5$, and P lies between .02 and .01
12. No. $P = .09$
13. No. χ^2 (corrected) $= 1.35$
14. No. $\chi^2 = .073$
15. Yes. Significant at the .05 level

CHAPTER 11

ANALYSIS OF VARIANCE

◇◆

The methods described under analysis of variance include (1) a variety of procedures called experimental designs, as well as (2) certain statistical techniques devised for use with these procedures. The statistics used in analysis of variance are not new (as they are sometimes thought to be) but are, in fact, adaptations of formulas and methods described earlier in this book. The experimental designs, on the other hand, are in several instances new, at least to psychology. These systematic approaches often provide more efficient and exact tests of experimental hypotheses than do the conventional methods ordinarily employed.

This chapter will be concerned with the application of analysis of variance to the important and often-encountered problem of determining the significance of the difference between means. This topic has been treated by classical methods in Chapter 9, and the present chapter will give the student an opportunity to contrast the relative efficiency of the two approaches and to gain, as well, some notion of the advantages and disadvantages of each. Treatment of other and more complex experimental designs through analysis of variance is beyond the scope of this book. After this introductory chapter, however, the interested student should be able to follow the more comprehensive treatments of analysis of variance in the references listed in the footnote.*

The plan of this chapter is to give, *first,* an elementary account of the

* Edwards, A. L., *Statistical Methods for the Behavioral Sciences* (New York: Rinehart, 1954).

McNemar, Q., *Psychological Statistics* (New York: John Wiley and Sons, 2nd ed., 1955).

Snedecor, G. W., *Statistical Methods* (5th ed.; Ames, Iowa: Iowa State College Press, 1956).

Walker, H. M., and Lev, J., *Statistical Inference* (New York: Henry Holt & Co., 1953).

Fisher, R. A., *Statistical Methods for Research Workers* (8th ed.; London: Oliver and Boyd, 1941).

Fisher, R. A., *The Design of Experiments* (London: Oliver and Boyd, 1935).

(The Fisher references will be difficult for the beginner.)

principles of variance analysis. The problem of determining the significance of the difference between two means will then be considered: (1)
when the means are *independent*, i.e., when the sets of measures from
which the M's are derived are *uncorrelated*, and (2) when M's are not
independent because of correlation among the different sets of measures
or scores.

I. HOW VARIANCE IS ANALYZED

1. When pairs of scores are added to yield a composite score

While the variability within a set of scores is ordinarily given by the
standard deviation or σ, variability may also be expressed by the "variance" or σ^2. A very considerable advantage of variances over SD's is the
fact that variances are often additive and the sums of squares, upon
which variances are based, always are. A simple example will illustrate
this. Suppose that we add the two *independent* (uncorrelated) scores X
and Y made by subject A on tests X and Y to give the composite score Z
(i.e., $Z = X + Y$). Now, if we add the X and Y scores for each person in
our group, *after* expressing each score as a deviation from its own mean,
we will have for any subject that

$$z = x + y$$

in which $z = Z - M_z$, $x = X - M_x$, and $y = Y - M_y$.

Squaring both sides of this equation, and summing for all subjects in
the group, we have in general that

$$\Sigma z^2 = \Sigma x^2 + \Sigma y^2$$

The cross product term $2\Sigma xy$ * drops out as x and y are independent
(uncorrelated) by hypothesis. Hence we find that the sum of the squares
in x plus the sum of the squares in y equals the sum of the squares in z.
Dividing by N, we have

$$\frac{\Sigma z^2}{N} = \frac{\Sigma x^2}{N} + \frac{\Sigma y^2}{N}$$

or

$$\sigma^2{}_z = \sigma^2{}_x + \sigma^2{}_y$$

Also

$$\sigma_z = \sqrt{\sigma^2{}_x + \sigma^2{}_y}$$

The equation in terms of variances is more convenient and more useful
than is the equation in terms of SD's. Thus if we divide each variance by
$\sigma^2{}_z$ we have

$$1 = \frac{\sigma^2{}_x}{\sigma^2{}_z} + \frac{\sigma^2{}_y}{\sigma^2{}_z}$$

* The formula is $r = \dfrac{\Sigma xy}{N\sigma_x\sigma_y}$ (p. 139). If $r = 0$, Σxy must also be zero.

which tells us what *proportion* of the variance of the composite Z is attributable to the variance of X and what proportion is attributable to the variance of Y. This division of total variability into its independent components cannot be readily done with SD's.

2. When two sets of scores are combined into a single distribution

The breakdown of total variability into its contributing parts may be approached in another way. When two sets of scores, A and B, are thrown together or combined into a single distribution (see p. 56), the sum of the squares of *all* of the scores taken from the M_T of the single total distribution is related to the component distributions A and B as follows:

$$\Sigma x^2{}_T = \Sigma x^2{}_A + \Sigma x^2{}_B + N_A d^2{}_A + N_B d^2{}_B$$

where $\Sigma x^2{}_T = SS$ * of deviations in distribution T from M_T;

$\Sigma x^2{}_A = SS$ of deviations in distribution A from M_A;

$\Sigma x^2{}_B = SS$ of deviations in distribution B from M_B.

N_A and N_B are the numbers of scores in distributions A and B, respectively; d_A and d_B are the deviations of the means of A and B from the mean of T, i.e., $(M_A - M_T)^2 = d^2{}_A$; $(M_B - M_T)^2 = d^2{}_B$.

The equation given above in terms of $\Sigma x^2{}_T$ is important in the present connection because it shows that the sum of the squares of deviations around the mean of a single distribution made up of two component distributions can be broken down into two parts: (1) the SS around the M's of the two sets of scores, viz., M_A and M_B, and (2) the sum of squares (times the appropriate N's) of the deviations of M_A and M_B from M_T. An illustration will make the application of this result to variance analysis clearer.

Table 38 shows three sets of scores, 5 for group A, 10 for group B, and 15 for group T which is made up of A and B. The sums of scores, the means and SS around the M's have been calculated for each group. It may be noted that $M_T = \dfrac{18 \times 5 + 21 \times 10}{15} = 20$; and that, in general,

$$M_T = \frac{(M_A \times N_A) + (M_B \times N_B)}{N_A + N_B} \quad \text{(p. 30)}.$$

Substituting the data from Table 38 in the sums equation above we find that

$$274 = 138 + 106 + 5(18 - 20)^2 + 10(21 - 20)^2$$

or

$$274 = 138 + 106 + 20 + 10$$

* SS = sum of squares.

TABLE 38   A and B are two distributions and T is a combination of the two

Distribution A	Distribution B	Distribution T (A + B)
25	17	25
15	20	15
18	26	18
22	18	22
10	20	10
	25	17
	19	20
	26	26
	18	18
	21	20
		25
		19
		26
		18
		21
Sum 90	210	300
M 18	21	20
Σx^2 138	106	274

Of the total SS (274), 244 (138 + 106) is contributed by the variability within the two distributions A and B, and 30 (20 + 10) is contributed by the variability between the means of the two distributions. This breakdown of total SS into the SS's *within* component distributions and *between* the M's of the combined distributions is fundamental to analysis of variance. The method whereby SS's can be expressed as variances will be shown later.

II. THE SIGNIFICANCE OF THE DIFFERENCE BETWEEN MEANS DERIVED FROM INDEPENDENT OR UNCORRELATED MEASURES OR SCORES (ONE CRITERION OF CLASSIFICATION)

1. When there are more than two means to be compared

The value of analysis of variance in testing experimental hypotheses is most strikingly demonstrated in those problems in which the significance of the differences among several means is desired. An example will illustrate the procedures and will provide a basis for the discussion of certain theoretical points.

Example (1)   Assume that we wish to study the effects of eight different experimental conditions designated A, B, C, D, E, F, G, H, upon performance on a sensorimotor task. From a total of 48 subjects, 6 are assigned at random to each of 8 groups and the same test is administered to all. Do the mean scores achieved under the 8 experimental conditions differ significantly?

Records for the 8 groups are shown in parallel columns in Table 39.

TABLE 39 Hypothetical experiment in which 48 subjects are assigned at random to 8 groups of 6 subjects each. Groups are tested under 8 different experimental conditions, designated respectively A, B, C, D, E, F, G and H

	A	B	C	D	E	F	G	H	
	64	73	77	78	63	75	78	55	
	72	61	83	91	65	93	46	66	
	68	90	97	97	44	78	41	49	
	77	80	69	82	77	71	50	64	
	56	97	79	85	65	63	69	70	
	95	67	87	77	76	76	82	68	
Sums	432	468	492	510	390	456	366	372	Grand Sum: 3486
M's	72	78	82	85	65	76	61	62	General Mean = 72.63

A. CALCULATION OF SUMS OF SQUARES

Step 1 Correction term $(C) = \dfrac{(3486)^2}{48} = 253{,}171$

Step 2 Total Sum of Squares

$$= (64^2 + 72^2 + \ldots + 70^2 + 68^2) - C$$
$$= 262{,}364 - 253{,}171 = 9193$$

Step 3 Sum of Squares *among* Means of A, B, C, D, E, F, G, and H

$$= \frac{(432)^2 + (468)^2 + (492)^2 + (510)^2 + (390)^2 + (456)^2}{6}$$
$$+ \frac{(366)^2 + (372)^2}{6} - C$$
$$= \frac{1540188}{6} - 253{,}171 = 3527$$

Step 4 Sum of Squares *within* Conditions A, B, C, D, E, F, G and H

$$= \text{Total SS} - \text{Among Means SS}$$
$$= 9193 - 3527 = 5666$$

TABLE 39 (*Continued*)

B. SUMMARY: ANALYSIS OF VARIANCE

Source of Variation	df	Sums of Squares	Mean Square (Variance)	SD
Among the means of Conditions	7	3527	503.9	
Within Conditions	40	5666	141.6	
Total	47	9193		11.9

$$F = \frac{503.9}{141.6} = 3.56$$

From Table F for
$df_1 = 7$ and $df_2 = 40$
F at .05 = 2.26
F at .01 = 3.14

C. TESTS OF DIFFERENCES BY USE OF t

For $df = 40$, $t_{.05} = 2.02$ (Table D)
$t_{.01} = 2.71$

$$SE_D = 11.9 \sqrt{\frac{1}{6} + \frac{1}{6}}$$
$$= 11.9 \times .577$$
$$= 6.87$$

$D_{.05} = 2.02 \times 6.87 = 13.9$
$D_{.01} = 2.71 \times 6.87 = 18.6$
Largest difference is between D and G = 24
Smallest difference is between G and H = 1

Distribution of mean differences	f
22–24	2
19–21	3
16–18	3
13–15	4
10–12	4
7–9	3
4–6	5
1–3	4
	28

Approximately 5 differences significant at .01 level

Approximately 10 differences significant at .05 level

Individual scores are listed under the 8 headings which designate the conditions under which the test was given. Since "conditions" furnishes the category for the assignment of subjects, in the terminology of analysis of variance there is said to be *one criterion of classification*. The first step in our analysis is a breakdown of the total variance (σ^2) of the 48 scores into *two* parts: (1) the variance attributable to the different conditions, or the variance among the 8 means, and (2) the variance arising from individual differences within the 8 groups. The next step is to determine whether the group means differ significantly *inter se* in view of the variability within the separate groups (individual differences). A detailed account of the calculations required (see Table 39) is set forth in the steps on pages 280–281.

Step 1

Correction term (C). When the SD is calculated from original measures or raw scores,* the formula $SD^2 = \dfrac{\Sigma x^2}{N} - C^2$ becomes $SD^2 = \dfrac{\Sigma x^2}{N} - M^2$. The correction ($C$) equals M directly in this form of the equation, since $C = AM - M$ and the AM (assumed mean) here is zero. Replacing σ^2 by $\dfrac{\Sigma x^2}{N}$ we have that $\dfrac{\Sigma x^2}{N} = \dfrac{\Sigma X^2}{N} - M^2$. Now, if the correction term M^2 is written $\dfrac{(\Sigma X)^2}{N^2}$ we can multiply this equation through by N to find that $\Sigma x^2 = \Sigma X^2 - \dfrac{(\Sigma X)^2}{N}$. In Table 39 the correction term $\dfrac{(\Sigma X)^2}{N}$ is 253,171. This correction is applied to the sum of squares, ΣX^2.

Step 2

Total sum of squares around the general mean. Since $\Sigma x^2 = \Sigma X^2 - \dfrac{(\Sigma X)^2}{N}$, we need only square and sum the original scores and subtract the correction term to find SS_T (sum of squares around the general mean of all 48 scores). In Table 39, squaring each score and summing we get a total of 262,364; and subtracting the correction, the final SS_T is 9193. This SS_T may also be computed by taking deviations around the general mean directly. The general mean is 72.63. Subtracting 72.63 from each of the 48 scores, squaring these x's and summing, we get 9193 checking the calculations from raw scores. The formula for sum of squares around the general mean is

$$SS_T = \Sigma X^2 - \frac{(\Sigma X)^2}{N} \tag{73}$$

(SS_T *around general mean using raw scores*)

* See page 278. In analysis of variance calculations it is usually more convenient to work with original measures or raw scores.

Step 3

Sum of squares among the means obtained under the 8 conditions. To find the sum of squares attributable to condition differences ($SS_{M's}$), we must first square the *sum* of each column (i.e., each condition), add these sums and divide the total by 6, the number of scores in each group or column. Subtracting the correction found in Step 1, we then get the final $SS_{M's}$ to be 3527. This $SS_{M's}$ is simply the SS of the separate group M's around the one general mean, multiplied by the number of scores in each column. We may carry out these calculations as a check on the result above. Thus for the present example:

$$SS_{M's} = 6[(72 - 72.63)^2 + (78 - 72.63)^2 + (82 - 72.63)^2$$
$$+ (85 - 72.63)^2 + (65 - 72.63)^2 + (76 - 72.63)^2$$
$$+ (61 - 72.63)^2 + (62 - 72.63)^2] = 3527$$

When, as here, we are working with raw scores, the method of calculation repeats Step 2, except that we divide the square of *each* column total by 6 (the number of scores in each column) before subtracting C. The general formula is

$$SS \; (among \; means) = \frac{(\Sigma X_1)^2}{n_1} + \frac{(\Sigma X_2)^2}{n_2} + \cdots + \frac{(\Sigma X_n)^2}{n_n} - C \qquad (74)$$

(SS *among means when calculation is with raw scores*)

When the number of scores in the groups differ, the squares of the column sums will be divided by different n's before the correction is subtracted (see page 288 for illustration).

Step 4

Sum of squares within conditions (individual differences). The SS within columns or groups (SS_w) always equals the SS_T minus the $SS_{M's}$. Subtracting 3527 from 9193, we have 5666. This SS_w may also be calculated directly from the data (see p. 303).

Step 5

Calculation of the variances from each SS and analysis of the total variance into its components is shown in the B part of Table 39. Each SS becomes a variance when divided by the degrees of freedom (df) allotted to it (p. 194). There are 48 scores in all in Table 39, and hence there are ($N - 1$) or 47 df in all. These 47 df are allocated in the following way.

The df for "among the means of conditions" are $(8 - 1)$ or 7, less by one than the number of conditions. The df *within* groups or within conditions are $(47 - 7)$ or 40. This last df may also be found directly: since there are $(6 - 1)$ or 5 df for each condition ($N = 6$ in each group), 5×8 (number of conditions) gives 40 df for within groups. The variance among M's of groups is $3527/7$ or 503.9; and the variance within groups is $5666/40$ or 141.6.

If N = number of scores in all and k = number of categories or groups, we have for the general case that

$$df \text{ for total SS} = (N - 1)$$
$$df \text{ for within groups SS} = (N - k)$$
$$df \text{ for among means of groups SS} = (k - 1)$$

Also: $(N - 1) = (N - k) + (k - 1)$

Step 6

In the present problem the null hypothesis asserts that the 8 sets of scores are in reality random samples drawn from the same normally distributed population, and that the means of conditions A, B, C, D, E, F, G and H will differ *only* through fluctuations of sampling. To test this hypothesis we divide the "among means" variance by the "within groups" variance and compare the resulting *variance ratio*, called F, with the F values in Table F. The F in our problem is 3.56 and the df are 7 for the numerator (df_1) and 40 for the denominator (df_2). Entering Table F we read from column 7 (midway between 6 and 8) and row 40 that an F of 2.26 is significant at the .05 level and an F of 3.14 is significant at the .01 level. Only the .05 and .01 points are given in the table. These entries mean that, for the given df's, variance ratios or F's of 2.26 and 3.14 can be expected once in 20 and once in 100 trials, respectively, when the null hypothesis is true. Since our F is larger than the .01 level, it would occur less than once in 100 trials by chance. We reject the null hypothesis, therefore, and conclude that the means of our 8 groups do in fact differ.

F furnishes a comprehensive or over-all test of the significance of the differences among means. A significant F does not tell us *which* means differ significantly, but that at least one is reliably different from some others. If F is not significant, there is no reason for further testing, as none of the mean differences will be significant (see p. 184). But if F is significant, we may proceed to test the separate differences by the t test (p. 191) as shown in Table 39 C.

Step 7

The best estimate which we can make of the uncontrolled variability arising from individual differences is given by the SD of 11.9 computed from the "within groups" variance given in Table 39 B. This SD is based upon *all* of our data and is a measure of subject variability *after* the systematic effects arising from differences in column means have been allowed for. In testing mean differences by the t test, therefore (Table 39 C), the SD of 11.9 is used throughout instead of the SD's calculated from the separate columns, A, B, C, D, E, F, G and H. The standard error of *any* mean (SE_M) is $\dfrac{SD_w}{\sqrt{N}}$ or $11.9/\sqrt{6} = 4.86$. And the SE of the difference (D) between any two means is $SE_D = \sqrt{4.86^2 + 4.86^2}$ or 6.87. A general formula for calculating SE_D directly is

$$SE_D = SD_w\sqrt{\frac{1}{N_1} + \frac{1}{N_2}} \tag{75}$$

(standard error of the difference between any two means in analysis of variance)

where SD_w is the within-groups SD, and n_1 and n_2 are the sizes of the samples or groups being compared.

The means of the 8 groups in Table 39 range from 61 to 85, and the mean differences from 24 to 1. To determine the significance of the difference between *any* two selected means we must compute a t ratio by dividing the given mean difference by its SE_D. The resulting t is then compared with the t in Table D for 40 df, viz., the number of df upon which our SD_w is based. A more summary approach than this is to compute that difference among means which for 40 df will be significant at the .05 or the .01 level and check our differences against these standards. This is done in Table 39 C. We know from Table D that for 40 df, a t of 2.02 is significant at the .05 level; and a t of 2.71 is significant at the .01 level. Since t = mean difference/SE_D, we may substitute 2.02 for t in this equation and 6.87 for SE_D to find that a difference of 13.9 is significant at the .05 level. Using the same procedure, we substitute 2.71 for t in the equation to find that a difference of 18.6 is significant at the .01 level.

Eight means will yield $\dfrac{(8 \times 7)}{2}$ or 28 differences. From the distribution of these 28 differences (Table 39 C) it is clear that approximately 5 differences are significant at the .01 level (i.e., are 18.6 or more); and approximately 10 at the .05 level (i.e., are 13.9 or more). The largest difference is 24 and the smallest is 1.

Several additional comments may serve to clarify and summarize the computations relating to Table 39.

(1) It must be kept in mind that we are testing the null hypothesis—namely, the hypothesis that there are *no* true differences among the 8 condition means. Said differently, the F ratio tests the hypothesis that our 8 groups are in reality random samples drawn from the same normally distributed population. The F test refutes the null hypothesis for means by demonstrating differences which cannot be explained by chance, i.e., differences larger than those which might occur from sampling accidents once in 100 trials, if the null hypothesis were true. In addition to the assumption of normality in the common population, we also assume, in using the F test, that the samples have *equal variances.*

(2) This second assumption of equal variances can be tested by means of Bartlett's test for homogeneity of variance.* Unless the samples are quite small, however, the experimental evidence shows that variances in the samples may differ considerably and the F test still be valid. A simple check on the equality of sample variances is to calculate the sum of squares for each group separately, divide by the appropriate df, and test the largest V against the smallest V using the F test. In Table 39, for example, the largest V is for Group G and the smallest for Group D. The sum of squares for Group G is 1540 and the df are $(6-1)$ or 5, so that $V_G = 308$. For Group D, the sum of squares is 302, and the df are again 5, so that $V_D = 60.4$. F is $308/60.4$ or 5.1 and the df are 5 and 5. From Table F we find that for 5/5 df, F must equal 5.05 to be significant at the .05 level; and 10.97 to be significant at the .01 level. The observed F of 5.1 is barely significant at the .05 level, and since the two V's tested are the extremes out of 8, we may feel sure that the 8 V's do not differ significantly the one from the other. It sometimes happens that the two extreme V's differ significantly, but the complete set of V's is homogeneous by Bartlett's test.

(3) The 47 df $(48-1)$ in the table are broken down into 7 df allotted to the 8 condition means and the 40 df allotted to individual differences (variations within groups or columns). Variances are calculated by dividing each SS by its own df.

(4) In problems like that of Table 39 (where there is only one criterion of classification) all 3 variances (total, among means, and within groups) are in effect estimates of the variance in the population from which our 8 samples have been drawn. Only two of these variances are *independent*: the variance among condition means and the variance within groups, since V_T is composed of these two. The two independent

* See Snedecor, G. W., *op. cit.*, pp. 285–289

estimates of the population variance are used in computing the variance ratio and making the F test.

Since the numerator in the F ratio is always the larger of the two V's and the denominator the smaller, F must be 1.00 or greater. This means that we are dealing with only the *right* (the positive) tail of the F distribution: that we are making a one-tailed test. This is the appropriate test, as we are interested in knowing whether the first V is equal to or greater than the second.

When samples are strictly random, these two estimates of the common V are equal and F is 1.00. Moreover, when F is 1.00, the variance among group means is no greater than the variance within groups; or, put differently, group means differ no more than do the individuals within the groups. The extent to which F is greater than 1.00 becomes, then, a measure of the significance of the differences among group means. The larger the F the greater the probability that group mean differences are greater than individual variation—sometimes called "experimental error."

(5) According to the traditional method of treating a problem like that of Table 39, 8 SD's would first be computed, one around each of the 8 column means. From these 8 SD's, SE's of the means and SE's of the differences between pairs of means would be computed. A t test would then be made of the difference between each pair of means and the significance of this difference determined from Table D.

Analysis of variance is an improvement over this procedure in several respects. In Table 39 we first compute an F ratio which tells us whether *any* mean differences are significant. If F is significant, we may then compute a single SE_D. This SE_D is derived from the SD_w calculated from the 8 groups after systematic mean differences have been removed. Moreover, this within-groups SD—based as it is upon all 48 scores and with 40 df— furnishes a better (i.e., more reliable) measure of uncontrolled (or experimental) variation in the table than could be obtained from SD's based upon only 8 scores and 7 df. Pooling of sums to obtain the within-groups SD is permissible, since the deviations in each group have been taken from their own mean.

(6) If the F test refutes the null hypothesis we may use the t test to evaluate mean differences. If the F test does not refute the null hypothesis there is no justification for further testing, as differences between pairs of means will not differ significantly unless there are a number of them— in which case one or two might by chance equal or approach significance.*

* In 100 strictly random differences, 5 will be significant at the .05 level; that is, 2½% will exceed 1.96σ at each end of the curve of differences (p. 214). Hence in 28 differences (Table 39 C) 1 or 2 might be significant at the .05 level ($28 \times .05 = 1.40$) if differences are randomly distributed around zero.

(7) When samples are strictly random and V's are equal, F is a valid test. However, in practice, sample sizes may be small and the assumption of equal V's precarious. Under these conditions, the F ratio is only an approximate test of significance. Repetition of the experiment, perhaps many times, is the only real guarantee against an erroneous conclusion.

TABLE 40 Solution of example (5), page 223, through methods of analysis of variance

SCORES

Class 1 ($N_1 = 6$)	Class 2 ($N_2 = 10$)
28	20
35	16
32	25
24	34
26	20
35	28
6⟌180	31
$M_1 = 30$	24
	27
	15
	10⟌240
	$M_2 = 24$

A. SUMS OF SQUARES

1. Correction: $(420)^2/16 = 11025$

2. $SS_T = 28^2 + 35^2 + \cdots + 15^2 - C$
   $= 11622 - 11025 = 597$

3. $SS_{M's} = \dfrac{(180)^2}{6} + \dfrac{(240)^2}{10} - C$
   $= 11160 - 11025 = 135$

4. $SS_w = 597 - 135 = 462$

B. ANALYSIS OF VARIANCE

Source	df	SS	MS(V)
Between means	1	135	135
Within classes	14	462	33
Total	15	597	

$F = \dfrac{135}{33} = 4.09$

$t = \sqrt{F} = 2.02$

From Table F
F at .05 level $= 4.60$
F at .01 level $= 8.86$

2. When there are only two means to be compared

In order to provide a further comparison of analysis of variance with the methods of Chapter 9, example (5), page 223, is solved in Table 40. This second example will show that when only two means are to be compared, the F test reduces to the t test.

Step 1

The sum of all of the 16 scores is $180 + 240$ or 420; and the correction (C) is, accordingly, $(420)^2/16$ or 11025 (see p. 282).

Step 2

When each score has been squared and the correction subtracted from the total, the SS around the general mean is 597 by formula (73), page 282.

Step 3

The sum of squares between means (135) is found by squaring the sum of each column, dividing the first by 6 (n_1) and the second by 10 (n_2) and subtracting C.

Step 4

The SS within groups is the difference between the SS_T and $SS_{between\ M's}$. Thus $SS_w = 597 - 135 = 462$.

Step 5

The analysis of variance is shown in Table 40. SS_T is divided into SS between means of groups and SS within groups. Since there are 16 scores in all, there are $(N-1)$ or 15 df for "total." The $SS_{M's}$ is allotted $(k-1)$ or 1 df ($k=2$). The remaining 14 df are assigned to within groups and may be found either by subtracting 1 from 15 or by adding the 5 df in Class 1 to the 9 df in Class 2. Mean squares or variances are obtained by dividing each SS by its appropriate df.

Step 6

The variance ratio or F is 135/33 or 4.09. The df for between means is 1 and the df for within groups is 14. Entering Table F with these dfs we read in column 1 and row 14 that the .05 level is 4.60 and the .01 level is 8.86. Our F of 4.09 does not quite reach the .05 level so that our mean difference of 6 points must be regarded as not significant. The difference between the two means $(30 - 24)$ is not large enough, therefore, to be convincing; or, stated in probability terms, a difference of 6 can be expected to occur too frequently to render the null hypothesis untenable.

When there are only two means to be compared, as here, $F = t^2$ or $t = \sqrt{F}$ and the two tests $(F$ and $t)$ give exactly the same result. In Table 40 B, for instance $\sqrt{F} = \sqrt{4.09}$ or 2.02 which is the t previously found in example (8) on page 223. From Table D we have found (p. 225) that for 14 df the .05 level of significance for this t is 2.14. Our t of 2.02 does not quite reach this level and hence (like F) is not significant. If we interpolate between the .05 point of 2.14 and the .10 point of 1.76 in Table D, our t of 2.02 is found to fall approximately at .07. In 100 repetitions of this experiment, therefore, we can expect a mean difference of 6 or more to occur about 7 times—too frequently to be significant under the null hypothesis.

3. Example (6), page 225, solved by analysis of variance

In problems requiring the comparison of two group means either F or t may be employed. From the standpoint of calculation, F is perhaps somewhat easier to apply. In example (6), page 225, it is easier to calculate t because raw scores are not given. But F may be calculated if desired in the following way. The general mean for the two groups is $(40.39 \times 31 + 35.81 \times 42)$ divided by 73, or 37.75: it is the weighted mean obtained from the two group means. The SS between the means of the groups of boys and girls is $31(40.39 - 37.75)^2 + 42(35.81 - 37.75)^2$ or 374.13; namely, the deviation of each group mean from the general mean weighted in each case by the N of the group.

To get the SS within groups we simply square each SD and multiply by $(N - 1)$, remembering that $SD^2 = \dfrac{\Sigma x^2}{(N - 1)}$ (p. 186). In example (6) we find that $(8.69)^2 \times 30 = 2265.48$; and $(8.33)^2 \times 41 = 2844.94$. The sum of these two is 5110.42, the SS within groups. The complete analysis of variance and F test are shown in Table 41; $F = 5.20$ and $t = \sqrt{F}$ or

2.28, checking the result given on page 225. Our F of 5.20 exceeds the .05 level of 3.98 but does not reach the .01 level of 7.01. As before, F and t give identical results.

TABLE 41 Solution of example (6), page 225, by analysis of variance

A. SUMS OF SQUARES AND GENERAL MEAN

1. General mean $= \dfrac{(40.39 \times 31 + 35.81 \times 42)}{73} = 37.75$

2. SS between means:
$$31(40.39 - 37.75)^2 + 42(35.81 - 37.75)^2 = 374.13$$

3. SS within groups:
$$30(8.69)^2 + 41(8.33)^2 = 5110.42$$

B. ANALYSIS OF VARIANCE

Source of Variation	df	Sums of Squares	Mean Square (Variance)
Between means	1	374.13	374.1
Within groups	71	5110.42	72.0

$F = 374.1/72 = 5.20$ From Table F

$t = \sqrt{F} = \sqrt{5.20} = 2.28$ $df = 1/71$

                                           F at .05 = 3.98

                                           F at .01 = 7.01

III. THE SIGNIFICANCE OF THE DIFFERENCE BETWEEN MEANS OBTAINED FROM CORRELATED GROUPS (TWO CRITERIA OF CLASSIFICATION)

1. When the same group is measured more than once (single group method)

Means are correlated when the two sets of scores achieved by the group from which the means were derived are correlated. When a test is given and then repeated, analysis of variance may be used to determine whether the mean change is significant. The experimental design here is essentially the same as that of the Single Group Method of Chapter 9, page 226. Hence example (8), page 227, is used in Table 42 to illustrate the methods of analysis of variance and to provide a comparison with the difference method of page 292.

TABLE 42   Solution of example (8), page 227, by analysis of variance

A. SUMS OF SQUARES

1. Correction $= (1240)^2/24 = \dfrac{1537600}{24} = 64066.67$

2. Total Sum of Squares $= 68952 - 64066.67 = 4885.33$

3. Between trials sum of squares:
$$\dfrac{(572)^2 + (668)^2}{12} - 64066.67 = 384.00$$

4. Among subjects sum of squares:
$$68391 - 64066.67 = 4324.33$$

5. Interaction sum of squares $= 4885.33 - (384.00 + 4324.33)$
$$= 177$$

B. ANALYSIS OF VARIANCE

Source of Variation	df	Sums of Squares	Mean Square (Variance)	SD
Between trials	1	384.00	384.00	
Among subjects	11	4324.33	393.12	
Interaction	11	177.00	16.09	4.01
Total	23	4885.33		

$F_{trials} = \dfrac{384}{16.09} = 23.87$

$F_{subjects} = \dfrac{393.12}{16.09} = 24.43$

$t = \sqrt{23.87} = 4.89$

From Table F

Trials	Subjects
$df = 1/11$	$df = 11/11$
F at .05 = 4.84	2.83
F at .01 = 9.65	4.48

The procedures for the analysis of variance in example (8) differ in at least two ways from the methods of Section II. First, since there is the possibility of correlation between the scores achieved by the 12 subjects on the first and fifth trials, the two sets of scores should not at the outset be treated as independent (random) samples. Secondly, classification is now in terms of *two* criteria: (*a*) trials and (*b*) subjects. Because of these two criteria, the total SS must be broken down into three parts: (*a*) SS attributable to trials; (*b*) SS attributable to subjects; and (*c*) a residual SS usually called "interaction." Steps in the calculation of these three variances, shown in Table 42 A, may be summarized as follows.

Step 1

Correction (C). As in Section II, $C = \dfrac{(\Sigma X)^2}{N}$. In example (8) C is $(1240)^2/24$ or 64066.67.

Step 2

Total SS *around general mean*. Again the calculation repeats the procedure of Section II.

$$SS_T = (50^2 + 42^2 + \cdots + 72^2 + 50^2) - 64066.67$$
$$= 68952 - 64066.67 = 4885.33$$

Step 3

SS *between the means of trials*. There are two trials of 12 scores each. Therefore,

$$SS_{trials} = \frac{(572)^2 + (668)^2}{12} - 64066.67$$
$$= 64450.67 - 64066.67 = 384.0$$

Step 4

SS *among the means of subjects*. A second "between means" SS is required to take care of the second criterion of classification. There are 12 subjects and each has two trials. Hence,

$$SS_{subjects} = \frac{112^2 + 82^2 + \cdots + 134^2 + 88^2}{2} - 64066.67$$
$$= 68391.00 - 64066.67 = 4324.33$$

Step 5

Interaction SS. The residual variation or interaction is whatever is left when the systematic effects of trial differences and subject differences have been removed from the total SS. Interaction measures the tendency for subject performance to vary along with trials: it measures the factors attributable *neither* to subjects *nor* trials acting alone, but rather to both acting together. Interaction is obtained most simply * by subtracting trials SS plus subjects SS from total SS. Thus

$$\text{Interaction SS} = SS_T - (SS_{subjects} + SS_{trials})$$
$$= 4885.33 - (384 + 4324.33)$$
$$= 177$$

Step 6

As before, SS's become variances when divided by their appropriate df. Since there are 24 trials in all we have $(24 - 1)$ or 23 df for the total SS. Two trials receive 1 df, and 12 subjects, 11. The remaining 11 df are assigned to interaction. The rule is that the df for interaction is the product of the df for the two interacting variables, here 1×11. In general if $N =$ total number of scores, $r =$ rows and $k =$ columns, we have

$$df \text{ for total SS} = (N - 1)$$
$$df \text{ for column SS (trials)} = (k - 1)$$
$$df \text{ for row SS (subjects)} = (r - 1)$$
$$df \text{ for interaction SS} = (k - 1)(r - 1)$$

The three measures of variance appear in Table 42. Note that we may now calculate two F's, one for trial differences and one for subject differences. In both cases the interaction variance is placed in the denominator of the variance ratio, since it is our best estimate of residual variance (or experimental error) after the systematic influences of trials and subjects have been removed. The F for trials is 23.87 and is much larger than the 9.65 we find in Table F for the .01 point when $df_1 = 1$ and $df_2 = 11$. This means that the null hypothesis with respect to trials is untenable and must be abandoned. The evidence is strong that real improvement took place from trial 1 to trial 5.

Ordinarily in most two-criteria experiments we are concerned primarily with one criterion, as here. It is possible, however (and sometimes desirable), to test the second criterion—viz., differences among subjects. The F for subjects is 24.43 and again is far larger than the .01 point of 4.46 in Table F for $df_1 = 11$ and $df_2 = 11$. It is obvious that some subjects were consistently better than others without regard to trial.

Since there are two trials, we have two trial means. Hence, if we compute a t from the F for trials, it should be equal to that found by the difference method. The F of 23.87 yields a t of $\sqrt{23.87}$ or 4.89 which checks the t of 4.89 on page 227.

* Interaction may be calculated directly from the data.

Computations needed for the difference method of example (8), page 227, are somewhat shorter than are those for analysis of variance, and the difference method would probably be preferred if one wished to determine only the significance of the difference between the two trial means. If, however, the significance of the differences in the second criterion (differences among subject means) is wanted, analysis of variance is more useful. Moreover, through a further analysis of variance we can determine whether individual differences (differences among subjects) are significantly greater than practice differences (differences between trials). Thus if we divide the $V_{subjects}$ by the V_{trials}, the resulting F is 393.12/384 or 1.02. For a $df_1 = 11$ and $df_2 = 1$, the .05 point is 243. Hence, in the present experiment, at least, we may feel quite sure that individual differences were no greater than practice differences. Since the reverse is usually true, the implication to be drawn is that practice in the present experiment must have been quite drastic: a conclusion borne out by the F test for trials.

IV. ANALYSIS OF COVARIANCE

In many experimental situations, especially in the fields of memory and learning, we wish to compare groups that are initially unlike, either in the variable under study or some presumably related variable. In Chapter 9, two methods were given for equating groups initially—having them "start from scratch." In the first method, experimental and control groups were made equivalent initially by person-to-person matching; and in the second method, groups were matched initially for mean and σ in one or more related variables. Neither of these methods is entirely satisfactory and neither is always easy to apply. Equivalent groups often necessitate a sharp reduction in size of N (and also in variability) when the matching of scores is difficult to accomplish. Furthermore, in matched groups it is often difficult to get the correlation between the matching variable and the experimental variable in the population from which our samples were drawn (p. 230).

Analysis of covariance represents an extension of analysis of variance to allow for the correlation between initial and final scores. Covariance analysis is especially useful to experimental psychologists when for various reasons it is impossible or quite difficult to equate control and experimental groups at the start: a situation which often obtains in actual experiments. Through covariance analysis one is able to effect adjustments in final or terminal scores which will allow for differences in some initial variable. (For many other uses of covariance the reader should consult the references on page 276.)

Table 43 presents a numerically simple illustration of the application of analysis of covariance. The data in example (2) are artificial and are purposely meager so that the procedure will not be swamped by the numerical calculations.

Example (2)   Suppose that 15 children have been given one trial (X) of a test. Five are then assigned at random to each of three groups, A, B, and C. After two weeks, say, Group A is praised lavishly, Group B scolded severely, and the test repeated (Y). At the same time, a second trial (Y) is also given to Group C, the control group, without comment.

TABLE 43   To illustrate covariance analysis

(Original data from Example [2])

	GROUP A (praised)			GROUP B (scolded)			GROUP C (control)		
	X_1	Y_1	X_1Y_1	X_2	Y_2	X_2Y_2	X_3	Y_3	X_3Y_3
	15	30	450	25	28	700	5	10	50
	10	20	200	10	12	120	10	15	150
	20	25	500	15	20	300	20	20	400
	5	15	75	15	10	150	5	10	50
	10	20	200	10	10	100	10	10	100
Sums	60	110	1425	75	80	1370	50	65	750
M's	12	22		15	16		10	13	

For all 3 groups: $\Sigma X = 185$ $\Sigma Y = 255$

$\Sigma X^2 = 2775$ $\Sigma Y^2 = 5003$ $\Sigma XY = 3545$

Step 1   Correction terms:

$$C_x = (185)^2/15 = 2282$$
$$C_y = (255)^2/15 = 4335$$
$$C_{xy} = \frac{185 \times 255}{15} = 3145$$

Step 2   Total SS

$$\text{For } x = 2775 - 2282 = 493$$
$$y = 5003 - 4335 = 668$$
$$xy = 3545 - 3145 = 400$$

TABLE 43 (*Continued*)

Step 3 Among Group Means SS

$$\text{For } x = \frac{60^2 + 75^2 + 50^2}{5} - 2282 = 63$$

$$y = \frac{110^2 + 80^2 + 65^2}{5} - 4335 = 210$$

$$xy = \frac{60 \times 110 + 75 \times 80 + 50 \times 65}{5} - 3145 = 25$$

Step 4 Within Groups SS

$$\text{For } x = 493 - 63 = 430$$
$$y = 668 - 210 = 458$$
$$xy = 400 - 25 = 375$$

Step 5 Analysis of Variance of X and Y scores, taken separately

Source of Variation	df	SS_x	SS_y	$MS_x(V_x)$	$MS_y(V_y)$
Among Means	2	63	210	31.5	105
Within Groups	12	430	458	35.8	38.2
Total	14	493	668		

$$F_x = \frac{31.5}{35.8} = .88$$

$$F_y = \frac{105}{38.2} = 2.75$$

From Table F

$df\ 2/12$

F at .05 level $= 3.88$

F at .01 level $= 6.93$

Neither F is significant. Mean differences on final trial approach significance. $F_x = .88$ shows that the experimenter was quite successful in getting random samples in Groups A, B, C.

Step 6 Computation of Adjusted SS for Y: i.e., $SS_{y.x}$

$$\text{Total SS} = 668 - \frac{(400)^2}{493} = 343$$

$$\text{Within SS} = 458 - \frac{(375)^2}{430} = 131$$

$$\text{Among M's SS} = 343 - 131 = 212$$

TABLE 43 (Continued)

Analysis of Covariance

Source of Variation	df	SS_x	SS_y	S_{xy}	$SS_{y.x}$	$MS_{y.x}(V_{y.x})$	$SD_{y.x}$
Among Means	2	63	210	25	212	106	
Within Groups	11 *	430	458	375	131	12	3.46
Total	13	493	668	400	343		

$$F_{y.x} = \frac{106}{12} = 8.83$$

From Table F

df 2/11

F at .05 level $= 3.98$

F at .01 level $= 7.20$

Step 7 Correlation and Regression

$$r_{total} = \frac{400}{\sqrt{493 \times 668}} = .70 \qquad\qquad b_{total} = \frac{400}{493} = .81$$

$$r_{\substack{among \\ means}} = \frac{25}{\sqrt{63 \times 210}} = .22 \qquad\qquad b_{\substack{among \\ means}} = \frac{25}{63} = .40$$

$$r_{within} = \frac{375}{\sqrt{430 \times 458}} = .84 \qquad\qquad b_{within} = \frac{375}{430} = .87$$

Step 8 Calculation of Adjusted Y Means

Groups	N	M_X	M_Y	$M_{Y.X}$ (adjusted)
A	5	12	22	22.3
B	5	15	16	13.7
C	5	10	13	15.0
General Means		12.3	17	17.0

$$M_{Y.X} = M_Y - b(M_X - GM_X)$$

For Group A: $M_Y - bx = 22 - .87(12 - 12.3) = 22.3$

B: $M_Y - bx = 16 - .87(15 - 12.3) = 13.7$

C: $M_Y - bx = 13 - .87(10 - 12.3) = 15.0$

* 1 df lost, see p. 194.

TABLE 43 *(Concluded)*

Step 9 Significance of differences among adjusted Y means

$$SD_{y.x} = \sqrt{12} = 3.46$$

$$SE_{M_{y.x}} = \frac{3.46}{\sqrt{5}} = 1.55$$

SE_D between any two adjusted means $= SD_{y.x} \sqrt{\dfrac{1}{N_1} + \dfrac{1}{N_2}}$

$$= 3.46\sqrt{\frac{1}{5} + \frac{1}{5}} = 3.46 \times .63 = 2.18 \qquad (75)$$

For $df = 11$, $t_{.05} = 2.20$; $t_{.01} = 3.11$ (Table D)

Significant difference at .05 level $= 2.20 \times 2.18 = 4.80$

Significant difference at .01 level $= 3.11 \times 2.18 = 6.78$

A differs significantly from both B and C at .01 level.

B and C are not significantly different.

We thus have three groups—two experimental and one control—with initial scores (X) and final scores (Y). The problem is to determine whether the groups differ in the final trial (Y) as a result of the incentives. The method permits us to determine whether initial differences in (X) are important and to allow for them if they are.

Table 43 gives the necessary computations. The following steps outline the procedure.

Step 1

Correction term (C). There are three correction terms to be applied to SS's, one for X, one for Y and one for the cross products in X and Y. Calculation of C_x and C_y follows the method of page 282. The formula for C_{xy} is $\dfrac{\Sigma X \times \Sigma Y}{N}$ or in our problem $\dfrac{185 \times 255}{15}$.

Step 2

SS *for totals*. Again we have three SS's for totals: SS_x, SS_y and SS_{xy}, of which only SS_{xy} is new. The formula for SS_{xy} is

$$SS_{xy} = \Sigma XY - C_{xy} \qquad (75a)$$

(sum of squares for xy in analysis of covariance)

The SS_{xy} is found by multiplying pairs of X and Y scores, summing over the range and subtracting C_{xy}: thus $(15 \times 30 + 10 \times 20 + \cdots + 10 \times 10) - 3145 = 400$.

Step 3

SS *among means of the three groups*. Calculations shown in Table 43 follow the method of page 283 for X and Y. The "among means" term for xy is the sum of the corresponding X and Y column totals (e.g., $60 \times 110 + 75 \times 80 + 50 \times 65$) divided by 5 and minus C_{xy}.

Step 4

SS *within groups*. For x, y, and xy these SS's are found by subtracting the "among means" SS's from the SS_T.

Step 5

A preliminary analysis of variance of the X and Y trials, taken separately, has been made in Table 43. The F test applied to the initial (X) scores ($F_x = .88$) falls far short of significance at the .05 level, from which it is clear that the X means do not differ significantly and that the random assignment of subjects to the three groups was quite successful. The F test applied to the final (Y) scores ($F_y = 2.75$) approaches closer to significance, but is still considerably below 3.88, the .05 level. From this preliminary analysis of variance of the Y means *alone* we must conclude that neither praise nor scolding is more effective in raising scores than is mere repetition of the test.

Step 6

The computations carried out in this step are for the purpose of correcting the final (Y) scores for differences in initial (X) scores. The symbol $SS_{y.x}$ means that the SS_y have been "adjusted" for any variability in Y contributed by X, or that the variability in X is held constant. The general formula (see p. 304) is

$$SS_{y.x} = SS_y - \frac{(S_{xy})^2}{SS_x} \tag{76}$$

(SS *in y when variability contributed by x has been removed or held constant*)

For SS_T we have that $SS_{y.x} = 668 - \dfrac{(400)^2}{493}$ or 343; for SS_{within} that

$SS_{y.x} = 458 - \dfrac{(375)^2}{430} = 131$. The SS for among means is the adjusted SS_T minus adjusted SS_{within}. This last $SS_{y.x}$ cannot readily be calculated directly.

From the various adjusted sums of squares the variances ($MS_{y.x}$) can now be computed by dividing each SS by its appropriate df. Owing to the restriction imposed by the use of formula (76) (reduction of variability in X) 1 df is lost and the analysis of covariance (Table 43) shows only 11 df for within groups instead of 12, and only 13 instead of 14 for total.

The value of analysis of covariance becomes apparent in Table 43 when the F test is applied to the adjusted *among* and *within* variances. $F_{y.x} = 106/12$ or 8.83, and is highly significant—far beyond the .01 level ($F_{.01} = 7.20$). This $F_{y.x}$ should now be compared with the F_y of 2.75 (p. 297) obtained *before* correcting for variability in initial (X) scores. It is clear from $F_{y.x}$ that the three final means—which depend upon the three incentives—differ significantly *after* they have been adjusted for initial differences in X. To find which of the three possible differences is significant or whether all are significant we must apply the t test (in Step 9).

Step 7

An additional step is useful, however, before we proceed to the t test for adjusted means. From the SS's in x, y and xy it is possible to compute several coefficients of correlation. These are helpful in the interpretation of the result obtained in Step 6. The general formula used is $r = \dfrac{\Sigma xy}{\sqrt{\Sigma x^2 \cdot \Sigma y^2}}$ (p. 139); it may be applied to the appropriate SS's for total, among means and within groups.

The within-groups correlation of .84 is a better measure of the relationship between initial (X) and final (Y) scores than is the total correlation of .70, as systematic differences in means have been eliminated from the within r. It is this high correlation between X and Y which accounts for the marked significance among Y means when the variability in X is held constant. High correlation within groups *reduces* the denominator of the variance ratio, $F_{y.x}$, while low correlation between X and Y means (namely, .22) does not proportionally affect the numerator. Thus we note that the within-groups variance of 38.2 is reduced through analysis of covariance to 12, while the among means variance is virtually unchanged (from 105 to 106). When correlation among scores is *high* and correlation among means *low* (as here), analysis of covariance will often lead to a significant F when analysis of variance fails to reveal significant differences among the Y means. These two r's may be used, therefore, in a preliminary way to decide whether analysis of covariance is worth while.

Regression coefficients for total, among means and within groups have been calculated by use of the formula $b = \dfrac{\Sigma xy}{\Sigma x^2}$ (p. 304). The b_{within} is the most nearly unbiased estimate of the regression of Y on X, since any systematic influence due to differences among means has been removed. Therefore b_{within} is used in the computation of the adjusted Y means in Step 8.

Step 8

Y means can be adjusted directly for differences in the X means by use of the formula $M_{Y.x} = M_Y - b(M_X - Gen.M_X)$* in which the regression coefficient, b, is the b_{within} of .87. M_Y is the original or uncorrected Y mean of a group; M_X is the corresponding X mean of a group and $Gen.M_X$ is the mean of *all* X scores. It will be noted that the B and C means receive more correction than the A mean which is only slightly changed.

$F_{y.x}$ tells us, it must be remembered (p. 298), that at least *one* of our adjusted Y means differs significantly from one other mean. To determine which mean differences are significant we must first compute the adjusted Y means and then test these differences by the t test.

Step 9

The $V_{y.x}$ is 12 (Table 43, Step 6, p. 298) as compared with the V_y of 38.2 (Table 43, Step 5, p. 297) and the $SD_{y.x}$ is $\sqrt{12}$ or 3.46. From formula (75) we find that the standard error of the difference between any two means is 2.18. For 11 df, t is 2.20 at the .05 and 3.11 at the .01 level. Substituting for $t_{.05}$ and SE_D in the equation $t = D/SE_D$, we obtain significant differences at the .05 level and .01 level of 4.80 and 6.78, respectively. It is clear by reference to Step 8 that the adjusted A mean is significantly higher than the B and C means (at the .01 level) but that B and C do not differ significantly. We may conclude, therefore, that when initial differences are allowed for, praise makes for significant changes in

---

* See p. 298. $y - bx =$ adjusted value of y, or $M_Y - bx = M_{Y.x}$. Substitute $x = (M_X - Gen.M_X)$ to give $M_{Y.x} = M_Y - b(M_X - Gen.M_X)$.

final score, but that scolding has no greater effect than mere repetition of the test. Neither of these last two factors makes for significant changes in test score.

V. SIGNIFICANCE OF THE DIFFERENCE BETWEEN SD's IN SMALL SAMPLES

When samples are small and uncorrelated (independent), the significance of the difference between two SD's can be determined by the F test, through the use of variances. Formula (62) is not accurate when N's are small, as the SD's from small samples drawn at random from a normally distributed population will tend to exhibit skewed distributions around the population σ.

To make an F test, divide the larger V by the smaller and evaluate the resulting F in terms of the appropriate df. We may illustrate the method with example (5), where $N_1 = 6$ and $N_2 = 10$, respectively. The first V is 110/5 or 22; and the second V is 352/9 or 39.1. The F ratio found by dividing the larger by the smaller of the variances, is 39.1/22 or 1.78. This F test gives the probability that the larger V is equal to or greater than the smaller: it is a one-tailed test (p. 217). In testing the differences between two V's we want a two-tailed test—a test of the probability of F's below as well as above 1.00. It is not necessary, however, to get a second V by dividing the smaller V by the larger V. All we need do is double the probability of the one ratio at the .05 and .01 points. This gives a two-tailed test at the .10 and .02 levels

Entering Table F with $df_1 = 9$ (df of the larger V) and with $df_2 = 5$ (df of the smaller V), we get an F of 4.78 at the .05 and of 10.17 at the .01 levels. Our observed F of 1.78 is far below the smaller of these F's and hence is not significant at the .10 level, much less at the .02 level. There is no evidence that the two groups differ in variability, whether measured in terms of V or SD.

APPENDIX TO CHAPTER 11

(a) Calculation SS_w [Example (1), p. 280]

Columns

A: $[64^2 + 72^2 + \ldots + 95^2] - \dfrac{(432)^2}{6} = 890$

B: $[73^2 + \ldots\ldots + 67^2] - \dfrac{(468)^2}{6} = 944$

C: $[77^2 + \ldots\ldots + 87^2] - \dfrac{(492)^2}{6} = 454$

Columns

$$D: \quad [78^2 + \ldots\ldots + 77^2] - \frac{(510)^2}{6} = 302$$

$$E: \quad [63^2 + \ldots\ldots + 76^2] - \frac{(390)^2}{6} = 710$$

$$F: \quad [75^2 + \ldots\ldots + 76^2] - \frac{(456)^2}{6} = 488$$

$$G: \quad [78^2 + \ldots\ldots + 82^2] - \frac{(366)^2}{6} = 1540$$

$$H: \quad [55^2 + \ldots\ldots + 68^2] - \frac{(372)^2}{6} = 338$$

$$\overline{5666}$$

(b) Derivation of the formula

$$SS_{y.x} = SS_y - \frac{(S_{xy})^2}{SS_x}$$

Let

$X =$ independent variable

$Y =$ dependent variable

$r_{xy} =$ correlation between X and Y

Then

$$\sigma^2_{y.x} = \sigma^2_y(1 - r^2_{xy}) = \sigma^2_y - \sigma^2_y r^2_{xy} \qquad \text{p. 179}$$

$$r^2_{xy} = \frac{(\Sigma xy)^2}{\Sigma x^2 \cdot \Sigma y^2} \qquad \text{p. 139}$$

Substituting,

$$\sigma^2_{y.x} = \sigma^2_y - \frac{(\Sigma xy)^2}{N\Sigma x^2}$$

In terms of SS:

$$SS_{y.x} = SS_y - \frac{(S_{xy})^2}{SS_x}$$

(c) Derivation of formula

$$b = \frac{\Sigma xy}{\Sigma x^2}$$

$$b = r\frac{\sigma_y}{\sigma_x} \qquad \text{p. 154}$$

$$r = \frac{\Sigma xy}{N\sigma_x\sigma_y}$$

Substituting

$$b = \frac{\Sigma xy}{N\sigma^2_x} = \frac{\Sigma xy}{\dfrac{N\sigma x^2}{N}}$$

$$= \frac{\Sigma xy}{\Sigma x^2}$$

PROBLEMS

1. In a learning experiment, 10 subjects are assigned at random to each of six groups. Each group performs the same task but under slightly different experimental conditions. Do the groups differ in mean performance?

	1	2	3	4	5	6	
	41	40	36	14	41	55	
	40	36	33	38	35	36	
	39	40	29	51	52	41	
	41	34	30	41	41	36	
	39	34	45	36	34	48	
	41	39	39	36	10	36	
	36	36	33	36	44	42	
	35	34	32	32	26	42	
	35	41	34	38	54	34	
	37	37	34	36	30	40	Grand sum
Sums	384	371	345	358	367	410	2235

2. Solve problem (2), page 243, by the methods of analysis of variance.
3. Twenty subjects are paired on the basis of their initial scores on a test. Ten (one member of each pair) are then assigned to an experimental and 10 to a control group. The experimental group is given special practice and both groups are retested. Data for final scores are as follows:

Pairs of Subjects

	1	2	3	4	5	6	7	8	9	10	Total
Control group	25	46	93	45	15	64	47	56	73	66	530
Experimental group	36	57	89	67	19	78	46	59	69	70	590

(a) Do the groups differ significantly in mean performance?
(b) Do subject pairs differ significantly?
(c) Check the result in (a) by taking the difference between pairs of scores, and testing the mean difference (by t test) against null hypothesis.

4. In the following table * the entries represent blood cholesterol readings taken from 18 patients in April and in May.

(a) Is the rise from April to May significant?
(b) Are there significant individual differences, regardless of month?
(c) From the column of differences, compute M_D and SD_D. Using the t test, measure of the significance of M_D against the null hypothesis. Compare with the result in (a)

* Fertig, John W., "The Use of Interaction in the Removal of Correlated Variation," *Biometric Bull.*, 1936, 1, 1–14.

Individual	April	May	Difference	Sum
1	158.0	190.5	32.5	348.5
2	158.5	177.0	18.5	335.5
3	137.5	172.0	34.5	309.5
4	145.5	152.5	7.0	298.0
5	130.5	147.0	16.5	277.5
6	141.0	127.0	−14.0	268.0
7	150.5	149.5	−1.0	300.0
8	142.5	152.5	10.0	295.0
9	148.0	147.0	−1.0	295.0
10	137.5	130.5	−7.0	268.0
11	137.0	133.0	−4.0	270.0
12	160.0	145.5	−14.5	305.5
13	145.0	124.5	−20.5	269.5
14	149.5	156.0	6.5	305.5
15	145.0	143.5	−1.5	288.5
16	132.5	146.0	13.5	278.5
17	139.0	148.0	9.0	287.0
18	151.0	161.0	10.0	312.0
Sum	2608.5	2703.0	94.5	5311.5
SS	379288.25	410872.0	4311.25	1576009.25

5. In an experiment by Mowrer,* previously unrotated pigeons were tested for clockwise postrotational nystagmus. The rate of rotation was one revolution in 1½ sec. An average initial score for each pigeon based upon 2 tests is indicated by the symbol X. The 24 pigeons were then divided into 4 groups of 6 each. Each group was then subjected to 10 daily periods of rotation under one of the experimental conditions indicated below. The rotation speed was the same as during the initial test and the rotation periods lasted 30 sec., with a 30-sec. rest interval between each period. Groups 1, 2 and 3 were practiced in a clockwise direction only. For Group 4 the environment was rotated in a counterclockwise direction. At the end of 24 days of practice, each group was tested again under the same conditions as on the initial test. These records are called Y.

* From Edwards, A. L., *Experimental Design in Psychological Research* (New York: Rinehart, 1950), p. 357.

GROUP 1 ROTATION OF BODY ONLY. VISION EXCLUDED		GROUP 2 ROTATION OF BODY ONLY. VISION PERMITTED		GROUP 3 ROTATION OF BODY AND ENVIRONMENT		GROUP 4 ROTATION OF ENVIRONMENT ONLY	
Initial X	Final Y	Initial X	Final Y	Initial X	Final Y	Initial X	Final Y
23.8	7.9	28.5	25.1	27.5	20.1	22.9	19.9
23.8	7.1	18.5	20.7	28.1	17.7	25.2	28.2
22.6	7.7	20.3	20.3	35.7	16.8	20.8	18.1
22.8	11.2	26.6	18.9	13.5	13.5	27.7	30.5
22.0	6.4	21.2	25.4	25.9	21.0	19.1	19.3
19.6	10.0	24.0	30.0	27.9	29.3	32.2	35.1
134.6	50.3	139.1	140.4	158.6	118.4	147.9	151.1

(a) Test the significance of the differences among X means. (Compute the among groups and within groups variance and use F test.)

(b) Do same as in (a) for the Y scores.

(c) By analysis of covariance test the differences among the adjusted means in Y. How much is the variance among Y means reduced when X is held constant?

(d) Compute the adjusted Y means, $M_{Y.X}$ by the method of p. 298.

(e) From the t test find that difference among adjusted Y means which is significant at the .05 level; at the .01 level.

ANSWERS

1. No. $F = \dfrac{50.8}{54.7}$ or .93, and differences among means may be attributed entirely to sampling fluctuations.

2. $F = 5.16$ and $t = 2.3$ $(\sqrt{F})$. Significant at .05 level.

3. (a) No. $F = \dfrac{180}{35.3} = 5.10$

   (b) Yes. $F = \dfrac{911.8}{35.3} = 25.83$

   (c) $t = \dfrac{6}{2.66} = 2.26 \quad t^2 = F = 5.11$

4. (a) No. $F = \dfrac{248.0}{112.22} = 2.21$, $df = 1/17$ and $F_{.05} = 4.45$ (Table F)

   (b) Not significant. $F = \dfrac{255.12}{112.22} = 2.27$, $df = 17/17$ and $F_{.05} = 2.30$

(c) $M_D = 5.25$; $SE_D = 3.53$. $t = \dfrac{5.25}{3.53} = 1.49$; $F = t^2 = 2.22$. $df = 17$

5. (a) Difference among X means not significant. $F_x = \dfrac{18.7}{23.1} = .81$

   (b) Y means differ significantly. $F_y = \dfrac{341.4}{24.9} = 13.7$. For df of 3/20, $F_{.01} = 4.94$.

   (c) $F_{y.x} = \dfrac{303.4}{19.8} = 15.3$. Variance among Y means is reduced 11%— from 341.4 to 303.4.

   (d) 9.3, 23.9, 18.6 and 24.9

   (e) 5.37; 7.34

PART III

SPECIAL TOPICS, CORRELATION AND TEST CONSTRUCTION

CHAPTER 12

THE SCALING OF MENTAL TESTS
AND OTHER PSYCHOLOGICAL DATA

◇◇

Various methods, many of them based upon the normal probability curve, have been used in the scaling of psychological and educational data. As used in mental measurement, a *scale* may be thought of as a continuum or continuity along which items, tasks, problems and the like have been located in terms of difficulty or some other attribute. The units of a scale are arbitrary and depend upon the method employed by the investigator. Ideally, scale units should be equal, have the same meaning, and remain stable throughout the scale. Some of the more useful scaling procedures will be described in this chapter.

I. THE SCALING OF TEST ITEMS

1. Scaling individual test items in terms of difficulty (σ scaling)

We sometimes wish to construct a test which is to contain problems or tasks graded in difficulty from very easy to very hard by known steps or intervals. If we know what proportion of a large group is able to solve each problem, it is comparatively easy to arrange our items in a percentage order of difficulty. Such an arrangement constitutes a scale, to be sure, but a crude one, as percentage differences are not satisfactory indices of differences in difficulty (p. 322).

If we are justified in assuming normality in the trait being measured, the *variability* (i.e., σ) of the group will give us a better scaling unit than will percentage passing (p. 310). Test items may be "set" or spaced in terms of σ difficulty at definite points along a difficulty continuum; their positions with respect to each other as well as with respect to some reference point or "zero" is then known in terms of a stable unit. To illustrate σ scaling, suppose that we wish to construct a scale for measuring "reasoning ability" (e.g., by means of syllogisms) in 12-year-olds; or a scale for measuring mechanical ingenuity in high-school juniors; or a scale for determining degree of suggestibility in college freshmen. The steps in constructing such a device may be outlined briefly as follows:

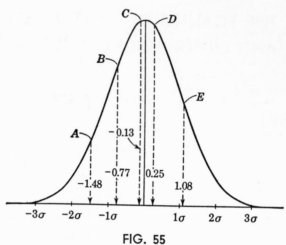

FIG. 55

(1) Compile a large number of problems or other test items. These should vary in difficulty from very easy to very hard, and should all sample the behavior to be tested.

(2) Administer the items to a large group drawn randomly from those for whom the final test is intended.

(3) Compute the percentage of the group which can solve each problem. Discard duplicate items and those too easy or too hard or unsatisfactory for other reasons. Arrange the problems retained in an order of percentage difficulty. An item done correctly by 90% of the group is obviously easier than one solved by 75%; while the second problem is less difficult than one solved by only 50%. The larger the percent passing the lower the item in a scale of difficulty.

(4) By means of Table A convert the percent solving each problem into a σ distance above or below the mean. For example: an item done correctly by 40% of the group is 10% or $.25\sigma$ above the mean. A problem solved by 78% is 28% (78% − 50%) or $.77\sigma$ below the mean. We may tabulate the results for 5 items, taken at random, as follows (see Fig. 55):

Problem A is solved by 93% of the group, i.e., by the upper 50% (the right half of the normal curve) plus the 43% to the *left* of the mean. This puts Problem A at a point -1.48σ from the mean. In the same way, the percentage distance of each problem from the mean (measured in the plus or minus direction) can be found by subtracting the percent passing

Problems	A	B	C	D	E
Percent solving:	93	78	55	40	14
Distance from the mean in percentage terms:	−43	−28	−5	10	36
Distance from the mean in σ terms:	−1.48	−.77	−.13	.25	1.08

from 50%. From these percentages, the σ distance of the problem above or below the mean is read from Table A.

(5) When the σ distance of each item has been established, calculate the σ distance of each item from the zero point of ability in the trait. A zero point may be located as follows: Suppose that 5% of the entire group fail to solve a single problem. This would put the level of zero ability 45% of the distribution below the mean, or at a distance of −1.65σ from the mean.[*] The σ value of each item in the scale may then be measured from this zero. To illustrate with the 5 problems above:

Problems	A	B	C	D	E
σ distance from mean:	−1.48	−.77	−.13	.25	1.08
σ distance from arbitrary zero, −1.65	.17	.88	1.52	1.90	2.73

The simplest way to find σ distances from a given zero is to subtract the zero point algebraically from the σ distance of each item from the mean. Problem A, for example, is −1.48 − (−1.65) or .17σ from the arbitrary zero; and problem E is 1.08 − (−1.65) or 2.73σ from zero.

(6) When the distance of each item from the established zero has been determined, the difficulty of each item with respect to each of the other items and with respect to zero is known—and the scaling is finished. The next steps depend upon the purposes of the investigator. He may select a large number of items separated by fairly small σ distances, so that his test covers a fairly wide range of talent. Or he may limit the range of talent from 2.50σ to −2.50σ and space out a limited number of items at wider intervals—separated by a .5σ, for example. Again, he may simply place his items along the base line of the normal curve and not attempt to set up equal difficulty steps. Norms may be determined for the final scale for children of different age levels or from different grades, or for adults in several occupational groups.

2. Scaling scores on a test

Instead of scaling separate test items, it is usually saving of time and effort to scale aggregates of items or total scores. In this section we shall

[*] This is, of course, an arbitrary, not a true zero. It will serve, however, as a reference point (level of minimum ability) from which to measure performance. The point −3.00σ is often taken as a convenient reference point.

outline two methods of scaling scores. These procedures are generally followed in constructing aptitude and achievement tests. They enable us to combine and compare scores originally expressed in different units.

(1) σ SCORES AND STANDARD SCORES

Let us suppose that the mean of a test is 122 and the σ is 24. Then if John earns a score of 146 on this test, his deviation from the mean is $146 - 122$ or 24. Dividing John's deviation of 24 by the σ of the test, we give him a σ score of 24/24 or 1.00. If William's score is 110 on this test, his deviation from the mean is $110 - 122$ or -12; and his score in σ units is $-.5$. Deviations from the mean expressed in σ terms are called σ scores, z scores, and reduced scores. Of these designations, σ score is certainly the most descriptive, but the other terms are often used. We have already used the concept of a σ score in the problems in Chapter 5, page 120.

The mean of a set of σ scores is always 0 (the reference point) and the σ is always unity or 1.00. As approximately half of the scores in a distribution will lie below and half above the mean, about half of our σ scores will be negative and half positive. In addition, σ scores are often small decimal fractions and hence somewhat awkward to deal with in computation. For these reasons, σ scores are usually converted into a new distribution with M and σ so selected as to make all scores positive and relatively easy to handle. Such scores are called *standard scores*. Raw test scores of the Army General Classification Test, for example, are expressed as standard scores in a distribution of $M = 100$ and $\sigma = 20$; subtests of the Wechsler-Bellevue are converted into standard scores in a distribution of $M = 10$ and $\sigma = 3$; and the tests of the Graduate Record Examination into standard scores in a distribution of $M = 500$ and $\sigma = 100$.

The shift from raw to standard score requires a linear transformation.* This transmutation does not change the *shape* of the distribution in any way; if the original distribution was skewed (or normal), the standard score distribution will be skewed or normal in exactly the same fashion. The formula for conversion of raw to standard score is as follows:

Let X = a score in the original distribution.

X' = a standard score in the new distribution

M and M' = means of the raw score and standard score distributions

σ and σ' = SD's of raw and standard scores

---

* When the equation connecting two variables, y and x, is that of a straight line, changing x's into y's involves a linear transformation. Formula (77) is the equation of a straight line, analogous to the general equation of a straight line, $y = mx + b$.

Then $\dfrac{X' - M'}{\sigma'} = \dfrac{X - M}{\sigma}$

or $X' = \dfrac{\sigma'}{\sigma}(X - M) + M'$ (77)

(*formula for converting raw scores to standard scores*)

An example will show how the formula works.

Example (*1*)   Given a distribution with Mean $= 86$ and $\sigma = 15$. Tom's score is 91 and Mary's 83. Express these raw scores as standard scores in a distribution with a mean of 500 and σ of 100.

By formula (77)

$$X' = \frac{100}{15}(X - 86) + 500$$

Substituting Tom's score of 91 for X we have

$$X' = 6.67(91 - 86) + 500$$
$$= 533$$

Substituting Mary's score of 83 for X,

$$X' = 6.67(83 - 86) + 500$$
$$= 480$$

In a distribution with a mean of 10 and a σ of 3, Tom's standard score would be 11 and Mary's 9; in a distribution with a mean of 100 and a σ of 20, Tom's standard score would be 107 and Mary's 96. Other scaling distributions may, of course, be employed.

Scores made by the same individual upon several tests cannot usually be compared directly owing to differences in test units. Thus a score of 162 on a group intelligence test and a score of 126 on an educational achievement examination cannot be compared meaningfully. If scores like these are expressed as standard scores, however, they can be compared *provided* the distributions of raw scores are of the same form. Fortunately, most distributions of scores are so nearly bell-shaped (p. 87) that no great error is made in treating them as normal. When we can assume normality, a score of 1.00σ on a mechanical aptitude test and a score of 1.00σ on a test of mechanical interests represent the same relative degree of achievement: both are exceeded by approximately 16% of those taking the two tests (Table A). A problem will illustrate further this important aspect of standard scores.

Example (*2*)   Given a reading test with a mean of 81 and σ of 12; and an arithmetic test with a mean of 33 and a σ of 8. Sue's score is 72 in reading and 27 in arithmetic. Assuming the distributions of reading and arithmetic scores to be of the same form (approximately normal), convert Sue's scores into a standard score distribution with Mean = 100 and σ = 20 and compare them.

In the reading test Sue's score is 9 below the mean of 81. Hence, her score is at $-.75\sigma$ ($-9/12$) and her new score is 85 ($100 - .75 \times 20$). In arithmetic Sue's score is 6 points below the mean; again her score is at $-.75\sigma$ and her new score 85 ($100 - .75 \times 20$). Sue's two standard scores are comparable, and are also *equivalent* (represent same degree of achievement) if our assumption of normality of distributions is tenable.

(2) NORMALIZING THE FREQUENCY DISTRIBUTION: THE T SCALE

Instead of σ scores, the obtained scores of a frequency distribution may be converted into a system of "normalized" σ scores by transforming them directly into equivalent points in a normal distribution. Equivalent scores indicate the same level of talent. Suppose that in a chemistry test, 20% of the group earn scores below John's score of 73. And that in a physics test, 20% again fall below John's score of 46. From Table A we know that 20% of the area of the normal probability curve falls below $-.84\sigma$ (30% falls between the mean and $.84\sigma$). Accordingly, John's scores of 73 and 46 are both equivalent to the "score" of $-.84\sigma$ in the normal distribution, and both represent the same level of achievement.

Normalized standard scores are generally called T scores. T scaling was devised by McCall [*] and first used by him in the construction of a series of reading tests designed for use in the elementary grades. The original T scale was based upon the reading scores achieved by 500 12-year-olds; and the scores earned by other age groups on the same reading test were expressed in terms of 12-year-old performance. Since this first use of the method, T scaling has been employed with various groups and with different tests so that it no longer has reference specifically to 12-year-olds nor to reading tests.

T scores are normalized standard scores converted into a distribution with a mean of 50 and σ of 10. In the σ scaling of individual items, the mean, as we know, is at zero and σ is 1.00. The point of reference, therefore, is zero and the unit of measurement is 1. If the point of reference is moved from the mean of the normal curve to a point 5σ below the mean, this new reference point becomes zero in the scale and the mean is 5. As shown in Figure 56, the σ divisions above the mean (1σ, 2σ, 3σ, 4σ, 5σ) become 6, 7, 8, 9 and 10; and the σ divisions below the mean (-1σ, -2σ, -3σ, -4σ, -5σ) are 4, 3, 2, 1 and 0. The σ of the distribution remains, of course, equal to 1.00.

[*] McCall, William A., *Measurement* (New York: Macmillan, 1939), Chap. 22.

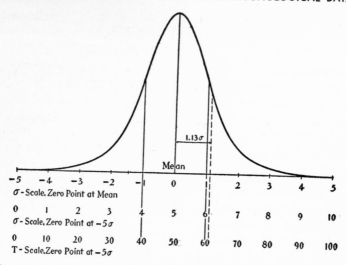

FIG. 56 To illustrate σ scaling and *T* scaling in a normal distribution
(The *T* is in honor of Thorndike and Terman.)

Only slight changes are needed in order to convert this σ scale into a
T scale. The *T* scale begins at −5σ and ends at +5σ. But σ is multiplied
by 10 so that the mean is 50 and the other divisions are 0, 10, 20, 30, 40,
50, 60, 70, 80, 90 and 100. The relationship of the *T* scale to the ordinary
σ scale is shown in Figure 56. Note that the *T* scale ranges from 0 to 100;
that its unit, i.e., *T*, is 1 and that the mean is 50. *T*, of course, equals .1 of σ
which is equal to 10. The reference point on the *T* scale is set at −5σ in
order to have the scale cover exactly 100 units. This is convenient but it
puts the extremes of the scale far beyond the ability ranges of most
groups. In actual practice, *T* scores range from about 15 to 85, i.e., from
−3.5σ to 3.5σ.

(3) CONSTRUCTING A *T* SCALE

The procedure to be followed in *T* scaling a set of scores can best be
shown by an example. We shall outline the process in a series of steps,
illustrating each step by reference to the data of Table 44.

(1) Compile a large and representative group of test items which vary in
difficulty from easy to hard. Administer these items to a sample of subjects
(children or adults) for whom the final test is intended.
(2) Compute the percent passing each item. Arrange the items in an order of
difficulty in terms of these percentages.
(3) Administer the test to a representative sample and tabulate the distribution
of total scores. Total scores may now be scaled as shown in Table 44 for

TABLE 44   To illustrate the calculation of T scores

(1)	(2)	(3)	(4)	(5)	(6)
Test Score	f	Cum. f	Cum. f below Score + 1/2 on Given Score	Col. (4) in %'s	T Scores
10	1	62	61.5	99.2	74
9	4	61	59	95.2	67
8	6	57	54	87.1	61
7	10	51	46	74.2	56
6	8	41	37	59.7	52
5	13	33	26.5	42.7	48
4	18	20	11	17.7	41
3	2	2	1	1.6	29
	$N = 62$				

62 subjects. In column (1) the test scores are entered; and in column (2) are listed the frequencies—number of subjects achieving each score. Two subjects had scores of 3, 18 had scores of 4, 13 scores of 5, and so on. In column (3) scores have been cumulated (p. 62) from the low to the high end of the frequency distribution. Column (4) shows the number of subjects who fall *below* each score plus one-half of those who earn the given score. The entries in this column may readily be computed from columns (2) and (3). There are no scores below 3 and 2 scores on 3, so that the number below 3 plus one-half on 3 equals 1. There are 2 scores below 4 [see column (3)] and 18 on 4 [column (2)]; hence the number of scores below 4 plus one-half on 4 is 2 + 9 or 11. There are 20 scores below 5 (2 + 18) and 13 scores on 5 [column (2)] so that the number below 5 plus one-half on 5 is 20 + 6.5 or 26.5. The reason why one-half of the frequency *on* a given score must be added to the frequency falling *below* that score is that each score is an interval—not a point on the scale. The score of 4, for example, covers the interval 3.5–4.5, midpoint 4.0. If the 18 frequencies on score 4 are thought of as distributed evenly over the interval, 9 will lie *below* and 9 *above* 4.0, the midpoint. Hence, if we add 9 to the 2 scores below 4 (i.e., below 3.5) we obtain 11 as the number of scores below 4.0, the midpoint of the interval 3.5–4.5. Each sum in column (4) is taken up to the *midpoint* of a score interval.

(4) In column (5) the entries in column (4) are expressed as percents of N (here 62). Thus, 99.2% of the scores lie below 10.0, midpoint of the interval 9.5–10.5; 95.2% of the scores lie below 9.0, midpoint of 8.5–9.5, etc.

(5) Turn the per cents in column (5) into T scores by means of Table G. T scores in Table G corresponding to percentages nearest to those wanted

are taken without interpolation, as fractional T scores are a needless refinement. Thus for 1.6% we take 1.79 (T score $= 29$); for 17.7% we take 18.41% (T score $= 41$), and so on.

In Table G, percentages lying to the *left* of (i.e., below) succeeding σ points expressed as T scores have been tabulated, rather than percents between the mean and given σ points as in Table A. In Table G, we are enabled, therefore, to read T scores directly; but the student will note that T scores can also be read from Table A. To illustrate with score 8 in Table 44, which has a percentage-below-plus one-half-reaching of 87.1, note that a score failed by 87.1% lies 37.1% (87.1% $-$ 50.0%) to the *right* of the mean. From Table A, we read that 37.1% of the distribution lies between the mean and 1.13σ. Since the σ of the T scale is 10, 1.13σ becomes 11 in T units; and adding 11 to 50, the mean, we get 61 as the required T score (see Fig. 56).

Figure 57 shows a histogram plotted from the distribution of 62 scores in Table 44. Note that the scores of 3, 4, 5, etc., are spaced at equal inter-

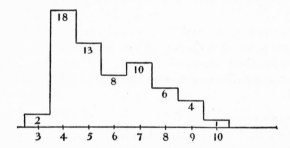

FIG. 57   Histogram of the sixty-two scores in Table 44

vals along the base line, i.e., along the scale of scores. When these raw scores are transformed into normalized standard scores—into T scores—they occupy the positions in the normal curve shown in Figure 58. The unequal scale distances between the scores in Figure 58 show clearly that, when normality is forced upon a trait, the original scores do not represent equal difficulty steps. In other words, normalizing a distribution of test scores alters the original test units (stretching them out or compressing them) and the more skewed the raw score distribution, the greater is the change in unit.

(4) ADVANTAGES OF THE T SCALE

In T scaling, what is actually being scaled is the percentile rank of the raw score. If Tom's PR on Test A is 84, his T score is 60—this being the

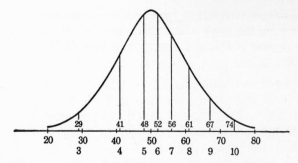

FIG. 58 Normalized distribution of the scores in Table 44 and Figure 57.
Original scores and *T* score equivalents are shown on base line.

point below which 84% of normal curve area falls. If Tom's *PR* on Test B
is 30, his *T* score is 45, etc.

T scores have general applicability, a convenient unit, and they cover a
wide range of talent. Besides these advantages, *T* scores from different
tests are comparable and have the same meaning, since reference is always
to a standard scale of 100 units based upon the normal probability curve.
T scaling forces normality upon the scores of a frequency distribution and
is unwarranted if the distribution of the trait in the *population* is not
normal. For the distributions of most mental abilities in the population, however, normality is a reasonable—and is often the only feasible
—assumption.

(5) THE STANINE SCALE

The stanine scale * is a condensed form of the *T* scale. Stanine scores
run from 1 to 9 along the base line of the normal curve constituting a
scale in which the unit is .5σ and the median is 5. The percentage of
scores in each stanine is shown in Figure 59. These percents have been

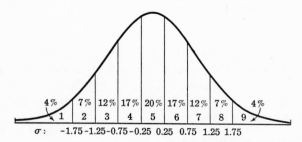

FIG. 59 Stanine scale showing percents on each score from 1 to 9

* Stanine is a contraction for "standard nine."

found from Table A as follows: Since 9.87% of the area of the normal curve falls between the median and .25σ, then 19.74% (i.e., 9.87 × 2) or 20% (to two digits) is found in the median interval (between ±.25σ). The median 20% of test scores, therefore, are all given the single stanine score of 5. The next 17% of area above 5 receives the stanine score of 6 (lies between .25σ and .75σ); the next 12% of area is scored 7 (lies between .75σ and 1.25σ); the next 7% is scored 8, and the upper 4% receives the stanine score of 9. In the lower half of the curve, the lowest 4% is given the stanine score of 1, the next 7% 2, the next 12% 3, and the next 17% 4. The two end stanines include what is left over in the tails of the curve and thus complete 100% of the area. If the scores on an aptitude test achieved by 100 students are arranged in order of size, the first 4 will receive a stanine of 1, the next 7 a stanine of 2, the next 12 a stanine of 3, and so on to the last 4 who receive a stanine score of 1.

The 125 Reading Scores found in Table 13 have been converted into stanines in Table 45. The procedure is to count 4%, 11%, 23% etc., into

TABLE 45 The stanine score system applied to the 125 reading scores taken from Table 13

Stanine scale	% in each interval (rounded)	Cum. %'s	Reading scores in each stanine interval
(1)	(2)	(3)	(4)
9	4	100	70+
8	7	96	64–69
7	12	89	59–63
6	17	77	54–58
5	20	60	51–53
4	17	40	46–50
3	12	23	41–45
2	7	11	34–40
1	4	4	25–33
	$N = 100$		

the distribution, setting up score intervals (approximately) to fit the stanine intervals. Note that any score 41–45 is scored 3, any score 51–53 is scored 5 and so on. In an ogive, stanine intervals of 4, 11, 23, etc., may be laid off on the Y axis and stanines corresponding to reading scores read directly from the graph.

(6) A COMPARISON OF T SCORES AND STANDARD SCORES

T scores are sometimes confused with standard scores, but the assumptions underlying the two sorts of measures are quite different. Table 46 repeats the data of Table 44 and shows the T score equivalents to the given raw scores. Standard scores with a mean of 50 and σ of 10 are listed

TABLE 46 Comparison of T scores and standard scores
(Data from Table 44)

Test Score	f	T Scores	Standard Scores $M = 50$, $\sigma = 10$
10	1	74	75
9	4	67	69
8	6	61	63
7	10	56	57
6	8	52	52
5	13	48	46
4	18	41	40
3	2	29	34

$$N = 62$$

For test scores:
$$M = 5.73$$
$$\sigma = 1.72$$

Equation for converting test scores into standard scores (see p. 313)

$$\frac{X - 5.73}{1.72} = \frac{X' - 50}{10}$$

$$X' = \frac{10X}{1.72} - \frac{57.3}{1.72} + 50$$

$$X' = 5.81X - 33.3 + 50$$

$$X' = 5.81X + 16.7$$

in column (4) for comparison with the T scores. These standard scores were calculated by means of formula (77) on page 313. The mean of the raw scores is 5.73 and the σ is 1.72. A mean of 50 and a σ of 10 were selected for the new standard score distribution so that these standard scores could be compared directly with T scores. Substituting in formula (77) we have

$$X' = 5.81X + 16.7$$

as our transformation equation. Putting 3, 4, 5, etc., for X in this equation we find X's of 34, 40, 46, etc. These X' scores will be found to correspond fairly closely to the T scores. This is often the case, and the more nearly normal the distribution of raw scores the closer the correspondence. The two kinds of scores are *not* interchangeable, however. With respect to original scores, T scores represent equivalent PR's in a normal distribution. Standard scores, on the other hand, always have the same *form* of distribution as raw scores, and are simply original scores expressed in σ units.

Standard scores represent the kind of conversion we make when we change inches to centimeters or kilograms to pounds; that is, the transformation is linear. Standard scores correspond exactly to T scores when the distribution of raw scores is strictly normal.

3. Percentile scaling

(1) DIRECT CALCULATION OF PERCENTILES

A child who earns a certain score on a test can be assigned a percentile rank (PR) * of 27, 42 or 77, say, depending upon his position in the score distribution. Percentile rank locates a child on a scale of 100 and tells us immediately what proportion of the group has achieved scores *lower* than he. Moreover, when a child has taken several tests, a comparison of his PR's provides measures of relative achievement, and these may be combined into a final total score. As a method of scaling test scores, PR's have the practical advantage of being readily calculated and easily understood. But the percentile scale also possesses marked disadvantages which limit its usefulness.

Percentile scales assume that the difference between a rank of 10 and a rank of 20 is the same as the difference between a rank of 40 and a rank of 50, namely, that percentile differences are equal throughout the scale. This assumption of equal percentile units holds strictly only when the distribution of scores is rectangular in shape; it does not hold when the distribution is bell-shaped, or approximately normal. Figure 60 shows graphically why this is true. In the diagram we have a rectangular distribution and a normal curve of the *same area* plotted over it. When the rectangle is divided into 5 equal segments, the areas of the small rectangles are all the same (20%) and the distances from 0 to 20, 20 to 40, 40 to 60, 60 to 80, and 80 to 100 are all equal. These percentiles, P_{20}, P_{40}, etc., have been marked off along the top of the rectangle.

Now let us compare the distances along the base line of the normal curve when these are determined by successive 20% slices of area. These base-line intervals can be found in the following way. From Table A we read that the 30% of area to the left of the mean extends to $-.84\sigma$. The first 20% of a normal distribution, therefore, falls between -3.00σ and $-.84\sigma$: covers a distance of 2.16σ along the base line. The second 20% $(P_{20}$ to $P_{40})$ lies between $-.84\sigma$ and $-.25\sigma$ (since $-.25\sigma$ is at a distance of 10% from the mean); and covers a distance of $.59\sigma$ along the base line. The third 20% $(P_{40}$ to $P_{60})$ lies between $-.25\sigma$ and $.25\sigma$: straddles the

---

* For method of computing PR's, see p. 65.

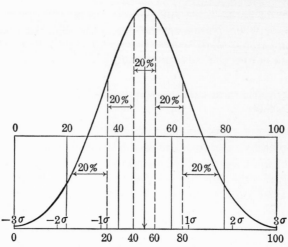

FIG. 60   To illustrate the position of the same five percentiles in rectangular and normal distributions

mean and covers .50σ on the base line. The fourth and fifth 20%'s occupy the same relative positions in the upper half of the curve as the second and first 20%'s occupy in the lower half of the curve. To summarize:

> First   20% of area covers a distance of 2.16σ
> Second 20% of area covers a distance of .59σ
> Third   20% of area covers a distance of .50σ
> Fourth 20% of area covers a distance of .59σ
> Fifth   20% of area covers a distance of 2.16σ

It is clear (1) that intervals along the base line from the extreme left end (0, to P_{20}, P_{20} to P_{40}, etc.) to the extreme right end of the normal curve are not equal when determined by successive 20% slices of area; and (2) that inequalities are relatively greater at the two ends of the distribution, so that the two end fifths are 4 times as long as the middle one.

Distributions of raw scores are rarely if ever rectangular in form. Hence equal percents of N (area) cannot be taken to represent equal increments of achievement and the percentile scale does not progress by equal steps. Betweeen Q_1 and Q_3, however, equal percents of area are more nearly equally spaced along the base line (see Fig. 60), so that the PR's of a child in two or more tests may be safely combined or averaged if they fall within these limits. But high and low PR's (above 75 and below 25) should be combined, if at all, with full knowledge of their limitations.

(2) PERCENTILE RANKS FROM THE NORMAL CURVE

Differences between points on the percentile scale may be allowed for by proper spacing when scores are to be represented by a profile. Table 47 shows the *PR*'s of various σ scores in the normal curve and their

TABLE 47 Percentile ranks in the normal curve expressed as σ scores and as *T* scores

PR	σ Score	T Score
99	2.33	73
95	1.64	66
90	1.28	63
80	.84	58
70	.52	55
60	.25	53
50	.00	50
40	−.25	47
30	−.52	45
20	−.84	42
10	−1.28	37
5	−1.64	34
1	−2.33	27

corresponding *T* scores. Unequal gaps between *PR*'s when compared with *T* score intervals at the middle and the ends of the scale are clearly apparent. Figure 61 shows graphically the performance of a twelfth-grade boy on the Differential Aptitude Tests. Percentile ranks on the chart have been marked off in such a way (larger at extremes, smaller at middle) as to accord with the normal form of distribution. *T* scores (along the *Y* axis) may be compared with *PR*'s. Note that James is very high in the mechanical and spatial tests, average in numerical and abstract, and low in verbal and spelling.

II. SCALING JUDGMENTS

1. The scaling of answers to a questionnaire

Answers to the queries or statements in most questionnaires admit of several possible replies, such as Yes, No, ?; or Most, Many, Some, Few, No; or there are four or five answers one of which is to be checked. It is often desirable to "weight" these different selections in accordance with the degree of divergence from the "typical answer" which they indicate.

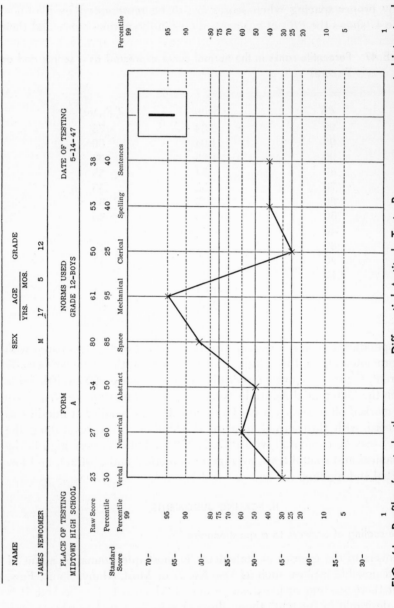

FIG. 61 Profile of a student's scores on Differential Aptitude Tests. Raw scores are converted into standard scores and into percentiles.

First we assume that the attitude or personality trait expressed in answering a given proposition is normally distributed. From the percentage who accept each of the possible answers to a question or statement, we then find a σ equivalent, which expresses the value or weight to be given that answer. The Internationalism Scale furnishes an example of this scaling technique. This questionnaire contains 24 statements upon each of which the subject is requested to give an opinion. Approval or disapproval of any statement is indicated by checking one of five possibilities "strongly approve," "approve," "undecided," "disapprove," and "strongly disapprove." The method of scaling as applied to statement No. 16 on the Internationalism Scale is shown in Table 48. This statement reads as follows:

16. All men who have the opportunity should enlist in the Citizens' Military Training Camps.
    Strongly approve   Approve   Undecided   Disapprove
    Strongly disapprove

TABLE 48   Data for statement No. 16 of the Internationalism Scale

Answers	Strongly Approve	Approve	Undecided	Dis-approve	Strongly Dis-approve
Percent checking	13	43	21	13	10
Equivalent					
σ values	−1.63	−.43	.43	.99	1.76
Standard scores	34	46	54	60	68

The percentage selecting each of the possible answers is shown in the table. Below the percent entries are the σ equivalents assigned to each alternative on the assumption that opinion on the question is normally distributed—that few will wholeheartedly agree or disagree, and many take intermediate views. The σ values in Table 48 have been obtained from Table H in the following way: Reading down the first column headed 0, we find that beginning at the upper extreme of the normal distribution, the highest 10% has an average σ distance from the mean of 1.76. Said differently, the mean of the 10% of cases at the upper extreme of the normal curve is at a distance of 1.76σ from the mean of the whole distribution. Hence, the answer "strongly disapprove" is given a σ equivalent of 1.76 (see Fig. 62).

To find the σ value for the answer "disapprove," we select the column headed .10 and running down the column take the entry opposite 13, namely, .99. This means that when 10% of the distribution reading from the upper extreme has been accounted for, the average distance from the mean of the next 13% is .99σ. Reference to Figure 62 will make this clearer. Now from the column headed 23 (13% + 10% "used up" or accounted for), we find entry .43 opposite 21. This means that when the

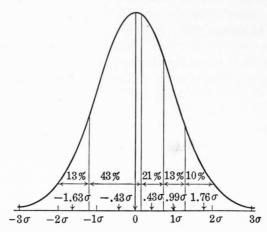

FIG. 62 To illustrate the scaling of the five possible answers to statement 16 on the Internationalism Scale

23% at the upper end of the distribution has been cut off, the mean σ distance from the general mean of the next 21% is .43σ, which becomes the weight of the preference "undecided." The weight of the fourth answer "approve" must be found by a slightly different process. Since a total of 44% from the upper end of the distribution has now been accounted for, 6% of the 43% who marked "approve" will lie to the *right* of the mean, and 37% to the *left* of the mean, as shown in Figure 62. From the column headed 44 in Table H, we take .08 (entry opposite 6%) which is the average distance from the general mean of the 6% lying just above the mean. Then from the column headed 13 (50% − 37%) we take entry .51 (now −.51) opposite 37%, as the mean distance from the general mean of the 37% just below the mean. The algebraic sum $\frac{-.51 \times .37 + .08 \times .06}{.43} = -.43$, which is the weight assigned to the preference "approve." The 13% left, those marking "strongly approve," occupy the 13% at the extreme (low end) of the curve. Returning to the column headed 0, we find that the mean distance from the general mean of the 13% at the extreme of the distribution is −1.63σ.

In order to avoid negative values, each σ weight in Table 48 can be expressed as a σ distance from -3.00σ (or -5.00σ). If referred to -3.00σ, the weights become in order 1.37, 2.57, 3.43, 3.99, and 4.76. Dropping decimals, and taking the first two digits, we could also assign weights of 14, 26, 34, 40, and 48. Again each σ value in Table 48 may be expressed as a standard score in a distribution the mean of which is 50 and the σ 10. The category "strongly approve" is -16 (-1.63×10) from the mean of 50, or at 34. Category "approve" is -4 ($-.43 \times 10$) from 50 or at 46. The other three categories have standard scores of 54, 60, and 68.

When all 24 statements on the Internationalism Scale have been scaled as shown above, a person's "score" (his attitude toward internationalism in general) is found by adding up the weights assigned to the various preferences which he has selected.

One advantage of σ scaling is that the units of the scale are equal and hence may be compared from item to item or from scale to scale. Moreover, σ scaling gives us a more accurate picture of the extent to which extreme or biased opinions on a given question are divergent from typical opinion than does some arbitrary weighting method.

2. Scaling ratings in terms of the normal curve

In many psychological problems individuals are judged for their possession of characteristics or attributes not readily measured by tests. Honesty, interest in one's work, tactfulness, originality are illustrations of such traits. Suppose that two teachers, Miss Smith and Miss Brown, have rated a group of 40 first-grade pupils for "social responsibility" on a 5-point scale. A rating of A means that the trait is possessed in marked degree, a rating of E that it is almost if not completely absent, and ratings of B, C and D indicate intermediate degrees of responsibility. Assume that the percentage of children assigned each rating is as shown below:

Social Responsibility

Judges	A	B	C	D	E
Miss Smith	10%	15%	50%	20%	5%
Miss Brown	20%	40%	20%	10%	10%

It is obvious that the second teacher rates more leniently than the first, and that a rating of A by Miss Smith may not mean the same degree of social responsibility as a rating of A by Miss Brown. Can we assign weights or numerical values to these ratings so as to render them comparable from teacher to teacher? The answer is Yes, provided we may assume that the distribution of social responsibility is normal in the population of first-grade children, and that one teacher is as competent a judge as the other. From Table H, we read the σ equivalents to the percents given each rating by Miss Smith and Miss Brown as follows:

	A	B	C	D	E
Miss Smith	1.76	.95	.00	−1.07	−2.10
Miss Brown	1.40	.27	−.53	−1.04	−1.76

These σ values are read from Table H in the same way as were the σ equivalents in the previous problem. If we refer each of our σ values to −3.00σ as an arbitrary origin or reference point, multiply each σ value by 10 and round to two digits, we have the following:

	A	B	C	D	E
Miss Smith	48	40	30	19	9
Miss Brown	44	33	25	20	12

Table H is valuable when one wishes to transmute various sorts of qualitative data into numerical scores. Almost any trait upon which relative judgments can be obtained may be scaled, provided we can assume normality of distribution in the general population.

3. Changing orders of merit into numerical scores

It is often desirable to transmute orders of merit into units of amount or "scores." This may be done by means of tables, if we are justified in assuming normality for the trait. To illustrate, suppose that 15 salesmen have been ranked in order of merit for selling efficiency, the most efficient salesman being ranked 1, the least efficient being ranked 15. If we are justified in assuming that "selling efficiency" follows the normal probability curve in the general population we can, with the aid of Table 49, assign to each man a "selling score" on a scale of 10 or of 100 points. Such a score will define ability as a salesman better than will a rank of 2, 5, or 14. The problem may be stated specifically as follows:

Example (3) Given 15 salesmen, ranked in order of merit by their sales manager, (*a*) transmute these rankings into scores on a scale of 10 points; (*b*) a scale of 100 points.

First, by means of the formula

$$Percent\ position = \frac{100(R - .5)}{N} \qquad (78)$$

(*formula for converting ranks into percents of the normal curve*)

TABLE 49   The transmutation of orders of merit into units of amount or "scores"

Example   If $N = 25$, and $R = 3$, Percentage Position is $\dfrac{100(3 - .5)}{25}$ or 10 (formula 78) and from the table, the equivalent rank is 75, on a scale of 100 points.

Percent	Score	Percent	Score	Percent	Score
.09	99	22.32	65	83.31	31
.20	98	23.88	64	84.56	30
.32	97	25.48	63	85.75	29
.45	96	27.15	62	86.89	28
.61	95	28.86	61	87.96	27
.78	94	30.61	60	88.97	26
.97	93	32.42	59	89.94	25
1.18	92	34.25	58	90.83	24
1.42	91	36.15	57	91.67	23
1.68	90	38.06	56	92.45	22
1.96	89	40.01	55	93.19	21
2.28	88	41.97	54	93.86	20
2.63	87	43.97	53	94.49	19
3.01	86	45.97	52	95.08	18
3.43	85	47.98	51	95.62	17
3.89	84	50.00	50	96.11	16
4.38	83	52.02	49	96.57	15
4.92	82	54.03	48	96.99	14
5.51	81	56.03	47	97.37	13
6.14	80	58.03	46	97.72	12
6.81	79	59.99	45	98.04	11
7.55	78	61.94	44	98.32	10
8.33	77	63.85	43	98.58	9
9.17	76	65.75	42	98.82	8
10.06	75	67.48	41	99.03	7
11.03	74	69.39	40	99.22	6
12.04	73	71.14	39	99.39	5
13.11	72	72.85	38	99.55	4
14.25	71	74.52	37	99.68	3
15.44	70	76.12	36	99.80	2
16.69	69	77.68	35	99.91	1
18.01	68	79.17	34	100.00	0
19.39	67	80.61	33		
20.93	66	81.99	32		

in which R is the rank of the individual in the series * and N is the number of individuals ranked, determine the "percentage position" of each man. Then from these percentage positions read the man's score on a scale of 10 or 100 points from Table 49. Salesman A, who ranks No. 1, has a percent position of $\dfrac{100(1 - .5)}{15}$ or 3.33, and his score from Table 49 is 9 or 85 (finer interpolation unnecessary). Salesman B, who ranks No. 2, has a percentage position of $\dfrac{100(2 - .5)}{15}$ or 10, and his score, accordingly, is 8 or 75. The scores of the other salesmen, found in exactly the same way, are given in Table 50.

TABLE 50   The order of merit ranks of 15 salesmen converted into normal curve "scores"

Salesmen	Order of Merit Ranks	Percentage Position (Table 49)	Scores Scale (10)	Scale (100)	PR's
A	1	3.33	9	85	97
B	2	10.00	8	75	90
C	3	16.67	7	69	83
D	4	23.33	6	64	77
E	5	30.00	6	60	70
F	6	36.67	6	57	63
G	7	43.33	5	53	57
H	8	50.00	5	50	50
I	9	56.67	5	47	43
J	10	63.33	4	43	37
K	11	70.00	4	40	30
L	12	76.67	4	36	23
M	13	83.33	3	31	17
N	14	90.00	2	25	10
O	15	96.67	1	15	3

It has been frequently pointed out that the assumption of normality in a trait implies that differences at extremes of the trait are relatively much greater than differences around the mean. This is clearly brought out in Table 50; for, while all differences in the order of merit series equal 1, the differences between the transmuted scores in the scale of 100 vary considerably. The largest differences are found at the ends of the series,

---

* A rank is an interval on a scale; .5 is subtracted from each R because its midpoint best represents an interval. E.g., $R = 5$ is the 5th interval, namely 4–5, and 4.5 (or $5 - .5$) is the midpoint.

the smallest in the middle. For example, the difference in score between A and B or between N and O is three times the difference between G and H. If selling ability is normally distributed, it is three times as hard for a salesman to improve sufficiently to move from second to first place as it is for him to move from eighth to seventh place.

The percentile ranks (PR's) of our 15 salesmen in example (3) have been entered in Table 50 for comparison with the normal curve scores. These PR's were calculated by the method given on page 68.

Another use to which Table 49 may be put is in the combining of incomplete order of merit ratings. To illustrate with a problem:

Example (4) Six graduate students have been ranked for research competence by 3 professors. Judge 1 knows all 6 well enough to rank them; Judge 2 knows only 3 well enough to rank them; and Judge 3 knows 4 well enough to rank them. Can we combine these orders into a composite when two are incomplete?

The data are as follows:

	Students					
	A	B	C	D	E	F
Judge 1	1	2	3	4	5	6
Judge 2		2		1		3
Judge 3	2		1		3	4

It seems fair that A should get more credit for ranking first in a list of six than D for ranking first in a list of three, or C for ranking first in a list of four. In the order of merit ratings, all three individuals are given the same rank. But when we assign scores to each person, in accordance with his position in the list, by means of formula (78) and Table 49, A gets 77 for his first place, D gets 69 for his, and C gets 73 for his. See table.

All of the ratings have been transmuted as shown in example (3). Separate scores may be combined and averaged to give the final order of merit shown in the table.

	Persons					
	A	B	C	D	E	F
Judge 1's ranking	1	2	3	4	5	6
score	77	63	54	46	37	23
Judge 2's ranking		2		1		3
score		50		69		31
Judge 3's ranking	2		1		3	4
score	56		73		44	27
Sum of scores	133	113	127	115	81	81
Mean	67	57	64	58	41	27
Order of Merit	1	4	2	3	5	6

By means of formula (78) and Table 49 it is possible to convert any set of ranks into "scores," if we may assume a normal distribution in the trait for which the ranking is made. The method is useful in the case of those attributes which are not easily measured by ordinary methods, but for which individuals may be arranged in order of merit, as, for example, athletic ability, personality, beauty, and the like. It is also valuable in correlation problems when the only available criterion * of a given ability or aptitude is a set of ranks. Transmuted scores may be combined or averaged like other test scores.

A word of explanation may be added with regard to Table 49. This table represents a normal frequency distribution which has been cut off at ±2.50σ. The base line of the curve is 5σ, divided into 100 parts, each .05σ long. The first .05σ from the upper limit of the curve takes in .09 of 1% of the distribution and is scored 99 on a scale of 100. The next .05σ (.10σ from the upper end of the curve) takes in .20 of 1% of the entire distribution and is scored 98. In each case, the percentage position gives the fractional part of the normal distribution which lies to the right of (above) the given "score" on base line.

PROBLEMS

1. Five problems are passed by 15%, 34%, 50%, 62%, and 80%, respectively, of a large unselected group. If the zero point of ability in this test is taken to be at -3σ, what is the σ value of each problem as measured from this point?

2. (a) The fifth-grade norms for a reading examination are Mean = 60 and $SD = 10$; for an arithmetic examination, Mean = 26 and $SD = 4$. Tom scores 55 on the reading and 24 on the arithmetic test. Compare his σ scores. In which test is he better?

   (b) Compare his standard scores in a distribution with M of 100 and SD of 20.

3. (a) Locate the deciles in a normal distribution in the following way. Beginning at -3σ, count off successive 10%'s of area up to $+3\sigma$. Tabulate the σ values of the points which mark off the limits of each division. For example, the limits of the first 10% from -3σ are -3.00σ and -1.28σ (see Table A). Label these points in order from -3σ as .10, .20, etc. Now compare the distances in terms of σ between successive 10 percent points. Explain why these distances are unequal.

   (b) Divide the base line of the normal probability curve (take as 6σ) into ten equal parts, and erect a perpendicular at each point of division. Compute the percentage of total area comprised by each

* For definition of a criterion, see p. 354.

division. Are these percents of area equal? If not, explain why. Compare these percents with those found in (*a*).

4. Fifty workers are rated on a 7-point scale for efficiency on the job. The following data represent the distributions of ratings (in which 1 is best and 7 worst) for two judges. Judge X is obviously very lenient and Judge Z is very strict. To make these two sets of judgments comparable, use the following three procedures:

(*a*) Percentile scaling: divide each distribution into 5 parts by finding successive 20%'s of N. Let A = first 20%, B the next 20%, and so on to E, the fifth 20%.

(*b*) Standard scores: Find the M and SD for each distribution and convert each rating into a common distribution with M of 50 and SD of 10.

(*c*) T scores: Find T scores corresponding to ratings of 1, 2, 3 . . . 7. Now compare Judge X's rating of 3 with Judge Z's rating of 3 by the three methods.

Judge X Rating	f	Judge Z Rating	f
1	5	1	2
2	10	2	4
3	20	3	4
4	5	4	5
5	4	5	20
6	4	6	10
7	2	7	5
N = 50		N = 50	

5. In a large group of competent judges, 77% rank composition A as better than composition B; 65% rank B as better than C. If C is known to have a σ value of 3.50 as measured from the "zero composition," i.e., the composition of just zero merit, what are the σ values of B and A as measured from this zero point?

6. Twenty-five men on a football squad are ranked by the coach in order of merit from 1 to 25 for all-around playing ability. On the assumption that general playing ability is normally distributed, transmute these ranks into "scores" on a scale of 100 points. Compare these scores with the PR's of the ranks, and with the stanines for each man.

7. (*a*) In accordance with their scores upon a learning test, 20 children are ranked in order of merit. Calculate the percentile rank of each child.

(*b*) If 60 children are ranked in order of merit, what is the percentile rank of the first, tenth, fortieth, and sixtieth?

8. On an Occupational Interest Blank, each occupation is followed by five symbols, L! L ? D D!, which denote different degrees of "liking" and "disliking." The answers to one item are distributed as follows:

L!	L	?	D	D!
8%	20%	38%	24%	10%

(a) By means of Table H convert these percents into σ units.

(b) Express each σ value as a distance from "zero," taken at -3σ, and multiply by 10 throughout.

(c) Express each σ value as a standard score in a distribution of mean 50, σ 10.

9. Letter grades are assigned three classes by their teachers in English, history, and mathematics, as follows:

Mark	English	History	Mathematics
A	25	11	6
B	21	24	15
C	32	20	25
D	6	8	20
F	1	2	8
	85	65	74

(a) Express each distribution of grades in percents, and by means of Table H transform these percents into σ values.

(b) Change these σ values into 2-digit numbers and into standard scores following the method on page 312.

(c) Find average grades [from (b)] for the following students:

Student	English	History	Mathematics
S.H.	A	B	C
F.M.	C	B	A
D.B.	B	D	F

10. Calculate T scores in the following problem:

Scores	f	Percent below given score Plus One-half Reaching	T score
91	2	99.5	76
90	4	98.0	71
89	6		
88	20		
87	24		
86	28		
85	40		
84	36		
83	24		
82	12		
81	4		
	200		

11. (a) Calculate T scores for the midpoints of the class intervals in the following distribution:

Scores	f	Percent below given interval Plus One-half reaching Midpoint	T score
40–44	8	94.6	66
35–39	12		
30–34	20		
25–29	15		
20–24	15		
15–19	5		
	75		

(b) Convert these 75 scores into the stanine scale.

ANSWERS

1. In order: 4.04; 3.41; 3.00; 2.69; 2.16.
2. (a) In neither, same score in both
   (b) Reading 90; arithmetic 90
3. (a)

	.00	.10	.20	.30	.40	.50	.60	.70	.80	.90	1.00
	−3.00	−1.28	−.84	−.52	−.25	0	.25	.52	.84	1.28	3.00
Diffs:		1.72	.44	.32	.27	.25	25	.27	.32	.44	1.72

   (b) Percents of area in order: .68; 2.77; 7.92; 15.92; 22.57; 22.57; 15.92; 7.92; 2.77; .68.
4. (a) C vs. A   (b) 52 vs. 61   (c) 50 vs. 60
5. B, 3.89; A, 4.63
6.

Rank:	1	2	3	4	5	6	7	8	9	10	11	12	13
Score:	89	80	75	71	68	65	63	60	58	56	54	52	50
PR's:	98	94	90	86	82	78	74	70	66	62	58	54	50
Stanine:	9	8	8	7	7	7	6	6	6	6	5	5	5

Rank:	14	15	16	17	18	19	20	21	22	23	24	25
Score:	48	46	44	42	40	37	35	32	29	25	20	11
PR's:	46	42	38	34	30	26	22	18	14	10	6	2
Stanine:	5	5	4	4	4	4	3	3	3	2	2	1

7. (a)

Rank	PR		Rank	PR
1	97.5		11	47.5
2	92.5		12	42.5
3	87.5		13	37.5
4	82.5		14	32.5
5	77.5		15	27.5
6	72.5		16	22.5
7	67.5		17	17.5
8	62.5		18	12.5
9	57.5		19	7.5
10	52.5		20	2.5

(b)

Rank	1	10	40	60
PR	99.2	84.2	34.2	0.8
PR (to nearest whole number)	99	84	34	1

8.

	L!	L	?	D	D!
(a)	−1.86	−.94	−.08	.80	1.76
(b)	11	21	29	38	48
(c)	31	41	49	58	68

9. (a)

		F	D	C	B	A
	English	−2.70	−1.74	−.65	.22	1.18
	History	−2.28	−1.38	−.53	.39	1.49
	Math.	−1.71	− .71	.13	.94	1.86

(b)

	ENGLISH		HISTORY		MATHEMATICS	
	−3.00σ	Stan. Score	−3.00σ	Stan. Score	−3.00σ	Stan. Score
A	42	62	45	65	49	69
B	32	52	34	54	39	59
C	24	44	25	45	31	51
D	13	33	16	36	23	43
F	3	23	7	27	13	33

(c) S.H., 36 or 56; F.M., 36 or 56; D.B., 20 or 40

10. T scores:
76, 71, 67, 62, 58, 54, 49, 44, 39, 34, 27

11. (a) T scores: 66, 59, 53, 47, 40, 32

(b)

Stanine scale	1	2	3	4	5	6	7	8	9
Score range:	15– 17	18– 21	22– 24	25– 28	29– 32	33– 36	37– 39	40– 43	44–

CHAPTER 13

RELIABILITY AND VALIDITY
OF TEST SCORES

◇◇

I. THE RELIABILITY OF TEST SCORES

A test score is called reliable when we have reasons for believing the score to be stable and trustworthy. Stability and trustworthiness depend upon the degree to which the score is an index of "true ability"—is free of chance error. The Stanford-Binet I.Q., for example, is known to be a dependable measure. Hence, if a child's I.Q. is reported to be 110 by a competent examiner, we feel confident that this "score" is a good estimate of the child's ability to handle tasks like those represented by the test. Scores achieved on unreliable tests are neither stable nor trustworthy. In fact, a comparison of scores made upon repetition of an unreliable test, or upon two parallel forms of the same test, will reveal many discrepancies—some large and some small—in the two scores made by each individual in the group. The correlation of the test with itself—computed in several ways to be described later—is called the *reliability coefficient* of the test.

1. Methods of determining reliability

There are four procedures in common use for computing the reliability coefficient (sometimes called the self-correlation) of a test. These are
(1) Test-retest (repetition)
(2) Alternate or parallel forms
(3) Split-half technique
(4) Rational equivalence
All of these methods furnish estimates of the reproducibility of test scores; sometimes one method and sometimes another will provide the better measure.

(1) TEST-RETEST (REPETITION) METHOD

Repetition of a test is the simplest method of determining agreement between two sets of scores: the test is given and repeated on the same group, and the correlation computed between the first and second set of scores. Although test-retest is sometimes the only available procedure, the method is open to several serious objections. If the test is repeated immediately, many subjects will recall their first answers and spend their time on new material, thus tending to increase their scores—sometimes by a good deal. Besides immediate memory effects, practice and the confidence induced by familiarity with the material will almost certainly affect scores when the test is taken for a second time. Moreover, transfer effects are likely to be different from person to person, If the net effect of transfer is to make for closer agreement between scores achieved on the two givings of the test than would otherwise be the case, the reliability coefficient will be too high. On the other hand, if the interval between tests is rather long (e.g., six months or more) and the subjects are young children, growth changes will affect the retest score. In general growth increases initial score by various amounts and tends to lower the reliability coefficient.

Given sufficient time interval between the first and second administration of a test to offset—in part at least—memory, practice and other carry-over effects, the retest coefficient becomes a close estimate of the *stability* of the test scores. In fact, when the test is given and repeated, the reliability coefficient is primarily a stability coefficient.

The test-retest method will estimate less accurately the reliability of a test which contains novel features and is highly susceptible to practice than it will estimate the reliability of test scores which involve familiar and well-learned operations little affected by practice. Owing to difficulties in controlling conditions which influence scores on retest, the test-retest method is generally less useful than are the other methods.

(2) ALTERNATE OR PARALLEL FORMS METHOD

When alternate or parallel forms of a test can be constructed, the correlation between Form A, for example, and Form B may be taken as a measure of the self-correlation of the test. Under these conditions, the reliability coefficient becomes an index of the *equivalence* of the two forms of the test. Parallel forms are usually available for standard psychological and educational achievement tests.

The alternate forms method is satisfactory when sufficient time has intervened between the administration of the two forms to weaken or eliminate memory and practice effects. When Form B of a test follows Form A closely, scores on the second form of the test will often be increased because of familiarity. If such increases are approximately con-

stant (e.g., 3 to 5 points), the reliability coefficient of the test will not be affected, since the paired A and B scores maintain the same relative positions in the two distributions. If the mean increase due to practice is known, a constant may be subtracted from Form B scores to render them comparable to those of Form A.

In drawing up alternate test forms, care must be exercised to match test materials for content, difficulty and form; and precautions must be taken not to have the items in the two forms too similar. When alternate forms are virtually identical, reliability is too high; whereas when parallel forms are not sufficiently alike, reliability will be too low. For well-made standard tests, the parallel forms method is usually the most satisfactory way of determining reliability. If possible, an interval of at least two to four weeks should be allowed between administrations of the test.

(3) THE SPLIT-HALF METHOD

In the split-half method, the test is first divided into two equivalent "halves" and the correlation found for these half-tests. From the reliability of the half-test, the self-correlation of the whole test is then estimated by the Spearman-Brown prophecy formula (79). The procedure, in detail, is to make up two sets of scores by combining alternate items in the test. The first set of scores, for example, represents performance on the odd-numbered items, 1, 3, 5, 7, etc.; and the second set of scores, performance on the even-numbered items, 2, 4, 6, 8, etc. Other ways of making up two half-tests which will be comparable in content, difficulty and susceptibility to practice are employed, but the odds-evens split is the one most commonly used. From the self-correlation of the half-tests, the reliability coefficient of the whole test may be estimated from the formula

$$r_{11} = \frac{2r_{\frac{1}{2}\mathrm{I}\,\mathrm{II}}}{1 + r_{\frac{1}{2}\mathrm{I}\,\mathrm{II}}} \qquad (79)$$

(Spearman-Brown prophecy formula for estimating reliability from two comparable halves of a test)

where r_{11} = reliability coefficient of the whole test

and

$r_{\frac{1}{2}\mathrm{I}\,\mathrm{II}}$ = reliability coefficient of the half-test, found experimentally.

When the reliability coefficient of the half-test $(r_{\frac{1}{2}\mathrm{I}\,\mathrm{II}})$ is .60, for example, the reliability coefficient of the whole test by formula (79) is $\dfrac{2 \times .60}{1 + .60}$ or .75.

The split-half method is employed when it is not feasible to construct parallel forms of the test nor advisable to repeat the test itself. This situation occurs with many performance tests, as well as with questionnaires and inventories dealing with personality variables, attitudes and interests. Performance tests (e.g., picture completion, puzzle solving, form boards) are often very different tasks when repeated, as the child is familiar with content and procedure. Likewise, many personality "tests" (as for example, the Rorschach) cannot readily be given in alternate forms, nor repeated, owing to changes in the subject's attitudes upon taking the test for the second time.

The split-half method is regarded by many as the best of the methods for measuring test reliability. One of its main advantages is the fact that all data for computing reliability are obtained upon *one* occasion; so that variations brought about by differences between the two testing situations are eliminated. A marked disadvantage of the split-half technique lies in the fact that chance errors may affect scores on the two halves of the test in the *same* way, thus tending to make the reliability coefficient too high. This follows because the test is administered only once. The longer the test the less the probability that effects of temporary and variable disturbances will be cumulative in one direction, and the more accurate the estimate of score reliability.

Objection has been raised to the split-half method on the grounds that a test can be divided into two parts in a number of ways, so that the reliability coefficient is not a unique value. This criticism is true only when items are all of equal difficulty; or when, as in personality inventories, items may take any order. It is true also, of course, in speed tests. In most standard tests (power tests) items are arranged in order of difficulty so that the split into odds and evens provides a unique determination of the reliability coefficient.

(4) THE METHOD OF "RATIONAL EQUIVALENCE"

The method of rational equivalence * represents an attempt to get an estimate of the reliability of a test, free from the objections raised against the methods outlined above. Two forms of a test are defined as "equivalent" when corresponding items, *a*, *A*, *b*, *B*, etc., are interchangeable; and when the inter-item correlations are the same for both forms. The method of rational equivalence stresses the intercorrelations of the items in the test and the correlations of the items with the test as a whole. Four

* Richardson, M. W., and Kuder, G. F., "The Calculation of Test Reliability Coefficients Based upon the Method of Rational Equivalence," *Journal of Educational Psychology*, 1939, 30, 681–687.

formulas for determining test reliability have been derived, of which the one given below is perhaps the most useful:

$$r_{11} = \frac{n}{(n-1)} \times \frac{\sigma^2_t - \Sigma pq}{\sigma^2_t} \tag{80}$$

(reliability coefficient of a test in terms of the difficulty and the inter-correlations of test items)

in which

r_{11} = reliability coefficient of the whole test
n = number of items in the test
σ_t = the *SD* of the test scores
p = the proportion of the group answering a test item correctly
$q = (1-p)$ = the proportion of the group answering a test item incorrectly

To apply formula (80) the following steps are necessary:

Step 1

Compute the *SD* of the test scores for the whole group, namely, σ_t.

Step 2

Find the proportions passing *each* item (p) and the proportions failing *each* item (q).

Step 3

Multiply p and q for each item and sum for all items. This gives Σpq.

Step 4

Substitute the calculated values in formula (80).

To illustrate, suppose that a test of 60 items has been administered to a group of 85 subjects; $\sigma_t = 8.50$ and $\Sigma pq = 12.43$. Applying (80) we have

$$r_{11} = \frac{60}{59} \times \frac{72.25 - 12.43}{72.25} = .842$$

which is the reliability coefficient of the test.

A simple approximation to formula (80) is often useful to teachers and others who want to determine quickly the reliability of short objective classroom examinations. It reads:

$$r_{11} = \frac{n\sigma^2_t - M(n - M)}{\sigma^2_t(n-1)} \tag{81}$$

(approximation to formula 80)

in which

r_{11} = reliability of the whole test
n = number of items in the test
σ_t = SD of the test scores
M = the mean of the test scores

Formula (81) is a labor saver since only the mean, SD and number of items in the test need be known in order to get an estimate of reliability. The correlation need not be computed between alternate forms or between halves of the test. Suppose that an objective test of 40 multiple-choice items has been administered to a small class of students. An item answered correctly is scored 1, an item answered incorrectly is scored 0. The mean test score is 25.70 and $\sigma_t = 6.00$. What is the reliability coefficient of the test? Substituting in (81) we have

$$r_{11} = \frac{40 \times 36.00 - 25.70(40 - 25.70)}{36 \times 39}$$
$$= .76$$

The assumption is made in the above formula that all test items have the same difficulty, i.e., that the same proportion of subjects, but not necessarily the *same persons*, solve each item correctly. In a power test the items cover a wide range of difficulty. Practice has shown, however, that formula (81) provides a fairly good index of the test's reliability even when the assumption of equal item difficulty is not satisfied. Rational equivalence formulas tend to underestimate somewhat the reliability coefficient as found by other methods. These formulas provide a minimum estimate of reliability—we may feel sure that the test is at least as reliable as we have found it to be.

The rational equivalence formulas are not strictly comparable to the three methods already outlined. Like the split-half technique, these formulas provide an estimate of the internal consistency of the test and thus of the dependability of test scores. Rational equivalence is superior to the split-half technique in certain theoretical aspects, but the actual difference in reliability coefficients found by the two methods is never large and is often negligible.

2. The effect upon reliability of lengthening or repeating a test

(1) THE RELIABILITY COEFFICIENT FROM SEVERAL APPLICATIONS OR REPETITIONS OF A TEST

The mean of 5 determinations of a child's height will usually be more trustworthy than a single measurement; and the mean of 10 determinations will be more dependable than the mean of 5. Increasing the length of a test or averaging * the scores obtained from several applications of the test or from parallel forms will also increase reliability. If the self-correlation of a test is not satisfactory, what will be the effect of doubling the test's length? To answer this question experimentally would require considerable time and work. Fortunately a good estimate of the effect of lengthening or repeating a test can be obtained by use of the Spearman-Brown prophecy formula:

$$r_{nn} = \frac{nr_{1I}}{1 + (n-1)r_{1I}} \tag{82}$$

(Spearman-Brown prophecy formula for estimating the correlation between n forms of a test and n comparable forms)

where r_{nn} = the correlation between n forms of a test and n alternate forms (or the mean of n forms vs. the mean of n other forms)
and
r_{1I} = the reliability coefficient of Test 1.

To illustrate, suppose that in a group of 100 college freshmen the reliability coefficient of an achievement test is .70. What will be the effect upon test reliability of tripling the length of the test? Substituting in (82), $r_{1I} = .70$ and $n = 3$, we have

$$r_{3III} = \frac{3 \times .70}{1 + 2 \times .70} = \frac{2.10}{2.40} = .87$$

Tripling the test's length, therefore, increases the reliability coefficient from .70 to .87. Instead of tripling the test's length, we might have administered 3 parallel forms of the test and averaged the 3 scores made by each examinee. The reliability of these averaged scores will be the same (as far as statistical factors are concerned) as the reliability obtained by tripling the length of the test.

(2) THE SPEARMAN-BROWN FORMULA APPLIED TO RATINGS

The Spearman-Brown formula may be used to estimate the reliability of ratings, paired comparisons and other judgments, as well as test scores. Suppose that in judging the competence of a group of employees, the ratings of two supervisors (both equally well acquainted with the ratees) correlate .50. How reliable are the averages of these two sets of ratings? By formula (79), $r_{2\,II} = \frac{2 \times .50}{1 + .50}$ or .67. If we had had 3 supervisors whose

---

* Mathematically, averaging the scores from 3 applications of a test gives the same result as increasing the length of the test 3 times.

ratings on the average correlated .50, the mean of these 3 sets of ratings would be $r_{3III} = \dfrac{3 \times .50}{1 + 2 \times .50}$ or .75. The confidence we can place in these estimates will depend upon how well the assumptions underlying the formula are met: whether the judges are in reality "equally well acquainted" with the ratees, are equally competent as judges, etc. In many instances, "stepped-up estimates" like these must be taken as rough approximations, useful but not exact.

(3) LENGTHENING THE TEST TO ATTAIN A DESIRED DEGREE OF RELIABILITY

The prophecy formula may also be used to find how many times a test should be lengthened or repeated in order to reach a given standard of reliability. Suppose that an educational achievement test has a reliability coefficient of .80. How much should we lengthen the test in order to ensure a reliability coefficient of .95? Substituting $r_{11} = .80$ and $r_{nn} = .95$ in formula (82), and solving this time for n, we have that

$$.95 = \frac{.80n}{1 + .80n - .80} = \frac{.80n}{.20 + .80n}$$

and

$$n = 4.75 \text{ or } 5 \text{ in whole numbers}$$

This achievement test must be 5 times its present length or 5 parallel forms must be given and averaged if the reliability coefficient is to reach .95.

(4) PRECAUTIONS TO BE OBSERVED IN USING THE PROPHECY FORMULA

Predictions of increased reliability by the Spearman-Brown formula are valid when the items or questions added to the test cover the same ground, are of equal range of difficulty, and are comparable in other respects to the items in the original test. Often these conditions are not well satisfied in practice. When this is true, Spearman-Brown formula predictions must be taken as approximations rather than at face value.

When the conditions for prediction are satisfied, there would seem to be no reason why the reliability coefficient of a test should not be boosted to almost any figure, simply by increasing the test's length. Such a result is highly improbable, however. In the first place, it is impractical to increase a test's length 10 or 15 times, for example. Not only is it difficult to find suitable material, but boredom, fatigue and other factors lead to diminishing returns. When the content added to the test is made strictly comparable to the original by a careful selection and matching of items, and when motivation remains substantially constant, the experimental evidence indicates that a test may be increased 5 or 6 times its original length and the prophecy formula will give a close estimate of the experimentally determined results. With greater increase in length the prophecy formula tends to "overpredict"—give higher estimated reliability coefficients than those actually found. Perhaps this is not especially serious, however, as a test which needs so much lengthening should probably be radically changed or discarded in favor of a better test.

3. Chance and constant errors

Many psychological factors affect the reliability coefficient of a test—fluctuations in interest and attention, shifts in emotional attitude, and differential effects of memory and practice. To these must be added environmental factors such as distractions, noises, interruptions, scoring errors, and the like. All of these variable and transitory influences are called "chance errors." To be truly chance, errors must affect a score in such a way as to cause it to vary up or down from its true value, as often one way as the other. Chance errors are by definition independent and uncorrelated. When for various reasons such errors are correlated, they can no longer be regarded as chance. Chance errors are sometimes called *errors of measurement.*

Constant errors, as distinguished from chance errors, work in only one direction. Constant errors raise or lower *all* of the scores on a test but do not affect the reliability coefficient. Such errors are easier to avoid than are chance errors and may sometimes be allowed for by subtracting two points, say, from a retest score to allow for practice.

II. RELIABILITY IN TERMS OF TRUE SCORES AND MEASUREMENT ERRORS

I. The reliability coefficient as a measure of true variance

A score on a mental test may be thought of as an index of the examinee's "true ability" * plus errors of measurement. If a score has a large component of ability and a small component of error, its reliability is high; and, contrariwise, if a test score has a small component of ability and a large error component, its reliability is low. The reliability coefficient becomes, then, a measure of the extent to which true ability exceeds error in the obtained scores. The relations of obtained score, true score, and error may be expressed mathematically as follows:

* True score = a measure which would be obtained by taking the mean of an an infinitely large number of measurements of a given individual on similar tests under similar conditions. A true score cannot, of course, be determined experimentally.

Let X = the obtained score for an individual on a test
$X_\infty{}^*$ = true score of the same individual
e = the variable (chance) errors

Then

$$X = X_\infty + e$$

or in deviation units

$$x = x_\infty + e$$

It can be shown that if chance errors and true scores are uncorrelated,

$$\sigma^2{}_x = \sigma^2{}_\infty + \sigma^2{}_e$$

That is, the variance of the obtained scores can be divided into *two* parts: the variance of the true scores and the variance of chance errors. If we divide both sides of the above equation by $\sigma^2{}_x$, we have

$$1 = \frac{\sigma^2{}_\infty}{\sigma^2{}_x} + \frac{\sigma^2{}_e}{\sigma^2{}_x}$$

showing that 100% of the obtained score variance can be resolved into the proportion contributed by true-score variance and the proportion contributed by error variance. When the fraction $\sigma^2{}_\infty/\sigma^2{}_x$ is large, reliability is high; when $\sigma^2{}_e/\sigma^2{}_x$ is large, reliability is low.

Under certain reasonable assumptions, namely, that true scores and errors are independent or *uncorrelated*, we may write:

$$r_{11} = \frac{\sigma^2{}_\infty}{\sigma^2{}_x}$$

and the reliability coefficient becomes a measure of the *proportion* of test variance which is true variance. We may also write

$$r_{11} = 1 - \frac{\sigma^2{}_e}{\sigma^2{}_x}$$

showing that when the proportion of error variance is low the reliability coefficient is high. Both of these formulas reveal the reliability coefficient to be an index of the precision of measurement. If the reliability coefficient of a test is .90, for example, we know that 90% of the variance of test scores is true-score variance, and only 10% error variance. If the reliability coefficient is .50, only 50% of score variance is attributable to true score variance, the other 50% being error variance.

* The symbol ∞ (infinity) is used to designate a true score.

2. Estimating true scores by way of the regression equation and the reliability coefficient

We have seen in the preceding section that the reliability coefficient is an index of the degree to which obtained score variance is a measure of true score variance—and is free of error variance. True scores cannot be found experimentally, but we can estimate an individual's true score by way of the regression equation, when we know the reliability coefficient. It can be shown mathematically that

$$\overline{X}_{\infty} = r_{11}X_1 + (1 - r_{11})M_1 \tag{83}$$

(true score estimated from the regression equation)

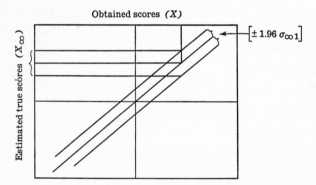

Obtained scores (X)

FIG. 63   True scores may be estimated from obtained scores by means of a regression equation. The parallel lines mark off the .95 confidence interval

in which

$$\overline{X}_{\infty} = \text{estimated true score on a test (Test 1, for example)}$$
$$X_1 = \text{obtained score on Test 1}$$
$$M_1 = \text{mean of Test 1 distribution}$$
$$r_{11} = \text{reliability coefficient of Test 1}$$

The standard error of an estimated true score is

$$SE_{\infty 1} = \sigma_1\sqrt{r_{11} - r^2_{11}} \tag{84}$$

(SE *of a true score estimated from a regression equation*)

where $SE_{\infty 1} =$ standard error of an estimated true score (predicted from an obtained score) in Test 1

and

$$r_{11} = \text{the reliability coefficient of Test 1.}$$

The example below shows how these formulas are applied.

Example (1)   The reliability coefficient of a test is .75, the M is 60 and the σ is 10. If John Brown has a score of 50 on the test, what is his estimated true score and its error of estimate? Compute the .95 confidence interval for John's true score.

Substituting in equation (83) we have that

$$\overline{X}_\infty = .75 \times 50 + .25 \times 60$$
$$= 52 \text{ (to nearest whole number)}$$

From equation (84), the SE of John's estimated true score is

$$SE_{\infty 1} = 10\sqrt{.75 - .56}$$
$$= 4 \text{ (to the nearest whole number)}$$

The .95 confidence interval for John's true score is $52 \pm 1.96 \times 4$ or 52 ± 8. We may feel quite sure, therefore, that the interval 44–60 contains John's true score. Note that John's estimated true score of 52 is nearer the mean of 60 than was his obtained score of 50. Scores *below* the test mean yield estimated true scores (regressed scores) which are closer in toward the mean. This is an illustration of the "regression effect" described on page 174. A diagram showing how a regressed true score may be estimated or predicted from an obtained score will be found in Figure 63.

A second example will demonstrate the considerable variation to be expected in an estimated true score, even when the reliability coefficient is high.

Example (2)   The M of the Stanford-Binet is 100 and the σ is 16. The reliability coefficient is .92. If Mary's I.Q. is 120, what is her estimated true I.Q. and its SE? Compute the .95 confidence interval for Mary's true I.Q.

From formula (83),

$$\overline{X}_\infty = .92 \times 120 + .08 \times 100$$
$$= 118 \text{ (to the nearest whole number)}$$

and the SE by (84) is

$$SE_{\infty 1} = 16\sqrt{.92 - .85}$$
$$= 4 \text{ (to the nearest whole number)}$$

The .95 confidence interval is $118 \pm 1.96 \times 4$ or 118 ± 8. The limits of the interval are 110 and 126—and the range is quite wide, 16 I.Q. points. It is clear that even when the reliability of a test is high, the prediction of true scores is subject to considerable error.

3. The index of reliability

An individual's true score on a test has been defined as the mean of a very large number of determinations made of the same person on the same test or on parallel forms of the test administered under standard conditions. The correlation between a set of obtained scores and their corresponding true counterparts is given by the formula

$$r_{1\infty} = \sqrt{r_{11}} \tag{85}$$

(correlation between obtained scores on a test and true scores in the function measured by the test)

in which $r_{1\infty}$ = the correlation of obtained and true scores

and r_{11} = the reliability coefficient of the Test 1.

The symbol ∞ (infinity) designates true scores (p. 346).

The coefficient $r_{1\infty}$ is called the index of reliability. It measures the dependability of test scores by showing how well obtained scores agree with their theoretically true values. The index of reliability gives the maximum correlation which the given test is capable of yielding in its present form. This is true because the highest correlation which can be obtained between a test and a second measure is between the test scores and their corresponding true scores.*

By squaring both sides of equation (85) we find that

$$r^2{}_{1\infty} = r_{11}$$

and the reliability coefficient (as before, p. 346) gives the *proportion* of the variance of the obtained scores which is determined by the variance of the true scores. Suppose that the reliability coefficient of a certain test is .64. Then 64% of the variance of obtained scores is attributable to the variance of true scores. Furthermore, since $r_{1\infty} = \sqrt{.64}$ or .80, we know that .80 is the highest correlation which this test is capable of yielding in its present form. If the reliability coefficient of a test is as low as .25, so that $r_{1\infty} = \sqrt{.25}$ or .50, it is obviously a waste of time to use such a test without lengthening it or otherwise improving it. A test whose index of reliability is only .50 is an extremely poor estimate of the function it is trying to measure. The index of reliability has no practical advantage over the reliability coefficient. It is useful mainly as a means of showing how r_{11} is a measure of true variance.

* Occasionally, chance may lead to a higher spurious correlation (p. 441).

4. The SE of an obtained score (the SE of measurement)

The effects of variable or chance errors in producing divergences of test scores from their true values is given by the formula

$$\sigma_{sc} = \sigma_1\sqrt{1 - r_{11}} \tag{86}$$

(standard error of an obtained score)

in which

σ_{sc} = the SE of an obtained score (also called the SE of measurement)
σ_1 = the standard deviation of test scores (Test 1)
r_{11} = the reliability coefficient of Test 1

The subscript *sc* indicates that this SE is a measure of the error made in taking an obtained score as an estimate of its true score. The example below provides an illustration of formula (86).

Example (3)   In a group of 300 college sophomores, the reliability coefficient of an Aptitude Test in mathematics is .75, the test *M* is 80 and the SD of the score distribution is 16. William achieves a score of 86. What is the SE of this score?

From formula (86) we find that

$$\sigma_{sc} = 16\sqrt{1 - .75}$$
$$= 8$$

and the odds are roughly 2:1 that the obtained score of *any* individual in the group of 300 does not miss its true value by more than ±8 points (i.e., ±1 SE_{sc}). The .95 confidence interval for William's true score is $86 \pm 1.96 \times 8$ or 70 to 102. Generalizing for the entire group of 300 sophomores, we may expect about 1/3 of their scores to be in error by 8 or more points, and 2/3 to be in error by less than this amount.

It is of interest to compare the estimate of William's true score given by (86) with that obtained by the methods of section 2, page 347. William's estimated true score is

$$\overline{X}_\infty = .75 \times 86 + .25 \times 80$$
$$= 84 \text{ (to the nearest whole number)}$$

and the $SE_{\infty 1}$ by (84) is

$$SE_{\infty 1} = 16\sqrt{.75 - .56}$$
$$= 7$$

We thus have an estimated true score of 84 with a $SE_{\infty 1}$ of 7 as against an obtained score of 86 (taken as an estimate of the true score) with an

SE_{sc} of 8. When using the SE_{x1}, the .95 confidence interval for the true score is $84 \pm 1.96 \times 7$ or from 70 to 98. This may be compared with the .95 confidence interval of 70 to 102 by the SE_{sc} method (p. 350). When the reliability coefficient is high (as here), little is to be gained by taking the estimated true score instead of the obtained score. But when the reliability coefficient is low, SE_{x1} is considerably smaller than SE_{sc} and the more precise method is to be preferred.

The student should note carefully the difference between the SE of estimate (see p. 160) and the SE_{sc}, i.e., the SE of an obtained score. The first SE enables us to say with what assurance we can predict an individual's score on Test A when we know his score on Test B (a different measure) and the correlation between the two. The prediction is made, of course, by way of the regression equation connecting the two variables. The SE_{sc} is also an estimate formula, but it tells us how adequately an obtained score represents its true score. The SE_{sc} is a better way of expressing the reliability of a test than is the reliability coefficient, as it takes into account the variability within the group as well as the self-correlation of the test (see p. 336).

5. Some other factors in reliability

(1) WHEN IS THE RELIABILITY COEFFICIENT SATISFACTORY?

How large a reliability coefficient we should require depends upon the nature of the test, the size and variability of the group, and the purpose for which the test was given. In order to differentiate between the means of two school grades of relatively narrow range, a reliability coefficient need be no higher than .50 or .60. If the test is to be used to make individual diagnoses (i.e., to separate pupil from pupil), its reliability coefficient for a single grade should be .90 or higher. Most of the authors of standard intelligence and educational achievement examinations report reliability coefficients of at least .90 between alternate forms of their tests. The reliability coefficient of a test is affected by the variability of the group (see below); and in reporting a reliability coefficient, the SD of the test distribution should always be given. The method used in computing the reliability should also be reported, as well as relevant information about the group and the testing procedures employed. Frequently teachers want to compare test results obtained from their classes with those cited in the literature. Such a comparison is impossible unless the author has outlined in some detail his methods of test administration and sampling procedures.

(2) THE EFFECTS OF DIFFERENT RANGES UPON RELIABILITY

The reliability coefficient of a test administered to a group of wide range of talent (e.g., to children from several school grades) cannot be compared directly with the reliability coefficient of a test administered to a group of relatively narrow spread, a single grade, for example. The self-correlation of a test (like any correlation coefficient) is affected by the variability of the group. The more heterogeneous the group, the greater the test variability and the higher the reliability coefficient. Figure 64

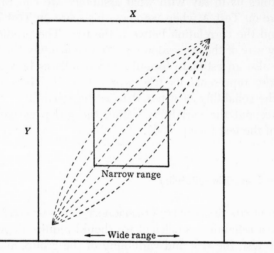

FIG. 64   Correlation within the narrow range (small rectangle) will be low (close to zero). Correlation in the wide range will be high (see p. 171)

shows how the correlation may be low in a group of restricted variability and at the same time quite high in a group of wider range (see p. 171).

If we know the reliability coefficient of a test in a wide range, we can estimate the reliability coefficient of the same test in a group of narrow range, provided the test is equally effective throughout both ranges. The formula is

$$\frac{\sigma_n}{\sigma_w} = \frac{\sqrt{1 - r_{ww}}}{\sqrt{1 - r_{nn}}} \tag{87}$$

(relation between σ's and reliability coefficients obtained in different stages when the test is equally effective throughout both ranges)

in which

σ_n and σ_w = the σ's of the test scores in the narrow and wide ranges, respectively

r_{nn} and r_{ww} = the reliability coefficients in the narrow and wide ranges

To illustrate, suppose that in grades 3–7 the reliability coefficient of an educational achievement test is reported to be .94 and the σ_w is 15.00. A teacher finds that in her fifth grade the σ_n is 5.00. Assuming the test to be just as effective in the single grade as in grades 3–7, what is the reliability coefficient in the narrow range? Substituting for σ_n, σ_w and r_{ww} in formula (87), we find r_{nn} to be .46. This means that a reliability coefficient of .46 in the narrow range (i.e., the restricted range) indicates as much score dependability as a reliability coefficient of .94 in a group in which the range is three times as wide.

Usually, perhaps, one wishes to estimate the reliability of a test given to a group of narrow range (e.g., a single grade) from data published for a standard test administered to groups of much greater spread. It is possible, also, if the assumption of equal effectiveness throughout both ranges holds true, to estimate from the reliability coefficient in a narrow range the most probable self-correlation of the test in a wider range. Formula (87) works both ways.

(3) RELIABILITY OF SPEED TESTS

Speed tests are tests in which the time limit imposed is so short that usually not all examinees can attempt all of the items. Speed tests differ from power tests in which ample time is allowed for all examinees to try every item. Speed tests are of low difficulty level, whereas in power tests the difficulty of the items increases steadily. The split-half technique and the rational equivalence methods should not be employed with speed tests. If there are relatively few errors—as will be true when the difficulty level is low—an odd-even split will give a correlation close to 1.00. Most examinees will have the same score in the two parts of the test. Sometimes the reliability of mazes used in animal learning experiments is estimated by correlating the time taken to learn the first and second halves of the maze. This procedure is rarely satisfactory. The first half of the maze is usually learned more quickly than the second half. Scores on the first half, therefore, will tend to be roughly the same for all, whereas scores on the second half will vary widely. There is little variability in the first half and much in the second. This situation leads to a half vs. half correlation which is close to zero. Parallel forms or test-retest are the methods to be used when speed is an important factor in the test score.

(4) RELIABILITY AT DIFFERENT PARTS OF THE TEST RANGE

The SE of an obtained score (p. 350) provides a general estimate of the dependability of a score over the entire range of the test. When the spread of ability is wide, however, agreement of scores on the two forms of the same test may differ considerably at successive parts of the scale—i.e., the test may not have equal discriminating power all along the scale. It is possible to refine our estimates of score reliability by computing the SE_{sc} for different levels of achievement. This has been done for the Stanford-Binet, a test which covers a very wide range of talent. The SE of an I.Q. of 130 and above, for example, is 5.24; for I.Q.'s of 90–109, 4.51; for I.Q.'s of 70 and below, 2.21, etc. The method of computing these differential SE_{sc}'s is given in the reference in footnote.*

III. THE VALIDITY OF TEST SCORES

The validity of a test, or of any measuring instrument, depends upon the fidelity with which it measures what it purports to measure. A home-made yardstick is entirely valid when measurements made by it are accurate in terms of a standard measuring rod. And a test is valid when the performances which it measures correspond to the same performances as otherwise independently measured or objectively defined. The difference between validity and reliability can be made clear, perhaps, by the following illustration. Suppose that a clock is set forward 20 minutes. If the clock is a good timepiece, the time it "tells" will be reliable (i.e., consistent) but will not be valid as judged by "standard time." The reliability of measurements made by scales, thermometers, chronoscopes, ammeters is determined by making repeated measurements of the same facts; and validity is found by comparing the data obtained from the instrument with standard (and sometimes arbitrary) measures. The validity of a test is found in the same manner. But since independent standards (i.e., criteria) are hard to get in mental measurement, the validity of a mental test can never be estimated as accurately as can the validity of a physical instrument.

Validity is a relative term. A test is valid for a particular purpose or in a particular situation—it is not *generally* valid. After World War I, several business concerns used the Alpha psychological test in the selection of applicants for routine clerical jobs. Those chosen often proved to be poor workers, indicating that the test was not a valid measure of the skills needed in many office jobs.

* McNemar, Q., "The expected average difference between individuals paired at random," *Jour. of Genetic Psychol.*, 1933, 43, 438–439.

I. Determining validity by means of judgments

What has been called "content validity" is employed in the selection of items in educational achievement tests, and in many trade tests. Standard educational achievement examinations represent the consensus of many educators as to what a child of a given age or grade should know about arithmetic, reading, spelling, history, and other subject fields. A test of English history or of geography is judged to be valid if its content consists of questions covering these areas. The validation of content through competent judgments is most satisfactory when the sampling of items is wide and judicious, and when adequate standardization groups are utilized.

Less defensible than content validity is the judgment process called "face validity." A test is said to have face validity when it appears to measure whatever the author had in mind, namely, what he thought he was measuring. Rating scales for various hypothesized traits, neurotic inventories, attitude scales, and even intelligence tests often can claim little more than face validity. Judgments of face validity are very useful in helping an author decide whether his test items are relevant to some specific situation (e.g., the military) or to specialized occupational experiences. Arithmetic problems dealing with military operations, for example, are more relevant to army jobs than are fictitious problems dealing with men rowing against a river, or the cost of papering a wall. Face validity is necessary, too, when we must decide what items are suitable for children and which are acceptable to adults. A feeble-minded man of 40 will feel affronted if asked how many fingers he has on his hand, whereas a child of 6 or 7 will regard the question as entirely proper (though easy). Face validity should never be more than a first step in testing an item; it should not be the final word.

2. Determining validity experimentally *

The validity of a test is determined experimentally by finding the correlation between the test and some independent criterion. A criterion may be an objective measure of performance, or a qualitative measure such as a judgment of the character or excellence of work done. Intelligence tests were first validated against school grades, ratings for aptitude by teachers, and other indices of ability. A trade test may be validated against time taken to carry out standard operations, amount done in a given time, or excellence of work. Personality, attitude and interest inventories are vali-

* See Anastasi, A., *Psychological Testing* (New York: Macmillan, 1954), Chap. 6.

dated in a variety of ways. One of the best is to check test predictions against actual outcomes. A high correlation between a test and a criterion is evidence of validity provided (1) the criterion was set up independently and (2) both the test and the criterion are reliable.

The index of reliability (p. 349) is sometimes taken as a measure of validity. The correlation coefficient, it will be recalled, gives the relationship between obtained scores and their theoretical true counterparts. If the reliability coefficient of a test is .81, for example, $r_{1\infty}$ is $\sqrt{.81}$ or .90. This means that the test measures true ability to the extent expressed by an r of .90.

3. Factorial validity

In the statistical method called *factor analysis,* the intercorrelations of a large number of tests are examined and if possible accounted for in terms of a much smaller number of more general "factors" or trait categories. The factors presumably run through the often complex abilities measured by the individual tests. It is sometimes found, for example, that 3 or 4 factors will account for the intercorrelations obtained among 15 or more tests. The validity of a given test is defined by its factor loadings— and these are given by the correlation of the test with each factor. A vocabulary test, for example, may correlate .85 with the verbal factor extracted from the entire test battery. This coefficient becomes the test's factorial validity.

Factor analysis is a specialized mathematical technique widely used and highly important in modern test construction. For a comprehensive account of its application to mental measurement, see Anastasi, *Psychological Testing,* Chapter 14.

4. Validity and the length of a test

Lengthening a test not only increases its reliability; it also increases its validity, thus rendering the test a better measure of its criterion. The effect upon the validity coefficient of increasing a test's length may be measured by the following formula:

$$r_{c(nx_1)} = \frac{nr_{cx_1}}{\sqrt{n + n(n-1)r_{11}}} \tag{88}$$

(correlation between a criterion (c) and (1) a test lengthened n times or (2) the average of n parallel forms of the test)

in which

$r_{c(nx_1)}$ = the correlation between the criterion (c) and n forms of Test X_1 or Test X_1 lengthened n times

r_{cx_1} = the correlation between the criterion (c) and the given Test X_1

r_{11} = reliability coefficient of Test X_1

n = number of parallel forms of Test X_1 or the number of times it is lengthened

The following example will illustrate formula (88)

> *Example* (4) Test A has a reliability coefficient of .70 and a correlation of .40 with the criterion (c). What would be the correlation of Test A with the same criterion (its validity coefficient) if the test were tripled in length?

Substituting $r_{11} = .70$, $r_{cx_1} = .40$ and $n = 3$ in (88), we have that

$$r_{c(3A)} = \frac{3 \times .40}{\sqrt{3 + 3 \times 2 \times .70}}$$

$$= .45$$

Thus, tripling the length of the test or averaging 3 administrations of the same test should increase the validity coefficient from .40 to .45. It may be noted that tripling the test's length also increases the reliability coefficient from .70 to .87 (p. 343). The increase in reliability with increase in validity shows the close relation between the two measures of test efficiency.

To find how much the test would have to be lengthened in order to reach a given level of validity, we can rearrange (88) and solve for n:

$$n = \frac{r^2_{c(nx_1)}(1 - r_{11})}{r^2_{cx_1} - r^2_{c(nx_1)} \times r_{11}} \tag{89}$$

(*amount by which a test must be lengthened in order to give a specified validity coefficient*)

Suppose that an oral trade test, Test T, has a reliability coefficient of .50 in a small group (narrow range of talent) and a criterion correlation of .30. How much lengthening is necessary in order that this test will yield a validity coefficient of .40? Substituting $r_{c(nx_1)} = .40$, $r_{11} = .50$ and $r_{cx_1} = .30$ in (89) and solving for n, we have that

$$n = \frac{.16 \times .50}{.09 - .16 \times .50}$$

$$= 8$$

Thus, Test T must be 8 times its present length in order for the validity coefficient to go from .30 to .40. Note that increasing Test T's length 8 times also raises its reliability coefficient from .50 to .89. It seems likely that a test which needs so much lengthening had best be abandoned in favor of a new test.

5. Dependence of validity on reliability

The correlation between a test and its criterion will be reduced or *attenuated* if either the test or the criterion or both are unreliable. In order to estimate the correlation between two sets of true scores, we need to make a correction which will take into account errors of measurement (chance errors). Such a correction is given by the formula

$$r_{\infty\infty \atop 1\,2} = \frac{r_{12}}{\sqrt{r_{1\mathrm{I}} \times r_{2\mathrm{II}}}} \qquad (90)$$

(correlation between Tests 1 and 2 corrected for attenuation)

in which

$r_{\infty\infty \atop 1\,2}$ = correlation between true measures in 1 and 2

r_{12} = correlation between obtained scores in 1 and 2

$r_{1\mathrm{I}}$ = reliability coefficient of Test 1

$r_{2\mathrm{II}}$ = reliability coefficient of Test 2

Formula (90) provides a correction for those chance errors which lower the reliability coefficients and thus reduce the correlation between test and criterion. Suppose the correlation between criterion (c) and Test A is .60, the reliability coefficient of c is .80 and the reliability coefficient of Test A is .90. What is the corrected correlation between c and A—the correlation freed of errors of measurement? Substituting in (90), we have

$$r_{\infty\infty \atop 1\,2} = \frac{.60}{\sqrt{.80 \times .90}}$$

$$= .71$$

as the estimated correlation between true measures in c and A. Our corrected coefficient of correlation represents the relationship which we should expect to get if our two sets of scores were perfect measures.

It is clear from formula (90) that correcting for chance errors will always raise the correlation between two tests—unless the reliability coefficients are both 1.00. Chance errors, therefore, *always* lower or attenuate an obtained correlation coefficient. The expression $\sqrt{r_{1\mathrm{I}} \times r_{2\mathrm{II}}}$ sets an upper limit to the correlation which we can obtain between two measures as they stand. In example (4), $\sqrt{.80 \times .90} = .85$; hence, Test A and the criterion c cannot correlate higher than .85, as otherwise their corrected r would be greater than 1.00.

Let us assume the correlation between first-year college grades (the criterion) and a general intelligence test is .46; the reliability of the intelligence test is .82; and the reliability of college grades is .70. The maximum correlation which we could hope to attain between these two measures is

$$r_{\infty\infty \atop 1\,2} = \frac{.46}{\sqrt{.70 \times .82}}$$

$$= .61$$

Knowing that the correlation between grades and general intelligence, corrected for errors of measurement, has a probable maximum value of .61 gives us a better notion of the "intrinsic" relationship between the two variables. At the same time, the investigator should remember that $r_{\infty\infty \atop 1\,2}$ of .61 is a theoretical, not a computed, value; that it gives an estimate of the relationship to be expected when tests are more effective than they actually were in the present instance. If many sources of error are present, so that considerable correction is necessary, it is better experimental procedure to improve the tests and the sampling than to correct the obtained r_{12}.

It is often (perhaps usually) true that the criterion is less reliable than the test or test battery. This will cause the battery to seem less valid than is actually the case. An experimenter, therefore, may correct a validity coefficient for attenuation in the criterion only, making no correction for unreliability in the tests. The formula for a one-way correction is

$$r_{\left(\frac{c}{\infty}\right)x} = \frac{r_{cx}}{\sqrt{r_{cc}}} \tag{91}$$

(validity correction for attenuation in the criterion only)

in which

> $r_{\left(\frac{c}{\infty}\right)x}$ = the correlation of the true criterion and the obtained test score
> r_{cx} = the correlation of criterion and obtained test scores
> r_{cc} = the reliability coefficient of the criterion (c)

The following example illustrates the use of (91):

> *Example* (5)   A comprehensive achievement examination correlates .38 with mean grade in the first year of a high school. The re-

liability coefficient of the grades is low, .57. What is the validity coefficient of the test battery when the criterion is corrected for attenuation?

Substituting in (91), $r_{cx} = .38$ and $r_{cc} = .57$, we have

$$\frac{r}{\left(\frac{c}{\infty}\right)x} = \frac{.38}{\sqrt{.57}}$$

$$= .50$$

The $r_{\left(\frac{c}{\infty}\right)x} = .50$ is a better estimate of the true validity of the achievement test than is the observed correlation of .38.

Workers with tests must be careful how they apply the attenuation formulas to correlations which have been averaged, as in such cases the reliability coefficients may actually be lower than the intercorrelations among the different tests. When this happens, corrected r's may be greater than 1.00—a result which is statistically and psychologically meaningless. Corrected r's close to 1.00 or even slightly greater than 1.00 may be taken as indicating complete agreement between true measures of the correlated variables, within the error of computation.

6. The relation of validity to reliability

There is a close connection between the two concepts, reliability and validity, in that both stress test efficiency. Reliability is concerned with the stability of test scores—does not go beyond the test itself. Validity, on the other hand, implies evaluation in terms of outside—and independent—criteria. Perhaps the greatest difficulty encountered in test validation is the problem of finding authentic criteria. Criteria must of necessity often be approximate and indirect, for if readily accessible and reliable criteria were available, these measures would be used instead of the tests. The purpose of a test is to find a measure which will be an adequate and time-saving substitute for criterion measures (e.g., school grades or performance records) obtainable only after long intervals of time.

To be valid a test must be reliable. A highly reliable test is always a valid measure of some function. Thus, if a test has a reliability coefficient of .90, its index of reliability is $\sqrt{.90}$ or .95. This means that the test correlates .95 with true measures of itself—these true measures constituting the criterion. A test may be theoretically valid, however, and show little or no correlation with anything else. The simple tapping test and the word cancellation tests are examples. Scores in these tests can be made highly reliable by lengthening or repeating the test so that the index of reliability is high. But the correlations of these tests with various criteria (e.g., speed or accuracy of factory work) are so low that they possess little practical validity in these situations.

7. Summary on the relation of validity and reliability

(1) The two concepts, reliability and validity, refer to different aspects of what is essentially the same thing, namely, test efficiency.

(2) A reliable test is theoretically valid, but may be practically invalid, as judged by its correlations with various independent criteria.

(3) A highly valid test cannot be unreliable since its correlation with a criterion is limited by its own index of reliability.

8. Validation of a test battery

A criterion of job efficiency, say, or of success in salesmanship may be forecast by a battery consisting of four, five, or more tests. The validity of such a battery is determined by the multiple correlation coefficient, R, between the battery and the criterion. The weights to be attached to scores on the subtests of the battery are given directly by the regression coefficients (p. 412).

If the regression weights are small fractions (as they often are), whole numbers may be substituted for them with little if any loss in accuracy. For example, suppose that the regression equation joining the criterion and the tests in a battery reads as follows:

$$c\ (criterion) = 4.32X_1 + 3.12X_2 - .65X_3 + 8.35X_4 + K(constant)$$

Dropping fractions and taking the nearest whole numbers, we have

$$c = 4X_1 + 3X_2 - 1X_3 + 8X_4 + K$$

Scores in Test 1 are multiplied by 4, scores in Test 2 by 3, scores in Test 3 by −1, and scores in Test 4 by 8, in order to provide the best forecast of c, the criterion. The fact that Test 3 has a negative weight does not mean that this test has no value in forecasting c, but simply that the best estimate of c is obtained by giving scores in Test 3 a negative value (p. 419).

IV. ITEM ANALYSIS

In preceding sections we have considered reliability and validity of test scores as being two aspects of a common attribute—namely, test efficiency. The adequacy of a test—whatever its purpose—depends upon the care with which the items of the test have been chosen. There are many approaches to the study of item analysis and the topic properly belongs in a book on test construction. We shall be concerned here, therefore, only with those features of item analysis which are primarily dependent upon statistical method. For a comprehensive discussion and summary of item analysis and its problems, see references listed in footnote.*

Item analysis will be treated under three heads (1) item selection, (2) item difficulty, and (3) item validity.

1. Item selection

The choice of an item depends, in the first instance, upon the judgment of competent persons as to its suitability for the purposes of the test. This is the "content validity" discussed on page 355. Certain types of items have proved to be generally useful in intelligence examinations. Problems in mental arithmetic, vocabulary, analogies, number series completion, for example, are found over and over again; so also are items requiring generalization, interpretation, and the ability to see relations. The validity of the items in most tests of educational achievement depends, as a first step, upon the consensus of teachers and educators as to the adequacy of the material included. Courses of study, grade requirements, and curricula from various parts of the country are carefully culled over by test makers in order to determine what content should be included in the various subject fields. In its preliminary form (before statistical analysis) the educational achievement test represents items carefully selected from all sources of information judged to be suitable.

Items chosen for aptitude tests, for tests in special fields, and items used in personal data sheets, interest and attitude tests are selected in the same manner. Such questions represent a consensus of experts as to the most relevant (and diagnostic) problems in the areas sampled.

2. Item difficulty

The difficulty of an item (problem or question) may be determined in several ways: (1) by the judgment of competent people who rank the

* Ross, C. C., and Stanley, J. C., *Measurement in Today's Schools* (New York: Prentice-Hall, 1954), Part II and Appendix B.

Lindquist, E. F. (ed.), *Educational Measurement* (Washington: American Council on Education, 1951), Part II.

Thorndike, R. L., *Personnel Selection* (New York: John Wiley and Sons, 1949), Chap. 8.

items in order of difficulty, (2) by how quickly the item can be solved, and (3) by the number of examinees in the group who get the item right. The first two procedures are usually a first step, especially when the items are for use in special aptitude tests, in performance tests, and in areas (such as music and art) where qualitative distinctions and opinions must serve as criteria. But the number right, or the proportion of the group which can solve an item correctly, is the "standard" method for determining difficulty in objective examinations. This is the statistical as contrasted with the judgmental approach to item validity.

(1) ITEM VARIANCE AND DIFFICULTY

The proportion (p) passing an item is an index of item difficulty. If 90% of a standard group pass an item, it is easy; if only 10% pass, the item is hard. When p = the percentage passing an item and q = the percentage failing, it can be shown that the SD of the item (its variability) is $\sqrt{pq}$ and its variance (σ^2) is pq. When p = .50 and q = .50, the item variance is .25. This is the *maximum variance* which an item can have; hence an item with a difficulty index of .50 (p = .50) brings out more individual differences (spreads the examinees out more) than a harder or easier item. In general, as p drops below .50 or goes above .50, the variance of the item steadily decreases. Thus, an item passed by 60% (and failed by 40%) has a variance of .24, and an item passed by 90% and failed by 10% has a variance of .09. The relation of item variance to difficulty can be shown in another way. If 5 examinees in a group of 10 pass an item and 5 fail (p = q = .50), there are 25 differentiations or discriminations possible as each of the 5 "passers" is separated from each of the 5 who fail ($5 \times 5 = 25$). If 6 pass and 4 fail, there are 24 differentiations, if 8 pass and 2 fail, 16. The larger the variance of the item, therefore, the greater the number of separations among individuals the test item is able to make. Other things being equal, items of moderate difficulty (40–50–60% passing) are to be preferred to those which are much easier or much harder.

(2) ITEM INTERCORRELATIONS AND RANGE OF DIFFICULTY

In item selection, not only must individual item difficulty be considered, but the intercorrelations of the items of the test as well. It is hardly ever feasible to compute all of the item intercorrelations. For a test of only 50 items, for example, there would be $\frac{50 \times 49}{2}$ or 1225 tetrachoric r's or phi coefficients. If the items of a test all correlate +1.00, then a single item will do the work of all. At the other extreme, if all item correlations are .00, the mean score of every examinee will tend to be about 1/2 of the total number of items for the following reason: when the items are independent (uncorrelated), the probability of passing any given item will depend upon its difficulty index. For the whole test (if items range from easy to hard) the probability would then be roughly 1/2 of all items. In mental tests, the intercorrelations among items are usually positive and fairly high, items close together in the scale correlating higher than items far apart.

In the absence of precise knowledge concerning item correlation, it is impossible to say exactly what is the best distribution of item difficulties. There is general agreement among test makers, however, that (1) for the sharpest discrimination among examinees, items should be around 50% in difficulty; that (2) when a certain proportion of the group (the upper 25%, for example) is to be separated from the remainder (the lower 75%), but comparisons within each group are of no special interest, difficulty indices should be close to 25%, i.e., the cutting point. Finally, (3) when item correlations are high (as is true in most educational achievement tests), and the talent range wide (over several grades), difficulty indices may range from high to low. The normal curve can be taken as a guide in the selection of difficulty indices. Thus, 50% of the items might have difficulty indices between .25 and .75; 25% indices larger than .75, and 25% smaller than .25. An item passed by 0% or 100% has no differentiating value, of course, but such items may be included in a test solely for the psychological effect. Difficulty indices within more narrow ranges may, of course, be taken from the normal curve.

(3) CORRECTING DIFFICULTY INDICES FOR CHANCE SUCCESS

It is important to try to estimate the number of examinees who get the right answer through correct knowledge or correct reasoning and to rule out answers which are based upon guesswork. In correcting for chance success, we assume that (1) wrong answers are due to absence of knowledge and that (2) to one who does not know the right answer, all of the response options are equally attractive. Under these assumptions, it is reasonable to expect that some of those who really did not know the right answer selected it by chance. A formula for correcting the difficulty index of an item for chance success is the following:

$$P_c = \frac{R - \dfrac{W}{(k-1)}}{N - HR} \tag{92}$$

(*to correct a difficulty index for chance success*)

in which

P_c = the percent who actually know the right answer
R = the number who get the right answer
W = the number who get the wrong answer
N = the number of examinees in the sample
HR = the number of examinees who do not reach the item (and hence do not try it)
k = the number of options or choices

To illustrate, suppose that a sample of 300 examinees take a test of 100 items, each item having 5 options. Suppose further that 150 answer item #46 correctly, that 120 answer it incorrectly, and that 30 do not reach the item and hence do not attempt it in the time limit. Instead of a difficulty index of .50, item #46 has a corrected difficulty index of .44. Thus

$$P_c = \frac{150 - \dfrac{120}{(5-1)}}{300 - 30}$$

$$= .44$$

The corrected value of the difficulty index is, to be sure, an approximation; but it probably gives a more nearly true measure than does the experimentally obtained percentage.

3. Item validity

(1) THE VALIDITY INDEX

The validity index of an item (i.e., its discriminative power) is determined by the extent to which the given item discriminates among examinees who differ sharply in the function (or functions) measured by the test as a whole. A number of methods have been devised for use in determining the discriminative power of an item. But biserial correlation (p. 375) is usually regarded as the standard procedure in item analysis. Biserial r gives the correlation of an item with total score on the test, or with scores in some independent criterion. The adequacy of other methods (some of them quite summary) is judged by the degree to which they are able to yield results which approximate those obtained by biserial correlation.

One method of determining validity indices, much favored by test makers, sets up extreme groups in computing the validity of an item. This procedure will be described here, as one of the best among several methods. *First,* the number who answer the item correctly in selected upper and lower subgroups is found. *Next,* the discriminative power of the item—its consistency with total score on the test—is gauged by the correlation (r_{bis}) of the item and the whole test. The biserial r is read from a table like that shown in abbreviated form in Table 51. The procedure in detail is as follows:

(1) Arrange the test papers in order of size for test score. Put the paper with the highest score on top.

(2) Assume that we have 200 examinees. Count off the top 27% of papers

TABLE 51 * Normalized biserial coefficients † of correlation as determined from proportions of correct responses in upper and lower 27 percent of the group

	PROPORTION OF CORRECT RESPONSES IN THE UPPER 27 PER CENT‡																									
	02	06	10	14	18	22	26	30	34	38	42	46	50	54	58	62	66	70	74	78	82	86	90	94	98	
02	00	19	30	37	43	48	51	55	58	61	63	66	68	70	72	73	75	77	79	80	82	84	86	88	91	02
06		00	11	19	26	31	36	40	44	47	50	53	56	59	61	64	66	68	71	73	76	78	81	84	88	06
10			00	08	15	21	26	30	34	38	41	45	48	51	54	57	60	63	65	68	71	74	77	81	86	10
14				00	07	12	18	22	27	31	34	38	42	45	48	51	54	57	60	63	67	70	74	78	84	14
18					00	06	11	16	20	25	28	32	36	39	43	47	49	53	56	60	63	67	71	76	82	18
22						00	06	10	15	19	23	27	31	34	38	42	45	49	52	56	60	63	68	73	80	22
26							00	05	09	14	18	22	26	30	33	37	41	44	48	52	56	60	65	71	79	26
30								00	04	09	13	17	21	25	29	33	37	40	44	49	53	57	63	68	77	30
34									00	04	09	13	17	21	25	29	33	37	41	45	49	54	60	66	75	34
38										00	04	08	13	16	20	25	29	33	37	42	47	51	57	64	73	38
42											00	04	08	12	16	20	25	29	33	38	43	48	54	61	72	42
46												00	04	08	12	16	21	25	30	34	39	45	51	59	70	46
50													00	04	08	13	17	21	26	31	36	42	48	56	68	50
54														00	04	08	13	17	22	27	32	38	45	53	66	54
58															00	04	09	13	18	23	28	34	41	50	63	58
62																00	04	09	14	19	25	31	38	47	61	62
66																	00	04	09	15	20	27	34	44	58	66
70																		00	05	10	16	22	30	40	55	70
74																			00	06	11	18	26	36	51	74
78																				00	06	12	21	31	48	78
82																					00	07	15	26	43	82
86																						00	08	19	37	86
90																							00	11	30	90
94																								00	19	94
98																									00	98
	02	06	10	14	18	22	26	30	34	38	42	46	50	54	58	62	66	70	74	78	82	86	90	94	98	

(Left axis label: PROPORTION OF CORRECT RESPONSES IN THE LOWER 27 PER CENT‡)

* This table is abridged from J. C. Flanagan's table of normalized biserial coefficients originally prepared for the Cooperative Test Service. It is included here with the generous permission of Dr. Flanagan and the Educational Testing Service of Princeton, New Jersey. This version is taken from Merle W. Tate, *Statistics in Education* (New York: The Macmillan Co., 1955), p. 364. Reproduced by permission.

† Decimal points are omitted.

‡ If the proportion of correct responses in the lower 27 percent exceeds that in the upper, enter the table with the lower 27 percent proportion at the top and attach a negative sign to the coefficient.

and the bottom 27%.* This puts 54 papers in the first pile and 54 in the second.

(3) Lay aside the middle 92 papers. These are used simply to mark off the two end groups.
(4) Tally the number in the top group which passes each item on the test; and the number in the bottom group which passes each item. Convert these numbers into percentages.
(5) Correct these percents for chance success.
(6) Entering Table 51 with the percent of successes in the two groups, read the biserial r from the intersecting column and row in the body of the table.
(7) Average the two percentages (top and bottom groups) to find the difficulty index of the item.

The following example will illustrate, for 5 sample items, how difficulty indices and validity indices are computed.

Example (6)   The data below were obtained from 5 items of an achievement test (multiple choice, 4 options). Find the difficulty and validity indices for each item.

Item #	% right in the top 27% (corrected)	% right in the bottom 27% (corrected)	Difficulty † Index	Validity ‡ Index
5	73	58	.65	.17
21	61	38	.49	.23
36	50	50	.50	.00
54	43	36	.39	.07
75	36	8	.22	.40

The difficulty index of each item is found by averaging the percents correct in the upper and lower groups. This percentage is approximate, but is accurate enough for most purposes and has the great advantage of easy computation. The discriminative power (validity index) of each item is read directly from Table 51. Thus, r_{bis} for the split 73–58 (item #5) and test score is .17; for the split 61–38, r_{bis} is .23, and so on.

The size of an acceptable validity index will depend upon the length of the test, the range of the difficulty indices, and the purposes for which the

* It has been shown that the discriminative power of an item is most accurately determined when item analysis is based on the top and bottom 27% rather than some other percentage of the distribution.

† It would be more accurate to determine the difficulty index from the whole sample.

‡ These indices were found by interpolation in the table; but the increase in accuracy in so doing is hardly worthwhile.

test is designed. If one has analyzed 200 items and wants a test of 100 items, he could take the 100 most valid items in terms of their validity indices. Some valid items according to this criterion might be discarded if their difficulty indices were unsatisfactory. In the example above, items #36 and 54 have no validity; item #75 is highly valid; and items #5 and 21 are fairly satisfactory. As a general rule, items with validity indices of .20 or more are regarded as satisfactory; but items with lower indices will often serve if the test is long. Items having zero validity are, of course, useless. These items and items having negative validity (a larger percent right in the bottom group than the top) must be discarded; or they must be carefully examined for ambiguities, inaccuracies and other errors.

An experimentally excellent but somewhat laborious method of validating a test is to remove the obviously poor items, and compute the correlation of the remaining total scores (in tentative form) and the criterion. Then again remove the less valid items and recompute the criterion correlation, repeating the process until diminishing returns appear. In one study, a test of 86 items of high validity had a better correlation with the criterion than did the whole set of 222 items. Much evidence showing the effects of item analysis can be cited.[*]

The r_{bis} read from Table 51 is a biserial, not a point biserial r (p. 380). This coefficient is less accurate than is the usual r_{bis} as it utilizes only about 1/2 of the test data—the middle 46% are not used. The loss of accuracy in these validity indices is of little consequence when they are used comparatively; and the ease of computation is a practical advantage.

(2) CROSS VALIDATION

The validation of a completed test should always be computed on a *new* sample—i.e., one different from that used in the item analysis. This process is called "cross validation." The validity of a test, when computed from the "standardization sample," will of necessity be exaggerated, as the items are so selected as to maximize differences between high and low scorers. Furthermore, the validity coefficient of the test will be increased by chance factors peculiar to the standardization sample.

The effects of chance factors upon validity can be shown in the following way: Suppose that the items on an aptitude test, specially designed for retail salesmen, have been so selected as to yield satisfactory validity indices in terms of the top and bottom 27%'s of a "standard" sample of sales personnel. Many irrelevant factors are likely to be present in this group, some of which will be correlated with scores on the test. Such factors will often be correlated with responses to the items in one extreme

* Anastasi, A., *op. cit.*, Chap. 7.

group more often than in the other. Unless the same incidental factors are present in a new group of retail salesmen to the same degree (which is not likely), the validity coefficient of the final (completed) test will be lower in the new groups than in the original standardization group. Validity correlations tend always to be spuriously high in the standard group, thus making cross validation necessary.

PROBLEMS

1. The reliability coefficient of a test is .60.
   (a) How much must this test be lengthened in order to raise its self-correlation to .90?
   (b) What effect will doubling the test's length have on its reliability? tripling the test's length?
2. A test of 50 items has a reliability coefficient of .78. What is the reliability coefficient of a test
   (a) having 100 items comparable to those of the original test?
   (b) having 125 items comparable to those of the original test?
3. A test of 75 items has a σ_t of 12.35. The $\Sigma pq = 16.46$. What is the reliability coefficient by the method of rational equivalence?
4. Estimate the reliability of the test in (3) above by formula (81) if the $M = 40$.
5. A test is administered to 225 students with the following results: $M = 62.50$, $\sigma = 9.62$ and $r_{11} = .91$.
   (a) If Bob Jones makes a score of 50 on this test, what is his estimated true score and its standard error?
   (b) What is the standard error of an obtained score of 50?
   (c) Compare the .95 confidence intervals for the true score as determined from the methods used in (a) and (b).
6. A given test has a reliability coefficient of .80 and σ of 20.
   (a) What is the index of reliability?
   (b) What is the SE of an obtained score on this test?
   (c) What is the estimated reliability of this test in a group in which σ is 15?
   (d) What proportion of the variance of scores in this test is attributable to "true" variance?
7. Show that when (a) the reliability coefficient of a test is zero, the standard error of a score equals the SD of the test; and that (b) when the reliability coefficient is 1.00, the SE_{sc} equals zero.
8. A test of mathematics correlates .52 with a test of mechanical aptitude. The reliability coefficient of the mathematics test is .82 and of the mechanical aptitude test is .76.
   (a) What is the correlation between the two tests when both have been corrected for chance errors?

(b) What is the maximum correlation which the mathematics test is capable of yielding?

(c) What is the correlation between fallible scores in mathematics and true scores in mechanical aptitude?

9. A test of 40 items has a validity coefficient of .45 with a criterion, and a reliability coefficient of .75. If the test is lengthened to 120 items compute
    (a) the new validity coefficient
    (b) the new reliability coefficient.

10. A group of 150 students take a test of 50 items, each item having 4 choices. Suppose that 80 answer item #34 correctly, that 50 answer it incorrectly, and that 20 do not try the item. What is the difficulty index of the item?

11. Show that if 50 examinees in 100 pass an item and 50 fail more individual differences are brought out than when different numbers pass and fail.

12. Given the following data for 5 items on an aptitude test, multiple choice, 4 options. The percentages have been corrected for chance success. Complete the table.

Item No.	% right in upper 27%	% right in lower 27%	Diff'y Index	Validity Index
23	81	54		
34	62	46		
45	56	23		
51	50	50		
63	47	58		

ANSWERS

1. (a) 6 times   (b) doubling, .75; tripling, .82
2. (a) .88   (b) .90
3. .90
4. .89
5. (a) 51.12; 2.69
   (b) 2.89
   (c) 45.85 to 56.39; 44.34 to 55.66
6. (a) .89   (b) 9.0   (c) .64   (d) 80%
8. (a) .66   (b) .91   (c) .60
9. (a) .49   (b) .90
10. .48
12. Difficulty indices: .67, .54, .39, .52, .53
    Validity indices: .31, .16, .35, .00, −.11

CHAPTER 14

FURTHER METHODS
OF CORRELATION

◇◇

In Chapter 6 we described the linear, or product-moment correlation method, and in Chapter 7 showed how, by means of r and the regression equations, one can "predict" or "forecast" values of one variable from a knowledge of the other. Test scores, as we have seen, represent a series of determinations of a continuous variable taken along a numerical scale. The correlation coefficient is valuable to psychology and education as a measure of the relationship between test scores and other measures of performance. But many situations arise in which the investigator does not have scores and must work with data in which differences in a given attribute can be expressed only by ranks (e.g., in orders of merit); or by classifying an individual into one of several descriptive categories. This is especially true in vocational and applied psychology and in the field of personality and character measurement. Again, there are problems in which the relationship among the measurements made is *nonlinear,* and cannot be described by the product-moment r. In all of these cases other methods of determining correlation must be employed; and the purpose of this chapter is to develop some of the more useful of these techniques.

I. CORRELATION FROM RANKS

Differences among individuals in many traits can often be expressed by *ranking* the subjects in 1–2–3 order when such differences cannot be measured directly. For example, persons may be ranked in order of merit for honesty, athletic ability, salesmanship, or social adjustment when it is impossible to *measure* these complex behaviors. In like manner, various products or specimens, such as advertisements, color combinations, compositions, jokes and pictures, which are admittedly hard to evaluate numerically may be put in order of merit for aesthetic quality, beauty, humor, or some other characteristic. In computing the correlation between two sets of ranks, special methods which take account of relative position have been devised. These techniques may also be applied to measurements (i.e., to scores) when these have been arranged in order of merit. If we have only a few scores—under 25, for example—it is often advisable to rank these scores and to compute the correlation coefficient ρ (read *rho*) by the rank-difference method, instead of computing r by the longer and more laborious product-moment method. Whenever N is small, the rank-difference method will give as adequate a result as that obtained by finding r; and ρ is much easier to compute.

1. Calculating ρ from ranked data

Table 52 shows how to compute the correlation from rank-differences.

TABLE 52   To illustrate the calculation of ρ (rho)

Traits	(1) Judge X	(2) Judge Y	(3) D	(4) D^2
A	2	1	1	1
B	1	2	−1	1
C	4	5	−1	1
D	3	6	−3	9
E	6	4	2	4
F	5	3	2	4
			0	20

$$\rho = 1 - \frac{6 \times 20}{6 \times 35} = .43 \qquad (93)$$

Six traits (A, B, C, D, E, F) believed to be important in the work of an executive have been ranked in order of merit by Judges X and Y. In column (3), the differences (D) between each pair of ranks is entered, Judge Y's ranks being subtracted from those of Judge X. The sum of the D's is zero. This calculation is of no value *per se*, but is a check on the computation to this point. Each D is now squared in column (4), and the column is summed to give ΣD^2. The coefficient of correlation, ρ, is given by the formula:

$$\rho = 1 - \frac{6 \times \Sigma D^2}{N(N^2 - 1)} \qquad (93)$$

(rank-difference correlation coefficient, ρ)

in which

$$\rho = \text{coefficient of correlation from rank differences}$$
$$\Sigma D^2 = \text{sum of the squares of differences in rank}$$
$$N = \text{number of pairs}$$

Substituting for $\Sigma D^2 = 20$, and $N = 6$, we have that $\rho = .43$.

2. Comparing ρ and r: the question of tied ranks

If the ranks in Table 52 are treated as scores, we may calculate r directly, using formula (30) in which scores are taken as deviations from an assumed mean of zero. Columns (3), (4) and (5) give the squares of the X's, the squares of the Y's, and the cross products XY.

	(1)	(2)	(3)	(4)	(5)
Traits	Judge X	Judge Y	X^2	Y^2	XY
A	2	1	4	1	2
B	1	2	1	4	2
C	4	5	16	25	20
D	3	6	9	36	18
E	6	4	36	16	24
F	5	3	25	9	15
	21	21	91	91	81

Substituting in (30), we have that

$$r = \frac{(6 \times 81) - (21 \times 21)}{\sqrt{[(6 \times 91) - 21^2][(6 \times 91) - 21^2]}}$$

$$= .43$$

which checks the coefficient, ρ, given by formula (93). When ranks are treated as scores, and there are no ties, $\rho = r$. But when there are tied positions, a correction should be added to ρ to have it equal r exactly. This correction is small * unless the number of ties is large and may usually be safely ignored and ρ taken as a close approximation to r. Table 53 shows how to handle ties in ranked data. The problem is to find the relationship between length of service and selling efficiency in a group of 12 salesmen. The names of the men are listed in column (1), and in column (2) opposite the name of each man is the number of years he has been in the service of the company. In column (3) the men have been ranked in

* See Edwards, A. L., *Statistical Methods for the Behavioral Sciences* (New York: Rinehart, 1954), pp. 427–429.

TABLE 53   The rank-difference method when there are tied ranks

(1)	(2)	(3)	(4)	(5)	(6)
Salesmen	Years of Service	Order of Merit (service)	Order of Merit (efficiency)	Diffs. in Ranks D	Diffs. Squared D^2
Walsh	5	9.5	11	−1.5	2.25
Stevens	2	11.5	12	− .5	.25
Brown	10	2.0	1	1.0	1.00
Perry	8	3.5	9	−5.5	30.25
Johnson	6	7.0	8	−1.0	1.00
Cohen	6	7.0	5	2.0	4.00
Williams	6	7.0	2	5.0	25.00
Smith	12	1.0	3	−2.0	4.00
Shapiro	2	11.5	10	1.5	2.25
Ferrari	7	5.0	7	−2.0	4.00
Hastings	5	9.5	4	5.5	30.25
Mitchell	8	3.5	6	−2.5	6.25
				0.0	110.50

12^2

$$\rho = 1 - \frac{6 \times 110.50}{12 \times 143} \qquad (93)$$

$$= .61$$

order of merit in accordance with their length of service. Smith who has been longest with the company is ranked #1; Brown whose service is next longest is ranked #2; and so on down the list. Note that Perry and Mitchell have the same length of service, and that each is ranked 3.5. Instead of ranking one man 3 and the other 4, or both 3 or both 4, we simply average the ranks and give each man a rank of 3.5. Johnson, Cohen, and Williams all have 6 years of service. Since they occupy ranks 6, 7 and 8, each is given the median rank of 7; and Walsh and Hastings who follow in the 9th and 10th places are each ranked 9.5. Finally, Stevens and Shapiro who are 11th and 12th in order, are both ranked 11.5.

The difference between each pair of ranks is entered in column (5), and in column (6) each D is squared. The sum of the column is 110.50. Substituting for ΣD^2 and for N, we have that $\rho = .61$. If we compute r by formula (30) as was done in Table 52, its value also is .61 (to two decimals). The agreement between ρ and r is to the second decimal despite the number of ties in the service rankings.

3. Testing the significance of ρ

The stability of an obtained ρ can be tested against the null hypothesis by means of Table 25. The number of degrees of freedom is $(N - 2)$. For Table 52, we find that for 4 df a coefficient of correlation must be .81 to be significant at the .05 level. It is clear, therefore, that our ρ of .43 is not significant. When the df are 10, an r of .58 is significant at the .05 level, and an r of .71 significant at the .01 level. Hence, in Table 53, the ρ of .61 is just significant at the .05 level.

4. Summary on rank-difference correlation

The product-moment method deals with the size of the measures (or scores) as well as with their positions in the series. Rank differences, on the other hand, take account only of the positions of the items in the series, and make no allowance for gaps between adjacent scores. Individuals, for example, who score 90, 89 and 70 on a test would be ranked 1, 2, 3 although the difference between 90 and 89 is much less than the difference betweeen 89 and 70. Accuracy may be lost in translating scores over into ranks, especially when there are a number of ties. In spite of its mathematical disadvantages, ρ provides a quick and convenient way of estimating the correlation when N is small, or when we only have ranks. With larger N's, the rank-difference coefficient is still useful for exploratory purposes.

II. BISERIAL CORRELATION

In many problems it is important to be able to compute the correlation beween traits and other attributes when the members of the group can be measured (given scores, for example) in the one variable, but can be classified into only *two* categories in the second or dichotomous variable. (The term "dichotomous" means "cut into two parts.") We may, for example, wish to know the correlation between M.A. and "social adjustment" in a group of nursery children, when our subjects are measured in the first trait, but are simply classified as "socially adjusted" or "socially maladjusted" in the second. Other instances of twofold classification with reference to some attribute are athletic–nonathletic, radical–conservative, "drop outs" and "stay ins" in school, socially minded–mechanically minded, seventh grade and above–below seventh grade. When we can assume that the trait in which we have made a two-way split would be found to be continuous and normally distributed were more information available, we may compute a biserial r between the set of scores and two-category groupings like those listed above. Under the conditions specified, this biserial r is an estimate of the product-moment r (see also p. 382).

Many test questions and various sorts of items are scored to give two responses: for example, problems are marked *Passed* or *Failed*, statements *True* or *False*, personality inventory items *Yes* or *No*, interest items *Like* or *Dislike*, and so on. When a two-category split cannot be regarded as representing an underlying normal distribution upon which an arbitrary division has been imposed, but is in fact two discrete groupings, the *point biserial r* is the appropriate measure of correlation.

1. Biserial r

(1) CALCULATION OF BISERIAL r

The calculation of biserial r is shown in Table 54. The data are a distribution of scores on a Music Appreciation Test achieved by 145 high-school seniors. The total distribution of 145 scores has been broken down

TABLE 54 To illustrate the computation of biserial r. The two subdistributions represent the scores achieved on a Music Appreciation Test by students with and without training in music

Scores	(1) Training Group f	(2) No-training Group f	(3) Total f	
85–89	5	6	11	$M_T = 71.35$, mean of all 145 scores
80–84	2	16	18	$\sigma = 8.80$, SD of all scores
75–79	6	19	25	$M_p = 77.00$, mean of trained group
70–74	6	27	33	
65–69	1	19	20	$M_q = 70.39$, mean of untrained group
60–64	0	21	21	
55–59	1	16	17	$p = .145$, proportion in Group No. 1
	$N_1 = 21$	$N_2 = 124$	$N = 145$	$q = .855$, proportion in Group No. 2

$$r_{bis} = \frac{77.00 - 70.39}{8.80} \times \frac{(.145 \times .855)}{.228} \qquad (94)$$

$$= .41$$

$$\sigma_{r_{bis}} = \frac{\left(\frac{\sqrt{.145 \times .855}}{.228} - (.41)^2 \right)}{\sqrt{145}} \qquad (95)$$

$$= .11$$

$u = .228$, height of ordinate separating .145 and .855 in a unit normal distribution (Table 56)

into two subdivisions, the first made up of 21 students who had training in music [column (1)], and the second of 124 students without any formal musical training [column (2)]. The problem is to find whether there is a correlation between test score and previous training in music. Training in music is dichotomized or split into two categories, but it may reasonably be thought of as a graduated variable ranging from high level at the one extreme to complete lack of training at the other. The first column of Table 54 gives the intervals of the test distribution. Column (1) is the distribution of scores achieved by the 21 students with training; and column (2) is the distribution of scores made by the 124 students without training. The sum of the f's for the two distributions gives the total distribution in column (3). Computation of biserial r may be outlined conveniently in the following steps:

Step 1

Compute M_p, the mean of the group of 21. Also, compute M_q, the mean of the untrained group of 124. In our example, $M_p = 77.00$ and $M_q = 70.39$.

Step 2

Compute σ for the whole distribution of 145 cases. In Table 54, $\sigma_{tot} = 8.80$.

Step 3

There are 21 or 14.5% of the sample in the trained group; and 124 or 85.5% in the untrained group. Assuming a normal distribution in musical training, upon which an arbitrary cut has been imposed at a point 35.5% above the mean, we have the situation pictured below:

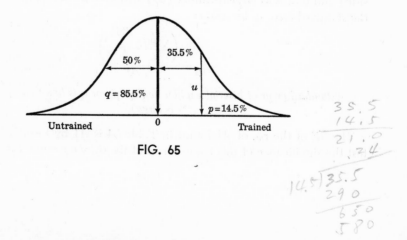

FIG. 65

The height of the ordinate of the normal curve (u) at the division point, i.e., at 35.5%, may be found from Table 56. This table gives the heights of the ordinates in a normal distribution of *unit* area, that is, with $N = 1.00$, $M = .00$, and $\sigma = 1.00$. Interpolating halfway between .35 and .36 in Table 56, we get a u-value of .228.

Step 4

Having computed M_p, M_q, σ, p and q, we find biserial r by substituting in the formula (94):

$$r_{bis} = \frac{M_p - M_q}{\sigma} \times \frac{pq}{u} \tag{94}$$

(biserial coefficient of correlation or biserial r)

in which

$M_p =$ the M of the group in the 1st category—usually the group showing superior or desirable characteristics

$M_q = M$ of the group in the second category or split

$\sigma = SD$ of the entire group

$p =$ proportion of the entire group in Category 1

$q =$ proportion of the entire group in Category 2 ($q = 1 - p$)

$u =$ height of the normal curve ordinate dividing the two parts, p and q.

In Table 54 $r_{bis} = .41$, indicating as might be expected a fairly strong association between training and test score on the Music Appreciation Test. Figure 66 shows schematically how the entire group is divided into two parts on the basis of training. The distance between the means of the two subgroups (M_p and M_q) is a measure of the effect of the split, i.e., of the effect of the dichotomy.

(2) THE STANDARD ERROR OF BISERIAL r

Provided neither p nor q is very small (less than .10 to be on the safe side) and that N is large, formula (95) will give a close approximation to the standard error of biserial r:

$$\sigma_{r_{bis}} = \frac{\left(\dfrac{\sqrt{pq}}{u} - r^2_{bis} \right)}{\sqrt{N}} \tag{95}$$

(standard error of biserial r when neither p nor q is less than .10 and N is large)

The *SE* of the r_{bis} of .41 found in Table 54 is .11 by formula (95). To test the significance of this r_{bis} in terms of its *SE*, we assume the sampling

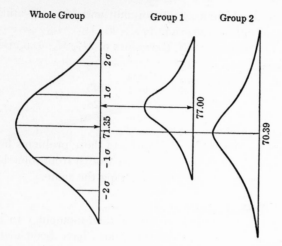

Whole Group   Group 1   Group 2

FIG. 66   To show relation between total group and two subgroups in biserial correlation. The distance between the means of Groups I and 2 is a measure of correlation. When the two means are equal, biserial *r* is zero.

distribution of r_{bis} to be normal around the population r, and $SE_{r_{bis}}$ to be the *SD* of this sampling distribution. The .99 confidence interval for the population r_{bis} is then from .13 to .69 (i.e., $.41 \pm 2.58 \times .11$). It appears that we can be quite confident of a positive relationship between training and the music test of at least .13, and probably the relation is much higher. A comparison of formula (95) with the classical formula for the *SE* of the product-moment r (p. 198) will show that $SE_{r_{bis}}$ is larger than SE_r and that it becomes increasingly larger as the difference between p and q widens: for example, from a split of $p = .50$ and $q = .50$ to one of $p = .95$ and $q = .05$. Formula (95) provides only an approximate measure of the stability of r_{bis} as the exact sampling distribution of biserial r is not known.

(3) AN ALTERNATIVE FORMULA FOR BISERIAL *r*

There is another formula for biserial r which is often more convenient to use than is formula (94). This is

$$r_{bis} = \frac{M_p - M_T}{\sigma} \times \frac{p}{u} \tag{96}$$

(*biserial coefficient of correlation in terms of* M_T, *the mean of the total sample*) in which M_T = the M of the entire group and M_p, σ, p and u have the same meaning as in formula (94).

Substituting in formula (96), the values of M_T, M_p, σ, p and u found in Table 54 we have

$$r_{bis} = \frac{77.00 - 71.35}{8.80} \times \frac{.145}{.228} = .41$$

which checks our previous result.

Formula (96) is especially well suited to those problems in which subgroups having different characteristics are drawn from some larger group, the mean of the larger group, M_T, remaining the same.

(4) SUMMARY ON BISERIAL r

Biserial r gives an estimate of the product-moment r to be expected for the given data when certain assumptions have been met. These are (1) continuity in the dichotomized trait, (2) normality of distribution, underlying the dichotomy, (3) a large N, and (4) a split that is not too extreme (the closer to .50 the better). Still further limitations to the use of biserial r should be noted. Biserial r cannot be used in a regression equation. This coefficient has no standard error of estimate, and the score predicted for all of the members of a group is simply the mean of that category. Biserial r is not limited as is r to a range of ± 1.00, rendering comparisons with other coefficients of correlation difficult.

2. The point biserial r

When items are scored simply as 1 if correct and 0 if incorrect, that is, as right or wrong, the assumption of normality in the distribution of right-wrong responses is unwarranted. In such cases the point biserial r rather than biserial r is appropriate. Point biserial r assumes that the variable which has been classified into two categories can be thought of as concentrated at two distinct *points* along a graduated scale or continuum. Examples of true dichotomies are male-female, living-dead, loyal-disloyal. Other traits or characteristics which constitute what are virtually genuine dichotomies (when the criteria are exact) are delinquent-nondelinquent, psychotic-normal, color blind-normal.

The formula for the point biserial r is

$$r_{pbis} = \frac{M_p - M_q}{\sigma} \times \sqrt{pq} \tag{97}$$

(point biserial r, a coefficient of correlation)

in which M_p and M_q are the means of the two categories, p is the proportion of the sample in the first group, and q is the proportion in the second group, and σ is the SD of the entire sample (p. 376).

The point biserial r is especially useful in the analysis of the items of a test, i.e., in item-test correlations. Table 55 shows the kind of data used in

TABLE 55 Calculation of point biserial r. To illustrate its value in item analysis. ($1 =$ item passed, $0 =$ item failed.)

(1)	(2)	(3)	(4)	(5)	(6)
Students	Test Criterion (X)	Item #13 (Y)	X^2	Y^2	XY
1	25	1	625	1	25
2	23	1	529	1	23
3	18	0	324	0	—
4	24	0	576	0	—
5	23	1	529	1	23
6	20	0	400	0	—
7	19	0	361	0	—
8	22	1	484	1	22
9	21	1	441	1	21
10	23	1	529	1	23
11	21	0	441	0	—
12	20	0	400	0	—
13	21	1	441	1	21
14	21	1	441	1	21
15	22	1	484	1	22
Sums:	323	9	7005	9	201

N_1 (number passing) $= 9$
N_0 (number failing) $= 6$

$$M_1 = \frac{201}{9} = 22.33$$

$$M_2 = \frac{122}{6} = 20.33$$

$p = .60$
$q = .40$

$$M_{tot} = \frac{323}{15} = 21.53$$

$$r_{p_{bis}} = \frac{22.33 - 20.33}{1.82}\sqrt{.60 \times .40} \quad (97)$$

$$\sigma_{tot} = 1.82$$

$$= .54$$

item analysis, except that in a real item analysis the sample would be very much larger and more than one item would be analyzed. For convenience in demonstrating the method, there are only 15 subjects in the group. These are listed in column (1) by number. Column (2) gives the total scores achieved by these subjects on a test (used as the criterion); and in column (3) the response of each student to item #13 on the test is shown. A 1 means that the item was passed, a 0 that it was failed. Columns (4), (5) and (6) are used later in the computation of the product-moment r, and are not needed for the computation of the point biserial r.

The computations at the bottom of the table are utilized in finding $r_{p_{bis}}$. N_1, the number who got the item right, is 9; and N_0, the number who got the item wrong, is 6. The mean of those passing or M_1 is 201/9 or 22.33; and the mean of those failing or M_2 is 122/6 or 20.33. The mean of the entire sample is 21.53; and the SD of the entire sample is 1.82. The proportion passing (p) is .60 and the proportion failing (q) is .40. Substituting in (97) we have that

$$r_{p_{bis}} = \frac{22.33 - 20.33}{1.82}\sqrt{.60 \times .40} \qquad (97)$$

$$= .54$$

and it seems clear that item #13 is substantially correlated with the criterion—is passed by high scorers more often than by low scorers. Items like #13 are good items, whereas items which correlate negatively or zero with the criterion are poor items.

The point biserial r is a product-moment r. To show this, we have computed r for the data of Table 55 by means of the formula

$$r = \frac{(N\Sigma XY) - (\Sigma X \cdot \Sigma Y)}{\sqrt{[(N\Sigma Y^2) - (\Sigma Y)^2][(N\Sigma X^2) - (\Sigma X)^2]}} \qquad \text{(see p. 143)}$$

Substituting the necessary data from Table 55 we have that

$$r = \frac{(15 \times 201) - (323 \times 9)}{\sqrt{[(15 \times 9 - (9)^2][(15 \times 7005) - (323)^2]}} = .54$$

thus checking the $r_{p_{bis}}$.

(1) SIGNIFICANCE OF POINT BISERIAL r

A point biserial r may be tested against the null hypothesis with the aid of Table 25. There are $(N - 2)$ degrees of freedom in the correlation table. To test the $r_{p_{bis}}$ of .54 obtained from Table 55, we enter Table 25 with 13 df to find that r must be .51 in order to be significant at the .05 level, and .64 to be significant at the .01 level. As our r of .54 just exceeds .51, it can be taken to be significant, though not highly so.

(2) COMPARISON OF BISERIAL r AND POINT BISERIAL r

On most counts $r_{p_{bis}}$ is a better—more dependable—statistic than r_{bis}. The point biserial r makes no assumptions regarding the form of distribution in the dichotomized variable; its range is ± 1.00; it may be used in a regression equation; and its standard error can be determined exactly. Point biserial r is always lower than r_{bis} for the same two variables, but this characteristic is not especially important, as both coefficients are rarely computed from the same data. In Table 54 $r_{p_{bis}} = \dfrac{77.00 - 70.39}{8.80} \times \sqrt{.145 \times .855}$ or .26 as against a r_{bis} of .41. In Table 55 where $r_{p_{bis}} = .54$, r_{bis} is .68. The point biserial r is a product-moment r and can be checked against r, as we saw in Table 55. This is usually not possible with r_{bis}. In favor of r_{bis},

TABLE 56   Ordinates (u) for given areas measured from the mean of a normal distribution with total area of 1.00

Area from the Mean	Ordinates (u)	Area from the Mean	Ordinates (u)
.00	.399	.26	.311
.01	.399	.27	.304
.02	.398	.28	.296
.03	.398	.29	.288
.04	.397	.30	.280
.05	.396	.31	.271
.06	.394	.32	.262
.07	.393	.33	.253
.08	.391	.34	.243
.09	.389	.35	.233
.10	.386	.36	.223
.11	.384	.37	.212
.12	.381	.38	.200
.13	.378	.39	.188
.14	.374	.40	.176
.15	.370	.41	.162
.16	.366	.42	.149
.17	.362	.43	.134
.18	.358	.44	.119
.19	.353	.45	.103
.20	.348	.46	.086
.21	.342	.47	.068
.22	.337	.48	.048
.23	.331	.49	.027
.24	.324	.50	.000
.25	.318		

however, it should be said that a normal distribution in the split variable is often a more plausible hypothesis than is the dubious assumption of a genuine dichotomy.

Biserial r and point biserial r are both useful in item analysis, but r_{bis} is ordinarily not as valid procedure (nor as defensible) as is $r_{p_{bis}}$. The coefficient r_{bis} has the distinct advantage over $r_{p_{bis}}$ in that tables are available from which we can read values of r_{bis} quickly and with sufficient accuracy for most purposes. All we need to know (p. 367) are the percentages passing a given item in selected upper and lower groups.

III. CORRELATION FROM FOURFOLD TABLES

I. Tetrachoric r

We have seen in the preceding section that when one variable is continuous and is expressed as test scores, and the other variable is dichotomous or in a twofold classification, biserial r or point biserial r provides an adequate measure of relationship between the two. An extension of the problem of finding the correlation between categories, to which the biserial method is not applicable, presents itself when *both* variables are dichotomous. We then have a 2×2 or fourfold table, from which a variety of the product-moment r, called tetrachoric r, may be computed. Tetrachoric r is especially useful when we wish to find the relation between two characters or attributes neither of which is measurable in scores, but both of which are capable of being separated into two categories. If we want to find the correlation between school attendance and current employment, for example, persons might first be classified into those who have graduated from high school and those who have not; and classified a second time into those who are presently employed and those who are unemployed. Or, if we wish to discover the relationship between intelligence and social maturity in first-graders, children might be classified as above or below average in intelligence, on the one hand, and as socially mature or socially immature, on the other. Tetrachoric correlation assumes that the two variables under study are essentially *continuous* and would be normally distributed if it were possible to obtain scores or exact measures and thus be able to classify both variables into frequency distributions.

(1) CALCULATION OF TETRACHORIC r

The diagrams below represent schematically the arrangement of a fourfold table. In the first table, entries are frequencies; in the second, proportions.

	−X−		
	−	+	
+	−+ B	++ A	A + B
Y			
−	−− D	+− C	C + D
	B + D	A + C	

	−X−		
	−	+	
+	b	a	(a + b) or p
Y			
−	d	c	(c + d) or q
	q′	p′	

Both variables, X and Y, are classified into two categories, marked + and −. Entries in cell A are + +, entries in D − −, so that concentration of frequencies into these two cells means close agreement and positive correlation. Concentration of entries in B and C (− + and + −) imply disagreement and negative correlation. For example, if X and Y represent two items on a test to be answered Yes or No, a clustering of tallies in cells A and D (Yes–Yes and No–No) means that the two items are positively correlated; a clustering of entries in B and C (No–Yes and Yes–No) that correlation is negative. Equal numbers of frequencies in each of the 4 cells means that there is no relationship and the correlation is zero. In the second diagram, a, b, c, and d are proportions so that $a + b + c + d = 1.00$.

The full equation for tetrachoric r is algebraically complex, and requires the solution of a quadratic equation in order to compute r. Fortunately, there are several useful approximations to r_t which are sufficiently accurate for most purposes; hence, the long formula will not be reproduced here. When two variables X and Y are divided close to the medians of each, so that $(A + B)$ and $(C + D)$ are virtually equal, and $(B + D)$ and $(A + C)$ also are nearly equal, the following equation will yield a good approximation to r_t:

$$r_t = \cos \left(\frac{180° \times \sqrt{BC}}{\sqrt{AD} + \sqrt{BC}} \right) \tag{98}$$

(approximate formula for tetrachoric r)

in which A, B, C and D are frequencies as shown in the first diagram above. The value of tetrachoric r is read from Table J which gives the cosines of angles from 0° to 90°. The sign of r_t is positive when the AD entries (agreements) exceed the BC entries (disagreements), and negative when the BC entries exceed the AD. When BC is greater than AD, put $\sqrt{AD}$ in the numerator instead of $\sqrt{BC}$. When correlation is negative, the minus sign is affixed by the experimenter.

Table 57 illustrates the computation or r_t. The problem is to find whether a larger number of successful than unsuccessful salesmen tend to

TABLE 57 To illustrate the calculation of r_t (100 salesmen)

$\overline{X}$ Variable

		Unsuccessful	Successful	Totals
$\overline{Y}$ Variable	Socially Well Adjusted	25 (B)	35 (A)	60 (A + B)
	Socially Poorly Adjusted	30 (D)	10 (C)	40 (C + D)
	Totals	55 (B + D)	45 (A + C)	N = 100 (A + B + C + D)

$$r_t = \cos\left(\frac{180° \times \sqrt{BC}}{\sqrt{AD} + \sqrt{BC}}\right)$$

$$= \cos\left(\frac{180° \times \sqrt{250}}{\sqrt{1050} + \sqrt{250}}\right)$$

$$= \cos 59° \qquad \text{From Table J } r_t = .52$$

---

be "socially well adjusted." The X variable is divided into two categories "successful" and "unsuccessful"; and the Y variable is divided into two categories "socially well adjusted" and "socially poorly adjusted." The sums of the rows show that 60 salesmen $(A + B)$ out of the sample of 100 are classed as socially adjusted; and that 40 salesmen $(C + D)$ are described as poorly adjusted socially. Substituting for $A = 35$, $B = 25$, $C = 10$ and $D = 30$ in formula (98) we have that

$$r_t = \cos\left(\frac{180° \times \sqrt{250}}{\sqrt{1050} + \sqrt{250}}\right)$$

$$= \cos 59°$$

From Table J the cosine of an angle of 59° is found to be .52 and, accordingly, $r_t = .52$. A very simple approximation to r_t can be found by first dividing AD by BC. Then, entering Table K with this ratio, we read r_t directly. In the present example, $AD/BC = 1050/250$ or 4.20. And from Table K the corresponding r_t is .51, checking the result obtained from formula (98). If BC is greater than AD, the ratio for use in Table K is BC/AD and the correlation is negative (disagreements exceed agreements). The experimenter affixes the minus sign.

Table 58 shows how r_t may be used in the evaluation of a test. The problem is to find whether a test of deductive reasoning (a syllogism

TABLE 58 Tetrachoric *r* in test evaluation (125 college juniors)

		X Variable		
		Nonscience Majors	Science Majors	Totals
Y Variable	Above Test Mean	30 (B)	44 (A)	74 $(A+B)$
	Below Test Mean	36 (D)	15 (C)	51 $(C+D)$
	Totals	66 $(B+D)$	59 $(A+C)$	125 $(A+B+C+D)$

$$r_t = \cos\left(\frac{180° \times \sqrt{450}}{(\sqrt{1584} + \sqrt{450})}\right)$$

$$= \cos 63° \qquad \text{From Table J } r_t = .45$$

test) will differentiate 59 college juniors majoring in science from 66 juniors majoring in literature and history (nonscience). The X variable is divided into science majors and nonscience majors; the Y variable into those above and those below the mean of the test (the mean established by the group as a whole). It should be noted that X is a true dichotomy, whereas Y is a continuous variable, arbitrarily divided into two parts. Substituting for $A = 44$, $B = 30$, $C = 15$ and $D = 36$ in formula (98) we have that

$$r_t = \cos\left(\frac{180° \times \sqrt{450}}{\sqrt{1584} + \sqrt{450}}\right)$$
$$= 63°$$

and from Table J the cosine of an angle of 63° is .45, so that $r_t = .45$. This r_t can be checked by dividing AD by BC and going to Table K. Since

$AD = 1584$ and $BC = 450$, $AD/BC = 3.52$. From Table K we get an r_t of .46 (to two decimals). As AD is greater than BC, r_t must be positive.

(2) RESTRICTIONS TO THE USE OF FORMULA (98); USE OF COMPUTING DIAGRAMS

Formula (98) and the AD/BC ratio work well when N is large and when the splits into X and Y are not too far removed from .50—fall, for example, between .40 and .60. For extreme cuts in X or in Y or in both (e.g., .95–.05, or .90–.10) neither formula (98) nor the AD/BC ratio gives accurate estimates of r_t and neither can be recommended. In Table 57, the proportions $(A + B)$ and $(A + C)$ are .60 and .45, respectively. In Table 58, these proportions are .59 and .47. Both splits lie in the .40–.60 range.

The investigator who finds it necessary to compute many tetrachoric r's will be well advised to use the computing diagrams devised by Thurstone and his coworkers.* These diagrams are not subject to the limitations as to split which apply to formula (98) and the AD/BC ratio. Moreover, they enable us to read (and check) the r_t directly from a graph as soon as we know the proportions within the 4 cells of the correlational table. For example, from Thurstone's charts, the r_t for Table 57 is .51, and for Table 58 is .45. Tetrachoric r's read from the computing charts are usually accurate to at least .01 when compared with r_t's from the full formula.

(3) STANDARD ERROR OF A TETRACHORIC r

The SE of a tetrachoric r is mathematically complex and is too long to be useful practically. Its derivation will be found in books dealing with mathematical statistics.† Tetrachoric r is most stable when (1) N is large and the cuts in X and in Y close to the median of each variable; and least stable when (2) N is small and the splits in X and Y depart sharply from .50. The standard error of r_t is from 50% to 100% larger than the SE of a product-moment r of the same size and based upon the same N. If r is computed from 100 cases, for example, r_t to be equally stable should be computed from at least 150 to 200 cases. Several approximations to the standard error formula for r_t will be found in Peters and Van Voorhis.

2. The phi coefficient (φ)

When statistical data fall into genuine dichotomies, they cannot be thought of as representing underlying normal distributions. Test items, for

* Chesire, L., Saffir, M., and Thurstone, L. L., *Computing Diagrams for the Tetrachoric Correlation Coefficient* (Chicago: Univ. of Chicago Bookstore, 1933).

† Peters, C. C., and Van Voorhis, W. R., *Statistical Procedures and Their Mathematical Bases* (New York: McGraw-Hill, 1940), pp. 370–375.

instance, are often scored True or False or Passed or Failed, with no intermediate answers being allowed. When the classification is truly discrete and the variables can take only one of two values, the ϕ coefficient is an appropriate measure of correlation. Phi may be used also with continuous variables which have been grouped into two categories, as for instance when two tests are split at the median. Phi bears the same relation to tetrachoric r as the point biserial bears to biserial r. The ϕ coefficient, like point biserial r, is a product-moment r and can be checked directly against r obtained from the same table.

The formula for ϕ is

$$\phi = \frac{AD - BC}{\sqrt{(A+B)(C+D)(B+D)(A+C)}} \tag{99}$$

(ϕ *coefficient of correlation*)

where A, B, C and D represent frequencies in the fourfold table (p. 385 for diagram). Expressed as proportions

$$\phi = \frac{ad - bc}{\sqrt{pq\,p'q'}}$$

Phi is perhaps most useful in item analysis when we want to know the item-item correlations. The computation of ϕ is shown in the following example.

Example (1) Two items X and Y are part of a test of 100 items. Item X is passed by 100 and failed by 125 students in a group of 225. Item Y is passed by 135 and failed by 90 in the same sample. Find the correlation between X and Y.

Item X e

	Failed	Passed	
Passed	55 B	80 A	135 A + B
Failed	70 D	20 C	90 C + D
	125	100	225

Item Y

Substituting for A, B, C and D in formula (99) we have

$$\phi = \frac{80 \times 70 - 55 \times 20}{\sqrt{135 \times 90 \times 125 \times 100}}$$

$$= .36$$

This value of ϕ may be compared with the product-moment r for the same data shown in Table 59. When we put $P = 1$ and $F = 0$, we can

TABLE 59 Product-moment r from a fourfold table. (Data from Example 1, p. 389.) (Passed = 1, Failed = 0.)

	X = 0	X = 1	f	y'	fy'	fy'^2	$x'y'$
Y = 1	55 (0)	80 (1) / 80	135	1	135	135	80
Y = 0	70 (0)	20 (0)	90	0	0	0	0
	125	100	225		135	135	80
x'	0	1					
fx'	0	100 = 100					
fx'^2	0	100 = 100					

$$\sigma_y = \sqrt{\frac{135}{225} - \left(\frac{135}{225}\right)^2}$$

$$= \frac{\sqrt{135 \times 90}}{225}$$

$$\sigma_x = \sqrt{\frac{100}{225} - \left(\frac{100}{225}\right)^2}$$

$$= \frac{\sqrt{100 \times 125}}{225}$$

$$c_y = \frac{135}{225}$$

$$c_x = \frac{100}{225}$$

$$r_{xy} = \frac{\dfrac{80}{225} - \dfrac{135 \times 100}{(225)^2}}{\dfrac{\sqrt{135 \times 90}}{225} \cdot \dfrac{\sqrt{100 \times 125}}{225}}$$

$$= \frac{80 \times 225 - 135 \times 100}{\sqrt{135 \times 90 \times 100 \times 125}}$$

$$= \frac{4500}{12324}$$

$$= .36$$

compute a product-moment r (see Table 59) which checks exactly with ϕ. The ϕ coefficient is not comparable to r_t for the same data as the two coefficients are not expressed in terms of the same scale. The r_t for Table 59 is .57—about .20 higher than the ϕ of .36. Also, in Tables 57 and 58 the r_t's are .52 and .45 (p. 387) whereas the ϕ's are .33 and .30.[*] In general, ϕ is from .15 to .30 less than the r_t from the same table. The gap between the two coefficients becomes greater as the split in either X or Y or in both departs from 50–50.

3. Significance of ϕ

The significance of ϕ may be determined through the relationship of ϕ to χ^2. χ^2 is related to ϕ by the following equation:

$$\chi^2 = N\phi^2 \qquad (100)$$

$$(\chi^2 \text{ as a function of } \phi)$$

and this relationship enables us to test an obtained ϕ against the null hypothesis. First, we convert ϕ to an equivalent χ^2, and then test χ^2. In Table 59 where ϕ is .36 and N is 225,

$$\chi^2 = 225 \times (.36)^2$$

$$= 29.2$$

which for 1 df (fourfold table) is highly significant—beyond the .01 level.

When N is large, there is another way to test ϕ against the null hypothesis. This is to compute a SE of a ϕ of .00 by the formula $SE = \dfrac{1}{\sqrt{N}}$. In Table 59, $SE_{\phi=0} = 1/\sqrt{225}$ or $1/15 = .07$. Our obtained ϕ of .36 is more than 5 times its SE (.36/.07) and hence is highly significant. The null hypothesis is rejected, therefore, as before.

4. Comparison or r_t and ϕ

As ϕ and r_t are both used to determine the relationship in a fourfold table, the student may be in doubt as to which coefficient is more suitable in a given case. The following summary indicates some of the advantages and disadvantages of each statistic.

(a) r_t is the better measure of relationship when N is large and when continuity in the variables and normality of distribution are safe assumptions. This would almost certainly be true when the variables are tests

[*] Recall that biserial r is also consistently lower than $r_{p_{bis}}$ (p. 383).

split at the medians. ϕ is the appropriate statistic when traits are truly dichotomous. ϕ is especially useful when item-item correlations are wanted.

(b) r_t ranges from $+1.00$ to -1.00 regardless of the relative sizes of the marginal totals. ϕ cannot equal 1.00 unless the cuts in X and Y are the same—i.e., unless $p = p'$ and $q = q'$. This restriction limits the upper range of ϕ, but does not destroy its value when item-item correlations are to be compared for the same data.

(c) The SE of r_t is difficult to compute and is always greater than the SE of the comparable r. To have the same stability as a product-moment r, r_t should be based upon twice the N (roughly) used in computing r. ϕ can easily be tested against the null hypothesis by means of its relation to χ^2.

(d) Under the assumption of (a), r_t is a good estimate of r. ϕ is a product-moment r and is equal to the r calculated from a fourfold table when 1 is assigned to a correct and 0 to an incorrect response.

IV. THE CONTINGENCY COEFFICIENT, C

The coefficient of contingency, C, provides a measure of correlation when each of the two variables under study has been classified into two or more categories. Table 60 shows the computation of C in a 4×4 fold classification. The table gives the joint distribution of 1000 fathers and sons with respect to eye color. The eye colors of the fathers are grouped into the 4 categories (columns) blue, gray, hazel and brown. The eye colors of the sons are classified into the same categories (rows). Each cell contains an observed value and an "independence" value in parentheses. The independence values give the number of matched eye colors to be expected on the hypothesis of chance. Each is computed as shown in section I of Table 60. To illustrate, from the top row we find that 335/1000 of *all* sons are listed as blue-eyed. This proportion should hold for the sons of the 358 blue-eyed fathers, if there is *no* association between father and son with respect to eye color. Since $335/1000 \times 358$ gives 120 as the number of blue-eyed fathers who can be expected to have blue-eyed sons by the operation of chance alone, this "independence" figure is to be compared with the 194 blue-eyed fathers who actually did have blue-eyed sons. In the same manner, expected or chance (independence) values are determined for the remainder of the cells in the table. When all of the independence values have been tabulated, we square each observed cell entry (see section II in the table) and divide by its chance value. The sum of these quotients yields S; and from S and N we calculate C by the equation

TABLE 60   To illustrate the calculation of C, the coefficient of contingency

	FATHER'S EYE COLOR				
	Blue	Gray	Hazel	Brown	Totals
Blue	(120) 194	(88) 70	(60) 41	(66) 30	335
Gray	(102) 83	(75) 124	(51) 41	(56) 36	284
Hazel	(49) 25	(36) 34	(25) 55	(27) 23	137
Brown	(87) 56	(64) 36	(44) 43	(48) 109	244
Totals	358	264	180	198	1000

(Son's Eye Color is the row label.)

I. Independence Values

$$\frac{335 \times 358}{1000} = 120 \qquad \frac{137 \times 358}{1000} = 49$$

$$\frac{335 \times 264}{1000} = 88 \qquad \frac{137 \times 264}{1000} = 36$$

$$\frac{335 \times 180}{1000} = 60 \qquad \frac{137 \times 180}{1000} = 25$$

$$\frac{335 \times 198}{1000} = 66 \qquad \frac{137 \times 198}{1000} = 27$$

$$\frac{284 \times 358}{1000} = 102 \qquad \frac{244 \times 358}{1000} = 87$$

$$\frac{284 \times 264}{1000} = 75 \qquad \frac{244 \times 264}{1000} = 64$$

$$\frac{284 \times 180}{1000} = 51 \qquad \frac{244 \times 180}{1000} = 44$$

$$\frac{284 \times 198}{1000} = 56 \qquad \frac{244 \times 198}{1000} = 48$$

II. Calculation of C

$$\frac{(194)^2}{120} = 313.6$$
$$\frac{(83)^2}{102} = 67.5$$
$$\frac{(25)^2}{49} = 12.8$$
$$\frac{(56)^2}{87} = 36.0$$
$$\frac{(70)^2}{88} = 55.7$$
$$\frac{(124)^2}{75} = 205.0$$
$$\frac{(34)^2}{36} = 32.1$$
$$\frac{(36)^2}{64} = 20.2$$
$$\frac{(41)^2}{60} = 28.0$$
$$\frac{(41)^2}{51} = 33.0$$
$$\frac{(55)^2}{25} = 121.0$$
$$\frac{(43)^2}{44} = 42.0$$
$$\frac{(30)^2}{66} = 13.6$$
$$\frac{(36)^2}{56} = 23.1$$
$$\frac{(23)^2}{27} = 19.6$$
$$\frac{(109)^2}{48} = 247.5$$

$$S = \overline{1270.7}$$
$$N = 1000$$
$$S - N = \overline{270.7}$$

$$C = \sqrt{\frac{S-N}{S}} = \sqrt{\frac{270.7}{1270.7}} = .46$$

$$C = \sqrt{\frac{S-N}{S}} \qquad (101)$$

(C, *the coefficient of contingency*)

in which S is the sum of the quotients and N is the size of the sample. In Table 60, the C is .46.

The sign to be attached to C depends on an inspection of the diagram. In Table 60 we note in the diagonal cells that in the blue-blue, gray-gray, hazel-hazel and brown-brown eye-color comparisons of father and son, the observed frequencies are almost twice their independence values. In the other 12 cells the expected (independence) values are larger than the observed, indicating that the observed or actual entries (nonmatchings) are less than the number to be expected by chance.

1. The relation of C to χ^2

Both C and χ^2 depend upon a comparison of observed and expected frequencies in the cells of a contingency table, and the one coefficient may be derived directly from the other. The *size* of C depends upon the extent to which the observed frequencies depart from their "chance" values. In formula (101), for example, when $N = S$, i.e., when the actual and expected entries are exactly the same, $C = 0.00$. C yields an index of correlation which under certain conditions is a good estimate of r. χ^2, on the other hand, provides a measure of the probability of association—of the existence of relation—but gives no quantitative measure of its size. C bears the following relationship to χ^2:

$$C = \sqrt{\frac{\chi^2}{N + \chi^2}} \qquad (102)$$

(C *in terms of* χ^2)

The χ^2 corresponding to the C of .46 in Table 60 is 268, which for 9 *df* is highly significant—far beyond the .01 level (see Table E). Accordingly, C may be regarded as highly significant. In Table 33 the association between eyedness and handedness was expressed by a χ^2 of 4.02, which for 4 *df* is not significant. By formula (102), the C for Table 33 is $\sqrt{\frac{4.02}{413 + 4.02}}$ or .10 (to two decimals)—a very small value. The standard error of C is complex and not very satisfactory and the significance of C is best tested by way of χ^2. Since our χ^2 of 4.02 is not significant, our C of .10 may be regarded as representing a negligible and not significant relationships between eyedness and handedness.

2. Relation of C and r

C is a good estimate of r when (1) the grouping is relatively fine—5×5 or finer; when (2) the sample is large; when (3) the two variables can legitimately be classified into categories; and when (4) we are justified in assuming normality in the categorized variables. These conditions are often hard to realize, and if a measure of relationship equivalent to r is wanted, it is often advisable to consolidate classes into a 2×2 table and compute ϕ or r_t. C has certain advantages over ϕ and r_t, however. In computing C no assumption need be made as to normality in the distributions of the two variables; in fact, any type of distribution, skewed or rectangular, may be utilized. This follows from the fact that C—like χ^2—depends upon the *divergences* of observed entries from those to be observed from those to be expected by chance, *not* upon form of distribution.

C possesses the disadvantage that it does not remain constant for the same data when the number of categories varies. For example, the C computed from a 3×3 table will not be comparable to the C for the same data arranged in a 5×5 table. Moreover, the maximum value which C can take will depend upon the fineness of grouping. When $k = $ the number of categories in the table, the maximum C is found from the equation $\sqrt{\frac{(k-1)}{k}}$. In a 3×3 table, the maximum C is .82, in a 5×5 table .89, and in a 10×10 table it is .95. A correction for grouping can be made by dividing the computed C by the maximum C for that classification. Thus, in Table 60, where C is .46, on dividing by .87 (maximum C for a 4×4 table), we get .53 as the value of C corrected for fineness of grouping.

Table 61 shows more clearly perhaps how C is an estimate of r when corrected for number of categories. The 100 cases in the sample have been prorated over the 5 diagonal cells, so that the correlation is as high as it can be for this classification. As shown in Table 61, however, C is only .89; but when divided by the maximum C for a 5×5 table, namely, by .89, the corrected C is 1.00.

A good plan is to use as fine a classification as the data allow (5×5 or finer, if feasible) in order that the maximum value of C will be as close to unity as possible. At the same time we must avoid a too-fine classification, as C is not stable when the entries in the cells are small (less than 5, say). A correction for broad categories—the opposite of fine grouping—may be applied. But this correction is hardly worth while unless the grouping is 4×4 fold or broader—and is small in any case.

C is not an entirely satisfactory statistic. Perhaps it is most useful to the clinical or social psychologist who wants a measure of correlation between

TABLE 61 C in a table in which the correlation is perfect

Y Variable	X Variable					Totals
					(4) 20	20
				(4) 20		20
			(4) 20			20
		(4) 20				20
	(4) 20					20
	20	20	20	20	20	100

I. Independence values

$$\frac{20 \times 20}{100} = 4 \text{ for each diagonal}$$

II. Calculation of C

$$\frac{20^2}{4} = 100 \text{ for each of 5 diagonal cells}$$

$$C = \sqrt{\frac{500 - 100}{500}} = \sqrt{.80}$$

$$= .89$$

two variables classified into more than two categories. The real difficulties in the interpretation of C have led many research workers to prefer χ^2 or else to convert C to χ^2.

V. CURVILINEAR OR NONLINEAR RELATIONSHIP

The relationship between the paired values of two sets of measures, X and Y, may be described in a general way as "linear" or "nonlinear." When the means of the arrays of the successive columns and rows in a correlation table follow straight lines (at least approximately), the regression is said to be linear or straight-line (p. 153). When the drift or trend of the means of the arrays (columns or rows) cannot be well described by a straight line, but can be represented by a *curve* of some kind, the regression is said to be curvilinear or in general nonlinear.

Our discussion in Chapter 6 was concerned entirely with linear rela-tionship, the extent or degree of which is measured by the product-moment coefficient of correlation, r. It sometimes happens in mental meas-urement, however, that the relationship between two variables is defi-nitely nonlinear; and when this is true, r is not an adequate measure of the degree of correspondence or correlation. When the regression is non-linear, a curve joining the means of successive arrays (in the columns, say) will fit these mean values more exactly than will a straight line. Hence, should a truly curvilinear relationship be described by a straight line, the scatter or spread of the paired values about the regression line will be greater than the scatter about the better-fitting regression curve. The smaller the spread of the paired scores about the regression line or the regression curve which relates the variables X and Y (or Y and X), the higher the relationship between the two variables. For this reason, an r calculated from a correlation table in which the regression is curvilinear will *always be less* than the true relationship. An example will make this situation clearer. The correlation between the following two short series, as given by the product-moment formula, is $r = .93$ [formula (27), p. 139]. The *true* correlation between the two series, however, is clearly

Variable X	Variable Y
1	.25
2	.50
3	1.00
4	2.00
5	4.00

perfect, since changes in Y are directly related to changes in X. As X increases by 1 (i.e., in arithmetic progression) Y doubles (i.e., increases in geometric progression). The reason why r is less than 1.00 becomes obvious as soon as we plot the paired X and Y values. As shown in Fig. 67, the relationship between X and Y is curvilinear, and is exactly described by a curve which passes through the successively plotted points. When linear relationship is forced upon these data, the plotted points do not fall along the straight line, and the product-moment coefficient, r, is less than 1.00. However, the correlation ratio, or coefficient of nonlinear relation-ship η (read as *eta*) for the given data is 1.00.

True nonlinear relationship is encountered in psychophysics and in experiments dealing with fatigue, practice, forgetting, and learning. Whenever an experiment is carried on to the point of diminishing returns, relationship will necessarily be curvilinear. Most mental and educational tests, however, when administered to large samples, exhibit linear or approximately linear relationships. The coefficient of correlation, r, therefore, has been employed in psychology and education to a far greater extent than has η; and for this reason the calculation of η is not given here.* If regression is significantly nonlinear, it makes considerable dif-

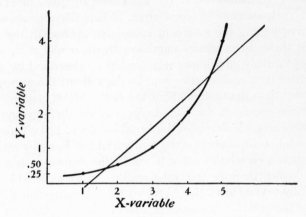

FIG. 67   To illustrate nonlinear relationship

ference whether η or r is the measure of relation. But if the correlation is low and the regression not significantly curvilinear, r will give as adequate a measure of relationship as η.

The coefficient of correlation has the advantage over η in that knowing r we can write down at once the straight-line regression equation connecting X and Y or Y and X. This is not possible with the correlation ratio. In order to estimate one variable from another (say, Y from X) when regression is nonlinear, a curve must be fitted to the means of the Y columns. The equation of this curve then serves as a "regression equation" from which estimates can be made.

* See references, p. 473.

PROBLEMS

1. Compute the correlation between the following two series of test scores by the rank-difference method and test its significance.

Individual	Intelligence Test Score	Cancellation Score (A Test + Number Group Checking Test)
1	185	110
2	203	98
3	188	118
4	195	104
5	176	112
6	174	124
7	158	119
8	197	95
9	176	94
10	138	97
11	126	110
12	160	94
13	151	126
14	185	120
15	185	118

[Note: The cancellation scores are in *seconds*; hence the two smallest scores numerically (i.e., 94) are highest and are ranked 1.5 each.]

2. Check the product-moment correlations obtained in problems 7 and 8, page 150, Chap. 6 by the rank-difference method.

3. The following data give the distributions of scores on the Thorndike Intelligence Examination made by entering college freshmen who presented 12 or more recommended units, and entering freshmen who presented less than 12 recommended units. Compute biserial r and its $SE_{r_{bis}}$.

Thorndike Scores	12 or more recommended units	Less than 12 recommended units
90–99	6	0
80–89	19	3
70–79	31	5
60–69	58	17
50–59	40	30
40–49	18	14
30–39	9	7
20–29	5	4
	186	80

4. The table below shows the distributions of scores on an achievement test earned by those students who answered 50% or more and those who answered less than 50% of the items in an arithmetic test correctly. Compute r_{bis} and the .99 confidence interval for the true r_{bis}.

Achievement Test	Subjects answering 50% or more of the items on arithmetic test correctly	Subjects answering less than 50% of the items on arithmetic test correctly
185–194	7	0
175–184	16	0
165–174	10	6
155–164	35	15
145–154	24	40
135–144	15	26
125–134	10	13
115–124	3	5
105–114	0	5
	120	110

5. Compute tetrachoric r for the following tables. Use the two methods described on pages 385–386.

   (1) Relation of alcoholism and health in 811 fathers and sons. Entries are expressed as proportions.

		SONS		
		Unhealthy	Healthy	Totals
FATHERS	Nonalcoholic	.343	.405	.748
	Alcoholic	.102	.150	.252
	Totals	.445	.555	1.000

   (2) Correspondence of Yes and No answers to two items of a neurosis inventory.

		QUESTION 1		
		No	Yes	Totals
QUESTION 2	Yes	83	187	270
	No	102	93	195
	Totals	185	280	465

6. (a) Compute ϕ coefficients for the two tables on page 244, example (11). Test the significance of ϕ by way of χ^2.

   (b) Compute r_t's for the same two tables. Which coefficient, r_t or ϕ, is the more appropriate?

(c) Compute ϕ for the table in problem 5 (2).

7. In the table below, compute $r_{p_{bis}}$ and r_{bis}. Which is the more appropriate coefficient for these data?

Scores on Miller Analogies Test	VA TRAINEES Failed in Program	Obtained Ph. D.
95–99	0	1
90–94	1	1
85–89	0	6
80–84	2	11
75–79	4	6
70–74	6	9
65–69	8	3
60–64	3	2
55–59	2	1
50–54	6	
45–49	2	
40–44	3	
35–39	1	
30–34	1	
	39	40

8. Calculate the coefficient of contingency, C, for the two tables given below.

(1)   MARRIAGE ADJUSTMENT SCORE OF HUSBANDS

		Very Low	Low	High	Very High	Totals
EDUCATION OF HUSBANDS	Graduate work	4	9	38	54	105
	College	20	31	55	99	205
	High School	23	37	41	51	152
	Grade School	11	10	11	19	51
	Totals	58	87	145	223	513

(2)   KIND OF MUSIC PREFERRED

		English	French	German	Italian	Spanish	Totals
NATIONALITY OF SUBJECT	English	32	16	75	47	30	200
	French	10	67	42	41	40	200
	German	12	23	107	36	22	200
	Italian	16	20	44	76	44	200
	Spanish	8	53	30	43	66	200
	Totals	78	179	298	243	202	1000

9. In the example above, convert the C's to χ^2's and test for significance.
10. Compute C from table in example 3, page 148, and compare with r.
11. (a) In the following table, compute r by the product-moment method.
    (b) Plot the relationship between X and Y as shown in Figure 67, page 398. Is the relation linear?

X	Y
1	1
2	2
3	4
4	8
5	16
6	32

ANSWERS

1. $\rho = .19$; not significant.
2. ρ's are .41 and .80.
3. $r_{bis} = .34 \qquad SE_{r_{bis}} = .07$
4. $r_{bis} = .47 \qquad .29$ to $.65$
5. (1) $r_t = -.09$ \qquad (2) $r_t = .34$
6. (a) $\phi = .25$ in first table and $\phi = .50$ in second table. Both ϕ's are significant.
    (b) $r_t = .42$ and $r_t = .72$; r_t is more appropriate for (1), ϕ for (2).
    (c) $\phi = .22$.
7. $r_{p_{bis}} = .56$; $r_{bis} = .70$. The first is more appropriate.
8. (1) $C = .24$ \qquad (2) $C = .40$.
9. (1) $\chi^2 = 31.35$; (2) $\chi^2 = 190.48$. Both are significant.
10. $C = .72$.
11. (a) $r = .91$. (b) Relationship is nonlinear and perfect.

CHAPTER 15

PARTIAL AND MULTIPLE CORRELATION

<<<<<<<<<<<<<<<<<<<<<<<<<<<<<<<<<<<<<<<<<<<<<<<<<<<<<<<<<<<<<>>>

I. THE MEANING OF PARTIAL AND MULTIPLE CORRELATION

Partial and multiple correlation represent an important extension of the theory and techniques of simple or 2-variable linear correlation to problems which involve three or more variables. The correlation between two variables is sometimes misleading and may be erroneous if there is little or no correlation between the variables other than that brought about by their common dependence upon a third variable (or several variables). Many attributes increase regularly with age from about 6 to 18, such as height, weight, physical strength, mental test scores, vocabulary, reading skills and general knowledge. Over a wide age range, the correlation between any two of these traits will almost certainly be positive and probably high, owing to the common maturity factor which is highly correlated with both variables. In fact, the correlation may drop to zero if the variability caused by age differences is eliminated. The factor of age can be controlled in two ways: (1) experimentally, by selecting children all of whom are of the same age; and (2) statistically, by holding age variability constant through partial correlation. In order to get children of the same or of nearly the same age, we may have to reduce drastically the sizes of our samples. Partial correlation, therefore, since it utilizes all of the data, is often to be preferred to experimental control.

If we let 1 = vocabulary score, 2 = height in inches, and 3 = age, $r_{12.3}$ represents the *partial* correlation between 1 and 2 (vocabulary and height) when 3 (age) has been held constant or "partialed out." The subscripts 12.3 mean that variable 3 is rendered constant, leaving the net correlation between 1 and 2. The subscripts in the partial correlation coefficient, $r_{12.345}$ mean that 3 variables, namely, 3, 4, 5, are partialed out from the correlation between 1 and 2. The numbers to the *right* of the decimal point represent variables whose influence is ruled out; those to the *left* represent the two correlated variables. Partial correlation is often useful in analyses in which the effects of some variable or variables are to be eliminated. But its chief value lies in the fact that it enables us to set up a multiple regression equation of two or more variables by means of which we can predict another variable or criterion.

The correlation between a set of obtained scores and the same scores predicted from the multiple regression equation is called a coefficient of multiple correlation. It is designated by the letter R (called multiple R). If $R_{1(234)} = .72$, this means that scores in variable (1) *predicted* from a multiple regression equation containing variables (2), (3) and (4) correlate .72 with scores *obtained* in variable (1). Expressed in another way, $R_{1(234)}$ gives the correlation between a criterion (1) and a *team* of tests (2, 3, 4). The variables in parentheses ( ) are the independent variables in the regression equation; whereas the variable outside of the parentheses, namely, (1), is the criterion to be predicted or estimated. Multiple R is always taken as positive (see p. 416).

The multiple regression equation is set up by way of partial correlation and its accuracy as a predicting instrument is given by the coefficient of multiple correlation, R. The meaning of partial and multiple correlation will be better understood when the student has worked through a problem like that given in Table 62.

TABLE 62 A 3-variable problem to illustrate partial and multiple correlation

---

PRIMARY DATA: $(N = 450)$

(1) Honor Points	(2) General Intelligence	(3) Aver. number of hours spent in study per week
$M_1 = 18.5$	$M_2 = 100.6$	$M_3 = 24$
$\sigma_1 = 11.2$	$\sigma_2 = 15.8$	$\sigma_3 = 6$
$r_{12} = .60$	$r_{13} = .32$	$r_{23} = -.35$

Step I   Equations for multiple regression are

$$\bar{x}_1 = b_{12.3}x_2 + b_{13.2}x_3 \quad \text{(deviation form)} \tag{106}$$

$$\bar{X}_1 = b_{12.3}X_2 + b_{13.2}X_3 + K \text{ (score form)} \tag{107}$$

TABLE 62 (Continued)

Step 2 Computation of partial r's *

$$r_{12.3} = \frac{.60 - .32(-.35)}{.947 \times .937} = .80 \tag{103}$$

$$r_{13.2} = \frac{.32 - .60(-.35)}{.800 \times .937} = .71$$

$$r_{23.1} = \frac{-.35 - .60 \times .32}{.800 \times .947} = -.72$$

Step 3 Computation of partial σ's

$$\sigma_{1.23} = 11.2 \times .800 \times .704 = 6.3 \tag{104}$$

$$\sigma_{2.13} = 15.8 \times .937 \times .600 = 8.9$$

$$\sigma_{3.12} = 6 \times .937 \times .704 = 4.0$$

Step 4 Computation of partial regression coefficients and regression equations

$$b_{12.3} = .80 \times \frac{6.3}{8.9} = .57 \tag{105}$$

$$b_{13.2} = .71 \times \frac{6.3}{4.0} = 1.12$$

and the regression equations become:

$$\overline{x}_1 = .57x_2 + 1.12x_3 \text{ (deviation form)}$$

$$\overline{X}_1 = .57X_2 + 1.12X_3 - 66 \text{ (score form)}$$

Step 5 Standard error of estimate

$$\sigma_{(est\ X_1)} = \sigma_{1.23} = 6.3 \tag{108}$$

Step 6 Multiple coefficient of correlation

$$R_{1(23)} = \sqrt{1 - \frac{(6.3)^2}{(11.2)^2}} \tag{109}$$
$$= .83$$

* In multiple correlation problems, the rounding of small decimal fractions often leads to considerable loss in accuracy in subsequent calculations. A practical rule is that in extracting square roots we should retain as many decimal places as there are variables in the problem. Thus, in a 3-variable problem we retain 3 decimal places; in a 4-variable problem, 4 places, and so on.

II. AN ILLUSTRATIVE MULTIPLE CORRELATION PROBLEM INVOLVING THREE VARIABLES

The most straightforward approach to the understanding of partial and multiple correlation, and of the somewhat involved techniques required, is through the detailed solution of a problem. The present section, therefore, will give a step-by-step application of the method to a 3-variable problem.

> *Example* (1) An investigator [*] wished to study the relationship of general intelligence and habits of study to academic success in a group of 450 college freshmen. Academic success was defined as the number of honor points earned by each student at the end of the first semester. A grade of A received 3 honor points, B 2, C 1, and D received 0. General intelligence was measured by a combination of group tests, and application to study was defined by the number of hours spent in study during the week. Information as to study habits was obtained from a questionnaire given to the students upon entrance. This questionnaire covered a variety of possible student activities, the topic of study not being unduly stressed. The reliability coefficient of the study reports (by retest after approximately 8 weeks) was .86.
>
> How well can we predict academic success (i.e., honor points) from a knowledge of general intelligence and application to study? The primary data are as follows:

$$N = 450$$

(1) Honor points	(2) General intelligence	(3) Study hours per week
$M_1 = 18.5$	$M_2 = 100.6$	$M_3 = 24$
$\sigma_1 = 11.2$	$\sigma_2 = 15.8$	$\sigma_3 = 6$
$r_{12} = .60$	$r_{13} = .32$	$r_{23} = -.35$

The solution of this problem is outlined in the following steps. A summary of the data and computations will be found in Table 62.

Step I. Writing the regression equations

First, we write down the multiple regression equation from which each student's honor points (1) will be predicted from his scores in general intelligence (2) and study hours (3). For 3 variables, our equation is

$$\overline{x}_1 = b_{12.3}x_2 + b_{13.2}x_3 \tag{106}$$

[*] May, Mark A., "Predicting academic success," *Jour. Educ. Psychol.*, 1923, 14, 429–440.

This equation is in deviation form; x_1 stands for honor points (the criterion), x_2 and x_3 are general intelligence and study hours, respectively. Note the resemblance of this equation to the simple regression equation for 2 variables—$y = b_{12} \cdot x$ (p. 154). Putting x_1 for y and x_2 for x, we may write the 2-variable equation as $\overline{x}_1 = b_{12} \cdot x_2$. Instead of using the letters x, y, z, etc., only x is used with identifying subscripts.

When written in score form, the multiple regression equation for 3 variables becomes

$$(X_1 - M_1) = b_{12.3}(X_2 - M_2) + b_{13.2}(X_3 - M_3) \tag{107}$$

or transposing and collecting terms

$$\overline{X}_1 = b_{12.3}X_2 + b_{13.2}X_3 + K \text{ (a constant)}$$

It is clear that in order to use this equation we must have the partial regression coefficients $b_{12.3}$ and $b_{13.2}$. These are given by formulas

$$b_{12.3} = r_{12.3} \frac{\sigma_{1.23}}{\sigma_{2.13}} \text{ and } b_{13.2} = r_{13.2} \frac{\sigma_{1.23}}{\sigma_{3.12}} \tag{105}$$

To replace the partial regression coefficients by their numerical values, we must first compute $r_{12.3}$ and $r_{13.2}$, the partial r's; and then $\sigma_{1.23}$, $\sigma_{2.13}$ and $\sigma_{3.12}$, the partial σ's. This is done in the following steps:

Step 2. Computing the partial r's

When (1) stands for honor points, (2) for intelligence and (3) for study hours, the partial $r_{12.3}$ is given by the equation

$$r_{12.3} = \frac{r_{12} - r_{13}r_{23}}{\sqrt{1 - r^2_{13}} \sqrt{1 - r^2_{23}}} \tag{103}$$

Substituting $r_{12} = .60$, $r_{13} = .32$ and $r_{23} = -.35$, we have that $r_{12.3} = .80$. This means that had *all* of our 450 freshmen studied the same number of hours per week, the correlation between honor points and general intelligence would have been .80 instead of .60. When students' study habits are alike, there is clearly a much closer relation between honor points earned and intelligence than there is when study habits vary.

The partial correlation between honor points (1) and study hours (3) when general intelligence (2) is a constant factor is given by the formula

$$r_{13.2} = \frac{r_{13} - r_{12}r_{23}}{\sqrt{1 - r^2_{12}} \sqrt{1 - r^2_{23}}} \tag{103}$$

Substituting for r_{13}, r_{12} and r_{23} (Table 62) we get a partial $r_{13.2}$ of .71 as against an r_{13} of .32. This result means that, had our group possessed the same level of general intelligence,* there would have been a much closer correspondence between academic success and study hours than there is when the students possess varying amounts of general ability. This is certainly the answer to be expected.

We need only two partial r's for the regression equation in Step 1, namely, $r_{12.3}$ and $r_{13.2}$. We have, however, computed $r_{23.1}$ for its analytic value and for illustration. The formula is

$$r_{23.1} = \frac{r_{23} - r_{12}r_{13}}{\sqrt{1 - r^2_{12}}\sqrt{1 - r^2_{13}}}$$

and substituting for r_{12}, r_{13} and r_{23} we have that $r_{23.1} = -.72$. This highly interesting result means that in a group in which every student earns the same number of honor points, the correlation between general intelligence and study hours would be much higher—*negatively*—than is the obtained r between general intelligence and study hours in a group of students in whom academic performance varies widely. The brighter the student the less he needs to study in order to reach a given standard of academic performance.

Step 3.   Partial σ's

The partial σ's, $\sigma_{1.23}$, $\sigma_{2.13}$ and $\sigma_{3.12}$ are given by the formulas

$$\sigma_{1.23} = \sigma_1 \sqrt{1 - r^2_{12}}\sqrt{1 - r^2_{13.2}} \qquad (104)$$

$$\sigma_{2.13} = \sigma_{2.31} = \sigma_2 \sqrt{1 - r^2_{23}}\sqrt{1 - r^2_{12.3}}$$

$$\sigma_{3.12} = \sigma_{3.21} = \sigma_3 \sqrt{1 - r^2_{23}}\sqrt{1 - r^2_{13.2}}$$

In the last two formulas, note that the order in which the variables (13) and (12) have been eliminated is changed to (31) and (21). It makes no difference in what order the variables to the right of the decimal are removed; and the changed orders save the calculation of one partial r, namely, $r_{23.1}$. Substituting for the r's and σ's, we find that $\sigma_{1.23} = 6.3$; $\sigma_{2.13} = 8.9$; and $\sigma_{3.12} = 4.0$. The variability of honor points (1) and general intelligence (2) are reduced by approximately one-half when the other two variables are held constant. The variability of study hours (3) is reduced by 1/3. This reduction in variability might have been predicted in view of the relatively high correlations among the three variables.

* By "same general intelligence" is meant the same score on the given intelligence tests.

Step 4. Computation of partial regression coefficients and of the multiple regression equation

From the partial σ's and the partial r's, the numerical values of the partial regression coefficients, $b_{12.3} = r_{12.3} \dfrac{\sigma_{1.23}}{\sigma_{2.13}}$ and $b_{13.2} = r_{13.2} \dfrac{\sigma_{1.23}}{\sigma_{3.12}}$ are found to be .57 and 1.12, respectively (Table 62). We may now, therefore, write the regression equation as

$$\bar{x}_1 = .57x_2 + 1.12x_3$$

and in score form

$$\bar{X}_1 = .57X_2 + 1.12X_3 - 66$$

Given a student's general intelligence score (X_2) and his study hours (X_3), we can estimate from this equation the most probable number of honor points ($\bar{X}_1$) he will receive at the end of the first semester. Suppose that student William Brown has an intelligence score of 120 and studies on the average 20 hours per week: how many honor points should he receive at the end of the term? Substituting $X_2 = 120$ and $X_3 = 20$ in the equation, we find that

$$\bar{X}_1 = (.57 \times 120) + (1.12 \times 20) - 66 = 25$$

and the most likely number of honor points William will receive—as predicted from his general intelligence score and his study habits—is 25.

Step 5. Standard error of estimate ($\sigma_{1.23}$)

Forecasts of honor points to be expected of entering freshmen must be made, of course, by way of a regression equation established upon groups from previous years. Each predicted score has an error of estimate (p. 160). For a multiple regression equation of 3 variables, the formula for $\sigma_{(est\ x_1)}$ is equal to $\sigma_{1.23}$ without any new computation.

The $\sigma_{(est\ x_1)}$ in our problem is 6.3, so that William's predicted score of 25 in honor points has an error of estimate of about 6 points. This means that the chances are 2 in 3 that William's predicted honor points will not miss the actual number he earns (or will earn) by more than ±6. In general, about 2/3 of all predicted honor point scores should lie within ±6 points of their earned values.

Step 6. Multiple coefficient of correlation, R

The final step in the solution of our 3-variable problem is the computation of the coefficient of multiple correlation. Multiple R is defined (p. 404) as the correlation between scores actually earned on the criterion (X_1) and scores predicted in the criterion from the multiple regression equation. For the data of Table 62, R gives the correlation between X_1 (honor points achieved) and $\overline{X}_1$ (honor points forecast) from the two variables (X_2) general intelligence and (X_3) study habits, when these two have been combined into a team by means of the regression equation. The formula for R when we have 3 variables is

$$R_{1(23)} = \sqrt{1 - \frac{\sigma^2_{1.23}}{\sigma^2_1}} \qquad (109)$$

In the present problem, $R_{1(23)}$ is .83. This means that when the most probable number of honor points which each student in our group of 450 will receive has been predicted from the regression equation given on page 405, the correlation between these 450 *predicted* scores and the 450 *earned* scores will be .83. Multiple R tells us to what extent X_1 is determined by the combined action of X_2 and X_3. Or, in the present problem, to what extent honor points are related to intelligence *and* study hours.

Summary

The multiple regression equation is used mainly for two purposes: (1) analysis and (2) prediction. In analysis, the purpose is to determine the importance or "weight" of each of a number of variables in contributing to some final result (e.g., a performance, called a criterion). The methods outlined in this section are not practicable when there are more than 4 variables. For multiple correlation problems, therefore, which involve a larger number of tests, it is advisable to use systematic methods to lessen the considerable amount of calculation.*

When the problem is one of predicting a criterion with a maximum degree of efficiency, the methods of Chapter 16 are recommended. In the Wherry-Doolittle Test Selection Method, the most efficient team of tests is selected one at a time from a larger number. Experience has shown that after the regression equation contains 4 or 5 variables, additional tests lead to negligible increases (if any) in multiple R. In fact, diminishing

---

* Efficient and timesaving methods are described in Chaps. 7 and 16 and Appendix A, of R. L. Thorndike's *Personnel Selection* (New York: John Wiley and Son, 1949).

returns (no increase or an actual decrease in R) may occur even earlier (see p. 420).

III. FORMULAS FOR USE IN PARTIAL AND MULTIPLE CORRELATION

1. Partial r's

The order of a partial r is determined by the number of its secondary subscripts. Thus, r_{12}, an entire or total r, is a coefficient of zero order; $r_{12.3}$ is a partial of the first order; $r_{12.345}$ is a partial of the third order. The last r has been freed of the influence of variables 3, 4 and 5.

The general formula for a partial r of any order is

$$r_{12.34\,\ldots\,n} = \frac{r_{12.34\,\ldots\,(n-1)} - r_{1n.34\,\ldots\,(n-1)}r_{2n.34\,\ldots\,(n-1)}}{\sqrt{1 - r^2_{1n.34\,\ldots\,(n-1)}}\,\sqrt{1 - r^2_{2n.34\,\ldots\,(n-1)}}} \qquad (103)$$

(partial r in terms of the coefficients of lower order—n variables)

From this formula, partial r's of any order may be found. In a 5-variable problem, for example, $(n-1) = 4$ and $n = 5$, so that $r_{12.345}$ becomes:

$$r_{12.345} = \frac{r_{12.34} - r_{15.34}r_{25.34}}{\sqrt{1 - r^2_{15.34}}\,\sqrt{1 - r^2_{25.34}}}$$

that is, in terms of partial r's of the second order. These second order r's must in turn be computed from r's of the first order; and these from r's of zero order.

2. Partial σ's

The partial standard deviation, $\sigma_{1.2345}$, denotes a partial σ which has been freed of the influence exerted upon its variability by variables 2, 3, 4 and 5. The general formula is

$$\sigma_{1.234\,\ldots\,n} = \sigma_1\sqrt{1 - r^2_{12}}\,\sqrt{1 - r^2_{13.2}}\,\sqrt{1 - r^2_{14.23}}$$
$$\ldots\,\sqrt{1 - r^2_{1n.23\,\ldots\,(n-1)}}$$
$$(104)$$

(partial σ for n variables)

In a 5-variable problem, $\sigma_{1.2345}$ would be written as

$$\sigma_{1.2345} = \sigma_1\sqrt{1 - r^2_{12}}\,\sqrt{1 - r^2_{13.2}}\,\sqrt{1 - r^2_{14.23}}\,\sqrt{1 - r^2_{15.234}}$$

The independent variables on the right of the decimal may be eliminated in more than one order without affecting the numerical result. Thus,

$\sigma_{2.13}$ and $\sigma_{3.12}$ may be written as $\sigma_{2.31}$ and $\sigma_{3.21}$. In this form, it is unnecessary to compute $r_{23.1}$, which is not needed in a 3-variable multiple regression equation (p. 404).

3. Partial regression coefficients (b's)

Partial regression coefficients may be found from the formula

$$b_{12.34\ldots n} = r_{12.34\ldots n} \frac{\sigma_{1.234\ldots n}}{\sigma_{2.134\ldots n}} \tag{105}$$

(partial regression coefficients in terms of partial coefficients of correlation and standard errors of estimate—n variables)

In a 4-variable problem, the regression coefficient is

$$b_{12.34} = r_{12.34} \frac{\sigma_{1.234}}{\sigma_{2.134}}$$

The b coefficients give the weights of the variables in the regression equation, i.e., the weights to be assigned to the scores in X_2, X_3, etc.

4. Multiple regression equation

The regression equation which expresses the relationship between a single variable, X_1, and any number of independent variables, X_2, X_3, $X_4 \ldots X_n$ may be written in deviation form as follows:

$$\bar{x}_1 = b_{12.34\ldots n}x_2 + b_{13.24\ldots n}x_3 + \cdots + b_{1n.23\ldots(n-1)}x_n \tag{106}$$

(regression equation in deviation form for n variables)

and in score form

$$\bar{X}_1 = b_{12.34\ldots n}X_2 + b_{13.24\ldots n}X_3 + \cdots + b_{1n.23\ldots(n-1)}X_n + K \tag{107}$$

(regression equation in score form for n variables)

The regression coefficients $b_{12.34\ldots n}$, $b_{13.24\ldots n}$, etc., give the weights to be attached to the scores in each of the independent variables when X_1 is to be estimated from all of these in combination. Furthermore, these regression coefficients give the weights which each variable exerts in determining X_1 when the influence of the other variables is excluded. From the regression equation we can tell just what role each of the several variables plays in determining the score in X_1, the criterion.

5. The *SE* of estimate in the multiple regression equation

All criterion scores (X_1) forecast from the multiple regression equation have a *SE* of estimate which tells the error made in taking estimated scores instead of earned scores. The *SE* of estimate is given directly by $\sigma_{1.2345\ldots n}$ as follows:

$$\sigma_{(est\ X_1)} = \sigma_{1.2345\ldots n} \tag{108}$$

(standard error of estimate for n variables)

In Table 62 the $SE_{(est\ X_1)}$ of an honor points prediction is 6.3. The chances are about 2 in 3, therefore, that the honor points forecast for *any* student will not be in error by more than about 6 points.

The $SE_{(est\ X_1)}$ which equals $\sigma_{1.23}$ shows the restriction in variability of honor points brought about by holding constant the influence of general intelligence (2) and study hours (3). The greater the reduction in the partial σ, the greater the influence upon its variability exerted by factors (2) and (3). Ruling out the variability in honor points attributable to intelligence and study reduces σ_1 from 11.2 to 6.3, or by nearly one-half. This means that students alike in general intelligence test score and in habits of study vary in scholastic achievement about one-half as much as do students in general.

From the multiple regression equation given in Table 62, X_1 can be predicted with a smaller error of estimate than from any other *linear* equation. Put differently, the $SE_{(est\ X_1)}$ is a minimum when the multiple regression equation is used to forecast X_1 scores. Predicted values of X_1 are, therefore, the best estimates of earned X_1's which can be made from a linear equation.

6. The coefficient of multiple correlation, *R*

The correlation between a single variable or criterion X_1 and $(n-1)$ independent variables combined by means of a multiple regression equation is given by the formula

$$R_{1(23\ldots n)} = \sqrt{1 - \frac{\sigma^2_{1.23\ldots n}}{\sigma^2_1}} \tag{109}$$

(multiple correlation coefficient in terms of the partial σ's for n variables)

When there are only 3 variables, (109) becomes

$$R_{1(23)} = \sqrt{1 - \frac{\sigma^2_{1.23}}{\sigma^2_1}}$$

If we replace $\sigma_{1.234\ldots n}$ in formula (104) by its value in terms of entire and partial r's [see (411)] we may write the general formula for $R_{1(234\ldots n)}$ as follows:

$$R_{1(234\ldots n)} = \sqrt{1 - [(1 - r^2_{12})(1 - r^2_{13.2}) \cdots (1 - r^2_{1n.23\ldots(n-1)})]}$$
(110)

(*multiple R in terms of partial coefficients of correlation for* n *variables*)

The independent variables may be eliminated in more than one order. Thus, $R_{1(23)}$ may be written $R_{1(32)}$, the second form serving as a check on the first.

Multiple R shows how accurately the scores from a given combination of variables represent the actual values of the criterion, when our independent variables are combined in the "best" linear equation. R is the maximum correlation obtainable from a linear equation connecting earned and predicted scores.

IV. THE SIGNIFICANCE OF A PARTIAL r, PARTIAL REGRESSION COEFFICIENT, b, AND MULTIPLE R

1. Significance of a partial r

The significance of a partial r may be determined most readily, perhaps, by way of the z transformation. The $SE_z = \dfrac{1}{\sqrt{N-3}}$ (p. 199), and the SE of the z corresponding to $r_{12.3}$ is $\dfrac{1}{\sqrt{N-4}}$. *One degree of freedom is subtracted from N for each variable eliminated,* in addition to the 3 already lost (p. 194). So for $r_{12.345}$ the SE of the corresponding z is $\dfrac{1}{\sqrt{N-3-3}}$ or $\dfrac{1}{\sqrt{N-6}}$. For the problem of Table 62, $r_{12.3} = .80$ and the corresponding z is 1.10 (Table C). The $SE_z = \dfrac{1}{\sqrt{N-4}}$ or $\dfrac{1}{\sqrt{450-4}}$ or .05 (to two decimals). The .95 confidence interval for the population z is $1.10 \pm 1.96 \times .05$ or from 1.00 to 1.20. Converting these z's back into r's, we have a .95 confidence interval from .76 to .83. Our obtained $r_{12.3}$ of .80, therefore, is highly stable; and there is little likelihood that the population r is zero.

Suppose that $r_{12.3456} = .40$ and $N = 75$. Is this partial r significant? The z corresponding to a r of .40 is .42 and the $SE_z = \dfrac{1}{\sqrt{N-7}}$: i.e., four df

are subtracted from $N - 3$ to give $N - 7$. Substituting $N = 75$, we have that $SE_z = \dfrac{1}{\sqrt{68}}$ or .12 (to two decimals). The .95 confidence interval for the population z is $.42 \pm 1.96 \times .12$ or from .18 to .66. When these z's are converted back into r's, we have a .95 confidence interval of .18 to .58.* The $r_{12.3456}$ is significant in the sense that the population r is not likely to be zero (the lower limit of the confidence range is .18). But the confidence interval is quite wide and the coefficient must be judged to be not very stable.

2. Significance of a regression coefficient (b)

The regression coefficient (b) has a SE as follows:

$$\sigma_{b_{12.34 \ldots m}} = \frac{\sigma_{1.234 \ldots m}}{\sigma_{2.34 \ldots m}\sqrt{N - m}} \tag{111}$$

(SE *of a multiple regression coefficient,* b)

in which

$m =$ the number of variables correlated
$N =$ size of sample
$(N - m) =$ degrees of freedom

In Table 62, the regression coefficient $b_{12.3}$ was .57. The $SE_{b_{12.3}}$ is

$$\sigma_{b_{12.3}} = \frac{6.3}{14.8 \times (\sqrt{450 - 3})} = .02 \text{ (to two decimals)}$$

The term $\sigma_{2.34 \ldots m}$ in the denominator reduces to $\sigma_{2.3}$ or $\sigma_2\sqrt{1 - r^2_{23}}$ when there are only 3 variables (p. 411). Substituting for $\sigma_2 = 15.8$ and $r_{23} = -.35$, $\sigma_{2.3} = 15.8\sqrt{1 - .35^2}$ or 14.8. From formula (111) the $SE_{b_{12.3}}$ is .02.

The .95 confidence interval for the $b_{12.3}$ of .57 is $.57 \pm 1.96 \times .02$ or from .53 to .61. The regression coefficient, therefore, is quite stable, and is highly significant.

The value of a SE of b lies in the fact that it tells us whether the given variable (X_2 in our example) is contributing anything to the prediction of the criterion by way of the multiple regression equation. If $b_{12.3}$ is not significantly greater than zero, the term containing $b_{12.3}$—and variable X_2—can safely be dropped from the regression equation.

* See Table C.

3. Significance of multiple R

(1) SE_R

Multiple R is always positive, always less than 1.00, and always greater than the zero order correlation coefficients, r_{12}, r_{13}, etc. The SE of a multiple R is given by the formula

$$SE_R = \frac{1 - R^2}{\sqrt{N - m}} \qquad (112)$$

(*standard error of a multiple* R)

where

$$m = \text{number of variables being correlated}$$
$$N = \text{size of sample}$$
$$(N - m) = \text{degrees of freedom}$$

In Table 62, $R_{1(23)}$ is .83, N is 450 and m is 3. Hence,

$$SE_R = \frac{1 - .83^2}{\sqrt{447}} = .01 \text{ (to two decimals)}$$

and the .95 confidence interval for the population R is $.83 \pm 1.96 \times .01$ or from .81 to .85. $R_{1(23)}$ is highly significant. When N is large and R high (as here), there is not much point in computing a SE_R.

Suppose that $R_{1(2345)} = .25$ and that $N = 41$. Is this R significant? Substituting in (112), we have

$$SE_R = \frac{1 - .25^2}{\sqrt{41 - 5}} = .16$$

and the .95 confidence interval for the population R is $.25 \pm 1.96 \times .16$ or from $-.06$ to .56. Multiple R is obviously not significant: the lower limit of the .95 confidence interval is negative and the population R could well be zero.

(2) CORRECTING MULTIPLE R FOR INFLATION

A multiple R computed from a sample always tends to be somewhat "inflated" with respect to the population R, owing to the accumulation of chance errors which tend to pile up since R is always taken as positive. The boosting of a multiple R is most pronounced when N is small and the number of variables in the problem quite large. An obtained R can be corrected or "shrunken" to give a better measure of the population R by use of the following formula:

$$\bar{R}^2{}_c = 1 - k^2 \frac{(N-1)}{(N-m)} \tag{113}$$

(*shrinkage formula for correcting an inflated multiple* R)

where

N = size of the sample
m = number of variables in the problem
$(N - m)$ = degrees of freedom
$k^2 = (1 - R^2)$

In the 3-variable problem in Table 62, $R = .83$, $N = 450$ and $m = 3$; $k^2 = (1 - .83^2)$ or $.31$. Substituting in (113) we have

$$\bar{R}^2{}_c = 1 - .31 \frac{(449)}{(447)}$$

and

$$\bar{R}_c = .83$$

and the correction is negligible.

The correction made by formula (113) may be considerable, however, when N is small, m is large and R is small. Let us consider the example given on page 416 in which $R_{1(2345)} = .25$ and $N = 41$. Is this R inflated? Substituting in formula (113) for $N = 41$, $m = 5$ and $k^2 = .94$, we have that

$$\bar{R}^2{}_c = 1 - .94 \frac{(40)}{(36)}$$

$$= -.04$$

and

$$\bar{R}_c = \sqrt{-.04} \text{ or essentially zero}$$

The obtained $R_{1(2345)}$ is not significantly greater than zero when corrected for inflation. Small multiple R's, small samples, and many variables always yield results to be interpreted with caution.

V. SOME PROBLEMS IN PREDICTING FROM THE MULTIPLE REGRESSION EQUATION

We have seen (p. 154) that the regression coefficients (i.e., the b's) are found from the σ's of the tests, and that these, in turn, depend upon the units in which the test is scored. The b coefficients give the weights of the *scores* in the independent variables, X_2, X_3, etc., but not the contributions of these variables without regard to the scoring system employed. The latter contribution is given by the "beta weights" described below.

I. The beta (β) coefficients

When expressed in terms of σ scores, partial regression coefficients are usually called beta coefficients. The beta coefficients may be calculated directly from the b's as follows:

$$\beta_{12.34\ldots n} = b_{12.34\ldots n}\frac{\sigma_2}{\sigma_1} \tag{114}$$

(beta *coefficients calculated from partial regression coefficients*)

The multiple regression equation for n variables may be written in σ scores as

$$\overline{z}_1 = \beta_{12.34\ldots n}z_2 + \beta_{13.24\ldots n}z_3 + \cdots + \beta_{1n.23\ldots(n-1)}z_n \tag{115}$$

(*multiple regression equation in terms of σ scores*)

Beta coefficients are called "beta weights" to distinguish them from the "score weights" (b's) of the ordinary multiple regression equation. When all of our tests have been expressed in σ scores (all means = .00 and all σ's = 1.00), differences in test units as well as differences in variability are allowed for. We are then able to determine from the correlations alone the relative weight with which each independent variable "enters in" or contributes to the criterion, independently of the other factors.

To illustrate with the data in Table 62, we find that $\beta_{12.3} = .57 \times \dfrac{15.8}{11.2}$ or .80 and that $\beta_{13.2} = 1.12 \times \dfrac{6.0}{11.2}$ or .60. From (115) above we get

$$\overline{z}_1 = .80z_2 + .60z_3$$

This equation should be compared with the multiple regression equation $\overline{x}_1 = .57x_2 + 1.12x_3$ in Table 62 which gives the weights to be attached to the *scores* in X_2 and X_3. The weights of .57 and 1.12 tell us the amount by which scores in X_2 and X_3 must be multiplied in order to give the "best" prediction of X_1. But these weights do not give us the relative importance of general intelligence and study habits in determining the number of honor points a freshman will receive. This information is given by the beta weights. It is of interest to note that, while the actual score weights are as 1:2 (.57 to 1.12), the independent contributions of general intelligence (z_2) and study habits (z_3) are in the ratio of .80 to .60 or as 4:3. When the variabilities (σ's) of our tests are all equal and scoring units are comparable, general intelligence has a proportionately greater influence than study habits in determining academic achievement. This is certainly the result to be expected.

2. Multiple R in terms of β coefficients

R^2 may be expressed in terms of the beta coefficients and the zero order r's:

$$R^2_{1(23\ldots n)} = \beta_{12.34\ldots n}r_{12} + \beta_{13.24\ldots n}r_{13} + \cdots + \beta_{1n.23\ldots (n-1)}r_{1n}$$
(116)

(*multiple* R^2 *in terms of* β *coefficients and zero order* r's)

For three variables (116) becomes

$$R^2_{1(23)} = \beta_{12.3}r_{12} + \beta_{13.2}r_{13}$$

From page 418 we find $\beta_{12.3} = .80$ and $\beta_{13.2} = .60$; and from Table 62 that $r_{12} = .60$ and $r_{13} = .32$. Substituting in (116), we get

$$R^2_{1(23)} = .80 \times .60 + .60 \times .32$$
$$= .48 + .19$$
$$R^2_{1(23)} = .67$$
$$R_{1(23)} = .82$$

$R^2_{1(23\ldots n)}$ gives the proportion of the variance of the criterion measure (X_1) attributable to the joint action of the variables $X_2, X_3 \ldots X_n$. As shown above, $R^2_{1(23)} = .67$; and, accordingly, 67% of whatever makes freshmen differ in (1) school achievement can be attributed to differences in (2) general intelligence and (3) study habits. By means of formula (116) the total contribution of .67 can be broken down further into the independent contributions of general intelligence (X_2) and study habits (X_3). Thus from the equation $R^2_{1(23)} = .48 + .19$, we know that 48% is the contribution of general intelligence to the variance of honor points, and 19% is the contribution of study habits. The remaining 33% of the variance of X_1 must be attributed to factors not measured in our problem.

3. Factors determining the selection of tests in a battery

The effectiveness with which the composite score obtained from a battery of tests measures the criterion depends (1) upon the intercorrelations of the tests in the battery as well as (2) upon the correlations of these tests with the criterion—their validity coefficients. This appears clearly in Table 63 in which the criterion correlation of each test is .30, but the intecorrelations of the tests of the battery vary from .00 to .60. When the tests are uncorrelated (all criterion r's being .30), an increase in size of the battery from 1 to 9 tests raises multiple R from .30 to .90.

TABLE 63 * Effect of intercorrelations on multiple correlation

Multiple R's for different numbers of tests, when criterion correlations (validities) of all tests are .30, and the intercorrelations are the same and vary from .00 to .60. Example: In a battery of 4 tests, all with validities of .30 and intercorrelations of .30, multiple R is .44.

Number of Tests	Size of Intercorrelations			
	.00	.10	.30	.60
1	.30	.30	.30	.30
2	.42	.40	.37	.34
4	.60	.53	.44	.36
9	.90	.67	.48	.37
20	†	.79	.52	.38

However, when the intercorrelations of the tests are all .60 and the battery is increased in size from 1 to 9 tests, multiple R goes from .30 to .37. Even when the number of tests in the battery is 20 multiple R is only .38.

A single test can add to the validity of a battery by "taking out" some of the as yet unmeasured part of the criterion. Such a test will show a high r with the criterion but relatively low r's with the other tests in the battery. (See Table 63 and Fig. 68.) Usually it is difficult to find tests,

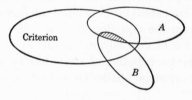

FIG. 68

after the first 4 or 5, which fulfill these requirements. In most group tests of general intelligence where the criterion is relatively homogeneous (ability to deal with abstract verbal relations, say) the subtests of a battery may exhibit high intercorrelations. This is true to a lesser degree of educational achievement tests and of many tests of aptitudes. When the criterion is a complex made up of a number of variables (job perform-

* From R. L. Thorndike, *Personnel Selection* (New York: John Wiley and Sons, 1949), p. 191.

† It is mathematically impossible for 20 tests all to correlate 0.30 with some measure and still have zero intercorrelations.

ance, success in salesmanship, or professional competence) it is easier to find tests of acceptable validity which will show low relationships with the other tests of the battery. But even here the maximum multiple R is often reached rather quickly (see p. 437).

A test may also add to the validity of a battery by acting as a "suppressor" variable. Suppose that Test A correlates .50 with a criterion—has good validity—while Test B correlates only .10 with the criterion but .60 with Test A. The $R_{1(23)} = .56$ despite the low validity of Test B. This is because Test B acts as a suppressor—takes out some of Test A's "nonvalid" variance, thus raising the criterion correlation of the battery (see Fig. 69). The weights of these two tests in the regression equation con-

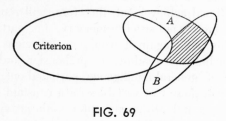

FIG. 69

necting the criterion with A and B are .69 and −.31. The negative weight of Test B serves to suppress that part of Test A not related to the criterion and thus gives a better (more valid) measure of the criterion than can be obtained with Test A, alone.

VI. LIMITATIONS TO THE USE OF PARTIAL AND MULTIPLE CORRELATION

Certain cautions in the use of partial and multiple correlation may be indicated in concluding this chapter.

(1) In order that partial coefficients of correlation be valid measures of relationship, it is necessary that all zero order coefficients be computed from data in which the regression is linear.

(2) The number of cases in a multiple correlation problem should be large, especially if there are a number of variables; otherwise the coefficients calculated from the data will have little significance. Coefficients which are misleadingly high or low may be obtained when studies which involve many variables are based on relatively few cases. The question of accuracy of computation is also involved. A general rule advocated by many workers is that results should be carried to as many decimals as there are variables in the problem. How strictly this rule is to be followed must depend upon the accuracy of the original measures.

(3) A serious limitation to a clear-cut interpretation of a partial r arises from the fact that most of the tests employed by psychologists probably depend upon a large number of "determiners." When we "partial out" the influence of clear-cut and relatively objective factors such as age, height, school grade, etc., we have a reasonably clear notion of what the "partials" mean. But when we attempt to render variability due to "logical memory" constant by partialing out memory test scores from the correlation between general intelligence test scores and educational achievement, the result is by no means so unequivocal. The abilities determining the scores in general intelligence *and* in school achievement undoubtedly overlap the memory test in other respects than in the "memory" involved. Partialing out a memory test score from the correlation between general intelligence and educational achievement, therefore, will render constant the influence of many factors not strictly "memory," i.e., partial out too much.

To illustrate this point again it would be fallacious to interpret the partial correlation between reading comprehension and arithmetic, say, with the influence of "general intelligence" partialed out, as giving the net relationship between these two variables for a constant degree of intelligence. Both reading and arithmetic enter with heavy, but unknown, weight into most general intelligence tests; hence the partial correlation between these two, for general intelligence constant, cannot be interpreted in a clear-cut and meaningful way.

Partial r's obtained from psychological and educational tests, though often difficult to interpret, may be used in multiple regression equations when the purpose is to determine the relative weight to be assigned the various tests of a battery. But we should be cautious in attempting to give psychological meaning to such residual, i.e., partial, r's. Several writers have discussed this problem, and should be referred to by the investigator who plans to use partial and multiple correlation extensively.

(4) Perhaps the chief limitation to R, the coefficient of multiple correlation, is the fact that, since it is always positive, variable errors of sampling tend to accumulate and thus make the coefficient too large. A correction to be applied to R, when the sample is small and the number of variables large, has been given on page 416. This correction gives the value which R would most probably take in the population from which our sample was drawn.

PROBLEMS

1. The correlation between a general intelligence test and school achievement in a group of children from 8 to 14 years old is .80. The correlation between the general intelligence test and age in the same group is .70; and

the correlation between school achievement and age is .60. What is the correlation between general intelligence and school achievement in children of the same age? Comment upon your result.

2. In a group of 100 college freshmen, the correlation between (1) intelligence and (2) the A cancellation test is .20. The correlation between (1) intelligence and (3) a battery of controlled association tests in the same group is .70. If the correlation between (2) cancellation and (3) controlled association is .45, what is the "net" correlation between intelligence and cancellation in this group? Between intelligence and controlled association? Interpret your results.

3. Explain why some variables are of such a nature that it is difficult to hold them "constant," and hence to employ them in problems involving partial correlation.

4. Given the following data for 56 children:

$$X_1 = \text{Stanford-Binet I.Q.}$$
$$X_2 = \text{Memory for Objects}$$
$$X_3 = \text{Cube Imitation}$$

$M_1 = 101.71$	$M_2 = 10.06$	$M_3 = 3.35$
$\sigma_1 = 13.65$	$\sigma_2 = 3.06$	$\sigma_3 = 2.02$
$r_{12} = .41$	$r_{13} = .50$	$r_{23} = .16$

(a) Work out the regression equation of X_2 and X_3 upon X_1, using the method of section II.

(b) Compute $R_{1(23)}$ and $\sigma_{(est\ x_1)}$.

(c) If a child's score is 12 in Test X_2 and 4 in Test X_3, what is his most probable score in X_1 (I.Q.)?

5. Given the following data for 75 cases:

$$X_1 = \text{criterion: average grades in freshman year in college}$$
$$X_2 = \text{average grade over 4 years of high school}$$
$$X_3 = \text{score on group intelligence test}$$

$M_1 = 78.00$	$M_2 = 87.20$	$M_3 = 32.80$
$\sigma_1 = 10.21$	$\sigma_2 = 6.02$	$\sigma_3 = 10.35$
$r_{12} = .67$	$r_{13} = .75$	$r_{23} = .63$

(a) Work out the regression equation of X_2 and X_3 on X_1.

(b) Compute $R_{1(23)}$ and $\sigma_{(est\ x_1)}$.

(c) If the minimum entrance requirements are a grade of 80 in high school and a score of 40 on the intelligence test, what grade in freshman class would you expect of a candidate who earned these scores?

6. Using the data in (5) above
(a) Find the .95 confidence interval for $r_{13.2} = .57$
(b) Find the .95 confidence interval for $b_{13.2} = .54$
(c) Is $R_{1(23)}$ significant at .01 level?
(d) Correct $R_{1(23)}$ for inflation.

7. Work out the regression equation of (5) above in terms of beta coefficients. What are the relative contributions of high-school grades and intelligence test scores to predicted performance in freshman class in college?

8. Let X_1 be a criterion and X_2 and X_3 be two other tests. Correlations and σ's are as follows:

$$r_{12} = .60 \qquad\qquad \sigma_1 = 5.00$$
$$r_{13} = .50 \qquad\qquad \sigma_2 = 10.00$$
$$r_{23} = .20 \qquad\qquad \sigma_3 = 8.00$$

How much more accurately can X_1 be predicted from X_2 and X_3 than from either alone?

9. Given a team of two tests, each of which correlates .50 with a criterion. If the two tests correlate .20
   (a) how much would the addition of another test which correlates .50 with the criterion and .20 with each of the other tests improve the predictive value of the team?
   (b) how much would the addition of two such tests improve the predictive value of the team?

10. Test A correlates .60 with a criterion and .50 with Test B, which correlates only .10 with the criterion. What is the multiple R of A and B with the criterion? Why is it higher than the correlation of A with the criterion?

11. Two absolutely independent tests, B and C, completely determine the criterion A. If B correlates .50 with A, what is the correlation of C and A? What is the multiple correlation of A with B and C?

12. Comment upon the following statements:
   (a) It is good practice to correlate E.Q.'s achieved upon two educational achievement tests, no matter how wide the age range.
   (b) The positive correlation between average AGCT scores by states and the average elevation of the states above sea level proves the close relationship of intelligence and geography.
   (c) The correlation between memory test scores and tapping rate in a group of 200 eight-year-old children is .20; and the correlation between memory test scores and tapping rate in a group of 100 college freshmen is .10. When the two groups are combined the correlation between these two tests becomes .40. This shows that we must have large groups in order to get high correlations.

ANSWERS

1. Partial $r = .67$
2. r (intelligence and cancellation) $= -.18$; r (intelligence and controlled association) $= .70$
4. (a) $\overline{X}_1 = 1.53X_2 + 3.02X_3 + 76$ (to nearest whole number)
   (b) $R_{1(23)} = .60$; $\sigma_{(est\ x_1)} = 10.93$
   (c) 107

5. (a) $\overline{X}_1 = .55X_2 + .54X_3 + 12$ (to nearest whole number)
   (b) $R_{1(23)} = .79$; $\sigma_{(est\ x_1)} = 6.23$
   (c) 78
6. (a) .39 to .71
   (b) .36 to .72
   (c) Yes. $R_{1(23)} = .79 \pm .04$
   (d) .78
7. $\overline{z}_1 = .32z_2 + .55z_3$. Intelligence contributes almost twice as much as high-school grades (1.7 :: 1)
8. From X_2 alone $\sigma_{(est\ x_1)} = 4.0$
   From X_3 alone $\sigma_{(est\ x_1)} = 4.3$
   From X_2 and X_3 together, $\sigma_{(est x_1)} = 3.5$
9. (a) R increases from .64 to .72 (b) R increases from .64 to .76
10. $R_{Cr(AB)} = .65$
11. $r_{AC} = .87$; and $R_{A(BC)} = 1.00$

CHAPTER 16

MULTIPLE CORRELATION
IN TEST SELECTION

◇◇

I. THE WHERRY-DOOLITTLE TEST SELECTION METHOD *

The method of solving multiple correlation problems outlined in Table 62 of Chapter 15 is adequate when there are only three (or not more than four) variables. In problems involving more than four variables, however, the mechanics of calculation become almost prohibitive unless some systematic scheme of solution is adopted (p. 410). The Wherry-Doolittle Test Selection Method, to be presented in this section, provides a method of solving certain types of multiple correlation problems with a minimum of statistical labor. This method selects the tests of the battery analytically and adds them one at a time until a maximum R is obtained. To illustrate, suppose we wish to predict aptitude for a certain technical job in a factory. Criterion ratings for job proficiency have been obtained and eight tests tried out as possible indicators of job aptitude. By use of the Wherry-Doolittle method we can (1) select those tests (e.g., three or four) which yield a maximum R with the criterion and discard the rest; (2) calculate the multiple R after the addition of each test, stopping the process when R no longer increases; (3) compute a multiple regression equation from which the criterion can be predicted with the highest precision of which the given list of tests is capable.

The application of the Wherry-Doolittle test selection method to an actual problem is shown in example (1) below. Steps in computation are outlined in order and are illustrated by reference to the data of example (1), so that the student may follow the process in detail.

---

* Stead, W. H., Shartle, C. L., *et al.*, *Occupational Counseling Techniques* (New York: American Book Co., 1940), Appendix 5.

I. Solution of a multiple correlation problem by the Wherry-Doolittle Test Selection Method

Example (1)   In Table 64 are presented the intercorrelations of ten tests administered in the Minnesota study of Mechanical Ability. The criterion—called the "quality" criterion—was a measure of the excellence of mechanical work done by 100 junior high-school boys. The tests in Table 64 are fairly representative of the wide range of measures used in the Minnesota study. Our immediate problem is to choose from among these variables the most valid battery of tests, i.e., those tests which will predict the criterion most efficiently. Selection of tests is made by the Wherry-Doolittle method.

TABLE 64   Intercorrelations of ten tests and a criterion

(Data from the Minnesota Study of Mechanical Ability *)

List of Tests ($N = 100$)

C = Quality criterion
1 = Packing blocks
2 = Card sorting
3 = Minnesota spatial relations boards, A, B, C, D
4 = Paper form boards, A and B
5 = Stenquist Picture I
6 = Stenquist Picture II
7 = Minnesota assembly boxes, A, B, C
8 = Mechanical operations questionnaire
9 = Interest analysis blank
10 = Otis intelligence test

	1	2	3	4	5	6	7	8	9	10
C	.26	.19	.53	.52	.24	.31	.55	.30	.55	.26
1		.52	.34	.14	.18	.21	.30	.00	.34	.00
2			.23	.14	.10	.24	.13	−.12	.23	.08
3				.63	.42	.39	.56	.22	.55	.23
4					.37	.30	.49	.24	.61	.56
5						.54	.46	.24	.23	.11
6							.40	.19	.13	.21
7								.40	.41	.13
8									.25	.18
9										.38

Steps in the solution of example (1) may be outlined in order.

* Paterson, D. G., Elliott, R. M., *et al.*, *Minnesota Mechanical Ability Tests* (Minneapolis: The University of Minnesota Press, 1930), Appendix 4.

Step 1

Draw up work sheets like those of Tables 65 and 66. The correlation coefficients between tests and criterion are entered in Table 64.

Step 2

Enter these coefficients *with signs reversed* in the V_1 row of Table 65.* The numbers heading the columns refer to the tests.

TABLE 65

					Tests					
	1	2	3	4	5	6	7	8	9	10
V_1	−.260	−.190	−.530	−.520	−.240	−.310	−.550	−.300	−.550	−.260
V_2	−.095	−.118	−.222	−.250	.013	−.090		−.080	−.324	−.188
V_3	−.010	−.049	−.097	−.091	.029	−.103		−.047		−.061
V_4	.005	−.034		−.057	.054	−.072		−.053		−.056
V_5	−.012	−.039			.062	−.065		−.051		−.018

$$\frac{V_1^2}{Z_1} = \frac{(-.550)^2}{1.000} = .3025; \frac{V_2^2}{Z_2} = \frac{(-.324)^2}{.832} = .1261; \frac{V_3^2}{Z_3} = \frac{(-.097)^2}{.563} = .0167;$$

$$\frac{V_4^2}{Z_4} = \frac{(-.057)^2}{.489} = .0066; \qquad \frac{V_5^2}{Z_5} = \frac{(-.065)^2}{.775} = .0054$$

Step 3

Enter the numbers 1.000 in each column of the row Z_1 in Table 66.

TABLE 66

					Tests					
	1	2	3	4	5	6	7	8	9	10
Z_1	1.000	1.000	1.000	1.000	1.000	1.000	1.000	1.000	1.000	1.000
Z_2	.910	.983	.686	.760	.788	.840		.840	.832	.983
Z_3	.853	.945	.563	.559	.786	.839		.831		.854
Z_4	.839	.931		.489	.748	.782		.829		.852
Z_5	.796	.927			.737	.775		.829		.637

$$\frac{1}{.832} = 1.202$$

$$\frac{1}{.563} = 1.776$$

$$\frac{1}{.489} = 2.045$$

* Correlation coefficients are assumed to be accurate to three or to four decimals in subsequent calculations to avoid the loss of precision which results when decimals are rounded to two places (see p. 405).

Step 4

Select that test having the highest $\dfrac{V_1{}^2}{Z_1}$ quotient as the *first* test of the battery. From Tables 65 and 66 we find that Tests 7 and 9 both have correlations of .550 with the criterion, and that these are the largest r's in the table. Either Test 7 or Test 9 could be selected as the first test of our battery. We have chosen Test 7 because it is the more objective measure of performance.

Step 5

Apply the Wherry shrinkage formula

$$\bar{R}^2 = 1 - K^2 \left(\frac{N-1}{N-m} \right) \tag{117}$$

in which $\bar{R}$ is the "shrunken" multiple correlation coefficient, the coefficient from which chance error has been removed.* This corrected R may be calculated in a systematic way as follows:

(1) Prepare a work sheet similar to that shown in Table 67.

TABLE 67

a	b	c	d	e	f	g	
m	$\dfrac{V_m{}^2}{Z_m}$	K^2	$\dfrac{N-1}{N-m}$	$\bar{K}^2$	$\bar{R}^2$	$\bar{R}$	Test #
0		1.0000	$(N=100)$				
1	.3025	.6975	1.000	.6975	.3025	.5500	7
2	.1261	.5714	1.010	.5771	.4229	.6503	9
3	.0167	.5547	1.021	.5663	.4337	.6586	3
4	.0066	.5481	1.031	.5651	.4349	.6595	4
5	.0054	.5427	1.042	.5655	.4345	.6591	6

(1) Enter 1.0000 in column c, row 0, under K^2. Enter $N = 100$ in column d.

(3) Enter the quotient $\dfrac{V_1{}^2}{Z_1}$ in column b, row 1. $\dfrac{V_1{}^2}{Z_1} = \dfrac{(-.550)^2}{1.000} = .3025$ †

(4) Subtract .3025 from 1.000 to give .6975 as the entry in column c under K^2.

* Wherry, R. J., "A New Formula for Predicting the Shrinkage of the Coefficient of Multiple Correlation," *Annals of Mathematical Statistics*, 1931, Vol. 2. 440–451.

† Quotient is taken to four decimals (p. 405).

(5) Find the quotient $\dfrac{(N-1)}{(N-m)}$ and record it in column d.

$(N-1) = 99$; and since m (number of tests selected) is 1, $(N-m)$ also equals 99 and $\dfrac{(N-1)}{(N-m)} = 1.000$.

(6) Write the product of columns c and d in column e: $.6975 \times 1.000 = .6975$.

(7) Subtract the column e entry from 1.000 to obtain $\bar{R}_2$ (the shrunken multiple correlation coefficient) in column f. In Table 67 the $\bar{R}^2$ entry, of course, is .3025.

(8) Find the square root of the column f entry and enter the result in column g under $\bar{R}$. Our entry is .5500, the correlation of Test 7 with the criterion. No correction for chance errors is necessary for one test.

Step 6

To aid in the selection of a *second* test to be added to our battery of one, a work sheet similar to that shown in Table 68 should be prepared. Calculations in Table 68 are as follows:

(1) Leave a_1 row blank.

(2) Enter in row b_1 the correlations of Test 7 (*first* selected test) with each of the other tests in Table 64. These r's are .300, .130, .560, etc., and are entered in the columns numbered to correspond to the tests. Enter 1.000 in the column for Test 7. In column $-C$ enter the correlation of Test 7 with the criterion *with sign reversed*, i.e., as $-.550$.

(3) Write the algebraic sum of the b_1 entries in the "Check Sum" column. This sum is 3.730.

(4) Multiply each b_1 entry by the *negative reciprocal* of the b_1 entry for Test 7, the *first* selected test. Enter these products in the c_1 row. Since the negative reciprocal of Test 7's b_1 entry is -1.000, we need simply write the b_1 entries in the c_1 row with signs reversed.

Step 7

Draw a vertical line under Test 7 in Table 65 to show that it has been selected. To select a *second* test proceed as follows:

(1) To each V_1 entry in Table 65, add algebraically the product of the b_1 entry in the criterion $(-C)$ column of Table 68 by the c_1 entry for each of the other tests. Enter results in the V_2 row. The formula for V_2 is $V_2 = V_1 + b_1$ (criterion) $\times c_1$ (each test). To illustrate, from Table 68 and Table 65 we have

For Test 1: $V_2 = -.260 + (-.550) \times (-.300) = -.260 + .165 = -.095$

TABLE 68

	1	2	3	4	5	6	7	8	9	10	—C	Check Sum	Test #
a_1	—	—	—	—	—	—	—	—	—	—	—	—	7
b_1	.300	.130	.560	.490	.460	.400	1.000	.400	.410	.130	-.550	3.730	
c_1	-.300	-.130	-.560	-.490	-.460	-.400	-1.000	-.400	-.410	-.130	.550	-3.730	
a_2	.340	.230	.550	.610	.230	.130	.410	.250	1.000	.380	-.550	3.580	9
b_2	.217	.177	.320	.409	.041	-.034	—	.086	.832	.327	-.324	2.051	
c_2	-.261	-.213	-.385	-.492	-.049	.041	—	-.103	-1.000	-.393	.389	-2.465	
a_3	.340	.230	1.000	.630	.420	.390	.560	.220	.550	.230	-.530	4.040	3
b_3	.088	.089	.563	.199	.146	.179	—	-.037	—	.031	-.097	1.161	
c_3	-.156	-.158	-1.000	-.353	-.259	-.318	—	.066	—	-.055	.172	-2.062	
a_4	.140	.140	.630	1.000	.370	.300	.490	.240	.610	.560	-.520	3.960	4
b_4	-.145	-.042	—	.489	.073	.058	—	.015	—	.324	-.057	.715	
c_4	.297	.086	—	-1.000	-.149	-.119	—	-.031	—	-.663	.117	-1.462	

431

For Test 4: $V_2 = -.520 + (-.550) \times (-.490) =$
$-.520 + .270 = -.250$

For Test 9: $V_2 = -.550 + (-.550) \times (-.410) =$
$-.550 + .226 = -.324$

(2) To each Z_1 in Table 66 add algebraically the product of the b_1 and c_1 entries for each test got from Table 68. Enter these results in the Z_2 row. The formula is $Z_2 = Z_1 + b_1$ (a given test) $\times c_1$ (same test). To illustrate, from Tables 65 and 68:
For Test 1: $Z_2 = 1.000 + (.300) \times (-.300) = 1.000 - .090 = .910$
For Test 4: $Z_2 = 1.000 + (.490) \times (-.490) = 1.000 - .240 = .760$
For Test 9: $Z_2 = 1.000 + (.410) \times (-.410) = 1.000 - .168 = .832$

Step 8

Now select the test having the largest $\dfrac{V_2{}^2}{Z_2}$ quotient, as the *second* test for our battery. The quantity $\dfrac{V_2{}^2}{Z_2}$ is a measure of the amount which the second test contributes to the squared multiple correlation coefficient, $\overline{R}^2$. From Tables 65 and 66 we find that Test 9 has the largest $\dfrac{V_2{}^2}{Z_2}$ quotient:
$$\frac{(-.324)^2}{.832} = .1261.$$

Step 9

To calculate the new multiple correlation coefficient when Test 9 is added to Test 7, proceed as follows:

(1) The quantity .1261 $\left(\dfrac{V_2{}^2}{Z_2}\right)$ is entered in column b, row 2 of Table 67.

(2) Subtract the ratio $\dfrac{V_2{}^2}{Z_2}$ from the K^2 entry in column c, row 1, and enter the result in column c, row 2; e.g., for the entry in column c, row 2, we have $.6975 - .1261$, or $.5714$.

(3) Find the quotient $\dfrac{(N-1)}{(N-m)}$. Since $N = 100$ and m (number of tests chosen) $= 2$, we have $\dfrac{(N-1)}{(N-m)}$ or $\dfrac{99}{98} = 1.010$, as the column d, row 2 entry.

(4) Record the product of the c and d columns in column e: $.5714 \times 1.010 = .5771$.

(5) Subtract .5771 (column e) from 1.000 to give .4229 as the entry in column f, row 2.

(6) Take the square root of .4229 and enter the result, .6503, in column g. This is the multiple coefficient $\bar{R}$ corrected for chance errors. It is clear that by adding Test 9 to Test 7 we increase $\bar{R}$ from .5500 to .6503, a substantial gain.

Step 10

Since $\bar{R}$ for Tests 7 and 9 is larger than the correlation for Test 7 alone, we proceed to add a *third* test in the hope of further increasing the multiple $\bar{R}$. The procedure is shown in Step 11.

Step 11

Return to Table 68 and

(1) Record in the a_2 row the correlation coefficient of the *second* selected test (i.e., Test 9) with each of the other tests *and* with the criterion. (Read r's from Table 64.) The correlation of Test 9 with the criterion is entered *with sign reversed* (i.e., as $-.550$).

(2) Enter the algebraic sum of the a_2 entries (i.e., 3.580) in the Check Sum column.

(3) Draw a vertical line down through the b_2 and c_2 rows for Test 7, the *first* selected test. This indicates that Test 7 has already been chosen.

(4) Compute the b_2 entry for each test by adding to the a_2 entry the product of the b_1 entry of the given test by the c_1 entry of the second selected test (i.e., Test 9). The formula is $b_2 = a_2 + b_1$ (given test) $\times c_1$ (*second* selected test). To illustrate:

For Test 2: $b_2 = .230 + (.130)(-.410) = .230 - .053 = .177$

For Test 6: $b_2 = .130 + (.400)(-.410) = .130 - .164 = -.034$

For Test 10: $b^2 = .380 + (.130)(-.410) = .380 - .053 = .327$

Compute b_2 entries for criterion and Check Sum column in the same way. For the criterion column we have $-.550 + (-.550)(-.410)$ or $-.324$. For the Check Sum column we have $3.580 + (3.730)(-.410)$ or 2.051.

(5) There are three checks for the b_2 row. (*a*) The entry for the *second* selected test (Test 9) should equal the Z_2 entry for the same test in Table 66. Note that both entries are .832. (*b*) The entry in the criterion column should equal the V_2 entry of the second selected test (Test 9) in Table 65; both entries are $-.324$. (*c*) The entry in the Check Sum column should equal the sum of all of the entries in the b_2 rows. Adding

.217, .177, .320, etc., we get 2.051, checking our calculations to the third decimal.

(6) Multiply each b_2 entry by the *negative reciprocal* of the b_2 entry for the *second* selected test (Test 9), and record results in the c_2 row. The negative reciprocal of .832 is -1.202. The c_2 entry for Test 1 is .217 $\times -1.202$ or $-.261$; for Test 2, $-.177 \times -1.202$ or $-.213$; and so on for the other tests. For the criterion column the c_2 entry is $(-.324) \times -1.202$ or .389; and for the Check Sum the c_2 entry is 2.051×-1.202 or -2.465.

(7) There are three checks for the c_2 entries. (*a*) The c_2 row entry of the second selected test (Test 9) should be -1.000. (*b*) The c_2 entry in the Check Sum column should equal the sum of all c_2 entries. Adding the c_2 entries in Table 68, we find the sum to be -2.465, the Check Sum entry. (*c*) The product of the b_2 and c_2 entries in the criterion column should equal the quotient $\dfrac{V_2{}^2}{Z_2}$ in column b, row 2, of Table 67 in absolute value. Note that the product $(-.324 \times .389) = -.1261$, thus checking our entry (disregard signs).

Step 12

Draw a vertical line under Test 9 in Table 65, to indicate that it has been selected as our second test. Then proceed as in Step 7 to compute V_3 and Z_3 in order to select a *third* test. The formula for V_3 is $V_3 = V_2 + b_2$ (criterion) $\times c_2$ (each test). The formula for Z_3 is $Z_3 = Z_2 + b_2$ (a given test) $\times c_2$ (same test). The third selected test is that one which has the largest $\dfrac{V_3{}^2}{Z_3}$ quotient in Table 65. This is Test 3, for which $V_3 = -.222 + (-.324)(-.385)$ or $-.097$; and $Z_3 = .686 + (.320)$ $(-.385) = .563$. The quotient $\dfrac{V_3{}^2}{Z_3} = .0167$.

Step 13

Entering .0167 $\left(\dfrac{V_3{}^2}{Z_3}\right)$ in column b, row 3, of Table 67, follow the procedures of Step 9 to get $\overline{R} = .6586$. Note that $\dfrac{(N-1)}{(N-m)} = 99/97$ or 1.021; and that the new $\overline{R}$ is larger than the .6503 found for the two tests, 7 and 9. We include Test 3 in our battery, therefore, and proceed to calculate a_3, b_3, and c_3 (Table 68), following Step 11, in order to select a *fourth* test.

Step 14

The a_3 entries in Table 68 are the correlations of Test 3 with each of the other tests including the criterion. The criterion correlation is entered in the $-C$ column with a negative sign (i.e., as $-.530$).

(1) The formula for b_3 is $b_3 = a_3 + b_1$ (given test) $\times c_1$ (third selected test) $+ b_2$ (given test) $\times c_2$ (third selected test). To illustrate,

For Test 1: $b_3 = .340 + (.300)(-.560) + (.217)(-.385) = .088$

For Test 4: $b_3 = .630 + (.490)(-.560) + (.409)(-.385) = .199$

Check the b_3 entries by Step 11 (5). (a) Note that the b_3 entry for the third selected test (Test 3) equals the Z_3 entry for Test 3 in Table 66, namely, .563. (b) The entry in the criterion column equals the V_3 entry of the third selected test (Test 3) in Table 65, i.e., $-.097$. (c) The Check Sum entry (1.161) equals the sum of the entries in the b_3 row.

(2) The formula for c_3 is $b_3 \times$ the negative reciprocal of the b_3 entry for the third selected test (Test 3). The negative reciprocal of .563 is -1.776. To illustrate the calculation for Test 5, $c_3 = .146 \times -1.776 = -.259$. Check the c_3 entries by Step 11 (7). (a) The c_3 row entry of the third selected test (Test 3) equals -1.000. (b) The c_3 entry in the Check Sum column, namely, -2.062, equals the sum of the c_3 row. (c) The product of the b_3 and c_3 entries in the criterion column (namely, $-.097 \times .172$) equals the quotient $\left(\dfrac{V_3{}^2}{Z_3}\right)$ (i.e., .0167) in absolute value.

Step 15

Repeat Step 12 to find V_4 and Z_4. The formula for V_4 is $V_4 = V_3 + b_3$ (criterion) $\times c_3$ (each test). Also, the formula for Z_4 is $Z_4 = Z_3 + b_3$ (a given test) $\times c_3$ (same test). For Test 4, $V_4 = -.091 + (-.097)(-.353)$ or $-.057$; and $Z_4 = .559 + (.199)(-.353)$ or .489. The quotient, $\dfrac{V_4{}^2}{Z_4}$, equals $\dfrac{(-.057)^2}{.489}$ or .0066. While none of the V_4 entries is large, Test 4 has the largest $\dfrac{V_4{}^2}{Z_4}$ quotient, and hence is selected as our fourth test. Enter .0066 $\left(\dfrac{V_4{}^2}{Z_4}\right)$ in column b, row 4, of Table 67. Follow the procedure of Step 9 to get $R \doteqdot .6595$. Note that $\dfrac{(N-1)}{(N-m)}$ is 99/96 or 1.031; and that the new $\overline{R}$ is but slightly larger than the $\overline{R}$ of .6586 found for the three tests, 7, 9, and 3. When $\overline{R}$ decreases or fails to increase, there is no point in adding new tests to the battery. The increase in $\overline{R}$ is so small as a result of adding Test 4 that it is hardly profitable to enlarge our battery by a fifth test. We shall add a fifth test, however, in order to illustrate a further step in the selection process.

Step 16

To choose a *fifth* test, calculate a_4, b_4, and c_4, following Step 11, and enter the results in Table 68. The a_4 entries are the correlations of the *fourth* selected test (Test 4) with each of the other tests including the criterion (*with sign reversed*).

(1) The formula for b_4 may readily be written by analogy to the formulas for b_3 and b_2 as follows: $b_4 = a_4 + b_1$ (given test) $\times c_1$ (*fourth* selected test) $+ b_2$ (given test) $\times c_2$ (*fourth* selected test) $+ b_3$ (given test) $\times c_3$ (*fourth* selected test). To illustrate

For Test 6: $b_4 = .300 + (.400)(-.490) + (-.034)(-.492)$
$+ (.179)(-.353) = .058$

For Test 10: $b_4 = .560 + (.130)(-.490) + (.327)(-.492)$
$+ (.031)(-.353) = .324$

Check the b_4 entries by Step 11 (5). (a) The b_4 entry for the *fourth* selected test (Test 4) equals the Z_4 entry for Test 4 in Table 66, namely, .489. (b) The entry in the criterion column equals the V_4 entry of the *fourth* selected test (Test 4), i.e., −.057. (c) The Check Sum (.715) equals the sum of the entries in the b_4 row.

(2) To find the entries c_4, multiply each b_4 by the *negative reciprocal* of the b_4 entry for the *fourth* selected test (Test 4). The negative reciprocal of .489 is −2.045. To illustrate

For Test 1: $c_4 = -.145 \times -2.045 = .297$.

Check the c_4 entries by Step 11 (7). (a) The c_4 row entry of the *fourth* selected test (Test 4) equals −1.000. (b) The c_4 entry in the Check Sum column, namely, −1.462, equals the sum of the c_4 row. (c) The product of the b_4 and c_4 entries in the criterion column (namely, $-.057 \times .117$) equals the quotient $\dfrac{V_4^2}{Z_4}$ (i.e., .0066) in absolute value.

Step 17

Repeat Step 12 to find V_5 and Z_5. $V_5 = V_4 + b_4$ (criterion) $\times c_4$ (each test); and $Z_5 = Z_4 + b_4$ (a given test) $\times c_4$ (same test). Test 6 has the largest $\left(\dfrac{V_5{}^2}{Z_5}\right)$ quotient (i.e., .0054) and its number is entered in column b, row 5, of Table 67. Following Step 9, we get $\bar{R} = .6591$. This multiple correlation coefficient is smaller than the preceding $\bar{R}$. We need go no further, therefore, as we have reached the point of diminishing returns and the addition of a sixth test will not increase the multiple $\bar{R}$. It may be noted that four (really three) tests constitute a battery which has the highest validity of any combination of tests chosen from our list of ten. The multiple $\bar{R}$ between the criterion and all ten tests would be somewhat lower—when corrected for chance error—than the $\bar{R}$ we have found for our battery of four tests. The Wherry-Doolittle method not only selects the most economical battery but saves a large amount of statistical work.

2. Calculation of the multiple regression equation for tests selected by the Wherry-Doolittle method

Steps involved in setting up a multiple regression equation for the tests selected in Table 68 may be set down as follows:

TABLE 69

	7	9	3	4	−C
c_1	−1.000	−.410	−.560	−.490	.550
c_2		−1.000	−.385	−.492	.389
c_3			−1.000	−.353	.172
c_4				−1.000	.117

Step 1

Draw up a work sheet like that shown in Table 69. Enter the c entries for the four selected tests (namely, 7, 9, 3, and 4) and for the criterion, following the order in which the tests were selected for the battery. When equated to zero, each row in Table 69 is an equation defining the beta weights.

For our four tests, the equations are

$$-1.000\beta_7 - .410\beta_9 - .560\beta_3 - .490\beta_4 + .550 = 0$$
$$-1.000\beta_9 - .385\beta_3 - .492\beta_4 + .389 = 0$$
$$-1.000\beta_3 - .353\beta_4 + .172 = 0$$
$$-1.000\beta_4 + .117 = 0$$

Step 2

Solve the fourth equation to find $\beta_4 = .117$.

Step 3

Substitute for $\beta_4 = .117$ in the third equation to get $\beta_3 = .131$.

Step 4

Substitute for β_3 and β_4 in the second equation to get $\beta_9 = .281$. Finally, substitute for β_3, β_4, and β_9 in the first equation to get $\beta_7 = .305$.

Step 5

The regression equation for predicting the criterion from the four selected tests (7, 9, 3, and 4) may be written in σ-score form by means of formula (115) as follows:

$$\bar{z}_c = \beta_7 z_7 + \beta_9 z_9 + \beta_3 z_3 + \beta_4 z_4$$

in which $\beta_7 = \beta_{c7.934}$; $\beta_9 = \beta_{c9.734}$; $\beta_3 = \beta_{c3.974}$;

$\beta_4 = \beta_{c4.973}$.

Substituting for the β's we have

$$\bar{z}_c = .305 z_7 + .281 z_9 + .131 z_3 + .117 z_4$$

To predict the criterion score of any subject in our group, substitute his scores in tests 7, 9, 3, and 4 (expressed as σ scores) in this equation.

Step 6

To write the regression equation in score form the β's must be transformed into b's by means of formula (114) as follows:

$$b_7 = \frac{\sigma_c}{\sigma_7} \beta_7; \; b_9 = \frac{\sigma_c}{\sigma_9} \beta_9; \; b_3 = \frac{\sigma_c}{\sigma_3} \beta_3; \; b_4 = \frac{\sigma_c}{\sigma_4} \beta_4.$$

The σ's are the SD's of the test scores: σ_7 of Test 7, σ_9 of Test 9, σ_c of the criterion, etc. In general, $b_p = \frac{\sigma_c}{\sigma_p} \beta_p$.

Step 7

The regression equation in score form may now be written

$$X_c = b_7 X_7 + b_9 X_9 + b_3 X_3 + b_4 X_4 + K \qquad * \ (107)$$

and the

$$\sigma_{est \ X_c} = \sigma_c \sqrt{1 - \overline{R}^2_{c(7934)}} \qquad (37)$$

3. Checking the β weights and multiple R

Step 1

The β weights may be checked by formula (116), in which R is expressed in terms of beta coefficients. In the present example, we have

$$R^2_{c(7934)} = \beta_7 r_{c7} + \beta_9 r_{c9} + \beta_3 r_{c3} + \beta_4 r_{c4}$$

in which c equals the criterion and the r's are the correlations between the criterion (c) and the Tests, 7, 9, 3, and 4. Substituting for the r's and β's (computed in the last section) we have

$$R^2_{c(7934)} = .305 \times .550 + .281 \times .550 + .131 \times .530 + .117 \times .520$$
$$= .1678 + .1546 + .0694 + .0608 = .4526$$
$$R_{c(7934)} = .6728$$

From $R^2_{c(7934)}$ we know that our battery accounts for 45% of the variance of the criterion. Also (p. 419) our four tests (7, 9, 3 and 4) contribute 17%, 15%, 7% and 6%, respectively, to the variance of the criterion.

Step 2

The R^2 of .4526 calculated above should equal $(1 - K^2)$ when K^2 is taken from column c, row 4, in Table 67. From Table 67 we find that $1 - K^2 = 1 - .5481$ or .4519 which checks the R^2 found above—and hence the β weights—very closely.

Step 3

It will be noted that the multiple correlation coefficient of .6728 found above is somewhat larger than the shrunken $\overline{R}$ of .6595 found between the

---

* This equation is not written for our four tests because means and SD's are not given in Table 64.

criterion and our battery of four tests in Table 67. The multiple correlation coefficient obtained from a sample always tends—through the operation of chance errors—to be *larger* than the correlation in the population from which the sample was drawn, especially when N is small or the number of test variables large. For this reason, the calculated R must be "adjusted" in order to give us a better estimate of the correlation in the population. The relationship of the $\overline{R}$, corrected for chance errors, to the R as usually calculated, is given by the following equation:

$$\overline{R}^2 = \frac{(N-1)R^2 - (m-1)}{(N-m)} \qquad * (118)$$

(*relation of* R *to* $\overline{R}$ *corrected for chance errors*)

Substituting .4526 for R^2, 99 for $(N-1)$, 96 for $(N-m)$ and 3 for $(m-1)$, we have from (118) that

$$\overline{R}^2 = \frac{99 \times .4526 - 3}{96} = .4355$$

and

$$\overline{R} = .6599 \text{ (see Table 67)}$$

The $\overline{R}$ of .6599 is the corrected multiple correlation between our criterion and test battery, or the multiple correlation coefficient estimated for the population from which our sample was drawn. In the present problem, shrinkage in multiple R is quite small (.6728 − .6599 = .0129) as the sample is fairly large and there are only four tests in the multiple regression equation.

4. Cautions in the use of the Wherry-Doolittle method

The Wherry-Doolittle method is most efficient when a few variables are to be selected from a much larger number. These selected tests may have higher correlations with the criterion than they normally would owing to sampling fluctuations and/or chance errors operating in our sample. When this is true, the resulting multiple R will be too high, and this will appear when correlations are computed from a second sample presumably similar to the first sample. Cross validation of this sort (p. 368) is especially necessary when the number of selected variables is small relative to the total number of variables. Multiple R, as we have seen, is inflated by the presence of chance errors and hence may appear to be much higher than it really is.

* See also formula (113).

II. SPURIOUS CORRELATION

The correlation between two sets of test scores is said to be *spurious* when it is due in some part to factors others than those which determine performance in the tests themselves. In general, spurious correlation arises from a failure properly to control conditions; and the most usual effect of this lack of control is a "boosting" or inflation of the correlation coefficient. Some of the common situations which may lead to spurious correlation are outlined in this section.

1. Spurious correlation arising from heterogeneity

We have shown elsewhere (p. 403) how a lack of uniformity in age level may lead to correlations which are misleadingly high. Failure to take account of heterogeneity introduced by the factor of age is a prolific source of error in correlational work. Within a group of boys 10 to 18 years old, for example, a substantial correlation will appear between strength of grip and memory span, quite apart from any intrinsic relationship, due solely to the fact that both variables increase with age. In stating the correlation between two tests, or the reliability coefficient of a test, one should always be careful to specify the range of ages, grades included, and other data bearing upon physical, mental and cultural differences, in order to show the degree of heterogeneity in the group. Without this information, the r may be of little value.

Heterogeneity is introduced by other factors than age. When alcoholism, degeneracy and bad heredity are all positively related, the r between alcoholism and degeneracy will be too high (because of the effect of heredity upon both factors) unless heredity can be "held constant." Again, assume that we have measured two distinctly different groups, 500 college seniors and 500 day laborers, upon a cancellation test and upon a general intelligence test. The mean ability in both tests will be definitely higher in the college group. Now, even if the correlation between the two tests is zero within each group taken separately, if the two groups are combined a positive correlation will appear because of the heterogeneity of the group with respect to age, intelligence and educational background. Such a correlation is, of course, spurious.

To be a valid measure of relationship, a correlation coefficient should be freed of the extraneous influences which affect the relationship between the two variables concerned. This is not always an easy task, as it is sometimes difficult to determine just what is extraneous. The correlation of a test with a battery of tests of which it is a part is theoretically spurious—higher than it would be were the test omitted from the battery. However, if we want to know which test best represents the entire battery such spurious correlations are quite useful.

2. Spurious index correlation

Even when three variables, X_1, X_2, and X_3, are uncorrelated, a correlation between the indices Z_1 and Z_2 (where $Z_1 = X_1/X_3$ and $Z_2 = X_2/X_3$) may appear which is as large as .50. To illustrate, if two individuals observe a series of magnitudes (e.g., Galton bar settings) independently, the absolute errors of observation (X_1 and X_2) may be uncorrelated, and still an appreciable correlation may appear between the errors made by the two observers, when these are expressed as *percents* of the observed magnitudes (X_3). The spurious element here, of course, is the common factor X_3 in the denominator of the ratios.

One of the commonest examples of a spurious index relationship in psychology is found in the correlation of I.Q.'s or E.Q.'s obtained from intelligence and achievement tests. If the I.Q.'s of 500 children ranging in age from 3 to 14 years are calculated from two tests, X_1 and X_2, the correlation is between $\dfrac{\text{M.A.}_1}{\text{C.A.}}$ and $\dfrac{\text{M.A.}_2}{\text{C.A.}}$. If C.A. were a *constant* (the same for all children) it would have no effect on the correlation and we would simply be correlating M.A.'s. But when C.A. varies from child to child there is usually a correlation between C.A. and M.A. which tends to increase the r between I.Q.'s—sometimes considerably.

3. Spurious correlation between averages

Spurious correlation usually results when the averages scores made by a number of different groups on a given test are correlated against the averages scores made by the same groups on a second test. An example is furnished by the correlations reported between *mean* intelligence test scores, by states, and such "educational" factors as number of schools, books sold, magazines circulated in the states, etc. Most of these correlations are high—many above .90. If average correlations by states are compared with the correlations between intelligence scores and number of years spent in school within the separate states, these latter r's are usually much lower. Correlations between averages become "inflated" because a large number of factors which ordinarily reduce the correlation within a single group cancel out when averages are taken from group to group. Average intelligence test scores, for instances, increase regularly as we go up the occupational scale from day laborer to the professions; but the correlation between intelligence and status (training, salary, etc.) at a given occupational level is far from perfect.

PROBLEMS

1. The following data were assembled for twelve large cities (of around 500,000 inhabitants) in a study of factors making for variation in crime.

X_c (criterion) = crime rate: number known offenses per 1000 inhabitants
$\quad\quad X_1$ = percentage of male inhabitants
$\quad\quad X_2$ = percentage of male native whites of native parentage
$\quad\quad X_3$ = percentage of foreign-born males
$\quad\quad X_4$ = number children under five per 1000 married women 15 to 44 years old
$\quad\quad X_5$ = number Negroes per 100 of population
$\quad\quad X_6$ = number male children of foreign-born parents per 100 of population
$\quad\quad X_7$ = number males and females 10 years and over, in manufacturing, per 100 of population

$M_c = 19.9 \quad M_1 = 49.2 \quad M_2 = 22.8 \quad M_3 = 10.2 \quad M_4 = 481.4 \quad M_5 = 4.7$
$\sigma_c = 7.9 \quad \sigma_1 = 1.3 \quad \sigma_2 = 7.2 \quad \sigma_3 = 4.6 \quad \sigma_4 = 74.4 \quad \sigma_5 = 4.0$
$\quad\quad\quad\quad\quad\quad M_6 = 13.1 \quad M_7 = 21.7$
$\quad\quad\quad\quad\quad\quad \sigma_6 = 4.2 \quad \sigma_7 = 4.3$

Intercorrelations

	1	2	3	4	5	6	7
C	.44	.44	−.34	−.31	.51	−.54	−.20
1		.01	.25	−.19	−.15	.01	.22
2			−.92	−.54	.55	−.93	−.30
3				.44	−.68	.82	.40
4					−.06	.52	.74
5						−.67	−.14
6							.21

(a) By means of the Wherry-Doolittle method select those variables which give a maximum correlation with the criterion.
(b) Work out the regression equation in score form (p. 159) and $\sigma_{(est\ X_c)}$.
(c) Determine the independent contribution of each of the selected factors to crime rate (to R^2).
(d) Compare R and $\bar{R}$. Why is the adjustment fairly large? (See p. 440.)
2. (a) What is the probable crime rate (from problem 1) for a city in which $X_6 = 15.0$, $X_1 = 50\%$? $X_5 = 6.0$?
(b) For a city in which $X_6 = 13$, $X_1 = 48\%$, and $X_5 = 5.0$?

(c) By how much does the use of multiple R reduce $\sigma_{(est\ X_c)}$?
3. In problem 4, page 423:
  (a) Work out the regression equation using the Wherry-Doolittle method.
  (b) How much shrinkage is there when $R_{1(23)}$ is corrected for chance errors (p. 429)?

ANSWERS

1. (a) The $\bar{R}$'s are, for Variable 6, .540; for Variables 6 and 1, .662; for Variables 6, 1 and 5, .692. $\bar{R}$ drops to .688 when Variable 7 is added.
  (b) $\bar{X}_c = -.52X_6 + 3.05X_1 + .79X_5 - 127$; $\sigma_{(est\ X_c)} = 5.7$
  (c) $R_{c(615)} = .15 + .22 + .20$. Variables 6, 1, and 5 contribute approximately 15%, 22% and 20%, respectively.
  (d) $R = .76$; $\bar{R} = .69$
2. (a) 22.4 per 1000 inhabitants
  (b) 16.5 per 1000 inhabitants
  (c) From 7.9 to 5.7 or about 28%.
3. (b) From .60 to .59

CHAPTER 17

DERIVATIONS OF KEY FORMULAS
AND SOME ADDITIONAL TECHNIQUES

◇◇◇

This chapter includes (1) the mathematical derivation of certain key formulas which appear in the text, and (2) several statistical techniques often useful in a specific case but not general enough in application to be put in the text. Students often want to know more about the formulas they use: where they come from, and what they do. And many times a specific procedure, not found in the text, fits a given problem.

I. The sum of the deviations of scores taken from the mean is always zero. (Chapter 3)

Let X_1, X_2, X_3,......X_n represent N scores. The mean is M; and x_1 x_2, x_3,......x_n are deviations of the X's from M. Then

$$X_1 - M = x_1$$
$$X_2 - M = x_2$$
$$X_3 - M = x_3$$
$$\vdots \qquad \vdots \qquad \vdots$$
$$X_n - M = x_n$$

$$\overline{\Sigma X - NM = \Sigma x}$$

Since, by definition, $M = \Sigma X/N$, $NM = \Sigma X$, and the left side of the summation in the final equation above is zero. Σx, of course, is also zero. Hence the sum of the squares of deviations from the mean is always a minimum—is always smaller than the sum of squared deviations taken from any other point. In a mechanical sense, the M is the *center of gravity* in the distribution.

2. Formula for the SD when deviations are taken from an arbitrary or assumed mean. (Chapter 3)

A. When scores are ungrouped:
    By definition (formula 12):

$$\sigma = \sqrt{\frac{\Sigma x^2}{N}}$$

$$\sigma = \sqrt{\frac{\Sigma(X-M)^2}{N}}$$

where X = any score and M is the mean of the distribution.

Expanding, $\sigma = \sqrt{\dfrac{\Sigma X^2}{N} - \dfrac{2M\Sigma X}{N} + NM^2}$

But $M = \dfrac{\Sigma X}{N}$ and substituting,

$$\sigma = \sqrt{\frac{X^2}{N} - 2M^2 + M^2}$$

or
$$\sigma = \sqrt{\frac{\Sigma X^2}{N} - M^2} \qquad \text{Formula (15), p. 53}$$

When scores are taken as deviations from an assumed mean of zero, the mean becomes the correction.

B. When scores are grouped into a frequency distribution:

Let X = any score

M = the mean

$x = X - M$

AM = assumed mean

$x' = X - AM$

i = interval

Then, $X = AM + x' \cdot i$ and

$$M = AM + \frac{\Sigma fx' \cdot i}{N} \qquad \text{(See Table 9, p. 51)}$$

Hence, $x = x' \cdot i - \dfrac{\Sigma fx'i}{N}$, since $x = (X - M)$

Squaring $x^2 = x'^2 i^2 - \dfrac{2x' i^2 \Sigma fx'}{N} + \left(\dfrac{fx'}{N}\right)^2 \cdot i^2$

Dividing by N, $\sigma = \sqrt{\dfrac{1}{N} \Sigma f \left(x'i - \dfrac{\Sigma fx' \cdot i}{N} \right)^2}$ and since $\sigma = \sqrt{\dfrac{\Sigma fx^2}{N}}$

$$\sigma = \sqrt{i^2 \left[\frac{\Sigma fx'^2}{N} - \left(\frac{\Sigma fx'}{N} \right)^2 \right]}$$

or $\qquad\qquad \sigma = i \sqrt{\dfrac{\Sigma fx'^2}{N} - c^2}$ $\qquad\qquad\qquad$ (14)

when $\qquad\qquad \dfrac{\Sigma fx'}{N} = \text{correction (c)}$

3. The normal probability distribution. (Chapter 5)

The meaning of the normal probability distribution may be clarified through two approaches: (1) by way of the binomial distribution, and (2) by deriving an equation to fit the known properties of the curve.

(1) We have seen (pp. 89-94) that the binomial expression $(p + q)^n$ approaches the normal form shown in Figure 21, when $p = q = \frac{1}{2}$ and n becomes infinitely large. The tendency for the distributions of many human traits to take the bell-shaped form suggests—but does not prove—that the occurrence of physical and mental traits in the general population may be determined by the operation of a very large number of genetic factors which combine by chance. The student of biology will see here the relationship to Mendel's theory.

(2) The equation * of the normal probability curve (Figure 21) as given on p. 96 is

$$y = \frac{N}{\sigma\sqrt{2\pi}} e^{\dfrac{-x^2}{2\sigma^2}}$$ (22)

in which $x =$ deviation of an X score from M_x

$\qquad y = $ " " a Y " " M_y

$\qquad N =$ number of cases

$\qquad \sigma =$ the standard deviation

$\qquad \pi = 3.1416$ a constant, the ratio of the circumference of a circle to its diameter

$\qquad e = 2.7183$, base of the Napierian system of logarithms

Examination of the above equation shows that

(a) when $x = 0$ (x is at the center of the curve), the term $e^{\dfrac{-x^2}{2\sigma^2}}$ equals 1.00, and $y_0 = \dfrac{N}{\sigma\sqrt{2\pi}}$. Thus y_0 is the maximum ordinate, and stands at the center

* Students unfamiliar with the calculus may not follow all of the details of this derivation, but they should understand its rationale.

of the curve. When $y = 0$, the equation becomes $\dfrac{1}{e^{\frac{x^2}{2\sigma^2}}} = 0$, and x approaches ∞ as y approaches zero. Hence it is clear that equation (22) has a maximum at the mean and that the curve (x-values) stretch to infinity in the $+$ and $-$ directions from the mean.

(b) since x in the formula is squared, either $+$ or $-$ values have the same effect, and the curve is bilaterally symmetrical.

T. L. Kelley * has proposed a differential equation, $\dfrac{dy}{dx} = C\,xy$ as a good starting point in our derivation. This equation has an origin at 0, and the slope of the curve is 0 both when $x = 0$ and $y = 0$. These are important characteristics of the normal probability curve.

We can integrate the expression $\dfrac{dy}{dx} = C\,xy$ in the following steps: †

$$dy \cdot \frac{1}{y} = -C\,x$$

or
$$\log y = \frac{-C\,x^2}{2} + k$$

or
$$y = k\,e^{\frac{-C\,x^2}{2}}$$

To evaluate the constant k, we must go to the moments ‡ of the distribution:

The zero moment is N or $k\sqrt{\dfrac{2\pi}{c}}$

1st   ''   '' 0

2nd   ''   '' $N \cdot \sigma^2$ or $\dfrac{k}{c}\sqrt{\dfrac{2\pi}{c}}$

Solving for c and k in the first and third equations of the moments, we find that $c = 1/\sigma^2$ and $k = N/\sigma\sqrt{2\pi}$. This gives finally by substitution in the third integral equation:

$$y = \frac{N}{\sigma\sqrt{2\pi}}\,e^{\frac{-x^2}{2\sigma^2}} \tag{22}$$

---

* Kelley, T. L., *Statistical Method* (New York: Macmillan Co., 1923), p. 94.

† All of the integrals used in this derivation were taken from Peirce, B. O., *A Short Table of Integrals* (Boston: Ginn and Co., 1910), pp. 62–63 especially.

‡ For meaning of moments, see Treloar, A. E., *Elements of Statistical Reasoning* (New York: John Wiley, 1939), Chapter 5.

Certain properties of the normal curve are important:

(a) the points of inflection in the curve are $\pm 1\ SD$ from the mean. These are the points at which the curve changes its direction from concave to convex.

(b) The Q or $PE = .6745\ SD$. One PE laid off in the $+$ and $-$ directions from the M includes the middle 50% of the cases (p. 99).

4. The product-moment (Pearson) coefficient of correlation.

Chapters 6 and 7 have given several formulas for the coefficient of correlation (r), and have illustrated many of their uses. The present section will outline a mathematical derivation for r.

A straightforward way of deriving r is to compute it from the regression equations. On page 157, we gave the equation of the straight line which passes through the origin as

$$y = mx$$

wherein m is the slope of the line, i.e., the tangent of the angle a which the line makes with the X-axis. (See Figure 41).

In Figure 70, a correlation diagram has been laid out in σ-units. These z-scores (p. 312) provide a scale in which the units are equal. Our goal is to set up a line $y = mx$ which will "best fit" the means of the columns

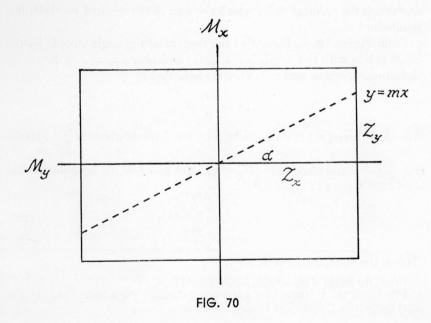

FIG. 70

(or rows).* The slope of the line $y = mx$ in Figure 70 is z_y/z_x which is also the tangent of the angle a. The degree of the relationship between y and x is measured by the tangent of the angle which the best fitting line makes with the X-axis. As the relation changes (see p. 131) the tangent of a also changes. It is 0 when the relation line coincides with the horizontal axis and 1.00 when it coincides with vertical axis. Hence, the tangent or r may be thought of as a measure of the correlation between x and y.

When $y = mx$

$(y - mx) = e$, is a residual, i.e., measures the amount by which the y predicted from x (mx) misses the actual value of y.

Squaring and summing: $\Sigma(y - mx)^2 = \Sigma e^2$ for the whole group.

In order to make Σe^2 a minimum (i.e., reduce the errors of measurement as much as possible), we must differentiate $\Sigma(y - mx)^2$ with respect to m and set the result equal to zero.†

$$\frac{\partial(\Sigma y^2 - 2m\Sigma xy + \Sigma x^2 m^2)}{\partial m} = -2\Sigma xy + 2m\Sigma x^2 = 0$$

Putting this last expression equal to zero and solving for m, we have that

$$m = \frac{\Sigma xy}{\Sigma x^2}$$

and this is the value of m for which the sum of the squared residuals is a minimum.†

From Figure 70, we know that the tangent of the angle a made by the relation line with the X-axis is $r = z_y/z_x$ and hence $z_y = r\, z_x$. Since, by definition, $z_x = x/\sigma_x$ and $z_y = y/\sigma_y$, we have that

$$y = r\frac{\sigma_y}{\sigma_x} \cdot x$$

The slope here (m) is $r\, \sigma_y/\sigma_x$ which by the formula above is $\dfrac{\Sigma xy}{\Sigma x^2}$. Hence

$r = \dfrac{\Sigma xy \cdot \sigma_x}{\Sigma x^2 \cdot \sigma_y}$; and since $\sigma_x = \sqrt{\dfrac{\Sigma x^2}{N}}$ and $\Sigma x^2 = \sigma_x{}^2 \cdot N$ we have finally that

$$r = \frac{\Sigma xy \cdot \sigma_x}{N\,\sigma^2{}_x \cdot \sigma_y}$$

$$\text{or } r = \frac{\Sigma xy}{N\,\sigma_x \cdot \sigma_y}$$

This is the standard formula for r.

* Only the means of the columns are considered here.
† Granville, W. A., *Differential and Integral Calculus* (New York: Ginn and Co., 1911), especially Chapter 3 on Maxima and Minima.

5. An interpretation of r in terms of displacement.

Another interpretation of *r* (see p. 175) which is often useful is provided by Table 70. Knowing the correlation between two sets of scores, we can read the probability that a student's score in the second test will miss his score in the first test, and by how much. Suppose, for example, that the correlation between an Aptitude Test and grades in high school is .60. Going down the first column in Table 70 to .60, we read that the chances are 29 in 100 that a student's grade will be in the same "tenth" of the distribution as his Aptitude score. The chances are 73 in 100 that the grade will not be "displaced" with reference to aptitude by more than one tenth of the grade distribution; and we may be virtually certain (chances are 99.2 in 100) that the grade will not be displaced with reference to aptitude by more than three tenths.

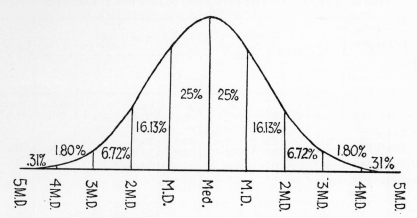

FIG. 71   Illustrating the division of the base of a normal surface of frequency into "tenths." M.D. = PE

Figure 71 shows the meaning of "tenths" of score. In the diagram, the baseline of a normal probability curve has been divided into 10 equal parts—5 on each side of the mean. The unit of measurement is the probable error ($PE = .6745\ \sigma$, p. 99). Just 25% of the cases in the distribution fall within that part of the curve $+$ and $- 1\ PE$ from the mean; 16.13% fall in the next two divisions on each side of the mean, and so on. The top and bottom tenths contain just .31 of 1%. All of these proportions can be verified from Table A. [$M.D.$ (mean deviation) $= PE$]

Another illustration will serve to clarify this interpretation in terms of displacement. Suppose that the WISC has been administered to 100 second grade children, and 6 months later is repeated. The correlation, say, is .80. For the WISC, the σ is 15 and the PE is approximately 10. Hence both distributions can be marked off into 10 equal IQ widths (see Figure 71). From Table 70 we know that 41 of the 100 children should—on the second test—have IQs in the same tenth as in the first test. There are 89 children who should not be displaced by more than one tenth, i.e., 10 IQ points in the second test, and virtually all vary by less than two tenths, i.e., 20 IQ points.

TABLE 70

Showing, for various amounts of correlation, the chances in 100 that the second measure of an individual will be in the same "tenth" of a distribution, not displaced more than 1 "tenth," 2 "tenths," etc. The sixth line is read as follows: In the case of a .50 correlation the chances are only 26 in 100 that an individual's second score will be in the same "tenth" of the distribution as his first score; the chances are 69 in 100 that his second score will not be displaced by more than 1 "tenth"; etc.

COEF-FICIENT OF CORRE-LATION	NUMBER OF "TENTHS" DISPLACEMENT							
	0	1	2	3	4	5	6	7
.00	19	53	77	91	97	99.2	99.8	99.9 +
.10	20	55	79	92	98	99.4	99.9	
.20	21	58	82	94	98	99.6	99.9 +	
.30	22	61	85	95	99.0	99.8	99.9 +	
.40	24	64	88	97	99.5	99.9 +		
.50	26	69	91	98	99.7	99.9 +		
.60	29	73	94	99.2	99.9 +			
.70	34	81	97	99.8	99.9 +			
.80	41	89	99.2	99.9 +				
.90	55	98	99.9 +					
.95	71	99.9						
.98	91							
1.00	100							

6. Semi-partial correlation.

We have seen (p. 407) that $r_{12.3}$ denotes the correlation between variables 1 and 2 with 3 constant: or more exactly with the variability introduced by 3 "partialled out" or eliminated from the correlation r_{12}. If variable 1 = height, variable 2 = weight, and variable 3 = age, then $r_{12.3}$ is the correlation between height and weight for children of the same age.

Another variety of controlled correlation, called semi-partial correlation, eliminates the influence of the third variable from only *one* of the two correlated variables. The formula for the correlation between Test #1 and that part of Test #2 which is independent of Test #3 may be written:

$$r_{1(2.3)} = \frac{r_{12} - r_{13}r_{23}}{\sqrt{1 - r_{23}^2}} \qquad (119)$$

(Coefficient of semi-partial correlation: variable 3 partialled out from variable 2)

To illustrate, suppose we have the following data from 150 high school students:

$$1 = \text{mathematics test}$$
$$2 = \text{grades in mathematics}$$
$$3 = \text{a verbal ability test}$$

$$r_{12} = .70 \qquad r_{13} = .10 \qquad r_{23} = .50$$

What is $r_{1(2.3)}$; that is, what is the semi-partial correlation between the mathematics test and teachers' grades in mathematics when verbal ability is eliminated from the teacher's grades? Substituting in (119) above, we have

$$r_{1(2.3)} = \frac{.70 - .10 \times .50}{.87} = .75$$

which means that by removing the variability in the teacher's grades induced by verbal ability scores, we raise the correlation between our mathematics test and grades by .05. Apparently when marking the students for mathematics, teachers were influenced somewhat by the verbal expression of the students. But the influence was not great.

For comparison, we may compute the partial correlation between mathematics test and grades with verbal ability scores constant.

$$r_{12.3} = \frac{.70 - .10 \times .50}{.995 \times .87} = .75$$

The result is the same as when verbal ability was partialled out of grades only. The obvious reason is the negligible correlation between the mathematics test and verbal ability; the only influence of the latter is on grades.

Semi-partial correlation can be extended to provide for the elimination of two or more variables from one of the two correlated tests, e.g., $r_{1(2.345)}$, where variables 3, 4, and 5 are controlled with respect to variable 2.*

* For additional formulas, see Dunlap, J., and Cureton, E., On the Analysis of Causation, Jour. Educ. Psychol., 1930, 21, 657.

7. Homogeneity of variance; tests of significance.

Sometimes an investigator wants to test the null hypothesis with reference to the means obtained from two samples differing sharply in variability. We pointed out on page 286 that t and F are valid tests of the null hypothesis for means when samples have been drawn at random from a normally distributed population. The means may or may not differ significantly and thus cause us to reject or accept the null hypothesis. But the variances in the samples are assumed in our tests of significance to be equal except for fluctuations of sampling. When variances differ significantly, the t and F tests are not valid, and a change in method is demanded. Two situations arise: when $N_1 = N_2$ and when N_1 does not equal N_2.

Case 1: When $N_1 = N_2$.

Consider the data in the table below: *

Sample	N	df	Means	x^2
1	10	9	35.8	1041.6
2	10	9	28.0	174.0
		18	7.8	1215.6

$$SD = \sqrt{\frac{1041.6 + 174.0}{18}} = 8.22 \qquad SE_D = 8.22\sqrt{\frac{20}{100}} \qquad \begin{array}{l} t = 7.8/3.67 \\ t = 2.12 \end{array}$$
$$= 3.67$$

The first sample of 10 cases was drawn from a normal population with $M = 30$ and $\sigma = 10$; and the second sample from a normal population with $M = 30$ and $\sigma = 5$. Hence the null hypothesis obviously should hold for the means of our two samples. But the assumption of equal variance is certainly not tenable.

Following the method outlined on page 224 and formulas (57) and (58), we get an SE_D of 3.67 from the pooled sums of squares used in computing the common SD. Since $M_1 - M_2 = 7.8$, t is 7.8/3.67 or 2.12. When $df = 18$, $P_{.05} = 2.10$, and we would reject the null hypothesis, though just barely. When the correct number of df is taken, namely, 9 or ½ total df, however, we have a $P_{.05} = 2.26$, and we can now clearly accept the null hypothesis, as we should.

The correct procedure when variances differ markedly and $N_1 = N_2$ is to take ½ of the df when reading $P_{.05}$ from Table D.

---

* Adapted with slight changes from Snedecor, G. W., *Statistical Methods* (Ames, Iowa: Iowa State College Press, 1956), pp. 97–98.

Case 2: When N_1 does not equal N_2.

When N_1 does not equal N_2, a modification of the method given above is required. In the table below, the sample of 13 has been drawn (as in the example above) from a normal population with $M = 30$ and $\sigma = 10$. And the second sample of 5 has been drawn from a normal population with $M = 30$ and $\sigma = 5$. Again it is clear that the null hypothesis for the means should be accepted.

Sample	N	df	P.05	Means	SD^2	SE^2 (means)
1	13	12	2.18	37.23	88.53	6.81
2	5	4	2.78	30.00	46.50	9.30
				7.23		16.11

$$SE_D = \sqrt{6.81 + 9.30} = 4.01 \qquad t' = 7.23/4.01 = 1.80$$

The SE_D is obtained from the two SE's taken separately, not pooled as before. The .05 level for testing t' is given approximately by the weighted mean of the two t's taken from Table D, for 12 and 4 degrees of freedom; and the two weights are the SE^2's of the means. Calculations are as follows:

For sample 1, the df are 12 and the $t_{.05} = 2.18$

" " 2 " " " 4 and the $t_{.05} = 2.78$

$$5\% \text{ level for } t' \text{ is } \frac{6.81 \times 2.18 + 9.30 \times 2.78}{16.11} = 2.52$$

The t' of 1.80 clearly falls below the .05 level of 2.52 and the null hypothesis is accepted.

This test is approximate and is subject to Type I errors (p. 219). The null hypothesis may be rejected when true. Perhaps the best plan is to repeat the test with increased samples.

Case 3: When there are more than two samples.

To test for homogeneity of variance when there are several samples, Bartlett's test is customarily used. It is given in detail in the reference below.*

* Snedecor, *op. cit.*, pp. 285–289.

TABLES

❖❖❖

TABLE A Fractional parts of the total area (taken as 10,000) under the normal probability curve, corresponding to distances on the baseline between the meun and successive points laid off from the mean in units of standard deviation

Example: between the mean and a point 1.38σ $\left(\dfrac{x}{\sigma} = 1.38\right)$ are found 41.62% of the entire area under the curve.

$\dfrac{x}{\sigma}$	.00	.01	.02	.03	.04	.05	.06	.07	.08	.09
0.0	0000	0040	0080	0120	0160	0199	0239	0279	0319	0359
0.1	0398	0438	0478	0517	0557	0596	0636	0675	0714	0753
0.2	0793	0832	0871	0910	0948	0987	1026	1064	1103	1141
0.3	1179	1217	1255	1293	1331	1368	1406	1443	1480	1517
0.4	1554	1591	1628	1664	1700	1736	1772	1808	1844	1879
0.5	1915	1950	1985	2019	2054	2088	2123	2157	2190	2224
0.6	2257	2291	2324	2357	2389	2422	2454	2486	2517	2549
0.7	2580	2611	2642	2673	2704	2734	2764	2794	2823	2852
0.8	2881	2910	2939	2967	2995	3023	3051	3078	3106	3133
0.9	3159	3186	3212	3238	3264	3290	3315	3340	3365	3389
1.0	3413	3438	3461	3485	3508	3531	3554	3577	3599	3621
1.1	3643	3665	3686	3708	3729	3749	3770	3790	3810	3830
1.2	3849	3869	3888	3907	3925	3944	3962	3980	3997	4015
1.3	4032	4049	4066	4082	4099	4115	4131	4147	4162	4177
1.4	4192	4207	4222	4236	4251	4265	4279	4292	4306	4319
1.5	4332	4345	4357	4370	4383	4394	4406	4418	4429	4441
1.6	4452	4463	4474	4484	4495	4505	4515	4525	4535	4545
1.7	4554	4564	4573	4582	4591	4599	4608	4616	4625	4633
1.8	4641	4649	4656	4664	4671	4678	4686	4693	4699	4706
1.9	4713	4719	4726	4732	4738	4744	4750	4756	4761	4767
2.0	4772	4778	4783	4788	4793	4798	4803	4808	4812	4817
2.1	4821	4826	4830	4834	4838	4842	4846	4850	4854	4857
2.2	4861	4864	4868	4871	4875	4878	4881	4884	4887	4890
2.3	4893	4896	4898	4901	4904	4906	4909	4911	4913	4916
2.4	4918	4920	4922	4925	4927	4929	4931	4932	4934	4936
2.5	4938	4940	4941	4943	4945	4946	4948	4949	4951	4952
2.6	4953	4955	4956	4957	4959	4960	4961	4962	4963	4964
2.7	4965	4966	4967	4968	4969	4970	4971	4972	4973	4974
2.8	4974	4975	4976	4977	4977	4978	4979	4979	4980	4981
2.9	4981	4982	4982	4983	4984	4984	4985	4985	4986	4986
3.0	4986.5	4986.9	4987.4	4987.8	4988.2	4988.6	4988.9	4989.3	4989.7	4990.0
3.1	4990.3	4990.6	4991.0	4991.3	4991.6	4991.8	4992.1	4992.4	4992.6	4992.9
3.2	4993.129									
3.3	4995.166									
3.4	4996.631									
3.5	4997.674									
3.6	4998.409									
3.7	4998.922									
3.8	4999.277									
3.9	4999.519									
4.0	4999.683									
4.5	4999.966									
5.0	4999.997133									

TABLE B Ordinates of the normal probability curve expressed as fractional parts of the mean ordinate, y_o

The height of the ordinate erected at the mean can be computed from $y_o = \dfrac{N}{\sigma\sqrt{2\pi}}$ where $\sqrt{2\pi} = 2.51$ and $\dfrac{1}{\sqrt{2\pi}} = .3989$. The height of any other ordinate, in terms of y_o, can be read from the table when one knows the distance which the ordinate is from the mean. For example: the height of an ordinate a distance of -2.37σ from the mean is $.06029\ y_o$. Decimals have been omitted in the body of the table.

$\dfrac{x}{\sigma}$	0	1	2	3	4	5	6	7	8	9
0.0	100000	99995	99980	99955	99920	99875	99820	99755	99685	99596
0.1	99501	99396	99283	99158	99025	98881	98728	98565	98393	98211
0.2	98020	97819	97609	97390	97161	96923	96676	96420	96156	95882
0.3	95600	95309	95010	94702	94387	94055	93723	93382	93024	92677
0.4	92312	91399	91558	91169	90774	90371	89961	89543	89119	88688
0.5	88250	87805	87353	86896	86432	85962	85488	85006	84519	84060
0.6	83527	83023	82514	82010	81481	80957	80429	79896	79359	78817
0.7	78270	77721	77167	76610	76048	75484	74916	74342	73769	73193
0.8	72615	72033	71448	70861	70272	69681	69087	68493	67896	67298
0.9	66689	66097	65494	64891	64287	63683	63077	62472	61865	61259
1.0	60653	60047	59440	58834	58228	57623	57017	56414	55810	55209
1.1	54607	54007	53409	52812	52214	51620	51027	50437	49848	49260
1.2	48675	48092	47511	46933	46357	45783	45212	44644	44078	43516
1.3	42956	42399	41845	41294	40747	40202	39661	39123	38569	38058
1.4	37531	37007	36487	35971	35459	34950	34445	33944	33447	32954
1.5	32465	31980	31500	31023	30550	30082	29618	29158	28702	28251
1.6	27804	27361	26923	26489	26059	25634	25213	24797	24385	23978
1.7	23575	23176	22782	22392	22008	21627	21251	20879	20511	20148
1.8	19790	19436	19086	18741	18400	18064	17732	17404	17081	16762
1.9	16448	16137	15831	15530	15232	14939	14650	14364	14083	13806
2.0	13534	13265	13000	12740	12483	12230	11981	11737	11496	11259
2.1	11025	10795	10570	10347	10129	09914	09702	09495	09290	09090
2.2	08892	08698	08507	08320	08136	07956	07778	07604	07433	07265
2.3	07100	06939	06780	06624	06471	06321	06174	06029	05888	05750
2.4	05614	05481	05350	05222	05096	04973	04852	04734	04618	04505
2.5	04394	04285	04179	04074	03972	03873	03775	03680	03586	03494
2.6	03405	03317	03232	03148	03066	02986	02908	02831	02757	02684
2.7	02612	02542	02474	02408	02343	02280	02218	02157	02098	02040
2.8	01984	01929	01876	01823	01772	01723	01674	01627	01581	01536
2.9	01492	01449	01408	01367	01328	01288	01252	01215	01179	01145
3.0	01111	00819	00598	00432	00309	00219	00153	00106	00073	00050
4.0	00034	00022	00015	00010	00006	00004	00003	00002	00001	00001
5.0	00000									

TABLE C Conversion of a Pearson *r* into a corresponding Fisher's *z* coefficient *

r	z	r	z	r	z	r	z	r	z	r	z
.25	.26	.40	.42	.55	.62	.70	.87	.85	1.26	.950	1.83
.26	.27	.41	.44	.56	.63	.71	.89	.86	1.29	.955	1.89
.27	.28	.42	.45	.57	.65	.72	.91	.87	1.33	.960	1.95
.28	.29	.43	.46	.58	.66	.73	.93	.88	1.38	.965	2.01
.29	.30	.44	.47	.59	.68	.74	.95	.89	1.42	.970	2.09
.30	.31	.45	.48	.60	.69	.75	.97	.90	1.47	.975	2.18
.31	.32	.46	.50	.61	.71	.76	1.00	.905	1.50	.980	2.30
.32	.33	.47	.51	.62	.73	.77	1.02	.910	1.53	.985	2.44
.33	.34	.48	.52	.63	.74	.78	1.05	.915	1.56	.990	2.65
.34	.35	.49	.54	.64	.76	.79	1.07	.920	1.59	.995	2.99
.35	.37	.50	.55	.65	.78	.80	1.10	.925	1.62		
.36	.38	.51	.56	.66	.79	.81	1.13	.930	1.66		
.37	.39	.52	.58	.67	.81	.82	1.16	.935	1.70		
.38	.40	.53	.59	.68	.83	.83	1.19	.940	1.74		
.39	.41	.54	.60	.69	.85	.84	1.22	.945	1.78		

* *r*'s under .25 may be taken as equivalent to *z*'s.

TABLE D Table of t, for use in determining the significance of statistics

Example: When the df are 35 and $t = 2.03$, the .05 in column 3 means that 5 times in 100 trials a divergence as large as that obtained may be expected in the positive *and* negative directions under the null hypothesis.

Degrees of Freedom	Probability (P)			
	0.10	0.05	0.02	0.01
1	$t = 6.34$	$t = 12.71$	$t = 31.82$	$t = 63.66$
2	2.92	4.30	6.96	9.92
3	2.35	3.18	4.54	5.84
4	2.13	2.78	3.75	4.60
5	2.02	2.57	3.36	4.03
6	1.94	2.45	3.14	3.71
7	1.90	2.36	3.00	3.50
8	1.86	2.31	2.90	3.36
9	1.83	2.26	2.82	3.25
10	1.81	2.23	2.76	3.17
11	1.80	2.20	2.72	3.11
12	1.78	2.18	2.68	3.06
13	1.77	2.16	2.65	3.01
14	1.76	2.14	2.62	2.98
15	1.75	2.13	2.60	2.95
16	1.75	2.12	2.58	2.92
17	1.74	2.11	2.57	2.90
18	1.73	2.10	2.55	2.88
19	1.73	2.09	2.54	2.86
20	1.72	2.09	2.53	2.84
21	1.72	2.08	2.52	2.83
22	1.72	2.07	2.51	2.82
23	1.71	2.07	2.50	2.81
24	1.71	2.06	2.49	2.80
25	1.71	2.06	2.48	2.79
26	1.71	2.06	2.48	2.78
27	1.70	2.05	2.47	2.77
28	1.70	2.05	2.47	2.76
29	1.70	2.04	2.46	2.76
30	1.70	2.04	2.46	2.75
35	1.69	2.03	2.44	2.72
40	1.68	2.02	2.42	2.71
45	1.68	2.02	2.41	2.69
50	1.68	2.01	2.40	2.68
60	1.67	2.00	2.39	2.66
70	1.67	2.00	2.38	2.65
80	1.66	1.99	2.38	2.64
90	1.66	1.99	2.37	2.63
100	1.66	1.98	2.36	2.63
125	1.66	1.98	2.36	2.62
150	1.66	1.98	2.35	2.61
200	1.65	1.97	2.35	2.60
300	1.65	1.97	2.34	2.59
400	1.65	1.97	2.34	2.59
500	1.65	1.96	2.33	2.59
1000	1.65	1.96	2.33	2.58
∞	1.65	1.96	2.33	2.58

TABLE E χ^2 Table. P gives the probability of exceeding the tabulated value of χ^2 for the specified number of degrees of freedom (df). The values of χ^2 are printed in the body of the table.*

df	0.95	0.90	0.80	0.70	0.50	0.30	0.20	0.10	0.05	0.02	0.01
1	0.00393	0.0158	0.0642	0.148	0.455	1.074	1.642	2.706	3.841	5.412	6.635
2	0.103	0.211	0.446	0.713	1.386	2.408	3.219	4.605	5.991	7.824	9.210
3	0.352	0.584	1.005	1.424	2.366	3.665	4.642	6.251	7.815	9.837	11.345
4	0.711	1.064	1.649	2.195	3.357	4.878	5.989	7.779	9.488	11.668	13.277
5	1.145	1.610	2.343	3.000	4.351	6.064	7.289	9.236	11.070	13.388	15.086
6	1.635	2.204	3.070	3.828	5.348	7.231	8.558	10.645	12.592	15.033	16.812
7	2.167	2.833	3.822	4.671	6.346	8.383	9.803	12.017	14.067	16.622	18.475
8	2.733	3.490	4.594	5.527	7.344	9.524	11.030	13.362	15.507	18.168	20.090
9	3.325	4.168	5.380	6.393	8.343	10.656	12.242	14.684	16.919	19.679	21.666
10	3.940	4.865	6.179	7.267	9.342	11.781	13.442	15.987	18.307	21.161	23.209
11	4.575	5.578	6.989	8.148	10.341	12.899	14.631	17.275	19.675	22.618	24.725
12	5.226	6.304	7.807	9.034	11.340	14.011	15.812	18.549	21.026	24.054	26.217
13	5.892	7.042	8.634	9.926	12.340	15.119	16.985	19.812	22.362	25.472	27.688
14	6.571	7.790	9.467	10.821	13.339	16.222	18.151	21.064	23.685	26.873	29.141
15	7.261	8.547	10.307	11.721	14.339	17.322	19.311	22.307	24.996	28.259	30.578
16	7.962	9.312	11.152	12.624	15.338	18.418	20.465	23.542	26.296	29.633	32.000
17	8.672	10.085	12.002	13.531	16.338	19.511	21.615	24.769	27.587	30.995	33.409
18	9.390	10.865	12.857	14.440	17.338	20.601	22.760	25.989	28.869	32.346	34.805
19	10.117	11.651	13.716	15.352	18.338	21.689	23.900	27.204	30.144	33.687	36.191
20	10.851	12.443	14.578	16.266	19.337	22.775	25.038	28.412	31.410	35.020	37.566
21	11.591	13.240	15.445	17.182	20.337	23.858	26.171	29.615	32.671	36.343	38.932
22	12.338	14.041	16.314	18.101	21.337	24.939	27.301	30.813	33.924	37.659	40.289
23	13.091	14.848	17.187	19.021	22.337	26.018	28.429	32.007	35.172	38.968	41.638
24	13.848	15.659	18.062	19.943	23.337	27.096	29.553	33.196	36.415	40.270	42.980
25	14.611	16.473	18.940	20.867	24.337	28.172	30.675	34.382	37.652	41.566	44.314
26	15.379	17.292	19.820	21.792	25.336	29.246	31.795	35.563	38.885	42.856	45.642
27	16.151	18.114	20.703	22.719	26.336	30.319	32.912	36.741	40.113	44.140	46.963
28	16.928	18.939	21.588	23.647	27.336	31.391	34.027	37.916	41.337	45.419	48.278
29	17.708	19.768	22.475	24.577	28.336	32.461	35.139	39.087	42.557	46.693	49.588
30	18.493	20.599	23.364	25.508	29.336	33.530	36.250	40.256	43.773	47.962	50.892

* Adapted from R. A. Fisher's *Statistical Method for Research Workers*, Oliver & Boyd, by permission of publishers.

TABLE F F-ratios for .05 (roman) and .01 (boldface) levels of significance

Degrees of freedom for smaller mean square	Degrees of freedom for greater mean square									
	1	2	3	4	5	6	8	12	24	∞
1	161.45 **4052.10**	199.50 **4999.03**	215.72 **5403.49**	224.57 **5625.14**	230.17 **5764.08**	233.97 **5859.39**	238.89 **5981.34**	243.91 **6105.83**	249.04 **6234.16**	254.32 **6366.48**
2	18.51 **98.49**	19.00 **99.01**	19.16 **99.17**	19.25 **99.25**	19.30 **99.30**	19.33 **99.33**	19.37 **99.36**	19.41 **99.42**	19.45 **99.46**	19.50 **99.50**
3	10.13 **34.12**	9.55 **30.81**	9.28 **29.46**	9.12 **28.71**	9.01 **28.24**	8.94 **27.91**	8.84 **27.49**	8.74 **27.05**	8.64 **26.60**	8.53 **26.12**
4	7.71 **21.20**	6.94 **18.00**	6.59 **16.69**	6.39 **15.98**	6.26 **15.52**	6.16 **15.21**	6.04 **14.80**	5.91 **14.37**	5.77 **13.93**	5.63 **13.46**
5	6.61 **16.26**	5.79 **13.27**	5.41 **12.06**	5.19 **11.39**	5.05 **10.97**	4.95 **10.67**	4.82 **10.27**	4.68 **9.89**	4.53 **9.47**	4.36 **9.02**
6	5.99 **13.74**	5.14 **10.92**	4.76 **9.78**	4.53 **9.15**	4.39 **8.75**	4.28 **8.47**	4.15 **8.10**	4.00 **7.72**	3.84 **7.31**	3.67 **6.88**
7	5.59 **12.25**	4.74 **9.55**	4.35 **8.45**	4.12 **7.85**	3.97 **7.46**	3.87 **7.19**	3.73 **6.84**	3.57 **6.47**	3.41 **6.07**	3.23 **5.65**
8	5.32 **11.26**	4.46 **8.65**	4.07 **7.59**	3.84 **7.01**	3.69 **6.63**	3.58 **6.37**	3.44 **6.03**	3.28 **5.67**	3.12 **5.28**	2.93 **4.86**
9	5.12 **10.56**	4.26 **8.02**	3.86 **6.99**	3.63 **6.42**	3.48 **6.06**	3.37 **5.80**	3.23 **5.47**	3.07 **5.11**	2.90 **4.73**	2.71 **4.31**
10	4.96 **10.04**	4.10 **7.56**	3.71 **6.55**	3.48 **5.99**	3.33 **5.64**	3.22 **5.39**	3.07 **5.06**	2.91 **4.71**	2.74 **4.33**	2.54 **3.91**
11	4.84 **9.65**	3.98 **7.20**	3.59 **6.22**	3.36 **5.67**	3.20 **5.32**	3.09 **5.07**	2.95 **4.74**	2.79 **4.40**	2.61 **4.02**	2.40 **3.60**

TABLE F—(Continued)

Degrees of freedom for smaller mean square	Degrees of freedom for greater mean square									
	1	2	3	4	5	6	8	12	24	∞
12	4.75 / 9.33	3.88 / 6.93	3.49 / 5.95	3.26 / 5.41	3.11 / 5.06	3.00 / 4.82	2.85 / 4.50	2.69 / 4.16	2.50 / 3.78	2.30 / 3.36
13	4.67 / 9.07	3.80 / 6.70	3.41 / 5.74	3.18 / 5.20	3.02 / 4.86	2.92 / 4.62	2.77 / 4.30	2.60 / 3.96	2.42 / 3.59	2.21 / 3.16
14	4.60 / 8.86	3.74 / 6.51	3.34 / 5.56	3.11 / 5.03	2.96 / 4.69	2.85 / 4.46	2.70 / 4.14	2.53 / 3.80	2.35 / 3.43	2.13 / 3.00
15	4.54 / 8.68	3.68 / 6.36	3.29 / 5.42	3.06 / 4.89	2.90 / 4.56	2.79 / 4.32	2.64 / 4.00	2.48 / 3.67	2.29 / 3.29	2.07 / 2.87
16	4.49 / 8.53	3.63 / 6.23	3.24 / 5.29	3.01 / 4.77	2.85 / 4.44	2.74 / 4.20	2.59 / 3.89	2.42 / 3.55	2.24 / 3.18	2.01 / 2.75
17	4.45 / 8.40	3.59 / 6.11	3.20 / 5.18	2.96 / 4.67	2.81 / 4.34	2.70 / 4.10	2.55 / 3.79	2.38 / 3.45	2.19 / 3.08	1.96 / 2.65
18	4.41 / 8.28	3.55 / 6.01	3.16 / 5.09	2.93 / 4.58	2.77 / 4.25	2.66 / 4.01	2.51 / 3.71	2.34 / 3.37	2.15 / 3.01	1.92 / 2.57
19	4.38 / 8.18	3.52 / 5.93	3.13 / 5.01	2.90 / 4.50	2.74 / 4.17	2.63 / 3.94	2.48 / 3.63	2.31 / 3.30	2.11 / 2.92	1.88 / 2.49
20	4.35 / 8.10	3.49 / 5.85	3.10 / 4.94	2.87 / 4.43	2.71 / 4.10	2.60 / 3.87	2.45 / 3.56	2.28 / 3.23	2.08 / 2.86	1.84 / 2.42
21	4.32 / 8.02	3.47 / 5.78	3.07 / 4.87	2.84 / 4.37	2.68 / 4.04	2.57 / 3.81	2.42 / 3.51	2.25 / 3.17	2.05 / 2.80	1.81 / 2.36
22	4.30 / 7.94	3.44 / 5.72	3.05 / 4.82	2.82 / 4.31	2.66 / 3.99	2.55 / 3.75	2.40 / 3.45	2.23 / 3.12	2.03 / 2.75	1.78 / 2.30
23	4.28 / 7.88	3.42 / 5.66	3.03 / 4.76	2.80 / 4.26	2.64 / 3.94	2.53 / 3.71	2.38 / 3.41	2.20 / 3.07	2.00 / 2.70	1.76 / 2.26

Degrees of freedom for smaller mean square

df										
24	4.26 / 7.82	3.40 / 5.61	3.01 / 4.72	2.78 / 4.22	2.62 / 3.90	2.51 / 3.67	2.36 / 3.36	2.18 / 3.03	1.98 / 2.66	1.73 / 2.21
25	4.24 / 7.77	3.38 / 5.57	2.99 / 4.68	2.76 / 4.18	2.60 / 3.86	2.49 / 3.63	2.34 / 3.32	2.16 / 2.99	1.96 / 2.62	1.71 / 2.17
26	4.22 / 7.72	3.37 / 5.53	2.98 / 4.64	2.74 / 4.14	2.59 / 3.82	2.47 / 3.59	2.32 / 3.29	2.15 / 2.96	1.95 / 2.58	1.69 / 2.13
27	4.21 / 7.68	3.35 / 5.49	2.96 / 4.60	2.73 / 4.11	2.57 / 3.78	2.46 / 3.56	2.30 / 3.26	2.13 / 2.93	1.93 / 2.55	1.67 / 2.10
28	4.20 / 7.64	3.34 / 5.45	2.95 / 4.57	2.71 / 4.07	2.56 / 3.75	2.44 / 3.53	2.29 / 3.23	2.12 / 2.90	1.91 / 2.52	1.65 / 2.06
29	4.18 / 7.60	3.33 / 5.42	2.93 / 4.54	2.70 / 4.04	2.54 / 3.73	2.43 / 3.50	2.28 / 3.20	2.10 / 2.87	1.90 / 2.49	1.64 / 2.03
30	4.17 / 7.56	3.32 / 5.39	2.92 / 4.51	2.69 / 4.02	2.53 / 3.70	2.42 / 3.47	2.27 / 3.17	2.09 / 2.84	1.89 / 2.47	1.62 / 2.01
35	4.12 / 7.42	3.26 / 5.27	2.87 / 4.40	2.64 / 3.91	2.48 / 3.59	2.37 / 3.37	2.22 / 3.07	2.04 / 2.74	1.83 / 2.37	1.57 / 1.90
40	4.08 / 7.31	3.23 / 5.18	2.84 / 4.31	2.61 / 3.83	2.45 / 3.51	2.34 / 3.29	2.18 / 2.99	2.00 / 2.66	1.79 / 2.29	1.52 / 1.82
45	4.06 / 7.23	3.21 / 5.11	2.81 / 4.25	2.58 / 3.77	2.42 / 3.45	2.31 / 3.23	2.15 / 2.94	1.97 / 2.61	1.76 / 2.23	1.48 / 1.75
50	4.03 / 7.17	3.18 / 5.06	2.79 / 4.20	2.56 / 3.72	2.40 / 3.41	2.29 / 3.19	2.13 / 2.89	1.95 / 2.56	1.74 / 2.18	1.44 / 1.68
60	4.00 / 7.08	3.15 / 4.98	2.76 / 4.13	2.52 / 3.65	2.37 / 3.34	2.25 / 3.12	2.10 / 2.82	1.92 / 2.50	1.70 / 2.12	1.39 / 1.60
70	3.98 / 7.01	3.13 / 4.92	2.74 / 4.07	2.50 / 3.60	2.35 / 3.29	2.23 / 3.07	2.07 / 2.78	1.89 / 2.45	1.67 / 2.07	1.35 / 1.53

TABLE F (Concluded)

Degrees of freedom for smaller mean square	Degrees of freedom for greater mean square									
	1	2	3	4	5	6	8	12	24	∞
80	3.96 / 6.96	3.11 / 4.88	2.72 / 4.04	2.49 / 3.56	2.33 / 3.26	2.21 / 3.04	2.06 / 2.74	1.88 / 2.42	1.65 / 2.03	1.31 / 1.47
90	3.95 / 6.92	3.10 / 4.85	2.71 / 4.01	2.47 / 3.53	2.32 / 3.23	2.20 / 3.01	2.04 / 2.72	1.86 / 2.39	1.64 / 2.00	1.28 / 1.43
100	3.94 / 6.90	3.09 / 4.82	2.70 / 3.98	2.46 / 3.51	2.30 / 3.21	2.19 / 2.99	2.03 / 2.69	1.85 / 2.37	1.63 / 1.98	1.26 / 1.39
125	3.92 / 6.84	3.07 / 4.78	2.68 / 3.94	2.44 / 3.47	2.29 / 3.17	2.17 / 2.95	2.01 / 2.66	1.83 / 2.33	1.60 / 1.94	1.21 / 1.32
150	3.90 / 6.81	3.06 / 4.75	2.66 / 3.91	2.43 / 3.45	2.27 / 3.14	2.16 / 2.92	2.00 / 2.63	1.82 / 2.31	1.59 / 1.92	1.18 / 1.27
200	3.89 / 6.76	3.04 / 4.71	2.65 / 3.88	2.42 / 3.41	2.26 / 3.11	2.14 / 2.89	1.98 / 2.60	1.80 / 2.28	1.57 / 1.88	1.14 / 1.21
300	3.87 / 6.72	3.03 / 4.68	2.64 / 3.85	2.41 / 3.38	2.25 / 3.08	2.13 / 2.86	1.97 / 2.57	1.79 / 2.24	1.55 / 1.85	1.10 / 1.14
400	3.86 / 6.70	3.02 / 4.66	2.63 / 3.83	2.40 / 3.37	2.24 / 3.06	2.12 / 2.85	1.96 / 2.56	1.78 / 2.23	1.54 / 1.84	1.07 / 1.11
500	3.86 / 6.69	3.01 / 4.65	2.62 / 3.82	2.39 / 3.36	2.23 / 3.05	2.11 / 2.84	1.96 / 2.55	1.77 / 2.22	1.54 / 1.83	1.06 / 1.08
1000	3.85 / 6.66	3.00 / 4.63	2.61 / 3.80	2.38 / 3.34	2.22 / 3.04	2.10 / 2.82	1.95 / 2.53	1.76 / 2.20	1.53 / 1.81	1.03 / 1.04
∞	3.84 / 6.64	2.99 / 4.60	2.60 / 3.78	2.37 / 3.32	2.21 / 3.02	2.09 / 2.80	1.94 / 2.51	1.75 / 2.18	1.52 / 1.79	

TABLE G   To facilitate the calculation of T scores

The percents refer to the percentage of the total frequency below a
given score +1/2 of the frequency on that score. T scores are
read directly from the given percentages.*

Percent	T score	Percent	T score
.0032	10	53.98	51
.0048	11	57.93	52
.007	12	61.79	53
.011	13	65.54	54
.016	14	69.15	55
.023	15	72.57	56
.034	16	75.80	57
.048	17	78.81	58
.069	18	81.59	59
.097	19	84.13	60
.13	20	86.43	61
.19	21	88.49	62
.26	22	90.32	63
.35	23	91.92	64
.47	24	93.32	65
.62	25	94.52	66
.82	26	95.54	67
1.07	27	96.41	68
1.39	28	97.13	69
1.79	29	97.72	70
2.28	30	98.21	71
2.87	31	98.61	72
3.59	32	98.93	73
4.46	33	99.18	74
5.48	34	99.38	75
6.68	35	99.53	76
8.08	36	99.65	77
9.68	37	99.74	78
11.51	38	99.81	79
13.57	39	99.865	80
15.87	40	99.903	81
18.41	41	99.931	82
21.19	42	99.952	83
24.20	43	99.966	84
27.43	44	99.977	85
30.85	45	99.984	86
34.46	46	99.9890	87
38.21	47	99.9928	88
42.07	48	99.9952	89
46.02	49	99.9968	90
50.00	50		

* T scores under 10 or above 90 differ so slightly that they cannot be read
as different two-place numbers.

	0	1	2	3	4	5	6	7	8	9	10	11	12	13	14	15	16	17	18	19	20	21	22	23
1	270	218	196	181	170	160	151	144	137	131	125	120	115	110	106	102	97	94	90	86	82	79	76	72
2	244	207	189	175	165	156	148	141	134	128	122	118	112	108	104	99	95	92	88	84	81	77	74	71
3	228	198	182	170	160	152	144	137	131	125	120	115	110	106	102	97	94	90	86	82	79	76	72	69
4	216	191	177	165	156	148	141	134	128	123	118	113	108	104	100	96	92	88	84	81	77	74	71	67
5	210	185	172	161	152	145	138	131	126	120	115	111	106	102	98	94	90	86	82	79	76	72	69	66
6	199	179	167	157	149	141	135	129	123	118	113	108	104	100	96	92	88	84	81	77	74	71	68	64
7	192	174	163	153	145	138	132	126	121	116	111	106	102	98	94	90	86	83	79	76	72	69	66	63
8	186	170	159	150	142	135	128	124	118	113	109	104	100	96	92	88	84	81	77	74	71	68	64	61
9	181	165	155	147	139	133	126	121	116	111	106	102	98	94	90	86	83	79	76	73	69	66	63	60
10	176	161	151	143	136	130	124	119	114	109	104	100	96	92	88	85	81	78	74	71	68	65	62	59
11	171	158	148	140	134	127	122	116	111	107	102	98	94	90	87	83	79	76	73	69	66	63	60	57
12	167	154	145	138	131	125	119	114	109	105	100	96	92	89	85	81	78	74	71	68	65	62	59	56
13	163	151	142	135	128	122	117	112	107	103	99	94	91	87	83	80	76	73	70	66	63	60	57	54
14	159	147	139	132	126	120	115	110	105	101	97	93	89	85	81	78	75	71	68	65	62	59	56	53
15	156	144	136	129	123	118	113	108	103	99	95	91	87	83	80	76	73	70	66	63	60	57	54	51
16	152	141	134	127	121	116	111	106	101	97	93	89	85	82	78	75	71	68	65	62	59	56	53	50
17	149	139	131	125	119	113	109	104	99	95	91	87	84	80	77	73	70	67	64	60	57	54	52	49
18	146	136	129	122	117	111	106	102	98	93	89	86	82	78	75	72	68	65	62	59	56	53	50	47
19	143	133	126	120	114	109	105	100	96	92	88	84	80	77	73	70	67	64	61	58	55	52	49	46
20	140	131	124	118	112	107	103	98	94	90	86	82	79	75	72	69	65	62	59	56	53	50	47	45
21	137	128	121	116	110	105	101	96	92	88	84	81	77	74	70	67	64	60	58	55	52	49	46	43
22	135	126	119	113	108	103	99	95	90	87	83	79	76	72	69	66	62	59	56	53	50	48	45	42
23	132	124	117	111	106	101	97	92	89	85	81	78	74	71	67	64	61	58	55	52	49	46	43	41
24	130	121	115	109	104	100	95	91	87	83	80	76	73	69	66	63	60	57	54	51	48	45	42	39
25	127	119	113	107	102	98	93	89	85	82	78	74	71	68	64	61	58	55	52	49	46	43	41	38
26	125	117	111	105	101	96	92	88	84	80	76	73	70	66	63	60	57	54	51	48	45	42	39	37
27	123	115	109	104	99	94	90	86	82	78	75	71	68	65	62	58	55	52	49	46	44	41	38	35
28	120	113	107	102	97	92	88	84	80	77	73	70	67	63	60	57	54	51	48	45	42	39	37	
29	118	111	105	100	95	91	87	83	79	75	72	68	65	62	59	56	53	50	47	44	41	38		
30	116	109	103	98	93	89	85	81	77	74	70	67	64	60	57	54	51	48	45	42	40			
31	114	107	101	96	92	87	83	79	76	72	69	65	62	59	56	53	50	47	44	41				
32	112	105	99	94	90	86	82	78	74	71	67	64	61	58	54	51	48	46	43					
33	110	103	98	93	88	84	80	76	73	69	66	63	59	56	53	50	47	44						
34	108	101	96	91	86	82	79	75	71	68	64	61	58	55	52	49	46							
35	106	99	94	89	85	81	77	73	70	66	63	60	56	53	50	47								
36	104	97	92	88	83	80	75	72	68	65	61	58	55	52	49									
37	102	96	91	86	82	78	74	70	67	63	60	57	54	51										
38	100	94	89	84	80	76	72	69	65	62	59	55	52											
39	98	92	87	83	79	75	71	67	64	61	57	54												
40	97	91	86	81	77	73	69	66	62	59	56													
41	95	89	84	80	75	72	68	64	61	58														
42	93	87	82	78	74	70	66	63	60															
43	91	85	81	76	72	69	65	62																
44	90	84	79	75	71	67	64																	
45	88	82	78	73	69	66																		
46	86	81	76	72	68																			
47	85	79	75	70																				
48	83	78	73																					
49	81	76																						
50	80																							

	24	25	26	27	28	29	30	31	32	33	34	35	36	37	38	39	40	41	42	43	44	45	46	47	48	49
1	69	66	63	60	57	54	51	48	45	43	40	37	35	32	29	27	24	21	19	16	14	11	09	06	04	01
2	67	64	61	58	55	52	50	47	44	41	39	36	33	31	28	25	23	20	18	15	13	10	08	05	03	
3	66	63	60	57	54	51	48	45	43	40	37	35	32	29	27	24	21	19	16	14	11	09	06	05		
4	64	61	58	55	52	50	47	44	41	39	36	33	31	28	25	23	20	18	15	13	10	08	05			
5	63	60	57	54	51	48	45	43	40	37	35	32	29	27	24	21	19	16	14	11	09	06				
6	61	58	55	53	50	47	44	41	39	36	33	31	28	25	23	20	18	15	13	10	08					
7	60	57	54	51	48	45	43	40	37	35	32	29	27	24	21	19	16	14	11	09						
8	58	55	52	50	47	44	41	39	36	33	31	28	25	23	20	18	15	13	10							
9	57	54	51	48	46	43	40	37	35	32	29	27	24	21	19	16	14	11								
10	56	53	50	47	44	41	39	36	33	31	28	25	23	20	18	15	13									
11	54	51	48	46	43	40	37	35	32	29	27	24	22	19	16	14										
12	53	50	47	44	41	39	36	33	31	28	25	23	20	18	15											
13	51	48	46	43	40	37	35	32	29	27	24	22	19	16												
14	50	47	44	42	39	36	33	31	28	25	23	20	18													
15	49	46	43	40	37	35	32	29	27	24	22	19														
16	47	44	42	39	36	33	31	28	26	23	20															
17	46	43	40	37	35	32	29	27	24	22																
18	44	42	39	36	33	31	28	26	23																	
19	43	40	38	35	32	30	27	24																		
20	42	39	36	34	31	28	26																			
21	40	38	35	32	30	27																				
22	39	36	34	31	28																					
23	38	35	32	30																						
24	36	34	31																							
25	35	32																								
26	34																									

TABLE H Mean σ-distances from the mean of various percents of a normal distribution

Average distance from the mean, in terms of σ, of each single percentage of a normal distribution (decimals omitted). Figures along the top of the table represent percentages of area from either extreme. Figures down the side of the table represent percentages measured from given points in the distribution.

Examples: The average distance from the mean of the highest 10% of a normally distributed group is 1.76σ (entry opposite 10 in first column). The average distance from the mean of the *next* 20% is $.86\sigma$ (entry opposite 20 in column headed 10). The average distance from the mean of the *next* 30% is

$$\frac{.26 \times .20 + (-.13 \times .10)}{.30}$$

or $.13\sigma$ (20% lie to the right of mean and 10% to left).

TABLE I   A table to infer the value of $\sqrt{1-r^2}$ from a given value of r

r	$\sqrt{1-r^2}$	r	$\sqrt{1-r^2}$	r	$\sqrt{1-r^2}$
.0000	1.0000	.3400	.9404	.6800	.7332
.01	.9999	.35	.9367	.69	.7238
.02	.9998	.36	.9330	.70	.7141
.03	.9995	.37	.9290	.71	.7042
.04	.9992	.38	.9250	.72	.6940
.05	.9987	.39	.9208	.73	.6834
.06	.9982	.40	.9165	.74	.6726
.07	.9975	.41	.9121	.75	.6614
.08	.9968	.42	.9075	.76	.6499
.09	.9959	.43	.9028	.77	.6380
.10	.9950	.44	.8980	.78	.6258
.11	.9939	.45	.8930	.79	.6131
.12	.9928	.46	.8879	.80	.6000
.13	.9915	.47	.8827	.81	.5864
.14	.9902	.48	.8773	.82	.5724
.15	.9887	.49	.8717	.83	.5578
.16	.9871	.50	.8660	.84	.5426
.17	.9854	.51	.8617	.85	.5268
.18	.9837	.52	.8542	.86	.5103
.19	.9818	.53	.8480	.87	.4931
.20	.9798	.54	.8417	.88	.4750
.21	.9777	.55	.8352	.89	.4560
.22	.9755	.56	.8285	.90	.4359
.23	.9732	.57	.8216	.91	.4146
.24	.9708	.58	.8146	.92	.3919
.25	.9682	.59	.8074	.93	.3676
.26	.9656	.60	.8000	.94	.3412
.27	.9629	.61	.7924	.95	.3122
.28	.9600	.62	.7846	.96	.2800
.29	.9570	.63	.7766	.97	.2431
.30	.9539	.64	.7684	.98	.1990
.31	.9507	.65	.7599	.99	.1411
.32	.9474	.66	.7513	1.00	.0000
.33	.9440	.67	.7424		

TABLE J Values of r_t taken as the cosine of an angle

Example: Suppose that $r_t = \cos 45°$. Then $\cos 45° = .707$, and $r_t = .71$ (to two decimals)

Angle	Cosine	Angle	Cosine	Angle	Cosine
0°	1.000	41°	.755	73°	.292
		42	.743	74	.276
5	.996	43	.731	75	.259
		44	.719	76	.242
10	.985	45	.707	77	.225
		46	.695	78	.208
		47	.682	79	.191
15	.966	48	.669	80	.174
16	.961	49	.656		
17	.956	50	.643	81	.156
18	.951			82	.139
19	.946	51	.629	83	.122
20	.940	52	.616	84	.105
		53	.602	85	.087
21	.934	54	.588		
22	.927	55	.574		
23	.921	56	.559	90	.000
24	.914	57	.545		
25	.906	58	.530		
26	.899	59	.515		
27	.891	60	.500		
28	.883				
29	.875	61	.485		
30	.866	62	.469		
		63	.454		
31	.857	64	.438		
32	.848	65	.423		
33	.839	66	.407		
34	.829	67	.391		
35	.819	68	.375		
36	.809	69	.358		
37	.799	70	.342		
38	.788				
39	.777	71	.326		
40	.766	72	.309		

TABLE K Estimated values of r_t corresponding to values of the ratio, AD/BC *

Example: If $AD/BC = 3.28$, the corresponding r_t is .44. Interpolation between AD/BC entries is not advised, as accuracy of the r_t values does not extend beyond the second decimal. If BC is larger than AD, find the ratio BC/AD and attach a negative sign to the r_t.

AD/BC	r_t	AD/BC	r_t	AD/BC	r_t
0 –1.00	.00	2.23–2.28	.31	5.81–6.03	.61
1.01–1.03	.01	2.29–2.34	.32	6.04–6.28	.62
1.04–1.06	.02	2.35–2.41	.33	6.29–6.54	.63
1.07–1.08	.03	2.42–2.48	.34	6.55–6.81	.64
1.09–1.11	.04	2.49–2.55	.35	6.82–7.10	.65
1.12–1.14	.05	2.56–2.63	.36	7.11–7.42	.66
1.15–1.17	.06	2.64–2.71	.37	7.43–7.75	.67
1.18–1.20	.07	2.72–2.79	.38	7.76–8.11	.68
1.21–1.23	.08	2.80–2.87	.39	8.12–8.49	.69
1.24–1.27	.09	2.88–2.96	.40	8.50–8.90	.70
1.28–1.30	.10				
		2.97–3.05	.41	8.91–9.35	.71
1.31–1.33	.11	3.06–3.14	.42	9.36–9.82	.72
1.34–1.37	.12	3.15–3.24	.43	9.83–10.33	.73
1.38–1.40	.13	3.25–3.34	.44	10.34–10.90	.74
1.41–1.44	.14	3.35–3.45	.45	10.91–11.51	.75
1.45–1.48	.15	3.46–3.56	.46	11.52–12.16	.76
1.49–1.52	.16	3.57–3.68	.47	12.17–12.89	.77
1.53–1.56	.17	3.69–3.80	.48	12.90–13.70	.78
1.57–1.60	.18	3.81–3.92	.49	13.71–14.58	.79
1.61–1.64	.19	3.93–4.06	.50	14.59–15.57	.80
1.65–1.69	.20				
		4.07–4.20	.51	15.58–16.65	.81
1.70–1.73	.21	4.21–4.34	.52	16.66–17.88	.82
1.74–1.78	.22	4.35–4.49	.53	17.89–19.28	.83
1.79–1.83	.23	4.50–4.66	.54	19.29–20.85	.84
1.84–1.88	.24	4.67–4.82	.55	20.86–22.68	.85
1.89–1.93	.25	4.83–4.99	.56	22.69–24.76	.86
1.94–1.98	.26	5.00–5.18	.57	24.77–27.22	.87
1.99–2.04	.27	5.19–5.38	.58	27.23–30.09	.88
2.05–2.10	.28	5.39–5.59	.59	30.10–33.60	.89
2.11–2.15	.29	5.60–5.80	.60	33.61–37.79	.90
2.16–2.22	.30				
				37.80–43.06	.91
				43.07–49.83	.92
				49.84–58.79	.93
				58.80–70.95	.94
				70.96–89.01	.95
				89.02–117.54	.96
				117.55–169.67	.97
				169.68–293.12	.98
				293.13–923.97	.99
				923.98–	1.00

* From Davidoff, M. D., and Goheen, H. W., *Psychometrika*, 1953, 18, 115–121, by permission.

TABLE OF SQUARES AND SQUARE ROOTS
OF THE NUMBERS FROM 1 TO 1000

TABLE OF SQUARES AND SQUARE ROOTS OF THE NUMBERS FROM 1 TO 1000

Number	Square	Square Root	Number	Square	Square Root
1	1	1.000	51	26 01	7.141
2	4	1.414	52	27 04	7.211
3	9	1.732	53	28 09	7.280
4	16	2.000	54	29 16	7.348
5	25	2.236	55	30 25	7.416
6	36	2.449	56	31 36	7.483
7	49	2.646	57	32 49	7.550
8	64	2.828	58	33 64	7.616
9	81	3.000	59	34 81	7.681
10	1 00	3.162	60	36 00	7.746
11	1 21	3.317	61	37 21	7.810
12	1 44	3.464	62	38 44	7.874
13	1 69	3.606	63	39 69	7.937
14	1 96	3.742	64	40 96	8.000
15	2 25	3.873	65	42 25	8 062
16	2 56	4.000	66	43 56	8.124
17	2 89	4.123	67	44 89	8.185
18	3 24	4.243	68	46 24	8.246
19	3 61	4.359	69	47 61	8.307
20	4 00	4.472	70	49 00	8.367
21	4 41	4.583	71	50 41	8.426
22	4 84	4.690	72	51 84	8.485
23	5 29	4.796	73	53 29	8.544
24	5 76	4.899	74	54 76	8.602
25	6 25	5.000	75	56 25	8.660
26	6 76	5.099	76	57 76	8.718
27	7 29	5.196	77	59 29	8.775
28	7 84	5.292	78	60 84	8.832
29	8 41	5.385	79	62 41	8.888
30	9 00	5.477	80	64 00	8.944
31	9 61	5.568	81	65 61	9.000
32	10 24	5.657	82	67 24	9.055
33	10 89	5.745	83	68 89	9.110
34	11 56	5.831	84	70 56	9.165
35	12 25	5.916	85	72 25	9.220
36	12 96	6.000	86	73 96	9.274
37	13 69	6.083	87	75 69	9.327
38	14 44	6.164	88	77 44	9.381
39	15 21	6.245	89	79 21	9.434
40	16 00	6.325	90	81 00	9.487
41	16 81	6.403	91	82 81	9.539
42	17 64	6.481	92	84 64	9.592
43	18 49	6.557	93	86 49	9.644
44	19 36	6.633	94	88 36	9.695
45	20 25	6.708	95	90 25	9.747
46	21 16	6.782	96	92 16	9.798
47	22 09	6.856	97	94 09	9.849
48	23 04	6.928	98	96 04	9 899
49	24 01	7.000	99	98 01	9 950
50	25 00	7.071	100	1 00 00	10 000

TABLE OF SQUARES AND SQUARE ROOTS—*Continued*

Number	Square	Square Root	Number	Square	Square Root
101	1 02 01	10.050	151	2 28 01	12.288
102	1 04 04	10.100	152	2 31 04	12.329
103	1 06 09	10.149	153	2 34 09	12.369
104	1 08 16	10.198	154	2 37 16	12.410
105	1 10 25	10.247	155	2 40 25	12.450
106	1 12 36	10.296	156	2 43 36	12.490
107	1 14 49	10.344	157	2 46 49	12.530
108	1 16 64	10.392	158	2 49 64	12.570
109	1 18 81	10.440	159	2 52 81	12.610
110	1 21 00	10.488	160	2 56 00	12.649
111	1 23 21	10.536	161	2 59 21	12.689
112	1 25 44	10.583	162	2 62 44	12.728
113	1 27 69	10.630	163	2 65 69	12.767
114	1 29 96	10.677	164	2 68 96	12.806
115	1 32 25	10.724	165	2 72 25	12.845
116	1 34 56	10.770	166	2 75 56	12.884
117	1 36 89	10.817	167	2 78 89	12.923
118	1 39 24	10.863	168	2 82 24	12.961
119	1 41 61	10.909	169	2 85 61	13.000
120	1 44 00	10.954	170	2 89 00	13.038
121	1 46 41	11.000	171	2 92 41	13.077
122	1 48 84	11.045	172	2 95 84	13.115
123	1 51 29	11.091	173	2 99 29	13.153
124	1 53 76	11.136	174	3 02 76	13.191
125	1 56 25	11.180	175	3 06 25	13.229
126	1 58 76	11.225	176	3 09 76	13.266
127	1 61 29	11.269	177	3 13 29	13.304
128	1 63 84	11.314	178	3 16 84	13.342
129	1 66 41	11.358	179	3 20 41	13.379
130	1 69 00	11.402	180	3 24 00	13.416
131	1 71 61	11.446	181	3 27 61	13.454
132	1 74 24	11.489	182	3 31 24	13.491
133	1 76 89	11.533	183	3 34 89	13.528
134	1 79 56	11.576	184	3 38 56	13.565
135	1 82 25	11.619	185	3 42 25	13.601
136	1 84 96	11.662	186	3 45 96	13.638
137	1 87 69	11.705	187	3 49 69	13.675
138	1 90 44	11.747	188	3 53 44	13.711
139	1 93 21	11.790	189	3 57 21	13.748
140	1 96 00	11.832	190	3 61 00	13.784
141	1 98 81	11.874	191	3 64 81	13.820
142	2 01 64	11.916	192	3 68 64	13.856
143	2 04 49	11.958	193	3 72 49	13.892
144	2 07 36	12.000	194	3 76 36	13.928
145	2 10 25	12.042	195	3 80 25	13.964
146	2 13 16	12.083	196	3 84 16	14.000
147	2 16 09	12.124	197	3 88 09	14.036
148	2 19 04	12.166	198	3 92 04	14.071
149	2 22 01	12.207	199	3 96 01	14.107
150	2 25 00	12.247	200	4 00 00	14.142

TABLE OF SQUARES AND SQUARE ROOTS—*Continued*

Number	Square	Square Root	Number	Square	Square Root
201	4 04 01	14.177	251	6 30 01	15.843
202	4 08 04	14.213	252	6 35 04	15.875
203	4 12 09	14.248	253	6 40 09	15.906
204	4 16 16	14.283	254	6 45 16	15.937
205	4 20 25	14.318	255	6 50 25	15.969
206	4 24 36	14.353	256	6 55 36	16.000
207	4 28 49	14.387	257	6 60 49	16.031
208	4 32 64	14.422	258	6 65 64	16.062
209	4 36 81	14.457	259	6 70 81	16.093
210	4 41 00	14.491	260	6 76 00	16.125
211	4 45 21	14.526	261	6 81 21	16.155
212	4 49 44	14.560	262	6 86 44	16.186
213	4 53 69	14.595	263	6 91 69	16.217
214	4 57 96	14.629	264	6 96 96	16.248
215	4 62 25	14.663	265	7 02 25	16.279
216	4 66 56	14.697	266	7 07 56	16.310
217	4 70 89	14.731	267	7·12 89	16.340
218	4 75 24	14.765	268	7 18 24	16.371
219	4 79 61	14.799	269	7 23 61	16.401
220	4 84 00	14.832	270	7 29 00	16.432
221	4 88 41	14.866	271	7 34 41	16.462
222	4 92 84	14.900	272	7 39 84	16.492
223	4 97 29	14.933	273	7 45 29	16.523
224	5 01 76	14.967	274	7 50 76	16.553
225	5 06 25	15.000	275	7 56 25	16.583
226	5 10 76	15.033	276	7 61 76	16.613
227	5 15 29	15.067	277	7 67 29	16.643
228	5 19 84	15.100	278	7 72 84	16.673
229	5 24 41	15.133	279	7 78 41	16.703
230	5 29 00	15.166	280	7 84 00	16.733
231	5 33 61	15.199	281	7 89 61	16.763
232	5 38 24	15.232	282	7 95 24	16.793
233	5 42 89	15.264	283	8 00 89	16.823
234	5 47 56	15.297	284	8 06 56	16.852
235	5 52 25	15.330	285	8 12 25	16.882
236	5 56 96	15.362	286	8 17 96	16.912
237	5 61 69	15.395	287	8 23 69	16.941
238	5 66 44	15.427	288	8 29 44	16.971
239	5 71 21	15.460	289	8 35 21	17.000
240	5 76 00	15.492	290	8 41 00	17.029
241	5 80 81	15.524	291	8 46 81	17.059
242	5 85 64	15.556	292	8 52 64	17.088
243	5 90 49	15.588	293	8 58 49	17.117
244	5 95 36	15.620	294	8 64 36	17.146
245	6 00 25	15.652	295	8 70 25	17.176
246	6 05 16	15.684	296	8 76 16	17.205
247	6 10 09	15.716	297	8 82 09	17.234
248	6 15 04	15.748	298	8 88 04	17.263
249	6 20 01	15.780	299	8 94 01	17.292
250	6 25 00	15.811	300	9 00 00	17.321

Number	Square	Square Root	Number	Square	Square Root
301	9 06 01	17.349	351	12 32 01	18 735
302	9 12 04	17.378	352	12 39 04	18.762
303	9 18 09	17.407	353	12 46 09	18.788
304	9 24 16	17.436	354	12 53 16	18.815
305	9 30 25	17.464	355	12 60 25	18.841
306	9 36 36	17.493	356	12 67 36	18.868
307	9 42 49	17.521	357	12 74 49	18 894
308	9 48 64	17.550	358	12 81 64	18.921
309	9 54 81	17.578	359	12 88 81	18.947
310	9 61 00	17.607	360	12 96 00	18.974
311	9 67 21	17 635	361	13 03 21	19.000
312	9 73 44	17 664	362	13 10 44	19.026
313	9 79 69	17.692	363	13 17 69	19.053
314	9 85 96	17.720	364	13 24 96	19.079
315	9 92 25	17.748	365	13 32 25	19.105
316	9 98 56	17.776	366	13 39 56	19.131
317	10 04 89	17.804	367	13 46 89	19.157
318	10 11 24	17 833	368	13 54 24	19.183
319	10 17 61	17.861	369	13 61 61	19.209
320	10 24 00	17.889	370	13 69 00	19.235
321	10 30 41	17.916	371	13 76 41	19.261
322	10 36 84	17 944	372	13 83 84	19.287
323	10 43 29	17 972	373	13 91 29	19.313
324	10 49 76	18.000	374	13 98 76	19.339
325	10 56 25	18.028	375	14 06 25	19.363
326	10 62 76	18.055	376	14 13 76	19.391
327	10 69 29	18.083	377	14 21 29	19.416
328	10 75 84	18.111	378	14 28 84	19.442
329	10 82 41	18.138	379	14 36 41	19.468
330	10 89 00	18.166	380	14 44 00	19.494
331	10 95 61	18.193	381	14 51 61	19.519
332	11 02 24	18.221	382	14 59 24	19.545
333	11 08 89	18.248	383	14 66 89	19.570
334	11 15 56	18.276	384	14 74 56	19.596
335	11 22 25	18.303	385	14 82 25	19.621
336	11 28 96	18.330	386	14 89 96	19.647
337	11 35 69	18.358	387	14 97 69	19.672
338	11 42 44	18.385	388	15 05 44	19.698
339	11 49 21	18.412	389	15 13 21	19.723
340	11 56 00	18.439	390	15 21 00	19.748
341	11 62 81	18.466	391	15 28 81	19.774
342	11 69 64	18.493	392	15 36 64	19.799
343	11 76 49	18.520	393	15 44 49	19.824
344	11 83 36	18.547	394	15 52 36	19.849
345	11 90 25	18.574	395	15 60 25	19.875
346	11 97 16	18.601	396	15 68 16	19.900
347	12 04 09	18.628	397	15 76 09	19.925
348	12 11 04	18.655	398	15 84 04	19.950
349	12 18 01	18.682	399	15 92 01	19.975
350	12 25 00	18.708	400	16 00 00	20.000

TABLE OF SQUARES AND SQUARE ROOTS—*Continued*

Number	Square	Square Root	Number	Square	Square Root
401	16 08 01	20.025	451	20 34 01	21.237
402	16 16 04	20.050	452	20 43 04	21.260
403	16 24 09	20.075	453	20 52 09	21.284
404	16 32 16	20.100	454	20 61 16	21.307
405	16 40 25	20.125	455	20 70 25	21.331
406	16 48 36	20.149	456	20 79 36	21.354
407	16 56 49	20.174	457	20 88 49	21.378
408	16 64 64	20.199	458	20 97 64	21.401
409	16 72 81	20.224	459	21 06 81	21.424
410	16 81 00	20.248	460	21 16 00	21.448
411	16 89 21	20.273	461	21 25 21	21.471
412	16 97 44	20.298	462	21 34 44	21.494
413	17 05 69	20.322	463	21 43 69	21.517
414	17 13 96	20.347	464	21 52 96	21.541
415	17 22 25	20.372	465	21 62 25	21.564
416	17 30 56	20.396	466	21 71 56	21.587
417	17 38 89	20.421	467	21 80 89	21.610
418	17 47 24	20.445	468	21 90 24	21.633
419	17 55 61	20.469	469	21 99 61	21.656
420	17 64 00	20.494	470	22 09 00	21.679
421	17 72 41	20.518	471	22 18 41	21.703
422	17 80 84	20.543	472	22 27 84	21.726
423	17 89 29	20.567	473	22 37 29	21.749
424	17 97 76	20.591	474	22 46 76	21.772
425	18 06 25	20.616	475	22 56 25	21.794
426	18 14 76	20.640	476	22 65 76	21.817
427	18 23 29	20.664	477	22 75 29	21.840
428	18 31 84	20.688	478	22 84 84	21.863
429	18 40 41	20.712	479	22 94 41	21.886
430	18 49 00	20.736	480	23 04 00	21.909
431	18 57 61	20.761	481	23 13 61	21.932
432	18 66 24	20.785	482	23 23 24	21.954
433	18 74 89	20.809	483	23 32 89	21.977
434	18 83 56	20.833	484	23 42 56	22.000
435	18 92 25	20.857	485	23 52 25	22.023
436	19 00 96	20.881	486	23 61 96	22.045
437	19 09 69	20.905	487	23 71 69	22.068
438	19 18 44	20.928	488	23 81 44	22.091
439	19 27 21	20.952	489	23 91 21	22.113
440	19 36 00	20.976	490	24 01 00	22.136
441	19 44 81	21.000	491	24 10 81	22.159
442	19 53 64	21.024	492	24 20 64	22.181
443	19 62 49	21.048	493	24 30 49	22.204
444	19 71 36	21.071	494	24 40 36	22.226
445	19 80 25	21.095	495	24 50 25	22.249
446	19 89 16	21.119	496	24 60 16	22.271
447	19 98 09	21.142	497	24 70 09	22.293
448	20 07 04	21.166	498	24 80 04	22.316
449	20 16 01	21.190	499	24 90 01	22.338
450	20 25 00	21.213	500	25 00 00	22.361

TABLE OF SQUARES AND SQUARE ROOTS—*Continued*

Number	Square	Square Root	Number	Square	Square Root
501	25 10 01	22.383	551	30 36 01	23.473
502	25 20 04	22.405	552	30 47 04	23.495
503	25 30 09	22.428	553	30 58 09	23.516
504	25 40 16	22.450	554	30 69 16	23.537
505	25 50 25	22.472	555	30 80 25	23.558
506	25 60 36	22.494	556	30 91 36	23.580
507	25 70 49	22.517	557	31 02 49	23.601
508	25 80 64	22.539	558	31 13 64	23.622
509	25 90 81	22.561	559	31 24 81	23.643
510	26 01 00	22.583	560	31 36 00	23.664
511	26 11 21	22.605	561	31 47 21	23.685
512	26 21 44	22.627	562	31 58 44	23.707
513	26 31 69	22.650	563	31 69 69	23.728
514	26 41 96	22.672	564	31 80 96	23.749
515	26 52 25	22.694	565	31 92 25	23.770
516	26 62 56	22.716	566	32 03 56	23.791
517	26 72 89	22.738	567	32 14 89	23.812
518	26 83 24	22.760	568	32 26 24	23.833
519	26 93 61	22.782	569	32 37 61	23.854
520	27 04 00	22.804	570	32 49 00	23.875
521	27 14 41	22.825	571	32 60 41	23.896
522	27 24 84	22.847	572	32 71 84	23.917
523	27 35 29	22.869	573	32 83 29	23.937
524	27 45 76	22.891	574	32 94 76	23.958
525	27 56 25	22.913	575	33 06 25	23.979
526	27 66 76	22.935	576	33 17 76	24.000
527	27 77 29	22.956	577	33 29 29	24.021
528	27 87 84	22.978	578	33 40 84	24.042
529	27 98 41	23.000	579	33 52 41	24.062
530	28 09 00	23.022	580	33 64 00	24.083
531	28 19 61	23.043	581	33 75 61	24.104
532	28 30 24	23.065	582	33 87 24	24.125
533	28 40 89	23.087	583	33 98 89	24.145
534	28 51 56	23.108	584	34 10 56	24.166
535	28 62 25	23.130	585	34 22 25	24.187
536	28 72 96	23.152	586	34 33 96	24.207
537	28 83 69	23.173	587	34 45 69	24.228
538	28 94 44	23.195	588	34 57 44	24.249
539	29 05 21	23.216	589	34 69 21	24.269
540	29 16 00	23.238	590	34 81 00	24.290
541	29 26 81	23.259	591	34 92 81	24.310
542	29 37 64	23.281	592	35 04 64	24.331
543	29 48 49	23.302	593	35 16 49	24.352
544	29 59 36	23.324	594	35 28 36	24.372
545	29 70 25	23.345	595	35 40 25	24.393
546	29 81 16	23.367	596	35 52 16	24.413
547	29 92 09	23.388	597	35 64 09	24.434
548	30 03 04	23.409	598	35 76 04	24.454
549	30 14 01	23.431	599	35 88 01	24.474
550	30 25 00	23.452	600	36 00 00	24.495

TABLE OF SQUARES AND SQUARE ROOTS—*Continued*

Number	Square	Square Root	Number	Square	Square Root
601	36 12 01	24.515	651	42 38 01	25.515
602	36 24 04	24.536	652	42 51 04	25.534
603	36 36 09	24.556	653	42 64 09	25.554
604	36 48 16	24.576	654	42 77 16	25.573
605	36 60 25	24.597	655	42 90 25	25.593
606	36 72 36	24.617	656	43 03 36	25.612
607	36 84 49	24.637	657	43 16 49	25.632
608	36 96 64	24.658	658	43 29 64	25.652
609	37 08 81	24.678	659	43 42 81	25.671
610	37 21 00	24.698	660	43 56 00	25.690
611	37 33 21	24.718	661	43 69 21	25.710
612	37 45 44	24.739	662	43 82 44	25.729
613	37 57 69	24.759	663	43 95 69	25.749
614	37 69 96	24.779	664	44 08 96	25.768
615	37 82 25	24.799	665	44 22 25	25.788
616	37 94 56	24.819	666	44 35 56	25.807
617	38 06 89	24.839	667	44 48 89	25.826
618	38 19 24	24.860	668	44 62 24	25.846
619	38 31 61	24.880	669	44 75 61	25.865
620	38 44 00	24.900	670	44 89 00	25.884
621	38 56 41	24.920	671	45 02 41	25.904
622	38 68 84	24.940	672	45 15 84	25.923
623	38 81 29	24.960	673	45 29 29	25.942
624	38 93 76	24.980	674	45 42 76	25.962
625	39 06 25	25.000	675	45 56 25	25.981
626	39 18 76	25.020	676	45 69 76	26.000
627	39 31 29	25.040	677	45 83 29	26.019
628	39 43 84	25.060	678	45 96 84	26.038
629	39 56 41	25.080	679	46 10 41	26.058
630	39 69 00	25.100	680	46 24 00	26.077
631	39 81 61	25.120	681	46 37 61	26.096
632	39 94 24	25.140	682	46 51 24	26.115
633	40 06 89	25.159	683	46 64 89	26.134
634	40 19 56	25.179	684	46 78 56	26.153
635	40 32 25	25.199	685	46 92 25	26.173
636	40 44 96	25.219	686	47 05 96	26.192
637	40 57 69	25.239	687	47 19 69	26.211
638	40 70 44	25.259	688	47 33 44	26.230
639	40 83 21	25.278	689	47 47 21	26.249
640	40 96 00	25.298	690	47 61 00	26.268
641	41 08 81	25.318	691	47 74 81	26.287
642	41 21 64	25.338	692	47 88 64	26.306
643	41 34 49	25.357	693	48 02 49	26.325
644	41 47 36	25.377	694	48 16 36	26.344
645	41 60 25	25.397	695	48 30 25	26.363
646	41 73 16	25.417	696	48 44 16	26.382
647	41 86 09	25.436	697	48 58 09	26.401
648	41 99 04	25.456	698	48 72 04	26.420
649	42 12 01	25.475	699	48 86 01	26.439
650	42 25 00	25.495	700	49 00 00	26.458

TABLE OF SQUARES AND SQUARE ROOTS—*Continued*

Number	Square	Square Root	Number	Square	Square Root
701	49 14 01	26.476	751	56 40 01	27.404
702	49 28 04	26.495	752	56 55 04	27.423
703	49 42 09	26.514	753	56 70 09	27.441
704	49 56 16	26.533	754	56 85 16	27.459
705	49 70 25	26.552	755	57 00 25	27.477
706	49 84 36	26.571	756	57 15 36	27.495
707	49 98 49	26.589	757	57 30 49	27.514
708	50 12 64	26.608	758	57 45 64	27.532
709	50 26 81	26.627	759	57 60 81	27.550
710	50 41 00	26.646	760	57 76 00	27.568
711	50 55 21	26.665	761	57 91 21	27.586
712	50 69 44	26.683	762	58 06 44	27.604
713	50 83 69	26.702	763	58 21 69	27.622
714	50 97 96	26.721	764	58 36 96	27.641
715	51 12 25	26.739	765	58 52 25	27.659
716	51 26 56	26.758	766	58 67 56	27.677
717	51 40 89	26.777	767	58 82 89	27.695
718	51 55 24	26.796	768	58 98 24	27.713
719	51 69 61	26.814	769	59 13 61	27.731
720	51 84 00	26.833	770	59 29 00	27.749
721	51 98 41	26.851	771	59 44 41	27.767
722	52 12 84	26.870	772	59 59 84	27.785
723	52 27 29	26.889	773	59 75 29	27.803
724	52 41 76	26.907	774	59 90 76	27.821
725	52 56 25	26.926	775	60 06 25	27.839
726	52 70 76	26.944	776	60 21 76	27.857
727	52 85 29	26.963	777	60 37 29	27.875
728	52 99 84	26.981	778	60 52 84	27.893
729	53 14 41	27.000	779	60 68 41	27.911
730	53 29 00	27.019	780	60 84 00	27.928
731	53 43 61	27.037	781	60 99 61	27.946
732	53 58 24	27.055	782	61 15 24	27.964
733	53 72 89	27.074	783	61 30 89	27.982
734	53 87 56	27.092	784	61 46 56	28.000
735	54 02 25	27.111	785	61 62 25	28.018
736	54 16 96	27.129	786	61 77 96	28.036
737	54 31 69	27.148	787	61 93 69	28.054
738	54 46 44	27.166	788	62 09 44	28.071
739	54 61 21	27.185	789	62 25 21	28.089
740	54 76 00	27.203	790	62 41 00	28.107
741	54 90 81	27.221	791	62 56 81	28.125
742	55 05 64	27.240	792	62 72 64	28.142
743	55 20 49	27.258	793	62 88 49	28.160
744	55 35 36	27.276	794	63 04 36	28.178
745	55 50 25	27.295	795	63 20 25	28.196
746	55 65 16	27.313	796	63 36 16	28.213
747	55 80 09	27.331	797	63 52 09	28.231
748	55 95 04	27.350	798	63 68 04	28.249
749	56 10 01	27.368	799	63 84 01	28.267
750	56 25 00	27.386	800	64 00 00	28.284

TABLE OF SQUARES AND SQUARE ROOTS—*Continued*

Number	Square	Square Root	Number	Square	Square Root
801	64 16 01	28.302	851	72 42 01	29.172
802	64 32 04	28.320	852	72 59 04	29.189
803	64 48 09	28.337	853	72 76 09	29.206
804	64 64 16	28.355	854	72 93 16	29.223
805	64 80 25	28.373	855	73 10 25	29.240
806	64 96 36	28.390	856	73 27 36	29.257
807	65 12 49	28.408	857	73 44 49	29.275
808	65 28 64	28.425	858	73 61 64	29.292
809	65 44 81	28.443	859	73 78 81	29.309
810	65 61 00	28.460	860	73 96 00	29.326
811	65 77 21	28.478	861	74 13 21	29.343
812	65 93 44	28.496	862	74 30 44	29.360
813	66 09 69	28.513	863	74 47 69	29.377
814	66 25 96	28.531	864	74 64 96	29.394
815	66 42 25	28.548	865	74 82 25	29.411
816	66 58 56	28.566	866	74 99 56	29.428
817	66 74 89	28.583	867	75 16 89	29.445
818	66 91 24	28.601	868	75 34 24	29.462
819	67 07 61	28.618	869	75 51 61	29.479
820	67 24 00	28.636	870	75 69 00	29.496
821	67 40 41	28.653	871	75 86 41	29.513
822	67 56 84	28.671	872	76 03 84	29.530
823	67 73 29	28.688	873	76 21 29	29.547
824	67 89 76	28.705	874	76 38 76	29.563
825	68 06 25	28.723	875	76 56 25	29.580
826	68 22 76	28.740	876	76 73 76	29.597
827	68 39 29	28.758	877	76 91 29	29.614
828	68 55 84	28.775	878	77 08 84	29.631
829	68 72 41	28.792	879	77 26 41	29.648
830	68 89 00	28.810	880	77 44 00	29.665
831	69 05 61	28.827	881	77 61 61	29.682
832	69 22 24	28.844	882	77 79 24	29.698
833	69 38 89	28.862	883	77 96 89	29.715
834	69 55 56	28.879	884	78 14 56	29.732
835	69 72 25	28.896	885	78 32 25	29.749
836	69 88 96	28.914	886	78 49 96	29.766
837	70 05 69	28.931	887	78 67 69	29.783
838	70 22 44	28.948	888	78 85 44	29.799
839	70 39 21	28.965	889	79 03 21	29.816
840	70 56 00	28.983	890	79 21 00	29.833
841	70 72 81	29.000	891	79 38 81	29.850
842	70 89 64	29.017	892	79 56 64	29.866
843	71 06 49	29.034	893	79 74 49	29.883
844	71 23 36	29.052	894	79 92 36	29.900
845	71 40 25	29.069	895	80 10 25	29.916
846	71 57 16	29.086	896	80 28 16	29.933
847	71 74 09	29.103	897	80 46 09	29.950
848	71 91 04	29.120	898	80 54 04	29.967
849	72 08 01	29.138	899	80 82 01	29.983
850	72 25 00	29.155	900	81 00 00	30.000

TABLE OF SQUARES AND SQUARE ROOTS—*Continued*

Number	Square	Square Root	Number	Square	Square Root
901	81 18 01	30.017	951	90 44 01	30.838
902	81 36 04	30.033	952	90 63 04	30.854
903	81 54 09	30.050	953	90 82 09	30.871
904	81 72 16	30.067	954	91 01 16	30.887
905	81 90 25	30.083	955	91 20 25	30.903
906	82 08 36	30.100	956	91 39 36	30.919
907	82 26 49	30.116	957	91 58 49	30.935
908	82 44 64	30.133	958	91 77 64	30.952
909	82 62 81	30.150	959	91 96 81	30.968
910	82 81 00	30.166	960	92 16 00	30.984
911	82 99 21	30.183	961	92 35 21	31.000
912	83 17 44	30.199	962	92 54 44	31.016
913	83 35 69	30.216	963	92 73 69	31.032
914	83 53 96	30.232	964	92 92 96	31.048
915	83 72 25	30.249	965	93 12 25	31.064
916	83 90 56	30.265	966	93 31 56	31.081
917	84 08 89	30.282	967	93 50 89	31.097
918	84 27 24	30.299	968	93 70 24	31.113
919	84 45 61	30.315	969	93 89 61	31.129
920	84 64 00	30.332	970	94 09 00	31.145
921	84 82 41	30.348	971	94 28 41	31.161
922	85 00 84	30.364	972	94 47 84	31.177
923	85 19 29	30.381	973	94 67 29	31.193
924	85 37 76	30.397	974	94 86 76	31.209
925	85 56 25	30.414	975	95 06 25	31.225
926	85 74 76	30.430	976	95 25 76	31.241
927	85 93 29	30.447	977	95 45 29	31.257
928	86 11 84	20.463	978	95 64 84	31.273
929	86 30 41	30.480	979	95 84 41	31.289
930	86 49 00	30.496	980	96 04 00	31.305
931	86 67 61	30.512	981	96 23 61	31.321
932	86 86 24	30.529	982	96 43 24	31.337
933	87 04 89	30.545	983	96 62 89	31.353
934	87 23 56	30.561	984	96 82 56	31.369
935	87 42 25	30.578	985	97 02 25	31.385
936	87 60 96	30.594	986	97 21 96	31.401
937	87 79 69	30.610	987	97 41 69	31.417
938	87 98 44	30.627	988	97 61 44	31.432
939	88 17 21	30.643	989	97 81 21	31.448
940	88 36 00	30.659	990	98 01 00	31.464
941	88 54 81	30.676	991	98 20 81	31.480
942	88 73 64	30.692	992	98 40 64	31.496
943	88 92 49	30.708	993	98 60 49	31.512
944	89 11 36	30.725	994	98 80 36	31.528
945	89 30 25	30.741	995	99 00 25	31.544
946	89 49 16	30.757	996	99 20 16	31.559
947	89 68 09	30.773	997	99 40 09	31.575
948	89 87 04	30.790	998	99 60 04	31.591
949	90 06 01	30.806	999	99 80 01	31.607
950	90 25 00	30.822	1000	100 00 00	31.623

REFERENCES

The following books will be useful to beginning students in psychology and education.

GUILFORD, J. P. *Fundamental Statistics in Psychology and Education*. 4th ed.; New York: McGraw-Hill Book Co., 1965.

McNEMAR, Q. *Psychological Statistics*. 3rd ed.; New York: John Wiley and Sons, 1962.

TATE, M. W. *Statistics in Education*. New York: Macmillan Co., 1955.

WALKER, HELEN M. *Elementary Statistical Methods*. New York: Henry Holt and Co., 1943.

More advanced books are:

EDWARDS, A. L. *Experimental Designs in Psychological Research*. New York: Henry Holt and Co., 1960.

FISHER, R. A. *Statistical Methods for Research Workers*. New York: Hafner Publishing Co., 1950.

LINDQUIST, E. F. *Statistical Analysis in Educational Research*. Boston: Houghton Mifflin Co., 1940.

SNEDECOR, G. W. *Statistical Methods*. 5th ed.; Ames, Iowa: Iowa State College Press, 1956.

WALKER, HELEN M. and LEV, J. *Statistical Inference*. New York: Henry Holt and Co., 1953.

Computation aids:

ARKIN, H. and COLTON, R. *Tables for Statisticians*. New York: Barnes and Noble, Inc., 1950.

BARLOW'S TABLES OF SQUARES, etc. London: E. and F. N. Spon, Ltd., 1935.

INDEX

◇◇◇

accuracy, standards of, in computation, 20–23

actuarial prediction, in correlation, 165–168

analysis of variance: principles of, 276–277; how variances are analyzed, 277–279; use of, in determining significance of differences, between independent means, 279–291, between correlated means, 291–295; in covariance, 295–303

array, in a correlation table, 130

attenuation: correction of correlation coefficients for, 358–360; assumptions underlying, 360

average: definition of, 27; of correlation coefficients, 172–173. *See also* mean, median, mode.

average deviation (AD): computation of, from ungrouped scores, 48; from grouped data, 48–49; when to use, 60

bar diagram, 80–82

beta coefficients: in partial and multiple correlation, 418–419; as "weights," 418; calculation of, in Wherry-Doolittle method, 437–439

bias in sampling. *See* sampling.

binomial expansion: use in probability, 89–93; graphic representation of, 93

biserial correlation (r_{bis}): use of in item analysis, 365–368; definition of, 375; calculation of, 376–378; standard error of, 378–379; alternate formula for, 379–380; point biserial coefficient, 380–382; comparison of biserial r and point biserial r, 383–384

central tendency, measures of, 27. *See also* mean, median, mode.

chi-square test, 253–254; as a measure of divergence from null hypothesis, 254–257; from the normal distribution, 257–258; correction (Yates) when table entries are small, 258–261; when entries are percentages, 262; in contingency tables, 262–265; additive property of, 266; relation to phi coefficient, 391

classification of measures, into a frequency distribution, 4–9

class interval: definition of, 4–6; methods of expressing, 6; midpoint of, 7–8; limits of, 7–9

coefficient: of variation (V), 57–59; of alienation, 177–178; of determination in correlation, 178–180

coefficient of correlation (r): meaning of, 122–125; as a ratio, 125–128; graphic representation of, 131; computation of, 134–142; computation of, mean at zero, 142–144; by difference formula, 145–146; effects of variability upon, 171–172; averaging of, 172–174; interpretations of, 175–177, 451–452; significance of, 198–202; derivation of formula for, 449–450

column diagram. *See* histogram.

computation, rules of, 21–23

confidence intervals, for population mean, 188–191

contingency, coefficient of (C), 392–394; relation to chi square, 394; comparison with r, 395–396

continuous series, meaning of, 2–3

correlation: linear, 122–124; as a ratio, 125–127; table of, 128–130; graphic representation of, 131; product-moment method in, 134–139; from ungrouped data, 139–147; difference formula in, 145–147; effects of errors of observa-

midpoint, of interval, 6–8

mode, 34–35; crude mode, 35; when to use, 39

moving average, in smoothing a curve, 13–15

multiple correlation: meaning of, 403–404; coefficient (R), 404; in 3-variable problem, 405–410; formulas for, 413–414; significance of, 416–417; shrinkage in, 416–417; beta coefficients in, 419–420; effects of intercorrelations upon, 420–422; limitations to the use of, 422; semi-partial, 452–453

multiple regression equation, for 3-variables, 405; for n variables, 412; partial regression coefficients in, 412; beta coefficients in, 418–419

nonlinear relationship, 396–398

nonparametric methods, 266–272; the sign test, 267; the median test, 268; the sum-of-ranks test, 271–272; value of, 272

normal probability curve, 87–89; illustrations of, 87–88; from binomial expansion, 89–93; in psychological measurement, 94–96; equation of, 96; properties of, 96–98; comparisons of distributions with, 102–105; use of, in various problems, 105–114; in scaling test scores, 314–318; in scaling judgments, 323–332; derivations of, 447–448

normality: divergences of frequency distribution from, 114–119; normalizing a frequency distribution, 314–317; T-scores and, 315–318

null hypothesis, 212, 247; in determining the significance of r, 200–202; in testing differences, 212, 246–247; advantages of, 212; testing against probable outcomes, 248–250; testing against normal curve, 251–253

numbers, rounded, 20; exact and approximate, 21

ogive, 69–72; percentiles and percentile ranks from, 71–74; smoothing of, 76; uses of, 76–78

order of merit, ranks, 328; changing into numerical values, 329

overlapping, defined, 108–110; in measurement of groups, 109–110

parallel forms of test, in reliability, 338–339

parameter, defined, 184

partial correlation: meaning of, 403–404; in analysis, 404; illustrated in 3-variable problem, 404–408; notation in, 407–408; formulas for partial r's, 411; significance of partial r's, 414–419; limitations to the use of, 421–422

percentages, standard error of, 197; compared with reference values, 234–235; difference between, 235–238; N needed for given significance level, 239–241

percentile ranks (PR), 65–69; from orders of merit, 68–69; curve of, 69–73; graphic method of finding, 71; uses of, 73–75; norms, 75–77; from the normal curve, 323

percentile scaling, 321–323; disadvantages of, 322–323

percentiles, 65–69; graphic determination of, 71–73; direct calculation of, 321–322

phi coefficient, 388–391; relation to χ^2, 391; comparison with r_t, 391–392

pie diagram, 82

prediction: from regression equation, 164–165; actuarial, 165–168; regression effect in, 174–175; from multiple regression equations, 409, 411–413, 438

probability, principles of, 89–94

probable error, relation to Q, 99; relation to σ, 99

product-moment correlational method, 134–139

quartile deviation (Q), 43–48; when to use, 60; stability of, 196

quartiles, Q_1 and Q_3, computation of, 43–47

range, as measure of variability, 42–43; when to use, 59; influence upon coefficient of correlation, 171–172

rank-difference method, of correlation, 371–374; significance of, 375; when to use, 375

ranks, converted into units of amount, 328–330

rational equivalence, method of, in test reliability, 340–342

rectangular distribution and normal, 322

regression coefficient, 154–156; in partial and multiple correlation, 412

regression effect, 174–175